RADICAL TECHNOLOGY

Edited by

PETER HARPER, GODFREY BOYLE and the editors of UNDERCURRENTS

Designed by **Roger Hall**

PANTHEON BOOKS

A Division of Random House, New York

Library of Congress Cataloging in Publication Data

Radical Technology.

Bibliography: pp. 267–96
Includes index.
1. Technology.   2. Human ecology.   I. Harper, Peter.
II. Boyle, Godfrey.   III. Undercurrents.
T47.R26   1976   338.6′3   75-10367
ISBN 0-394-73093-3

FIRST AMERICAN EDITION   Manufactured in the United States of America

---

First and most important of all, thanks to our contributors, whose
names appear alongside their articles or pictures, and without
whose efforts this book would not exist.

But a large number of other people have conspired with us to
make *Radical Technology* as a whole greater than the sum of its
individual parts. At the top of the bill are *Tony Durham, Martin
Ince, Barbara Kern* and *Pat Coyne*, of the *Undercurrents* editorial
team, who assembled a great deal of the material in the
'Communications', 'Food' and 'Materials' sections.

Next comes that visionary Rapidograph-wielder, *Cliff Harper*,
closely followed by *Annabel*, who scanned the manuscripts with
eagle eyes and pounced unerringly on every woolly thought that
dared to stray in.

Then there are our red-eyed, nimble-fingered typesetters;
Caroline, Moggs, Shirley and Janet; the people at *The Catalogue*,
who by introducing us to Wildwood House catalysed this book;
Ollie Caldecott and *Dieter Pevsner*, our publishers, who maintained
a straight face and cheerful disposition in spite of our absurd
delays and equally-absurd excuses; *Brian Dax*, who produced processed pictures sometimes better than the originals; *Jenny Fleet*,
who picked her way skilfully through a maze of copyrights and
picture permissions, and *Carol Overby*, who took over from her at
the 11th hour; and *Zoe Richmond-Watson*, who purged the boards
of all erros adn mispelingz*%.

A whole host of other people have also helped in a multitude of
major and minor ways. They include, in more-or-less random order:
BRAD, BSSRS, COMTEK, Robin Clarke, RadTech, Pauline
Faulkes, The Golfball Girl, Martyn Partridge, Peter Sommer, Phil
Steadman, James Thring, Gerry Smith, Simon Longland, Martin
Spring, Nick Lumsden, Jenny Pennings, Nick Saunders, The Street
Farmers, Abner Stein, Andre Schiffrin, Martin Lipson, Joy Watt,
Geoff Watts, Nigel Thomas, Woody.

**Dedicated
To Sparty
if he only knew**

CONTENTS

Imagination is seizing power

PREFACE

This is a book about technologies that could help create a less oppressive and more fulfilling society. It argues for the growth of small-scale techniques suitable for use by individuals and communities, in a wider social context of humanised production under workers' and consumers' control.

The book is not a blueprint. We don't imagine we have all the answers. Some of the proposals made may turn out to be misconceived. But we cannot know in advance which will, and which won't. We have kept the range as broad as possible, ranging from the sensible and piecemeal ('we used to do that during the war') through the straightforwardly radical (for example, workers' self-management) to the more-or-less utopian (say, repopulation of the countryside). This gives a considerable variety, reinforced by the idiosyncracies of the authors, who each interpreted their brief in different ways. Some of the articles are very technical, others more practical; some detailed, some giving just the broad outlines. They often contradict one another. This simply reflects the state of the art: a crazy-holy repertoire of theory and practice from which we can grow what we think fits the dream.

It is not a recipe book, although it does contain detailed instructions about some things. Some authors got carried away and wrote definitive monographs on their subjects. We didn't have the heart to cut all these, so there are some quite meaty pieces here and there. But on the whole it's a general turn-on book, broad rather than deep, aiming at making clearer how technical alternatives might work in a transformed society, and as part of the process of creating one. We have tried to keep just enough detail to give you an idea how it might feel to do these things yourselves.

Some readers might feel that because we concentrate so much on small-scale technology, we have emphasised only the home and neighbourhood, and therefore the technologies of consumption, at the expense of the factory and workplace, and the technologies of production. To some extent this is true. But it is not because we underrate the importance of basic industry. It is because (a) what is need-ed in the factories is not change of technology but of control, work-patterns, and products; and (b) because we want to show alternatives which will partly *replace* factory production. The organisation of factory work is beyond the framework we chose, but we try to show wherever possible, where the present proposals relate to it. Other 'gaps' in our coverage (for example medicine, education and many others) are more sketchily filled in in the Directory/Bibliography at the end of the book.

The organisation of the material is simple enough It is laid out in sections, each with a short editorial introducing the individual articles and explaining (if necessary) their claim to represent 'radical technology'. In between the sections are interviews with theorists and practitioners of radical technology, which explain themselves, and a series of drawings by Cliff Harper which we call **Visions**. The Visions are a very important part of the book, because they correct a bias toward hardware which any technology book suffers from. It is so much easier to draw *things* than relationships or feelings or organisations, and the hardware always tends to come over more vividly. In the Visions, we have tried to express the social context of Radical Technology, situations which, although they may look utopian, really could be implemented now if sufficiently large groups of people got themselves together. Truly, they are our visions (and Cliff's) of 'how it could be', and 'pictorial theses' to be criticised, modified or taken further, first in the head and then in the fields and streets.

The book begins and ends with attempts to define the scope of 'Radical Technology', firstly with a short account of its bastard origins and the currents of thought which have influenced it, and finally with a lengthy bibliographic essay and directory of heroes, practitioners, critics, wild ideas, and almost-sober intentions.

It took a lot more hard work than we expected to get this wretched book together, and we're sick of the sight of it, so now we're off for a bit of breakfast.

Over to you.

INTRODUCTION

Given that modern capitalist industrial societies are morally contemptible, ruthlessly exploitative, ecologically bankrupt, and a hell of a drag to live in, is there anything we can do to change them?

Let us grant that remedial gimmicks such as economic growth jags, foreign aid, Billy Graham, catalytic afterburners, and lobotomy on demand are not going to do the trick.

Let's face it, nobody has all the answers. But something has got to be done, and this book is a compilation of proposals which we think are going in the right direction. 'We' are a group of friends who for the past four years have been producing a magazine (*Undercurrents*) under the slogan 'Radical Science and People's Technology'. It always saves a lot of trouble to have a strong party line, and trying to work this out, we are perpetually tracking the elusive beast which we now call 'Radical Technology' in order to cage it once and for all. In spite of all our efforts it remains at large. Who knows where it will strike next?

But to resume the hunt: the word 'radical' literally means 'going to the root', and accordingly 'radical technology' implies a fundamental re examination of the role of technology in modern societies. It also implies a commitment to the ideals of the political Left. Let's say we're into *liberation*. We have to break through the political, economic, social, and psychological forces that constrain and oppress us. The trouble is these forces hold one another together in a web of mutual reinforcement so consistent that it's hard to know where to begin loosening their grip: patterns of ownership, status games, the way you work, what you learned at school, what the neighbours think, who gives the orders, what turns you on, what you see on TV, what you can or cannot buy . . . . Technology is one of these also, but we think it's a good place to get your fingers in the crack. Out of that assumption a syncretic model is developing which is both descriptive and normative, and suggests that real socialism will require a reassessment of the whole basis of productive activity: machines, methods, products, work-places, work-

patterns, training, allocation of work, loci of control, reward systems, distribution, pricing, economic co-ordination, attitudes, engineering principles, conventional scientific theory . . . .

Where does this 'model' come from? You can only ever see it out of the corner of your eye, so it's difficult to say. But we can identify a number of influences which have accumulated over the years, starting in the febrile days of the late '60s, when young scientists and technologists — and even some old ones — were dropping out like flies into spaces of personal and political discovery they never dreamed existed.

CRITICS OF INDUSTRIAL SOCIETY

Industrialisation hasn't always been an easy pill to swallow, and it has had its critics. In the past few decades, as Western capitalism moved into high gear for its assault on the consumerist Parnassus, a new version of 19th century pessimism emerged, with critics arguing from several different standpoints that the whole thing was quite intolerable. Writers like Huxley, Mumford, Ellul, Marcuse, Roszak and Illich hardly constituted a coherent school of thought, but they had in common a belief that modern-technological-industrial society itself engendered most of the problems, not just particular forms of it, such as capitalism. This implied dismantling the technostructure and decentralising into a simpler, more spartan and generally rural, form. Some critics went even further and asserted that the scientific world-view itself — objective, analytic, reductionistic, dispassionate, manipulatory — was the root of modern alienation. This implied a romantic, even mystical, reconstruction that drew inspiration from pre-industrial technologies and 'primitive' cultures (see Bibliography 2.52). Well, some of us fell for this and some of us didn't, but it certainly made us think about technology and 'modern consciousness' and what being human was all about.

COUNTER-CULTURE

Meanwhile, it was hard to be young in the sixties and not get caught up in the wild cultural revolution against the dominant values of industrial culture — reliability, ambition, obedience, technical rationality, privacy, competitiveness, consuming, mask-wearing etc — influencing and influenced by the anti-industrial intellectuals. The freaks were into relationships, communalism, head trips, being rather than having or doing. *Their* technologies (apart from domes, beads, and candles) were *inner* technologies, for exploring worlds in the head, and creating a mode, a mood, a vision, a way of seeing and feeling more alive. It was true the freaks tended to be parasitic on society as a whole, living in the interstices. But they were cheap to run and they pioneered a whole

Moloch devouring the workers. From Fritz Lang's *Metropolis*

new life style of hedonic poverty. Some of us got into that trip and were never the same again.

ECOLOGY

Another plague of the late sixties was the Apocalyptic Mania. Some of us caught this very badly. We did get over it eventually, but what remained was an awareness the Old Left never had, and still hesitates to take into account, of the physical and biological constraints on global human action. You can't go on growing forever, increasing energy consumption, use of raw materials, population; and you can't treat the biosphere like an infinite rubbish dump. Suspecting a basic incompatability between industrial technology and long term environmental stability, many people felt that the only really safe technologies in the long run were those which imitated 'Nature' as far as possible, or at least treated her with appropriate deference. This led them to the familiar criteria of arcadian technology in smallness, frugality, antiquity, rural setting, use of natural materials, and the cult of 'self-sufficiency'. More pragmatically, it spawned 'biotechnics' or 'Low-impact Technology', and all the familiar gadgetry of renewable-resource devices like windmills, solar collectors, methane digestors etc, of which this book has its due share.

THE THIRD WORLD

The spectacle of advanced technology applied in the non-industrial countries was extraordinary, even under the aegis of a 'benign' aid programme. It reduced rather than increased employment, produced luxury goods for the ruling class rather than essentials for the masses, accentuated the disparity of city and countryside, eroded old skills and exchange patterns, and created a tremendous dependence on foreign supplies of material, parts and technical assistance. 'Development' did take place, if GNP is any witness, but in a hideously distorted form. As an alternative it was suggested (originally by Schumacher) that smaller-scale, labour-intensive technics based on local skills and resources — 'intermediate technology' — would allow more even development, production geared to real needs, and greater self-reliance. This impressed us as further testimony of the evils of Big Technology and of the remarkable 'Taming Power of the Small'.

The only missing ingredient was socialism. At this point, inevitably, China enters the story. She was practising many principles of radical technology in a strikingly original way, reviving the old arts and blending them with the new; decentralising factories; judiciously combining big and small technology so as to get the best out of those; using natural materials and waste-products; encouraging self-reliance at all levels; and creating a balance of mental and manual work in a context of rigorous equality and guaranteed welfare rights. What was important to us was that the Chinese seemed to invert the conventional strategy. Instead of putting the sole emphasis on economic growth and hoping that social benefits would accrue as a side effect, the Chinese set out to establish social justice and minimum living standards, and found that economic growth appeared as if from nowhere. They put people before economics and the heavens did not fall down, even at a GNP per capita of under $200 — whatever that might mean in China's case. It can be done. The Chinese were, and remain, an inspiration.

The taming power of the small

THE ANARCHO-UTOPIAN TRADITION

Right from the beginning we were all socialists of one kind or another. We didn't need any persuading that capitalism had to go. And yet, many of the things we felt were most wrong in capitalist society were heartily approved by many others who called themselves socialists. We began to realise that there are two great streams of socialist thought. One, represented by Marxists and social democrats, however deep its disagreement with capitalism, at least shared its rational, materialist values of Progress, Science, Efficiency, Specialisation, Growth, Centralised Power, and fascination with the numbing achievements of smart-ass technology like Apollo and Concorde. And this was not all. They seemed to have a model of social development similar in many respects to the ideology of corporate liberalism: that society should be organised for maximum production, with the products themselves being the principal rewards, offered as compensation for the inevitable alienations of life and work in an industrial economy. Of course, under these tough-and-realistic forms of socialism, distribution would be fairer, work safer, products more rational, and public services much better. This was not in question. But the basic separation of production and consumption, the assumption of alienation-with-compensation, and technocratic criteria for social priorities, was broadly the same as liberal capitalism. Even the projected future was similar. Provided we all worked hard and behaved ourselves, eventually a state would arrive ('post-industrial society', 'communism') in which machines would take over most of the work and we could all go out and play.

But the *other* great stream of socialist thought, represented by the anarchists and utopians, looked at things quite differently. At first one could hardly take them seriously. They seemed to believe that the subtle human satisfactions should be given priority over production requirements; that life should be satisfying in all its aspects; that power should flow from below; that the action is not all in the city; that production and consumption need not be segregated in the factory and the home, but could be fused in the community; that revolutions are born of hope, not despair.

It is probably true that in the 19th century all this was hopelessly impractical — premature as they say — but later examples of local or regional economy run by anarchist collectives, although short-lived for external reasons, encouraged us a great deal. It became obvious that there were no technical or economic reasons why decentralised, participatory producer- and consumer-control production systems could not be set up which would be quite 'efficient' enough to provide all the necessities and a good deal more. The main obstacle to realising it may be merely that people hardly dare believe it could be true. It became clear that part of our task was to persuade them that it was. What do we do while waiting for the revolution? We let our imaginations off the leash and get on with building parts of the post-revolutionary society wherever and whenever we can.

What emerges from these varied influences is a jumble of theories and elements:

A theory of technology and society which insists that we *can* control technology, but if we don't it will control us;

Recognition of physical and biological constraints on human activity;

Social structure emphasising group autonomy and and control from the bottom up;

A bias towards simplicity and frugality in life and technology wherever possible;

Preference for direct gratification in production rather than through the medium of commodities;

An exploratory rather than a dogmatic application of the theory (such as it is . . .);

Willingness to learn from unlikely sources such as 'primitive' cultures and technologies, 'mystical' experiences or abilities, and even liberal social theory.

This may seem a strange chimera. Well, we have no monopoly on radical technology. Make up your own criteria if you don't like these.

Two topics deserve more comment. One is the question of romantic sensibility in technology, and related to it, economic restraint as a positive and deliberate life style. A focus on 'inner life' may be far more rational than we think in terms of buzzes received for effort expended. Neither need it be incompatible with a fine command of the hardware — as Robert Pirsig demonstrated in *Zen and the Art of Motorcycle Maintenance.* Likewise, frugal life-games may be far more efficient than opulence-games in terms

The biggest turn-on of all

SELF-MANAGED SWEAT

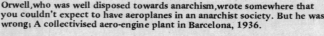

Orwell, who was well disposed towards anarchism, wrote somewhere that you couldn't expect to have aeroplanes in an anarchist society. But he was wrong; A collectivised aero-engine plant in Barcelona, 1936.

of resources needed for satisfaction gained — down there in the lower reaches of of the marginal utility curves.

The other topic, in many ways complementary to the last, concerns the nature of production and how small-scale community technologies can fit into a wider national or regional economy. Some goods *must* be mass-produced centrally. It is possible but unlikely that 'alternative technologies' could be introduced in factories. What is really needed is change of ownership; change in the patterns of immediate control; change of work-organisation on the shop floor; and change of products. And this in a context of *reduced* factory work, as useless production is progressively cut out, and the output of useful goods and services increases at the community and household levels. Of course, rotation of work, adjustments of money and other rewards, consultation with consumers, variable hours, and so on, all have to be continually debated. The aim is an optimum balance of public, community, and private production.

What's the next step? Most of the ideas that have been around for some time can be found in this book. The programme continues in its ad hoc way. We finish this little hunting party with a few of the ideas we are working on/thinking about/wondering if. There's more in the Bibliography.

◆*Community projects:* self-building; community workshops (see **Vision** No 5); community gardening (see **Vision** No 1); patient-controlled medical centres; zero-profit enterprises; self-organised projects by unemployed people; swap-shops and recycling depots; tool-sharing schemes; food conspiracies; consumer takeovers of established co-ops.

◆*Industry:* workers' co-operative takeovers in existing firms; alternative product possibilities; campaigns for the right to do socially useful work; community and consumer consultation; special retraining schemes; support for strikes and sit-ins.
◆*Alternatives for scientists and technologists:* a network of 'free range' technologists engaged in community work, repairs, evening classes, and research; science based living collectives; wandering technical tinkers; new courses in technical colleges, univers ities, polytechnics, and schools; directories of alternative work for scientists and technologists.
◆*Land reform:* campaigns for measures to break up large holdings; forms of collective ownership, community land trusts; repopulation of countryside; national self-sufficiency in food; city allotments.
◆*Rural communities:* conversion of conventional farms and derelict land to intensive husbandry; new rural villages (see **Vision** No 3); clearing house for information on available land; small industrial projects; directories of part time work; exchanges between city and country; courses in new techniques.
◆*Legal and economic changes:* campaign for guaranteed annual income; flexible work times; new laws concerning communal groups and collective ownership; alternative finance, credit unions, community levies.
◆*Analysis:* economic analysis of particular alternatives; radical Technology Assessment; 'malemployment analysis' — what work is actually useless? Planning for transition to a low-energy society; encouragement of radical technology and radical economics thesis topics for students.

That's all. There is a lot of work to do, but one of the nicest discoveries one can make is to realise that work is the biggest turn-on of all if you think it's worthwhile and you control it yourself. Kropotkin said something nice about this:

'**Struggle that all may live this rich, overflowing life, and be sure that in doing so you will find a happiness that nothing else can give.**'

FOOD

The technology of food production is unquestionably the most important of all human technologies. Human beings can survive without all the other basic techniques we cover in this book: without Energy, Shelter, Tools, Materials, Communications. But not without food and water.

So in this Food Section, after a brief look at the evils of Agribusiness, we concentrate on practical advice about how to grow food in various situations. John Seymour shows how the self-sufficient smallholder in the country can produce all the food he needs, and more, while at the same time freeing himself from the chains of the fertiliser and pesticide companies. Lawrence D. Hills then demonstrates how the town or suburban dweller with a patch of ground can also begin to grow a major portion of his food requirements.

Both of these articles are, of course, based on the natural, organic approach to food production which excludes the use of artificial fertilisers, but John Davy and Dr Koepf take the concept of organic husbandry a stage further. In their article, they suggest that organic farmers will achieve the best results by harmonising themselves with the subtle terrestrial and cosmic forces which everywhere vibrate about us, unseen but powerful.

Next we turn to some forms of food production which may seem unorthodox, at least in the West, but which can be highly productive: Tree Farming, Fish Farming, and Hydroponics.

Hydroponic techniques are rejected by some growers as 'too artificial', even though organic nutrients can be used, and even though in some urban situations where there is little or no soil it is difficult to think of any other practical way of growing food. We think it is beyond the scope of this section to attempt to resolve the conflict between these views.

Neither do we feel we should attempt to resolve the conflict between the unashamedly-carnivorous views of John Seymour and the forceful plea for vegetarianism made by Tony Joyce.

Essential to any discussion on food is information on *how much* food, and what varieties of food, are

up in an attractive and palatable way. John Seymour describes some simple methods of food preservation, and Monica Hill explains the essentials of one of many approaches to cookery: Macrobiotics. But we cannot pretend that in the few thousand words in this section we can do more than scratch the surface of this vast subject. Even the books in the Bibliography provide only starting points . Moreover, techniques for increasing individual and regional self-sufficiency in food form only one element — though a very important one — in the overall struggle for liberation from the power of the State and Big Business in all spheres. The various food production techniques described here all imply, in varying degrees, major political changes, of which Land Reform is the most important.

But the experience of growing one's own food is one which, people find, changes their heads significantly, and gives them confidence in their own ability to challenge the monopoly of state and corporate power in wider fields. You've got to start somewhere, and the garden is a better place than most.

needed by the body to keep it performing healthily and efficiently. John Shore looks at our bodily needs and how they can best be satisfied.

Equally-essential, after you've grown your food, are techniques for storing it until it's needed, together with methods for serving it

Martin Ince & Barbara Kern

AGRIBUSINESS

The ancient art of agri*culture* has today become the modern 'science' of agri*business,* where culture has been taken out of husbandry, and where ecological principles have become dominated by economic principles. Over the past few decades, the replacement of crafts and the continuous introduction of innovation has fundamentally changed the nature of food production.

The first innovation was the replacement of labour by machine. The number of 'horseless' machines on farms increased from 350,000 in 1942 to over three million in 1953. Machines increased the effectiveness of the system by imposing an apparent technological order on the workforce. The resulting increase in organizational efficiency, by raising the proportion of output to input, appeared to legitimate the authoritarian and hierarchical relations of production that accompanied this process.

A second basic innovation was the introduction of the 'package deal'—the combined use of artificial fertilisers, new pesticides and new plant strains—during the late 50's and early 60's. In the UK, nitrogen consumption quadrupled and potassium consumption doubled in the 20 years after 1950. Insecticides were the first pesticides to be widely used, but now herbicides are used in greater quantities. Plant breeders concentrated on producing strains that were resistant to the new waves of pests. Corn varieties were selected to produce less straw. A mini 'green revolution' took place.

WHAT ARE THE ADVANTAGES OF SUCH A SYSTEM?

Above all else agribusiness is claimed to be *efficient.* But it is necessary to challenge the term 'efficiency'. Efficiency in terms of *what?*

Not in terms of *energy,* anyway. British wheat growers produce 2.2 energy units for each unit expended; potato growers produce 1.1 units, and sugar beet, when refined to sugar, gains only 0.49 units. Battery eggs produce 0.16 and broiler chickens produce 0.11 units of energy for every one expended. Compare this performance with that of Yucatan maize farmers who produce 13-29 units of food energy, and primitive gardeners in New Guinea who produce 20 units, for each energy unit expended. Energy inputs into the agribusiness system are increasing enormously, but the food energy produced is rising only marginally. For instance in the US, food energy consumed has risen from about 150 kcal.10^{12} in 1940 to about 250 kcal.10^{12} in 1970, whereas energy input rose from 700 kcal.10^{12} in 1940 to 2250 kcal.10^{12} in 1970.

Nor is agribusiness efficient in terms of *productivity*—that is, output per acre. Yields in England and Wales of barley and wheat increased from 17.4 and 19.0 cwt per acre (cpa) during 1940-44, to 28.5 and 32.1 cpa for 1961-65. Production of wheat rose from 1½ million tons to 3.4 million tons, and output of barley from 2.2 million tons to 5.7 million tons, during the same period. These increases were accompanied by extensive monoculturing of crops and the establishment of larger farms as the main food producers.

Since then, however, yields have stabilised. The five year average for 1966-70 of these crops was *down* on the previous five year average in England and Wales. The yield per acre was 27.9 cwts per acre for barley, and 31.4 cpa for wheat. It is true, however, that yields have now improved slightly, the 71-73 average being 34.6 cpa for wheat, 31.3 cpa for barley.

It is not even true to say that the 'efficiency' of agribusiness is determined solely by economic criteria. Agribusiness is efficient by only one economic criterion—the ratio of gross monetary output to input. All other considerations, including productivity, are secondary. Thus, following the definition of the Ministry of Agriculture, Fisheries and Food, there are two sorts of farms: *high-performance (HP) farms*—those with the highest ratio of output per £100 input—which have "higher net incomes, specialise more and have lower labour, rent and machinery costs per acre"; and *low-performance (LP) farms*—the quarter of farms with the lowest such ratio. The advantage of large farms is clear—reduced labour and machinery costs per acre. But the productivity (i e. output per acre) bears no relationship to this measure of performance.

Dust another fifteen miles to go . . . of quiet combines, cool clean air, communal chitchat, and changing countryside.

Low-performance dairy, livestock and cropping farms produce outputs comparable to those of similar 'high-performance' farms, for most size groups. So-called 'low-performance' *mixed* farms (of all sizes) consistently outyielded 'high-performance' farms during 1970-72. *LP* farms produced £85 per acre, *HP* farms £65 per acre on average. The greatest discrepancy occurred on the larger farms (over 1800 acres), where high-performance farms produced only 70 per cent of the output of low-performance farms. High-performance farms had, of course, a higher return on labour input (about £550 compared to £410 per £100) and higher net farm income (about £29 compared to £7 per £100). And these are the determinants of efficiency.

Thus, talk of making our farms more efficient in order to provide for increased food demands is pure mystification. Agribiz efficiency does *not* produce more food automatically, nor is that a measure of its success. It produces more efficient *labour,* more efficient *capital,* and if it produces more *food,* well so much the better, but that is a secondary consideration. The drive to increase the technical efficiency of the food production process is in fact a drive to maximise the creation of surplus value, or *profit.*

WHAT ARE THE OBVIOUS COSTS?

These can be considered in three parts: exploitation of nature; exploitation of labour; and the associated political costs.

◆ *Exploitation of Nature: direct pollution.* The most widely known pollutive effect is that caused by pesticides, the major undesirable properties of which are persistence, broad range of activity, and widespread use. All the members of the organochlorine group, which includes DDT and Dieldrin, are powerful and persistent. It was the use of Dieldrin, Aldrin, and Heptachlor as seed dressings on wheat that first aroused attention as to possible side effects of insecticides in this country. In the springs of 1960 and 1961 bird deaths increased alarmingly, causing a public outcry. Game birds and predatory mammals and birds were affected. It was shown that the deaths were not solely due to the oral toxicity of pesticides, but that certain predators had been declining in numbers since World War II. This decline was linked with a reduction in the shell thickness, caused by increase in the production of enzymes—which broke down the oestrogen necessary for controlling calcium deposition. Thus, instead of simply asking the question "how much pesticide will kill an animal?" it became clear that the possible long term effects on animal populations had to be investigated.

Attention was then focused mainly on DDT, as it was the most widely used of the powerful and persistent pesticides. The main cause for concern was its build up in food chains, especially in aquatic fauna. The effects on soil fauna could still be measured even 12 years after application. The main drawback to DDT use became the build up of resistance among insect populations to the chemical. Thus, the withdrawal of use of DDT in the US was due more to the recognition of its future non-profitability than to the recognition of its harmful effects on biological systems.

Long term studies concerning other pesticides' effects on soil populations have been notoriously sparse, and often poor. Most soil micro-biological work has been carried out totally ignoring the role of soil mesofauna. Thus, the long term effects of medium persistent herbicides (eg. Simazine) or soil sterilants have yet to be established. Much basic research needs to be done before the bland reassurances of the Agribiz companies can be accepted.

Serious short term problems have so far occurred only rarely in practice. All insecticides are highly soluble in fatty tissues and kill by disrupting nerve impulse transmissions. Schradan, an organophosphate, caused many bird deaths in the 50's, but was replaced by more selective compounds of low toxicity.

Fertilisers, too, cause pollution problems. Artificial nitrates, unlike their organic counterparts, are not retained by the soil. Thus, they are essentially 'leached' into waterways. Not only is this a waste—which, considering that it takes five tons of oil to produce one ton of fertiliser, cannot be afforded—but it creates overfertilisation of vegetation in waterways. This process is called *eutrophication,* and it reduces the available oxygen for fish life. Nit*rates* can also be transformed to nit*rites,* which are a threat to watercourses, and are especially dangerous to children. This possibility is likely to increase as nitrates are being used in ever-increasing amounts, despite price rises due to increased energy costs.

The effects of continued fertiliser dressings can also cause two further sorts of damage to the soil. When acidification, caused by leaching, is not rectified by liming, damage to soils may ensue. Long lasting damage has also occurred by excessive application of micronutrients such as Boron.

The recent change to using excreta as unamended fluid slurry, instead of good old straw-composted material (farmyard manure), has also brought its pollution problems. These include transfer of organic material to streams via surface runoff, accumulation of elements in plants at concentrations undesirable to animal health, and further leaching of nitrates to groundwater. It can also block soil pores, reducing aeration, and thus reducing the nitrification process. Carryover of disease is also encouraged by the loss of oxidation properties.

◆ *Exploitation of Nature: degradation of ecosystems* While pollution affects ecosystems directly, there are other ways in which natural balances can be affected. The most profound alteration is caused by the very nature of agriculture—the aeration of large areas of single crops. Without agriculture there would be no such thing as pests.

That said, however, there is no need for Agribiz to exaggerate the problem by its insistent mono-culturing, whether it be by the yellow peril of monotonous barley or by the green slums of commissioned forest.

Biological controls have been degraded in various ways. The one that has attracted most attention is the removal of hedgerows. Although the president of the National Farmers Union has been heard to remark that "evidence shows that there is no loss of natural controls by removal of hedgerows, providing there are other hedgerows nearby", there is a lot of evidence to the contrary. In some studies yields have been improved by 20 per cent. Another method of degradation is straw burning after cropping. This was only made 'economic' when the carryover of stem pathogens, due to continuous corn crops, increased. Such measures are born of economic necessity rather than sensible husbandry or sane ecology. It is interesting to calculate the energy wastage in straw burning.

Another example of how modern methods create problems rather than solve them, is provided by the use of insecticides which may kill the natural predators, thus giving rise to new pests which avoid the primary insecticide. A classic example of this is the appearance of red spider mites in orchards, as a major pest. Similarly, the ability of insects continually to become immune to insecticides means that ever-new formulations are required. "Still, it makes for good business—if what you need is another pesticide, sir!"

A final word on the subject of natural controls. Imagine you do find that dream dome with a plot of land of your own; you may well be unable to grow anything organically, especially if your land backs onto a pea farm. Even if you manage to avoid the spray, and your plants are kept covered, the natural predators probably won't escape the ugly fingers of capitalism.

◆ *Exploitation of Labour* In the past 20 years, half of the workforce—a total of 400,000 people—has moved from the land: a telling indictment of the outdoor conditions created by agribusiness. Although some see this as a move to greater labour efficiency, it is probable that the total number of people involved with food production is still the same—the rest being employed in factories producing fertilisers, pesticides, and lots more surplus value.

Since 1956, according to the statistics, 2009 people (over two per week), including 334 children under the school-leaving age, have lost their lives through accidents on farms in England and Wales. The largest proportion of these have been caused by tractors overturning, or from falls. Legislation has now curbed this figure. Since the introduction of the Agriculture Act (1952) there has been only one fatal accident due to pesticide use up to 1972. Prior to the bill there had been eight fatalities on farms. But in 1972 there were four fatalities.

Most accidents with pesticides, however, have occurred away from the land. Nearly a hundred people have died from accidentally drinking Paraquat, for instance. The dangers of liver damage due to long term, low level exposure to DDT (and other chlorinated hydrocarbons) is most acute to those *manufacturing* the compound. The dangers of liver damage have now been underlined by the

recent discovery that another chlorinated hydro-carbon (Vinyl Chloride) causes liver cancer. The acute toxicity of organophosphates has likewise been associated with dangers of handling, rather than long term ecological damage.

Agricultural workers are prone to other diseases by virtue of their contact with soil and animals, yet the only diseases recognised as occupational hazards are dermatitis, Weil's disease and Farmers Lung. Agricultural workers are in fact subject to many other diseases, including brucellosis and tetanus. Agribusiness techniques have also exposed workers for prolonged periods to severe dust hazards in grain driers and silos. The long term hazards of these dusts are not known. And any chance of agricultural workers being afforded the same protection as industrial workers (meagre though that is) has just been eliminated by the exclusion of the Agricultural Inspectorate from the New Safety and Health at Work Bill.

Increased mechanisation has brought with it the costs that have been associated with automation in other industries. Regard for profits rather than ergonomics has meant that many older tractor drivers suffer from back complaints, and deafness. More insidiously, machines have created job specialisation, isolation, repetitive tasks, so that conditions of work bear little resemblance to 'the outdoor life.' A more realistic view of modern farming than contented cows portrayed in butter and cream adverts, would be of the dairyman in his concrete and steel 'herring bone' parlour milking 80 cows, three times a day, with the only respite being a visit from the vet.

Probably the worst exploitation is concerned with housing. Tradition has required that farm-workers live at the place of employment, often in a tied cottage. Because of this, and the acute housing shortage now felt in rural areas, workers have to tolerate housing conditions that elsewhere would be unacceptable; cottages are too often damp, cramped and without proper sanitation. There are also geographic disadvantages regarding shopping, transport and education.

◆ *Political costs.* The tied cottage is also at the base of the iniquitous distribution of power in landed circles. Rather than being paid a respectable wage, workers are accustomed to having a tied cottage. It means that they lack bargaining power, since their homes are at risk as well as their jobs.

The geographical isolation between workers on neighbouring farms has been further exaggerated by the division of labour within each farm. Whereas previously many jobs were carried out communally, this is now confined to harvest times: and even here there is the specialisation of driving, gathering, and bagging. This in turn has led to weak unionisation, with little militancy. The one area where significant militancy has occurred seems to be in the orchards of California—though in Belgium recently 4000 took to the roads with flails and bird scarers.

In the UK, however, farmers are now acquiring a reputation for militancy. It is not difficult to see why. More and more they are caught in a bind.

'The Great Outdoor Life'—a study of alienation.

Food prices continue to soar, yet *produce* prices are controlled by other interests—the government, the Common Market, and the food companies. Not only are they shackled by world capitalist forces and speculation, they are increasingly being reduced to the status of technicians/sharecroppers for industry. They have become dependent on food processors (for example, pea industries) not only to buy their crops, but also to tell them when to plant and to supply the capital to buy their package deal. Farms have had to increase in size (the number of farms in Canada, for instance, declined by 20 per cent from 1961-71) to withstand fluctuations in return on capital, and to make possible the necessary investment in machines and fertilisers in order to guarantee high yields.

In doing so, farmers become further dependent on the farm supply sectors of industry. It is dependency on virtual monopolies in each area; Massey-Ferguson, David Brown, Ford, and John Deere dominate farm machinery; ICI, Fisons and Shellmex control fertilisers; Fisons, May and Baker, Geigy and Shellstar are the leaders in pesticides; and the infamous seven major oil giants, control the fuel supplies.

The centralisation of power from the land to the boardrooms of Agribiz is exaggerated still further by the system's dependence on one man for the supply of phosphate rock. Mohammed Lamrani of Morocco controls a third of the exports, and more than one half of the export growth, of phosphate rock. And as for oil . . .

The influence of Agribusiness also dictates governmental research to such an extent that virtually all money in this field goes to 'articulating the paradigm of pesticide and fertiliser usage'. Rothamsted Research Station is built on super-phosphate. Virtually no research is undertaken on organic husbandry, and very little on biological control mechanisms. Yet again, the economic method is propagated under the guise of the scientific method.

PROSPECTS FOR THE FUTURE?

It is now recognised that energy is power—that energy is just as unequally distributed as wealth, and lies in the same few hands. It is not so widely recognised that this truth applies equally to food.

The staggering increases in food prices in the last two years are *not* due to a sudden increase in the world population. Something new is happening to world food supplies. It started in 1972 when three problems emerged. For the first time, the USSR entered the US market and purchased 400 million bushels of wheat. Secondly, the production advances that came to be lumped under the phrase 'green revolution' began to level off. Finally, the richer countries, all experiencing boom times, sharply increased their consumption of meat. This last factor may be the reason why the USSR decided to enter the wheat market at the time it did. The Russians needed greatly increased supplies of grain to produce meat; previous shortages had always been accommodated, and the '72 harvest was the fifth best ever for them. But as a result of Russian purchases in '72, the grain reserves in the US fell from 120 million tons to 21 million tons.

The USSR's entry into the consumer and capitalist market has had two main effects. It has created such a sensitivity in the market that speculation is widespread, and it is better to invest in food than in money. This sensitivity has exposed the weakness in the whole system. For instance, when the anchovies recently returned to Peru's coast it meant that the underdeveloped countries would be better able to afford their own, much needed protein, but that soya bean farmers in the US would suffer.

It is clear, however, that underdeveloped countries are in general *not* going to benefit. The change in the market has meant that the US has assumed greater control over distribution. The US was the main exporter for eight of the 20 commodities which showed the greatest increases in prices during 1972. The rest of the developed countries controlled a further eight. The under-developed countries controlled only four, but were the main exporters of the 20 commodities with the lowest price increases of all the 67 world commodities. Which isn't much consolation for countries like Mozambique which have been 'encouraged' to produce cash crops at the expense of home-consumed food crops. The increase of control by the US also had more obvious political effects. Critical supplies of wheat were denied to the Chilean Government under Allende—even though Chile offered to pay cash. When Allende was over thrown, the US approved the sale, and even offered credit.

Meanwhile, as a few businessmen made money and gained power from the market's uncertainty, pressure was increased on producers to produce more. This was the case in the UK just as much as elsewhere. The recent inflation of land prices (prices tripled in two years), coupled with the annual loss of 50,000 acres of urbanisation, exacerbates the problem still further. These pressures will dictate that 'efficiency' must become still more 'efficient' with all the absurd contradictions that that entails.

WHAT CAN BE DONE?

'Alternative' forms of agriculture, as outlined in the pages that follow, can and do challenge many of the implicit values of agribusiness. For instance, we are constantly reminded that we live in a consumer society. The public's willingness to accept an homogenous final product is indispensable in the transition from labour intensive agriculture to highly specialised automated agribusiness. The manipulation is built into the final product itself. Thus, by creating an *apparent* choice in relatively unimportant aspects, such as the size and colour of eggs, the *real* choice of nutritive value, price and ecological impact is obscured. But by insisting on consideration of these factors alternative agriculture can challenge the values of agribusiness.

However, it is not enough merely to pose the alternatives; it is necessary also to challenge the economic system within which agribusiness is founded. To do so from an agricultural perspective requires certain novel forms of organisation. Organisation around and among farmworkers is essential, but as we have seen, this is difficult because of problems inherent in the unusual position of such workers. Hence other challenges are also necessary. Two possibilities are open. The formation of cooperatives—not consumer cooperatives alone, but also productive and distributive cooperatives—needs to be encouraged in order to reduce the control of agrimonopolies. It will also be necessary to ignore all the rules of the capitalist game and just *landgrab,* in order to illustrate forcefully the inequities of land distribution. Both efforts should succeed in diversifying both the means of production and the crops that it produces.

Indeed the emphasis throughout should be on diversification. Diversification in understanding the problems as being not merely technical or economic, but political too. Diversification in approach, not merely being towards alternatives but to challenging the system directly in as many ways as possible. And diversification in the end product, away from monocultures and dependency on a few distant technocrats, towards natural systems controlled by the people working them.

Charlie Clutterbuck

ANIMAL FARM

It is absurd even to guess at the acreage necessary to support a person, because land varies enormously in productiveness, and so do husbandmen. But it may help to know that well-farmed land of good quality, without imported fertilizer but with animal manure, will grow two tons of wheat an acre or eight tons of potatoes. Vegetable requirements can be produced on a very small acreage indeed but Man (vegetarians included) cannot live on vegetables alone—that is if you mean vegetables in the accepted sense, excluding grains. Anyone who says "I am completely self-supporting because I grow all my own vegetables" is talking nonsense.

The aim should be the integration of soil, plant and animal that is found in nature, but guided by the knowledge of Man. The common urban belief that animals are inefficient because animal protein requires more land to produce than vegetable protein is a fallacy, as every countryman who's forked a heap of animal manure on his potato patch must know. For although it is true that an animal only transforms a small proportion of the vegetable food that it eats into food for man (or other predators) it is not true that the vegetable matter not so transformed is wasted. It is transmuted, in fact, into a better manure for the land than it would have been. Your rumen is your best compost heap.

The stockless holding can only maintain its fertility by importing fertilizer from outside itself. The amount of waste vegetable matter that can be composted grown on the holding is never enough to maintain fertility. The great stockless agribusiness farms of Eastern England and the grain belts of America continue because of vast amounts of imported ammonium sulphate, and the vegan self-supporter buys or begs farmyard manure from his animal-keeping neighbours or his land gradually becomes sterile. The amount of shit produced by a human is almost negligible.

If a Briton has his fair share of Britain he will have about half an acre of good arable land per member of his family, but as most people elect to live in towns we can at least double that and assume five acres of land for a family of four. To maintain and increase the fertility and health of this area without imported fertilizer, herbicides or pesticides demands a great *variety* of both plants and animals. A thorough rotation of crops must always be practised, for one crop is not affected by the diseases of another, and one species makes different demands on the soil and puts different residues back into it.

The same applies to animals: all grazing, browsing and rooting animals suffer from internal parasites. Keep one species too long on one patch and parasites will build up to lethal proportions. Follow one species by another and each species' parasites will die when ingested by another species.

Different species also make different demands on grazing. Thus adult cattle can eat long coarse grass

SALLY SEYMOUR

This illustration, like those that follow, is taken from John and Sally Seymour's book *Self-Sufficiency* (Faber and Faber, 1973).

and should be put first on to new grass. Sheep and horses crop close to the ground and should follow cattle. Goats like scrub and bush country and prefer leaves to grass. Horses suffer on too lush grass— they thrive on poor grazing. Pigs eat grass too but will thrive in woodland and can mine deep down for roots, underground insects and the like. Geese will thrive on good short grass but need grain to fatten them. Hens also eat grass and clover but need grain to lay eggs. They eat weed seeds and insects, harmful and otherwise. Ducks and geese of course thrive on wet land and on water. To deny ducks open water, as agribusiness does, is as cruel as keeping hens in battery cages. Ducks eat the snails that cause liver-fluke.

Let us imagine that a family takes over five acres of scrubland. First put pigs on to it, concentrated say at half a dozen pigs on half an acre. Electric-fence them or contain them with pig-netting, or else tether them, but if there are trees and bushes you can't tether. Take a small piece of land at a time, pig it for three months, then burn the scrub and level, and plant crops. When all the land is thus cleared (pigs will clear almost anything) gradually establish a proper rotation.

Put say two acres down to ley (this means temporary grass-and-clover), an acre to corn, an acre

SALLY SEYMOUR

some of your grass for hay every year. Clamp roots—fodder beet is one of the best, mangolds are fine for milk-production in the winter, marrow-stemmed kale, rape and hungry-gap-kale are winter fodder too—to be grazed off *in situ.* In the summer work for the winter. Remember, Britain is not New Zealand where grass grows for ten months of the year.

On your acre kept for gardening follow a rotation too. Of course the fruit patch cannot be rotated, but it is better to plant standard (ie high) hard fruit trees so that you can graze underneath them with ruminants or ringed pigs, and necessary that you heavily muck (farmyard manure) soft-fruit trees nearly every year. Brassica (cabbage tribe) love lime, so if necessary lime before them. Peas and beans (leguminosae) follow comfortably brassica. 'Roots' (parsnips, carrots, salsify, turnips, beet) come nicely after leguminosae. Potatoes come well after them, but muck *heavily* for potatoes. Always pig the land after you have lifted the potatoes—the pigs will get what you left. Then lime—then brassica again. Remember that in the garden and the field, leguminosae (beans, peas, clovers, lucerne) *make* nitrogen, so the more you can grow the less you will miss the artificial fertilizer bag.

Now, on such a holding, everything benefits by everything else. Nothing is wasted. All crop residue and kitchen refuse goes to either pigs, poultry or cattle. Straw from corn is used for litter for pigs and cattle and turned by them into lovely muck. Oats straw, though, is fed to cattle and horses to supplement hay. All shit from all animals goes back into the land. Skimmed milk from butter-making goes to fattening pigs, calves, or young poultry, whey

to other crops. Subdivide your two acres of grass, put young cattle on first (because it will be free of lung-worm) follow them with old cattle, follow these with sheep and your horse, and follow these with geese. After three years plough (or *pig*) one acre of grass and plant say half an acre of wheat, the rest with potatoes and jerusalem artichokes. The three years of grass will have improved the soil enormously. After you've harvested the spuds and such of the jerusalem artichokes (well-dubbed *fartichokes* by the irreverent) as you want for soup and seed, shove the pigs on to clear the remains. Follow the roots with spring barley and oats, the wheat with roots. Undersow the spring barley and oats with grass-and-clover seed and thus you will have half an acre of fresh 'ley' (grass-and-clover) to run your calves on next year. Follow the half that you have put again to roots with spring corn undersown with grass-and-clover. The famous Norfolk Four Course Rotation is: wheat—roots—barley—grass-and-clover. Follow this on your four acres of farm-cropped land and you won't go far wrong. You will grow all the wheat you need for bread, the barley you need for beer and animal feed, and the grass you need for grazing and hay and your land will improve in humus-content, structure and fertility from year to year until it becomes the equal of any land in the world.

If it needs lime, lime it from time to time. Cut

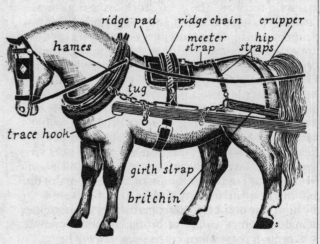

Labels: *ridge pad*, *ridge chain*, *crupper*, *hames*, *meeter strap*, *hip straps*, *tug*, *trace hook*, *girth strap*, *britchin*

SALLY SEYMOUR

from cheese-making the same. Pigs will fatten on barley-meal and whey or skimmed milk. After corn-harvest follow the scythe with hens. They will eat the spilled corn and also the weed seeds. Move hens in moveable arks over grassland—their manuring and scratching does great good. Aim to grow all your own protein—fish-meal is now £150 a ton and going up and the fish-meal plants denude the seas. Pulses of all sorts (the seeds of leguminosae) are high in protein—especially soya beans; good grass-and-clover cut *young* and made into hay and silage is also high in protein; fodder beet is fairly high; dairy by-products are high; but corn (wheat, barley, oats, rye,

SALLY SEYMOUR

maize) is fairly low. Experiment with high-protein crops and defy the debt-collector from the 'farmer's co-op'.

Hens will lay eggs on young grass and grain alone. Hens will go broody and rear their own chicks much better than an incubator can. Let them. Sows will farrow twice a year out of doors with the meagrest of shelters and provided you don't keep them on the same land more than four months at a time will never get ill. Two cows will provide you with milk, butter and cheese, help the pigs and poultry with their by-products, help the land with their manure, and give you two calves a year for beef, or for money if you are squeamish. The pigs will do much of your cultivating, but a mare also will help enormously. She will live on what you can produce on the holding alone, work amazingly quickly and well (she is ten times *faster* than a garden cultivator) and will do what no tractor in the world has ever done yet — reproduce her species.

One more thing. Plant trees somewhere on your holding, and leave some wilderness for wild plants and animals. The Earth was not created *just* for our benefit.

John Seymour

COMPOST CULTURE

Anything written on organic gardening must begin with making a compost heap. This is the essential recycler that makes it possible to garden without chemical fertilisers.

There are many systems of composting and the oldest and easiest was invented in China some four thousand years ago. Had the Chinese invented water sanitation instead, they would have starved their land of potash as well as humus. Today, we can only hope that they will not take a great 'leap forward' to chemical fertilisers for they could still ruin the fertility of their soil by copying our follies rather than developing their own methods towards greater ecological efficiency.

In small gardens some kind of compost bin is desirable to hold the heat in, for tidiness and to avoid the need for turning. Those who have plenty of bricks or breeze blocks can build one like a square cornered 'U', with slots in each side of the open end to take removable boards for the front. Wooden ones can be built like topless and bottom-less 'cold frames' three to four feet high, also with removable board fronts.

If you are making a brick bin, dip your bricks in a bucket of water or soak them with a watering can, so the cement will stick to their surfaces. Set the bricks or blocks so the joints do not come one above the other (any wall provides a model) and leave a few half inch wide gaps at intervals for extra ventilation. Secondhand bricks are good bin-making material, but corrugated iron and sheet asbestos are poor insulators. Wood is excellent and if it is creosoted and then given a coat of black or green bitumen paint, which, unlike ordinary paint, sticks on top of this most preservative undercoat, it could last twenty years.

Start the heap by setting two double rows of brickends running from the back to the front of the heap and protruding under the bottom of the board front. These should be on the soil, for no bin should have a cement floor which prevents the worms getting in, and which makes it impossible to move. Wooden bins (and those made with posts at the corners and inch mesh wire netting with opened out cartons string-stitched inside them to hold in the heat and moisture) can be moved round the

FOOD

HDRA

Above: **General view of compost heaps. The man with the machine is chopping up stemmy chrysanthemums into small pieces ready for the compost heap.** *Right:* **General view of the inside of a compost box showing brick ventilation underneath. Spot the black cat.**

garden, leaving extra rich patches wherever your compost heap has rested.

On top of the brick air channels, spread tough refuse such as brussel sprout or cabbage stumps smashed with an axe back on something hard so that they rot eventually. Add herbaceous plants, or tomato haulm, to prevent the lawn mowings or sappy weeds blocking the draught. Then pile on your first eight inch layer of weeds and garden rubbish.

Compost making is like baking bread—there are many methods but all are ways of using bacteria and fungi to make a product we want—compost is as 'unnatural' as a flint axe, a loaf of bread, a glass of beer, or a chunk of cheese. An easy way is to pile up your weeds in front of the bin and every morning take down the compost bucket from under the kitchen sink and tip it on your heap, before covering it with two or three forkfuls of rubbish to keep off birds and dogs. Then empty over it a bucket full of what is politely known as 'Household Liquid Activator', which is one part of urine to three parts of water.

This is the best activator of all because it supplies nitrogen as ammonium carbonate—which favours some highly efficient cellulose breaking bacteria, and contains almost all the potassium we take in with our food. Analyses of sewage and municipal compost only show a trace of potash, because it has been washed away in the effluent and wasted in growing the algae that cause eutrophication in water-courses, so recycle your potash through your compost heap to feed your soil. There are no disease bacteria carried by urine in temperate climates, though in tropical countries the eggs of the bilharzia parasite are carried.

If everyone used this activator, (also known as 'Chairman Mao's Favourite') we should save thousands of tons of potash fertiliser, and make better compost more cheaply than we do. There are, of course, many organic and inorganic activators which can be used according to the directions on the packets that grow more expensive every year, but everyone has his or her private supply that costs nothing. Chemical closet contents can be used as an activator, but the problem is to get enough vegetable waste to go with this in winter.

Many people are working on designs for a methane gas generator that will run on our bodily wastes and kitchen and garden rubbish. Such generators will enable us to use the heat our compost produces to cook our vegetables, and heat and light our homes, yet still have enough left in the residue to 'power' the earthworms, soil bacteria and all the life in our soils on which fertility depends. How exactly we shall use our methane residues in our gardens remains to be discovered by research.

A good compost heap should reach 160-170° F during its first ten days, and the heat will then fall as the fungi take over. This temperature will cook weed seeds like grains of rice and kill out the spores of plant diseases. If you wish to improve the compost breakdown, just turn the heap, forking it out of the bin, clearing the air channels and forking it back again, which produces a second heating and better breakdown. If your heap gets too wet, cover it with a square of old carpet which will hold the heat in and let the steam out; if too dry, cover with old polythene bags so that moisture condenses on their undersides and runs back into the heap, which will also need watering in dry weather. In winter it is easy to waste the potash and other plant foods in rainy or snowy weather, so rig a permanent or removable roof with room to get under for adding the day's contributions.

These can include potato peelings, tea leaves, coffee grounds, and all kitchen wastes other than plastics, nylon, manmade fibres, bones and vacuum cleaner dust. (This last item used to be included, but modern vacuum cleaners appear to include lead alloys, which add lead pollution to your soil, apart from the lead from petrol which blows in through your windows if you live in a town. Milk bottle tops and the foil some people use round roasts can be 149 parts per million lead, and the lead worn off from type is the reason why the proportion of newspaper in compost should be kept below 10%).

Most gardeners can manage two fillings of a compost heap in a year—one made in summer for autumn use, and an autumn and winter heap for spring. If you have large quantities of grass available from a playing field use this mixed with weeds, and add layers of enough lime to whiten the surface every eight inches. Then thrust stakes down into the air channels while you are building the heap, pulling them out afterwards to give extra ventilation.

But if you have dead leaves available, and these are sometimes delivered free by council roadmen, do *not* include them in the compost heap. Instead, make a wire netting surrounded enclosure and stack it full of leaves, treading them down, and watering them if they are in the best place for the stack, which is in dry shade under trees where nothing much will grow. Dead leaves take about two years to decay with the help of woodland fungi, and despite all that is said by orthodox writers with an eye to the firms that advertise peat, there are no poisonous leaves. Oak and beech make the best leafmould, but plane and chestnut leaves will rot in time, taking perhaps three years. Leafmould has its plant foods locked up by the tannins and is available in providing the moisture-retaining and soil-lightening power of humus. Use it as well as, not instead of, compost, and those who have sandy soils or clays that bake hard in summer should dig or rotavate all they can into their gardens.

If you have an old garden that is overgrown, borrow or hire a rotary mower like a Hayter and a rotavator. You may have to hire the service of the operator of the latter, too, but it will probably be

Sward garden. This is a no-digging technique involving a clover bed

worthwhile, especially if the garden is on clay or was part of a field. Clear the rough grass with the mower to use in your first compost heap, then rotavate it three times in dry weather with about three weeks between each. This will kill out the couch grass by letting the air in, and even destroy some of the docks, but before each rotavation go over and pick up any growing root sections for burning.

This clean sweep policy is vastly better than clearing small corners and dotting rose, currant and gooseberry bushes in them, for it uses your one opportunity to reduce weed roots to humus and kill out the millions of weed seeds that are waiting to germinate under the jungle. Never have your land ploughed, unless it is also cultivated and given two heavy harrowings, for ploughing only merely gives a ridged surface through which docks will grow.

If you have a bed of nettles, cut them with the rotary mower every six weeks. They make excellent compost material and you will kill them out in about two years. This policy also kills bracken in time. Those who are short of compost material and have spare space should buy the sunflower seed sold cheaply for parrot food and sow this an inch deep and a foot apart each way, pulling up the plants when they are four feet high, before the stems get too woody to break down easily.

Old gardens are often short of lime. You can check the lime content with a soil tester, which contains a kind of liquid litmus paper and a colour chart to give the 'pH' of your soil, which is the unit in which acidity or alkalinity is measured. Neutral, which is what you need, is pH 7.0, and though you can compensate for deficiencies by adding slaked lime to the quantity indicated by the tester, mushroom compost is a better answer. This consists of straw, dried blood, horse manure and ground chalk, and brings good humus as well as lime to give a good start to a new garden before any compost is ready. Do not buy the more elaborate kind of soil testing kit because these give their ' answers ' in terms of what chemical fertilisers are ' required '.

Potatoes should have the best of the compost which is ready in the spring, because they show the better flavour from compost most strongly. If yours is a small garden, plant Duke of York, because it can be lifted to scrape new when it is in full flower,

FOOD

and left to die down by August when it will keep a long way through the winter. The best keeping potatoes are Desiree for flavour, and Maris Piper which is not only excellent on taste but resists potato eelworm. This is found in old gardens and allotments and brings small foliage that turns yellow early and tiny tubers. Maris Page is the tastiest of the potato blight resisting kinds, and those who dislike scabby skins (which few gardeners worry about because the skins peel off) can try Pentland Crown and Ulster Concord, for baking in their jackets.

Spacings and quantities, timings and sowing seasons would take too much space to give here, but details are available free for a stamped addressed envelope in *Dig for Survival* issued by the Henry Doubleday Research Association, Bocking, Braintree, Essex. This Association of organic gardeners also gives away a booklet on safe pest control methods called *In Place of Poisons.*

As the potatoes are dug, plant cabbages such as Winter Monarch (bred for raw eating in salads as well as cooking) or Christmas Drumhead in August, and from July till the end of August put in leaks. These should have been sown in April and put in by merely dropping a plant, roots down, into a hole about eight inches deep thrust in to the soil with a 'dibber' or a pointed broken fork handle. Fill the hole with water and after perhaps two hoeings to keep the weeds down, they need no more work. Leeks are perhaps the ideal winter crop, for though they only grow about an inch thick from August planting they provide an excellent source of vitamin C in the leaves if these

are only shortened by about three inches, instead of being cut to stumps as they are by greengrocers.

Two other good winter crops are khol-rabi and Chinese radish, both sown in July a foot between rows and thinned to six inches apart. Both are left in the ground until about March, for pulling as required, and both are best grated raw for salads. Chinese Rose, the radish, is mild tasting compared with ordinary radishes though with the same flavour, and even though it runs to seed in the spring the roots do not go woody and strong. Khol-rabi has a swollen stem, so it starts by looking like a crazy turnip growing above ground, and its nutty flavour is wasted by cooking, as is the vitamin C, which is 37 mg per 100 gm raw, but only 8.9 after boiling for 30 minutes as directed by orthodox cookery books.

Many vegetarians are organic gardeners, and all vegetarians should be, for they gain most by the flavour improvement from compost cultivation. Parsnips, sown in April or even early May so they are not woody are also nicer raw than cooked, but the finest value for root salads is Cook's Delight beet, so called because it needs no cooking. Sown in March for summer eating, and in May to store through the winter (between layers of peat in a box in a dry shed like carrots) it will grow more food value to the square yard than almost anything that is easy in a small garden. Each stands up out of the ground for up to a foot and can grow to 4lb. without growing woody. It never bleeds, so a large one can stay in the fridge for grating day after day.

Another bargain for space is Sutton's Windermere lettuce, which is a frilly kind for maximum vitamin C, with thick midribs for highest carbohydrate and leaf protein that bring the average specimen up to 1lb. a lettuce. Their real garden value lies in the fact that they can last for more than a month from a single sowing, if the thinnings are transplanted about eight inches apart each way. Successive growing from March till August will keep up a supply right into the autumn. In a very small garden a vegetarian who concentrated on Windermere, Cook's Delight, and Chinese Rose,

Left above: **Japanese pumpkins—harvested in October and sown through the winter to make pumpkin soup and eggless lemon curd.** *Left below:* **High protein beans—daffa beans grown in the survival garden as a storable winter protein source.** *Below:* **Ladybird larva attacking aphids-greenfly.** *Opposite:* **Tagetes Minuta, the weedkiller plant which also prevents potato eel worm.**

HDRA

khol-rabi and leeks for winter would probably grow the most food for least trouble to supplement rice, pulses, or pea tribe grains such as lentils or beans.

Another value vegetable is onions from sets (small bulbs) planted in March an inch deep, with care taken to prevent any of the brown skin showing the sparrows where they are, on well firmed soil. They need none of the attention of seed onions and are immune to onion fly. Dig them and dry them in bunches in August with time to plant late cabbages such as January King after them.

Vegetables of the cabbage family, brussel sprouts, cabbage, cauliflowers, broccoli, savoys, turnips, radishes, Chinese radish and khol-rabi should be concentrated together because they are all subject to clubroot disease, for which there is no organic remedy and no completely effective chemical one either. Farmers control it by rotating their crops for it dies out in the soil after nine years, and by liming and keeping to pH 7.0 it can be kept down. Gardeners can rarely rest their soil this long.

One old remedy is to drop three inch long sections of rhubarb stem down the dipper holes at planting time, which can be effective, but research continues (at the Henry Doubleday Research Association) to find a better one. Organic gardeners should keep their cabbage crops together so the soil gets some rest, and if they have trouble, grow sprouting broccoli, which has some resistance. Potatoes too should be like lightning—never striking the same place twice, but the onion family, peas and beans, and the beet and lettuce order can even follow each other for five years in succession without a build-up of disease problems.

Whatever may be claimed about pest and disease resistance from compost growing, this is never 100% sure, and caterpillars, cabbage aphids and white fly are problems for all gardeners. Organic gardeners however control them as far as possible by sparing our friends so they may eat our foes. The best all-round spray is nicotine, made by simmering 2 oz. of filter tip cigarette ends (ask in your local cinema if you are a non-smoker) in a quart of water for half an hour, filtering through a cloth and diluting with six parts of water for aphids, and four for cabbage caterpillars. This mixture is a powerful poison, but spares ladybirds, their larvae and hoverfly larvae, which are the best aphid eaters, and is spent in twenty-four hours, unlike DDT, aldrin and dieldrin which keep on killing towards *Silent Springs.* Boil it up as you want it—no child will mistake your tin of cigarette ends for a soft drink, as 80 people so far have taken Paraquat for coca-cola and died.

The ideal remedy for blackfly, our commonest aphid, on broad beans, is to sow them in November and take off the soft tips which the aphids attack as soon as the pest appears. Take them up when the crop is eaten in July, then plant sprouting broccoli to enjoy from March to May, and pull out in time for outdoor tomatoes, to ripen mostly off the plants for bottling to last the year round, and after these sow broad beans again. This is the kind of cropping routine that gets a quart of production out of a pint pot of room in a small garden, which is as important as packing in the words into a tiny space in this book, in relation to all that there is to say and learn about organic gardening.

Lawrence D. Hills.

FOOD

BIODYNAMIC AGRICULTURE

During the past century, agriculture and horticulture have greatly increased yields, drastically reduced the labour needed, and developed more consistent products. Why, then, should we look for alternatives?

We are coming to see the price that has been paid—in loss of quality and nutritional value, disruption of ecological balances bringing increasingly expensive problems of disease and pest control, and a heavy dependence on fossil fuels and other non-renewable raw materials.

The biodynamic approach to farming is an alternative approach which has been under development in many countries all over the world since 1924. It is based on an understanding of living nature deriving from Rudolph Steiner's anthroposophy. Its emphasis is on enhancement of biological activity in soil, plants and animals.

Like any other type of farming, success depends above all on good husbandry—skill, experience and much attention to detail. Biodynamic farming has much in common with good organic farming—the use of carefully planned rotations, composting, companion planting and so on. But it adds to such practices the use of some special preparations and sprays (described in more detail below), and a detailed attention to the rhythms of sun and moon in planting, cultivating and harvesting. These methods arise out of a conception of the farm as an organism within the larger organism of the earth, which itself lives within an organised universe. But before considering this, what makes for a truly biological practice of farming?

Natural plant communities, undisturbed by man, follow a law of succession, of step-by-step changes, until the system as a whole arrives at a climax. It has then achieved maximum stability in relation to outside influences, and is nearly 'self sufficient'. But its productivity, in terms of capacity to feed human beings, is usually minimal. A rational farming system must therefore learn how to achieve a comparable stability, a healthy balance— but at a much higher level of productivity.

It seems to be widely believed that the basis of organic farming systems is the use of organic manures. These play an important part, of course, together with the use of crop residues, and the inclusion in rotations of leguminous plants such as clovers and pulses. These measures help restore organic matter broken down and released by cultivation.

But equally important are the balance of crops which exhaust and crops which renew the soil, and mixed planting within the farm area to control weeds, soil-borne pests, and soil-borne diseases such as the club root which afflicts brassicas. Mixed stands of grains being grown for feeding stuff usually bring better yields and lower risk of crop failure. Such grains can also be grown mixed with beans, peas or vetches, so that one field provides

Applying biodynamic spray in Sweden.

BEATA BERGSTROM

both a concentrated feeding stuff and nitrogenous fertilisation of the soil.

Similar methods of intercropping and planting can be used in gardens. Companion plants bring enhanced flavour and improved pest and disease control, if properly carried out. (Relevant literature is referred to in the Bibliography).

In preparing organic manures and composts, a proportion of animal manures is crucial in humid temperate climates (this does not hold to the same extent in warm humid climates), so that a healthy farm will carry a mixture of crops and livestock. The materials available for composting will vary from place to place, but the essential principles remain the same. The mixtures to be composted should contain carbonaceous litter and nitrogen-containing materials in a ratio of about 25:one, together with, if possible, not less than 5% by volume of soil. The pile must be moist but not wet, and structured so as to allow continued but not too intensive aeration (good dimensions are 6-9ft wide at base, 3-5ft high). Biodynamic treatment of compost heaps will be described below.

Well-matured and ripened composts can be applied at almost any time and for any crop. Crops which are heavy feeders may benefit from partially matured composts.

The above measures are fundamental to all sound organic farming methods, as well as to the biodynamic approach. But the latter is concerned with two polar groups of factors influencing plant

including dandelion, oak and yarrow. These are added to manures and composts after preparation, and have the effect of improving the overall quality of the resulting composts, including a higher holding capacity for nutrients, and improved growth-regulating influence on the root systems of crop plants. These effects have been well-demonstrated in a number of experimental programmes.

When biodynamic (and sometimes organic) farming is dubbed 'muck and magic', there might seem to be an element of 'magic' in the careful observance of certain cosmic rhythms in biodynamic practice. This derives from suggestions from Rudolph Steiner, which have been followed up in quite extensive experimental programmes. Only recently has science at large shown signs of taking seriously the possibility of detectable influences of moon rhythms and solar cycles on life on earth. But these are just one aspect of a variety of cosmic rhythms which are not without effect on the life of earth, which is itself organised in complex cycles and rhythms.

There is now some good experimental evidence that by observing appropriate patterns in sowing, cultivating, and application of preparations, definite effects are obtained on the yields and quality of cereal and root crops. It is not just a matter of sowing or planting at new or full moon. A significant factor is the sideral cycle of the moon with respect to the constellations of the zodiac. (A recently completed thesis at the University of Giessen reports some of the latest findings).

This is obviously a significant and intriguing line for further research, and must in due course have far-reaching effects on our conception of the relation of life on earth to the surrounding universe. Nevertheless, it should be emphasised that taking account of cosmic rhythms, while it may be a valuable addition to, is no substitute for, conventional farming skills, good husbandry and practical experience. And while cosmic factors may be universal, the terrestrial ones are enormously variable from place to place, so that an essential part of good farming is to acquire an intimate understanding of the soils and the climate of each particular farm.

When biodynamic methods are applied with skill and care, the results are quite soon apparent in the general health of crops and soil, and (sometimes even more markedly) in the health and performance of livestock.

NUTRITIONAL QUALITY

The nutritional value of produce is most usually assessed in terms of quantities of protein, carbo-hydrates, vitamins, minerals etc. There is nothing wrong with such an assessment as long as it is realised that it is a very partial view of true quality. Products of nature are, in a sense, like works of art, and their quality resides in the composition of various elements into a whole. Our healthy senses are an important and natural guide to assessing these 'works of art', whose qualities are expressed, among other things, in scent and smell, flavour,

growth and the life of the soil. The terrestrial factors include water, soil nutrients, and growth-regulating and disease-controlling factors in the soil. Cosmic influences include the light, warmth and rhythms of the atmosphere and the surrounding cosmos. In a healthy farm, the terrestrial and cosmic factors are maintained in a harmonious balance.

Composts and sound husbandry are essential. But the biodynamic farmer has at his disposal some special preparations to strengthen and maintain this balance. These preparations, first described by Steiner in his lectures on agriculture, are applied in very small quantities (it should be remembered that life processes can be affected by very small quantities of trace elements, plant hormones and other active substances in soil and plant tissues). The following preparations are in regular use: Two sprays, no. 500 and no. 501. No. 500, which is prepared from cow dung, is sprayed on moderately damp soil before sowing or planting. It has a quickening effect on soil life. The second spray, no. 501, is based on silica. It is sprayed on growing plants, and enhances the effects of light and warmth, increases resistance to fungal attack, enhances flavour and improves ripening of fruit and seed. Observations by growers, and quite extensive programmes of experiment, have led to specific modes of applying this preparation in accordance with stages of growth and cosmic rhythms.

A second set of preparations is based on the flowers or other parts of several common plants, texture, keeping qualities etc. Here the contrast between organically and chemically grown produce is immediately apparent. The smell of a cabbage being cooked immediately betrays its horticultural history. It should not be imagined that these qualities are mere frills to the nutritional value. The activation of taste and smell play an important part in stimulating and regulating the whole digestive process, in which there are subtleties as delicate as those in the life of the soil. We are gradually becoming aware that the qualities of the sense impressions by which we are surrounded can work into our mental and physical health. We should not be surprised if food which is inwardly disordered in its composition (even if this is not very obvious as taste and smell) brings disorder into our physical and mental health. There is a large and little explored field of research here, which will not be properly appreciated until qualitative questions about nutrition are taken as seriously as quantitative ones.

On purely quantitative measures, organically and biodynamically grown produce often shows clearly superior features in terms of vitamins, mineral content, and true protein. But at least as significant is the *balance* of these components. Some experiments in Sweden have recently highlighted this by comparing the protein, nitrate and vitamin content of spinach and other plants grown in varying conditions of light and shade. The chemically treated plants, even when grown in full light, show characteristics of growth in shade—a higher proportion of crude protein and nitrate, but a lower content of vitamin C and true protein. The organically grown, and still more the biodynamically grown plants, show a more harmonious and mature balance of these components which derives from a healthier balance of the terrestrial and cosmic growth factors.

Biodynamic research has made considerable use of a technique of sensitive crystallisation which supplements conventional quantitative analysis, and shows something of the quantitative constitution of a plant or a product as a whole. The test depends on learning to 'read' characteristic patterns of copper chloride crystals formed when water is evaporated from a solution in a shallow dish. Very different patterns result according to whatever small quantities of organic substances for test are added to the solution. It is a highly sensitive method which requires carefully controlled conditions and much experience to use properly, but there is now a considerable body of experimental literature on it. It has proved a valuable additional aid in exploring the difficult problem of quality in terms of the total balance and composition of components. The illustration on this page is given merely as an example of the kind of work in progress.

The emphasis on the total composition of foodstuffs as 'works of art' is reflected in biodynamic agriculture in the concept of a farm itself. Here, too, real health and lasting productivity depend on creating the right balance and

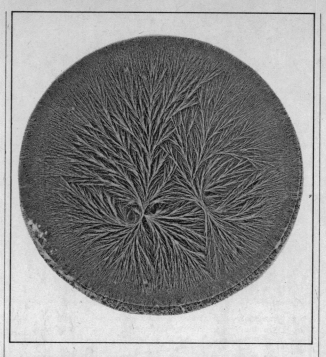

U. KOEPF

relationships between all the members of the farm 'community'—plants, animals, man, soil, water, air, light and cosmic rhythms. This is not a romantic ideal, but quite simply the basis for a truly ecological farming method. It will also lead to a much healthier relationship to the total energy resources of the earth. Some recent work at Sussex University and elsewhere has shown the enormous dependence of modern 'scientific' agriculture on huge supplies of energy imported either as manufactured fertilisers and farm chemicals, or more directly as fuel for enormous machines. Irrespective of their effects on the soil, plants and livestock, such methods are quite inapplicable on a world scale for any length of time, particularly in the less developed regions of the earth. A truly ecological thinking would long ago have made this obvious. In so far as such thinking develops, it must lead inevitably towards organic, and then into biodynamic agriculture.

MARKETING

Marketing of biodynamic produce began in parts of Europe under the trade mark 'Demeter' as early as 1928, and despite severe setbacks during the last war, has since expanded to a considerable trade. The trademark is a guarantee of defined standards of production, nutritional quality and storage procedures. Various staple foods, fruits, vegetables, some animal products and preserves, are available with this trademark, which involves annual inspections of crops by a biodynamic advisory service, together with spot testing and continued research. For a good many products, maintaining the standards means developing regional systems for supply and marketing. (The elaborate industrialised systems for food processing, packaging and long distance shipment, although partly necessary in present conditions, do not support real quality). In Great Britain, a working

BEATA BERGSTROM

(*Left*) Sensitive crystalization of extract from whole young rye plant. (*Above*) On the farm at Emerson College, Sussex: a healthy farm landscape with fields, grasses, trees, hedges, woods—and biodynamic farmers!

group of the Biodynamic Agricultural Association is responsible for putting the Demeter trademark system into effect.

TRAINING

It should be obvious that much of the training for biodynamic farming means acquiring the normal variety of professional farming skills required for any farming method. Practical experience on working farms or gardens is essential. Advice and guidance on the use of biodynamic methods and preparations can be obtained from various sources (see Bibliography), but it should be appreciated that biodynamic farming is more than a method: it is based on a view of the earth, and of man's relation to it, which is rooted ultimately in Steiner's anthroposophy, and it is not possible to go very deeply into biodynamics without exploring the wider context of outlook and life practice which this involves.

The biodynamic associations in many countries of Europe and in the United States offer a variety of conferences and introductory courses, as well as information. A school for biodynamic farming and gardening is based at Emerson College in Forest Row, Sussex, and offers a one-year course which includes practical work and some instruction in crop and animal husbandry and gardening, as well as an orientation in the fundamentals of the biodynamic approach.

CONCLUSION

Industrialised agriculture has gone to all kinds of extremes, not least the creation of a global network of production and transport of agricultural and food products, so that it is not at all impossible that British citizens will soon be eating yoghurt produced in New Zealand while New Zealanders consume yoghurt produced in Britain. In reaction to aberrations of this kind, there is now much talk

among those interested in the organic movement of 'self sufficiency'. Here there are obvious dangers of an opposite extreme, leading to a multiplicity of small, self-centred and fundamentally egotistic islands looking after their own interests and ignoring everyone else's.

True ecological thinking should bring a realisation of a deep truth in a principle which played a great part in the outlook of the Middle Ages, namely the fact that in the living world, the whole is found in each part, while each part is a member of a larger whole: the microcosm is an image of the macrocosm.

In practical biological terms, this means that every living organism is in one sense 'self-sufficient', in that it is a whole, self-regulating and self-maintaining. But at the same time it is an organic part of a larger environment, in a relation of mutual dependence. What applies to a single living organism extends also to groups of organisms, to a farm, a landscape, a region, and ultimately to the whole earth itself. There is no such thing in reality as a completely self-sufficient farm (unless someone succeeds in the science-fiction dream of enclosing themselves in a sealed plastic bubble). For the biodynamic farm, what matters is not self-sufficiency for its own sake, but the *relationships* between the various parts of the farm, and the relationship of the farm as a whole to its nearer and further surroundings. The farmer will feel himself responsible for a particular part of the earth, and will try to make it into a healthy organism, a living work of art. But at the same time, he will never forget that his farm is part of the life of a region, and of the whole earth, and that the life of the earth itself is part of a wider cosmic life of which we are little aware at present. No 'methods' of any kind are likely to bear full fruit unless backed by an awareness of this kind.

Dr. H.H. Koepf and John Davy

FOOD GLORIOUS FOOD

There are a few things which constitute good food, and many things which are eaten which are not foods at all. One definition of food is "any non-poisonous, organic substance that we can transform into living tissue" *(1)*. No single food is able to sustain health. We require a mixed and *balanced* diet.

A low energy diet aims at conserving energy— that is, taking the essential proteins, fats, carbohydrates, vitamins, minerals, enzymes and water direct from their sources without wastage *(2)*. These key elements are contained in most of the foods that you can grow and preserve yourself. Carbohydrates, vitamins, minerals and dietary fibre can all be provided by raw fruits and vegetables, preferably fresh, and our need for proteins and fats can be satisfied from plant or animal sources.

Food only becomes part of the body after being dismantled by the action of teeth, saliva, gastric juices, enzymes, muscular movements of the intestines and absorption by the bloodstream. The processes of chemical breakdown and build-up in the body are called metabolism.

PROTEIN

Our bodies need protein for growth, repair and enzyme formation; any excess is wasted by oxidation to provide energy or body fat. But over-consumption of protein accelerates the metabolism, strains the liver and kidneys and can cause calcium deficiency.

The total amount of protein in a food gives no indication of the amount *available* to the body and there is a wide disagreement on protein requirements. But the important thing is not so much to count grammes of protein as to make sure we do not waste it. We can cut down on our protein requirements by eating plant protein instead of meat.

If we examine the efficiency of various food production systems we find that leafy crops such as comfrey, alfalfa, kale and spinach can produce 26 times more protein per acre than beef cattle. Legumes average 10, cereals 5, and milk 2 times more protein per acre than beef. *(3)*.

Plant proteins provide 70 per cent of the world's supply, yet people still believe that animal protein is essential. But according to the HMSO *Manual of Nutrition (4)*; "If protein in the diet is supplied from . . . a very carefully chosen selection of vegetable foods, the amount required may be as little as if it came from animal sources alone, because the variety of amino acids available may enable the body to turn it economically into human protein." Which means that in a garden or allotment of suitable size, we can grow all the foods needed for a healthy diet.

The simplest sources of protein, in order of directness, are leaf and root vegetables, fruits and nuts, legumes and cereals, goat's milk, yoghurt, cheese and free-range eggs. In leaves, roots and fruits, however, the large proportion of inedible fibre, and the water-to-protein ratio, makes them unsuitable as a protein source—though the protein can be extracted by processing *(5)*.

PROTEIN COMBINATIONS

In the body, proteins are dismantled into the 22 amino acids. Of these, 14 can be synthesized by the body, while the other 8, called essential amino acids (EAAs) may be supplied in the diet. Growing children also require arginine and histidine. Body protein can only be formed efficiently if all the 8 EAAs are combined in one meal in correct proportions. A meal slightly deficient in one or more EAAs will give less protein than a correctly balanced meal.

What is this correct amino acid pattern? Mother's milk combines the EAAs, fats and less important nutrients in ideal proportions for the nutrition of babies. Only two per cent of cow's milk protein is wasted through incomplete digestion and absorption *(6)*. However, our requirements change during weaning and when growth is complete.

Some nutritionists have taken the egg as the ideal EAA pattern *(7)*. The egg is given a net protein utilization (NPU) of 100 per cent (NPU is the proportion of nitrogen intake that is retained). NPU values for foods can be found in *(8)* and *(9)*. The importance of NPU is stressed in *(8)* and its companion volume *(10)*, which contains many recipes for foods combined to increase protein utilisation. Fig 1 gives one example.

VITAMINS AND MINERALS

Vitamins and minerals are essential for good health and are closely associated with the regulation of the metabolism. They are found in most fresh, unprocessed foods, especially raw fruits and vegetables, and are needed regularly in small amounts. (Likely deficiencies, however, are B12 and D) The water-soluble vitamins (C and the B group) are easily destroyed or lost, usually down the drain with the cooking water. B vitamins, abundant in brewers yeast and sprouted wheat, are concerned with the release of energy from foods. Vitamin C, essential for growth, the healing of wounds, healthy teeth and bones is obtained if plenty of fresh raw fruit and vegetables are eaten.

The body has a limited ability to synthesize vitamin K and D. D is essential for calcium and phosphorus absorption, healthy bones and teeth.

Of the B vitamins, Biotin can be synthesized, and Nicotinic acid can be formed from the amino-acid trytophan. B12 prevents primary anaemia and is made in the intestine by *E.coli* bacteria, but usually too low down for absorption. Other sources are brewers yeast, wheat germ, soybeans and comfrey. Vitamins A, E and P are all available from plant sources.

Enzymes, regulators of chemical processes are destroyed and minerals such as magnesium are leached away during cooking.

FATS AND CARBOHYDRATES

These supply the calories of energy needed to move

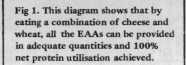

Fig 1. This diagram shows that by eating a combination of cheese and wheat, all the EAAs can be provided in adequate quantities and 100% net protein utilisation achieved.

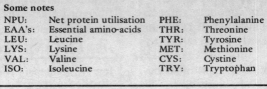

Some notes

NPU:	Net protein utilisation	PHE:	Phenylalanine
EAA's:	Essential amino-acids	THR:	Threonine
LEU:	Leucine	TYR:	Tyrosine
LYS:	Lysine	MET:	Methionine
VAL:	Valine	CYS:	Cystine
ISO:	Isoleucine	TRY:	Tryptophan

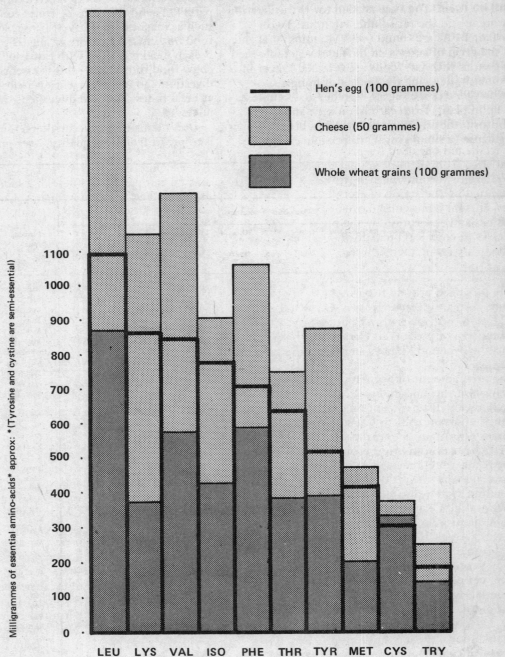

Complimentary effect of whole wheat and cheese amino-acids

Whole wheat grains have a NPU of only 43%, due to deficiencies in all EAA's (57% in Lysine) except Cystine.
Hen's egg is almost ideal, with a NPU of 94%.
By adding 50 grammes of cheese to the 100 grammes of wheat we can make up the deficiencies and get a NPU of 100%.

FOOD

and warm the body. Though fats supply more energy, carbohydrates are quite adequate and too much saturated fat should be avoided. If taken in excess, fats and carbohydrates are converted into body fat.

The three essential fatty acids (EFAs) must be supplied in the diet since the body cannot synthesize them. They are needed for the utilization of carotene and the fat-soluble vitamins. Two important EFAs are found (with vitamins A, D and E) in the germ of cereals, in nuts and vegetable seed oils. If eaten with fat, foods are retained longer in the stomach, delaying the feeling of hunger.

Carbohydrates are sugars, starches and celluloses built up in plants from carbon dioxide and water by photosynthesis. Sugars are starches broken down into glucose (a simple sugar) to provide energy.

Cellulose is not digestible but provides essential fibre or bulk to the diet. Lack of fibre causes intestinal disorders.

HEALTH AND ECONOMY

Eat foods whole for a balanced diet. The core of apples contains 24 times more iodine than the other parts (11) and the skins of fruits contain minerals such as magnesium. Harvest, rinse, scrub and prepare food *immediately* before eating. Digestion is easier if each meal is started with raw food. Enjoy and chew food thoroughly; this is essential for good digestion and helps prevent over-eating. Drinking at meal times dilutes and weakens the digestive juices.

Don't patronise supermarkets, their philosophy is to profit from low-quality, *over-processed, over-*

Table 1. Nutritional value of various vegetables.

Vegetable	Composition per ounce									Planting time	Harvest time
	Protein (g)	K calories	Calcium (mg)	Iron (mg)	Vit A (pg)	Thiamine (mg)	Riboflavine (mg)	Nicotinic Acid (mg)	Vit C (mg)		
Asparagus	0.7	7	6	0.3	78	0.05	0.06	0.5	10	Permanent bed	
Broad beans	2.0	19	9	0.3	6	0.08	0.01	1.4	9	Feb—May	June—Aug
Butter beans	5.2					0.15	0.20			May	Oct
Haricot beans	6.1	73	51	1.9	—	0.13	0.08	0.6	—	May	Nov
Runner beans	0.3	4	9	0.2	14	0.01	0.03	0.4	6	May—June	July—Oct
Beetroot	0.5	12	9	0.2	—	—	0.01	0.1	1	April—June	Sept—Oct
Broccoli	1.0	10	35	0.9	770	0.04	0.07	0.3	25	Mar—May	Oct—May
Brussels sprouts	1.0	9	8	0.2	19	0.03	0.05	0.4	28	Mar—April	Nov—Mar
Cabbages	0.4	8	18	0.3	14	0.02	0.01	0.1	17	Mar or May, June	June or Jan—Feb
Carrots	0.2	7	14	0.2	850	0.02	0.01	0.2	2	April	Oct
Cauliflower	1.0	7	5	0.2	1	0.03	0.03	0.4	20	April—Aug	Sept—June
Celery	0.3	2	15	0.2		0.01	0.01	0.1	2		Nov—Mar
Chard	0.7	7	25	0.9	550	0.02	0.05	0.1	9	Aug or May	Mar—July or Sept—Oct
Chicory	low nutritional value										
Cucumbers	0.03	4	7	0.3	—		0.01	0.1	3	April	July—Oct
Kale	1.7	15	71	0.8	860	0.05	0.07	0.6	53	April	Jan—April
Kohlrabi					210				11	April—June	July—Sept
Leeks					86					April	Nov—May
Lettuces	0.3	3	7	0.2	50*	0.02	0.02	0.1	4	Mar—Aug	May—Nov
Onions	0.3	7	9	0.1	—	0.01	0.01	0.1	3	Mar	Sept
Parsnips	0.5	14	16	0.2	—	0.03	0.03	0.1	4	April	Nov
Peas	1.6	18	4	0.5	14	0.09	0.04	1.0	7	Mar—July	July—Nov
Potatoes	0.6	22	2	0.2	—	0.03	0.01	0.5	5.5	April	Sept
Pumpkins					120						
Radishes		5	9	0.4	3	0.01	0.02	0.3	7	Mar—Sept	April—Oct
Rhubarb	0.2	2	29	0.1	3	—	0.02	0.1	3	Permanent bed	
Spinach	0.8	6	20	0.9**	284	0.03	0.06	0.4	17	Feb—Aug	May
Sweetcorn	1.0	28	—	—	25	0.04	0.03	0.4	3	May	Aug—Sept
Tomatoes	0.3	4	4	0.1	33	0.02	0.01	0.2	6	April—May	Aug—Oct
Turnip root	0.2	5	16		—		0.01	0.2	7	April—June or Aug	June—Aug or Feb
Turnip greens			28	0.9	850	0.03	0.10	0.2	29		

*   varies depending on how green the lettuce is; the figure is much higher for an open dark-green type, lower for a blanched or closely hearted type.

**   Oxalic acid in spinach interferes with absorption of calcium and iron, making them unavailable to the body, by forming insoluble salts. Spinach should not be eaten too green, although reasonable quantities are beneficial.

These nutritional values are not meant to be absolutely correct; foods contain slightly different nutrients depending on how fresh they are, what time of day they were picked, how they were grown. The values are mostly from McCance and Widdowson's tables given in appendix A of the Government's Manual of Nutrition (HMSO 1970). It is known that the variety of the plant grown affects the nutritional qualities, sometimes very significantly; for example, a Ribston Pippin apple contains 30.60 mg of Vitamin C per 100 grams, while Golden Delicious contains only 8.20 mg. This sort of information is hard to come by, as little work has been done in this area. Organic gardeners insist that their produce has higher nutritional value than chemically fertilised produce. This may be true, since it has been shown that although fertilisers boost the yields of potatoes, for example, the water content of the potatoes is much higher.

packaged food-substitutes. Refined carbohydrates can cause illness. Try to get foods fresh from their source. High water content foods (organically grown apples, cabbage, etc.) can supply better liquid than taps, endless cups of tea, coffee, cola or alcohol. Make a habit of sprouting nutritious grains and protein-rich legumes *(2),* which are delicious with grated, raw salads *(12).* Make your own yoghurt *(13)* and to make sure you get good food value; grow your own fruit and vegetables *(14).*

John Shore

REFERENCES

(1) Shelton, H.H. (1969) *Health for the Millions* Natural Hygiene Press, USA

(2) Shore, J. (1974) 'Organic Living Experiment' *Undercurrents* 6 and 8, London

(3) Wokes, F. (1968) 'Proteins' *Plant Foods in Human Nutrition* Pergamon, London

(4) Min.Agric.Fish.Food (1970) *Manual of Nutrition* HMSO, London

(5) Byers, M., Green, S.H. and Pirie, N.W. (1965) *Nutrition* 19, 63

(6) Fox and Cameron (1968) *A Chemical Approach to Food and Nutrition* Univ. of London Press, London

(7) FAO/WHO (1965) *Protein Requirements* Report 37, Rome

(8) Lappe, F. (1971) *Diet for a Small Planet* Friends of the Earth/ Ballantine, New York

(9) FAO (1970) *Amino-Acid Content of Foods and Biological Data on Protein,* Rome

(10) Ewald, E. (1973) *Recipes for a Small Planet* Ballantine Books, New York

(11) Bircher-Benner (1971) *Fruit Dishes and Raw Vegetables* C.W. Daniel, Essex (30p)

(12) Bircher, R. (1961) *Eating Your Way to Health* Faber and Faber, London

(13) Hills, H.C. (1970) *Housewives Help* Vol 2, Henry Doubleday Research Assoc, Essex (20p)

(14) Hills, L.D. (1974) *Dig for Survival* Henry Doubleday Research Assoc. (3p) 20 Convent Lane, Bocking, Braintree, Essex

Table 2. Amount of nutrients per month provided by 10 sq ft of ground under different vegetable crops.

Vegetable	Yield per 10 feet of row (lbs)	Months to grow	Distance between rows (inches)	Yield per 10 sq ft (lbs)	Protein (g)	K calories	Calcium (mg)	Iron (mg)	Vit A (pg)	Thiamine (mg)	Riboflavine (mg)	Nicotinic Acid (mg)	Vit C (mg)	Others
Asparagus	3.5	12 (permanent)	50	0.84	0.8	225	7	0.4	88	0.05	0.07	0.55	11.2	
Broad beans	5.0	4	20	3.00	24	225	107	3.6	73	0.95	0.12	16.50	107.5	
Butter beans	5	5	24	2.5	42					1.2	1.60			
Haricot beans	0.7	6	18	0.5	7.5	91	63	2.3	—	0.17	0.1	0.75	—	
Runner beans	15	4	24	7.5	9	120	270	6.0	425	0.3	0.9	12.00	180	
Beetroot	9	4	8	13.5	27	665	483	10.5	—		0.52	5.25	52	High Catalase
Broccoli	9	10	24	4.5	7	73	253	6.7	5,850	0.29	0.51	2.15	180	Pantothenic Acid
Brussels sprouts	5	12	24	2.5	3	30	27	0.7	63	0.1	0.17	1.33	93	
Cabbage, summer	15	3	24	7.5	16	320	717	12.0	518	0.8	0.4	4.00	680	
Cabbage, winter	15	8	24	7.5	6	120	270	4.5	194	0.3	0.15	1.50	255	
Carrots	10	6	8	15.0	8	180	400	8.0	40,000	0.8	0.6	8.00	80	
Cauliflower, summer	10	4	30	4.0	16	120	80	8.2	16	0.48	0.48	6.40	320	
Cauliflower, winter	10	10	30	4.0	6	48	32	1.3	6	0.19	0.19	2.56	128	
Celery	7	8	24	3.5	2	14	105	1.4	—	0.07	0.07	0.70	14	
Chard, summer	10	4	15	8.0	22	225	800	28.3	17,625	0.64	1.6	3.20	288	
Chard, winter	10	8	15	8.0	11	112	400	14.4	8,813	0.32	0.8	1.60	144	
Cucumber	9	6	50	2.2	—	25	41	1.7	—	—	0.06	0.60	17	
Kale, borecole	3	6	30	1.2	5	48	227	2.4	2,716	0.16	0.22	1.94	168	High Vit E, K
Kale, rape	3	12	30	1.2	3	24	113	1.2	1,358	0.08	0.11	0.97	84	
Kohlrabi	25	3	12	2.5					2,800				147	
Leeks	7.5	7.5	12	7.5					858					
Lettuces	7.5	3	8	11.25	18	180	420	12.0	3,000	1.2	1.2	6.00	240	
Onions	8.5	6	8	12.75	10	240	305	3.8	—	0.35	0.35	3.50	103	
Parsnips	11	7	15	8.8	10	290	320	4.0	—	0.66	0.66	1.21	80	
Peas	6.5	4	24	3.25	21	235	52	6.5	181	1.18	0.52	13.00	91	
Potatoes	15	5	27	6.7	13	470	43	4.3	—	0.64	0.21	10.70	116	Pantothenic Acid + Pyrodoxine
Radishes	1.5	1	9	2.0		160	293	11.2	96	0.32	0.64	0.96	224	
Rhubarb	10	12 (permanent)	36	3.33	1	9	128	0.4	13	0.0	0.09	0.44	13	
Spinach, summer	5	2	9	6.66	43	320	1,070	48.0	15,150	1.6	3.2	21.35	915	
Spinach, winter	5	7	9	6.66	12	90	306	13.7	4,329	0.46	0.91	6.10	261	
Sweetcorn	7.5	4	30	3.00	12	335	—	—	300	0.48	0.36	4.80	36	
Tomatoes	20	5	36	6.66	6	85	85	2.0	727	0.43	0.21	4.26	128	
Turnip, summer	13	2	9	17.53	21*	535+	2,690	38.7	27,220	2.01	4.27	27.80	1,675	
Turnip, winter	13	6	9	17.33	7*	180+	897	13.0	9,087	0.67	1.42	9.27	558	

*   Turnip, root plus greens

**   These yields are averages from several sources and could vary considerably; much higher yields are suggested by experienced gardeners.

Yields and analyses based on:
Bist and Ward: *The Garden Controversy*
L.D. Hills: *Grow Your Own Fruit and Vegetables*
V.H. Mottram: *Human Nutrition*
W.G. Smith: *Gardening for Food*
HMSO: *Manual of Nutrition*
HMSO: *Home Preservation of Fruit and Vegetables*

Patricia Pringle

A QUESTION OF BALANCE

Zen-macrobiotics is a way of nourishing yourself. It is part of a way of life commonly known as Zen-buddhism, originating in ancient China, and practised by Zen-buddhist monks in and outside of monasteries. The purpose of Zen-macrobiotics is to keep your body's bio-chemical process operating at full capacity with a minimum wastage of physical or mental energy.

It was George Oshawa, a little Japanese fellow, who first brought Zen-macrobiotics to the West. When he was 16, orthodox Western medicine gave him no more than two years to live, as he was suffering from TB. Indeed his whole family had already died suffering from illnesses that could not be cured by conventional 'scientific' methods. Having nothing much to lose, he turned to ancient Chinese medicine, and came up not with acupuncture but with Zen-macrobiotics. He lived happily to the age of 67.

contractive and inward moving. Yin is matriarchal, cold, dark, receptive, earth and water, fluid, and changeable in expression as the face of the moon. Yang is patriarchal, heat, light, creative, air and fire, rigid, and constant in expression as the light of the sun. It may seem odd, that Yin, or female motion, is termed as both expansive and receptive, the latter seeming to indicate impressionability and passivity. The way it works is that Yin, by its very unformed, dispersive drive to expansion, invites, and receives, Yang rigidity and contraction, whereby a specific form or shape is created, depending on the integrational Yin-Yang pattern at that moment. In that way, light divides darkness, and planets, by pursuing their orbits in space, define time. By being obstructed in its expansion, Yin is thrown back on itself, and thereby regenerates, instead of dissolving into nothingness. And by having an expansive force to combat, Yang can actually realise its formative powers in matter. It is important to relate this Yin-Yang principle to food, because physically speaking you are what you eat, and like every other form, the human body has an inherent balance, created by

When he started propagating this diet in the Fifties, he very much emphasized its medicinal use in curing ourselves from our welfare diseases, and the fact that it is part of a philosophy and a way of life was not made quite clear enough. Consequently, the real purpose and principles of macrobiotics have frequently been misunderstood. Like the idea that eating macrobiotically will increase your consciousness. It won't. What it increases is your sensual perceptivity. Or that it is a sober diet with very strict rules to follow, whereas the whole meaning of Zen-macrobiotics is to grasp a principle so basic and so essential to every form of life that it can be applied to any individual situation, circumstance, or metabolism.

This principle evolved from the concept of dual forces, antagonistic and complementary, and it is used to understand the laws according to which these forces integrate and create. The Chinese term them Yin and Yang, in the West we tend to think of them as positive and negative, while bio-chemistry defines them as acid-alkaline, or potassium and sodium. Yin is expansive, outward moving. Yang is

the interaction of the two forces.

Imagine your body like a see-saw, one end extreme Yang the other extreme Yin. Keeping it poised in balance, so that a constant harmony is established on which you can base your (eventual) increase of consciousness, can be done by fortifying the centre through eating foods whose Yin-Yang balance is close to your own molecular structure. However, most people feed on foods that only strengthen one end of the see-saw or the other. As the body has to cope with these excesses, the centre is extensively strained, and thereby prone to all sorts of diseases. We are conditioned to believe that physical suffering is quite natural, to a degree, but that's not really true. There is such a thing as physical perfection, practically attainable. It's a question of balance.

There are as many different ways to achieve this balance as there are people, but whole grains, for example, contain a lot of trace elements essential to the well-functioning of the human system, and the variety and quantity eaten can be adapted to any individual's needs. Brown rice, for example has a

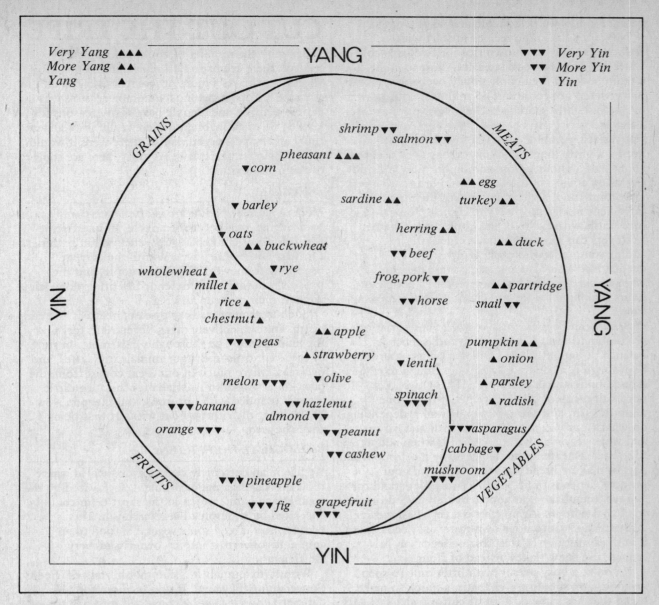

Very Yang ▲▲▲
More Yang ▲▲
Yang ▲

YANG

▼▼▼ Very Yin
▼▼ More Yin
▼ Yin

GRAINS

MEATS

shrimp ▼▼   salmon ▼▼

pheasant ▲▲▲

▼corn

▼ barley

sardine ▲▲

▲▲ egg
turkey ▲▲

▼ oats
▲▲ buckwheat

herring ▲▲

▲▲ duck

wholewheat ▲
millet ▲

▼ rye

▼▼ beef

frog, pork ▼▼

rice ▲

▼▼ horse

▲▲ partridge
snail ▼▼

chestnut ▲

YIN

YANG

▼▼▼ peas

▲▲ apple

pumpkin ▲▲

▲ strawberry

▼ lentil

▲ onion

melon ▼▼▼

▼ olive

spinach
▼▼▼

▲ parsley

▲ radish

▼▼▼ banana

▼▼ hazlenut
almond ▼▼

▼▼▼asparagus

orange ▼▼▼

cabbage▼

▼▼ peanut

mushroom
▼▼▼

▼▼ cashew

FRUITS

VEGETABLES

▼▼▼ pineapple

▼▼▼ fig

grapefruit
▼▼▼

YIN

Yin-Yang potassium-sodium ratio of 5 to 1, which is the Yin-Yang ratio closest to that of the human body. Brown rice also contains protein, fat, silicium, magnesium, phospher, calcium, and vitamin B_1. Oats and corn are rich in fat, oats and barley are rich in mineral salts, whole wheat and buckwheat are rich in protein. All grains contain iron, calcium, phosphorous, magnesium, protein, sugar, and an assortment of vitamins.

In choosing fruits and vegetables you can't go far wrong if you stick to what grows naturally (not in greenhouses) within a 500 mile radius. Avoid potatoes, tomatoes and eggplant. The Yin-Yang ratio in a potato is 512 to 1, so it's very very Yin, and known to be poisonous when consumed in excesses. Most animal foods and their by-products are chemically treated, and for that reason should be avoided.

Macrobiotics is not to be confused with vegetarianism, and if you can find organic meat, go ahead and eat it, just remember it's nourishing the extreme Yang end of your imaginary physical see-saw, so if taken in large quantities it will upset your

equilibrium. Wild birds, fresh fish and shellfish are preferable in terms of balance.

In determining what is best for you, you use the Yin-Yang principle to analyse your environment physiologically. A cold climate will produce predominantly Yang feeds, while a hot, or Yang climate, will produce Yin feeds. Whether a fruit or vegetable is more Yin or Yang can be seen partly by observing its form, size, and colour. If you cut open an orange, for example, you'll see the lines of its flesh almost explosively radiate outwards, and it contains a lot of acidy liquid, which is enough at first sight to qualify it as a fairly Yin fruit. If you're in Morocco or California it's a harmonius thing to eat there, because that is where it naturally grows. Up north you had better get your vitamin C out of rosehip or hibiscus tea, as all that acidy juice makes you prone to colds. The diagram shows how most foods are rated on Yin-Yang terms, so you can see for yourself what sort of balance you are keeping now, and where there is room for improvement. Experimenting is the best way to find out where you're at, foodwise (or otherwise) and remember

FOOD

you are your own best medicineman or woman.

Now for some basic recipes to start with:

◆ *Rice:* use one cup brown rice for two cups cold water and ½ a teaspoon sea-salt. Allow to come to a rapid boil and then cook slowly over a low flame in a covered pot for about 45 minutes, until bottom of pot is slightly scorched. The yellow part is most Yang and very good because it's richest in minerals. For variety, combine with red soya beans, which need a slightly longer cooking time, so put them on about half an hour before adding the rice, and add salt when almost finished. Rice and beans are a very important food, and can be used as the main ingredient in a great variety of dishes. You can also mix lentils with the rice, and cook these together. Leftovers can be used to make croquettes by adding water and whole wheat flour, then deepfrying. Wheat, barley and rye are delicious when cooked whole, but they require a couple of hours soaking in water and about 1½ hour cooking time.

◆ *Bread:* can be made out of almost any variation or combination of whole flours, and is most balanced when unyeasted, unless you use sourdough. Sourdough is made by leaving your dough to stand around under a wet cloth for a day or two. You need half a cup of oil to 4½ cups of flour, one teaspoon salt, and about ½ cup of water, depending on what flour you use. Mix flour, salt and oil first, and work very well with your hands when adding the water. Kneading the dough is the most important part of making bread, and the quality of your product depends on it. When kneaded let stand for ½ hour, then bake it at approximately 375 degrees for 1 to 1½ hours. Again, this is a very basic recipe, you can adjust it to your own taste and needs, mix it with raisins, nuts, dates, sesame seeds, or, for crunch, use some flakes instead of flour.

If you're a busy person with little time to spend on food, you should try chapatis, a quick to make bread that has survived a lot of cultural changes. Mix equal portions of wheatflour and cornflour. Salt to taste. Add water until dough doesn't stick to your fingers. Flatten with your hands or roll out and bake in pan over low flame for about ten minutes. Try buckwheat flour and unbleached white flour, too. Make chapati extremely thin. When making pies and pastries use more oil than you would for bread.

◆ *Stews:* vegetable stews are good when you use quite a bit of tamari (soya sauce) or miso (soya bean paste), and become very nice casseroles if you add some flour. Take care not to make it lumpy. Always use vegetables that are in season.

I said earlier there were no rules to follow, just a principle to understand and apply, but there is one thing you should never do, and that is use sugar. Both brown and white sugar can't be broken down into body sugar, so they clog up the bloodstream and they're plain poison.

Peace and harmony to you.

Monica Hill

CUT OUT THE TRIPE

Judging by the number of cookbooks on the subject, there seems to be a revival in interest in vegetarianism. As a more or less strict vegetarian I'm going to set down the most common reasons why people become one. People have many reasons for kicking the meat habit and there really isn't such a thing as a typical vegetarian. If there were it would be much easier to explain. Anyway, here are some of the main reasons:

INHUMANITY

Modern animal production is often a very unpleasant business, especially for the animal. In its extreme form chickens are kept tightly enclosed in batteries for their entire short lives. Within the current economic framework this is inevitable, and the process is in fact being extended to other domestic animals such as sheep and pigs.

Such treatment leads to disease, neurosis and early death, and subjectively many vegetarians feel that the animals must be thoroughly miserable. In spite of some controls in Britain animals still suffer, and overseas, where much of our meat comes from, the position is worse. In Australia for instance cattle are still branded with hot irons, and sheep in New Zealand get their throats cut without first being anaesthetised.

BIOLOGICAL INEFFICIENCY

We live in an extremely overcrowded world where food shortage is a major problem, aggravated by the meat eating habit, which in the short term could be alleviated by widespread vegetarianism. This is because if you feed some vegetable food to an animal it converts it into its own tissues very inefficiently.

With farm animals it is common to talk of 'Feed Conversion Efficiency'. If you feed ten tons of barley to cows it may be converted into one ton of cow, ie with 10 per cent Feed Conversion Efficiency. As only half the cow is eaten the efficiency is in fact only five per cent. This means that in this case you could feed twenty hungry people with the barley that is needed to produce meat for one person.

The efficiency of most animal production systems is lower than this so that food production using animals as an intermediary can be still more extravagant. We can't afford much meat in an overpopulated world. Generally speaking dairy production has a greater biological efficiency than meat.

Much of the world's wildlife resources are also threatened by meat hungry people who can't produce enough of it on their farms.

HEALTH REASONS

There are several of these. The first is fat. Farm animals today, like humans, are far too fat. This means that when you eat meat you get much more fat than is natural and healthy. Wild animals just don't have those white streaks of fat that we see in

all the meat in butchers' shops. Animal fat today is recognised as a major killer. Thousands of people in Britain die from heart disease every year, and one of the main causes is thought to be too much animal fat—particularly cholesterol. If you want to be a survivor don't eat meat.

Farm animals, like most fruit and vegetables, are not organically grown. Because the consequences of this are generally less well known than the consequences of eating too much cholesterol I'll mention it in a bit more detail. Farm animals today are subjected to mass medication on a grand scale throughout their lives. They are dosed, drenched, and injected with a whole range of agrochemicals designed to keep the parasites of intensive agriculture at bay. Needless to say, some of these substances are present in the animal when it is slaughtered. Also, some animals are dosed with other substances such as hormones and antibiotics and so on that have been shown to have serious side effects. These haven't yet been demonstrated in the people who eat the meat but it's enough to scare off some of us.

Farm animals, being grass eaters, also consume the agrochemicals that are applied to their food. These may accumulate in their bodies, as DDT is shown to do. When we eat meat we may be eating the accumulated agrochemicals of huge amounts of vegetable food—much more than we could ever eat directly. Although DDT is no longer applied to the land it is still present in the grass and therefore in the animals that eat it. Also, there are still some agrochemical poisons being applied to the land, such as cadmium in superphosphate fertilizer, that can accumulate in the meat of farm animals.

Animal foods often contain parasites such as flukes and tapeworms, and disease-causing organisms, whereas foods of plant origin do not. There are plenty of sick Germans who can attest to the foolishness of eating raw meat.

ECONOMIC CONSIDERATIONS

Animal production, because it involves the consumption of huge amounts of plant material (much of which could be eaten by humans) is very expensive. Despite the sale of cheaply produced foreign meat in Britain, it still costs more than plant foods. People living on a small budget simply can't afford meat. Although meat is a concentrated source of several nutrients they are relatively expensive. Whatever nutrient you need there is a cheaper form to be found in the plant kingdom or dairy products—so why waste money?

TECHNOLOGICAL INEFFICIENCY

Modern farming systems rely very heavily on complex technology, as opposed to labour and relatively simple machinery. Technology-intensive agriculture uses large amounts of agrochemicals and fuel to keep going. It is thus very dependent on non-renewable resources such as fossil fuels, whereas pretechnological agriculture depended mainly on renewable resources of human labour.

In our small island where we eat more than we grow, our sustained food production is very precarious. We really can't expect to be able to continue our animal-based agriculture in a shrinking world. We could however feed ourselves completely on a predominantly vegetarian diet. The example of the 10 tons of barley producing the half ton of edible cow shows this. As the "post-industrial" age draws closer it seems that vegetarianism offers the only hope for the future.

Although animal production can be de-technologised, this can only be at the expense of reduced output. When resources are tight we will need all our spare technology for plant production. In the past, whenever there has been a food crisis in Britain, the first types of foodstuffs to be affected have been the least biologically efficient. In 1940–1945 the biggest cutbacks were in beef cattle, with smaller reductions in more efficient energy converters like dairy cattle and pigs. Plant production actually increased.

I think we are beginning to see this again now. Meat prices are rising much faster than those of cereals. Farmers are moving out of meat production because people are now eating the grains that previously went to cattle.

Britain is slowly but surely entering a vegetarian era compatible with its chronic food shortage and the realization that energy- and technology-intensive agriculture can't last for *ever*.

Tony Joyce

AFTER THE GOLDFISH

In the far East, 'back yard' fish ponds are an important source of protein for many families. As a result, one or two varieties of *Tilapia* and Grass Carp fish have been developed for this purpose; they could, perhaps, be bred for conditions in this country. Most *Tilapia* varieties need high day-temperatures in order to achieve maximum growth. One type, namely *Tilapia rendalli*, has been successfully introduced to the river waters of St. Helens, Lancashire. It survives chiefly because of the waste heat dumped into the river by local industrial plant. Perhaps more importantly, *Tilapia* are resistant to high levels of pollution and low levels of oxygen—a combination not uncommon to this part of the world.

Tilapia rendalli, (also known as *Tilapia melanopleura*) and its cousin *Tilapia tholloni* are two varieties which feed exclusively on low-grade vegetable matter. For this reason they can be fed on kitchen waste, such as vegetable peelings and coffee grounds, when they have grown bigger than 4—5 cms in length. In many far Eastern countries, the habit of throwing sewage into the fish ponds is common practice, and enhances the growth of the fish (although exposed, untreated sewage can be hazardous to human health).

For breeding a suitable variety of *Tilapia* for this climate, it may prove profitable to look firstly at temperature control, since *Tilapia* are inclined to over-reproduction at their optimum temperatures of 20—21°C (68—70°F).

One omnivorous variety with a lower reproductive potential is *Tilapia sparrmani* which will tolerate temperatures as low as 8°C (46—47°F). *Tilapia* grow

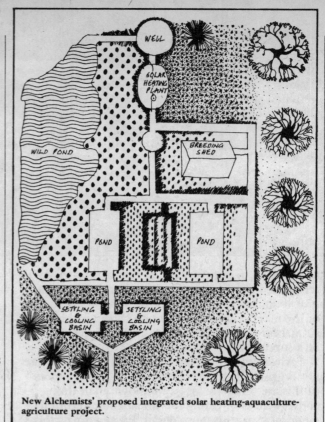

New Alchemists' proposed integrated solar heating-aquaculture-agriculture project.

quickly if fed daily:— my pair of *T. mossambica* (omnivores) grew from 1½ inches to 4 inches in their first six months, and to a fat 6 inches length in their second six months. Most fish automatically stop growing when they reach a size related to their pond-dimensions (although I have seen *Tilapia* almost as big as their tanks). By continuously circulating the water in and out of their tanks, it is possible to trick

Tilapia	Ducks	Fresh water 'mussels'	Crayfish	Catfish
Yield: up to 3,000 kg/hectare of live fish stocked at 3,000 fingerlings 1 hectare	*Yield:* 200 ducks/hectare	*(Lampsilis claibournensis)*	There are over 100 species of crayfish in US, all edible. Research will be needed to select most suitable species, although one of *Orconectes spp* might be best for pond culture	All ponds will drain into either of two cooling/settling basins designed to insure that thermally organically enriched water does not pass out of the system
Food input: virtually nil as they feed upon phytoplankton. Fertilization necessary (see ducks)	*Food input:* nourishment mainly from the pond, some duck feed necessary and research into most appropriate source needed	*Yield:* minimum of 200 kg/hectare of shelled mussel meats used as food crop, being eaten fried or in soups and shells for buttons and ornaments	*Yield:* up to 1,000 kg/hectare	Yellow bullheads *(Ictalurus natalis)* and 'mussels' which are tolerant of turbidity and enriched waters will be stocked to provide a further source
Harvesting: Tilapia will be harvested in the fall, and small breeding facilities maintained over winter, at 25°C	*Fertilization:* recent research in Czechoslovakia demonstrated duck manure produces more nutritious and digestible varieties of phytoplankton than commercial phosphate fertilizers	*Food input:* virtually nil, and its filtering action has been shown to increase fish production (bass and bluegills) by 40%	*Food input:* it is not known in this polyculture system if extra crayfish food will be needed to maintain yields in pure crayfish ponds. Culturists often add hay, potatoes, cracked corn, etc	of good quality food and fishing for the community's children
Breeding: monosex cultures to prevent stunting or overpopulation, hybrid strains 100% male from *Tilapia hornorum* *Tilapia mossambica*	*Pens* designed so that duck wastes enter ponds	*Source of soil:* their waste products known as 'mussel mud' make superb soil-fertilizers for vegetable production. One pond will be left drained each year, and planted to vegetable crops. Duck wastes and 'mussel mud' will make fertilizer input unnecessary.		After draining the sediment will be added to winter garden or vegetable garden
Tilapia will not survive winter outside of artificially heated ponds, consequently they will not upset natural ecosystems if they accidentally escape				

New Alchemy Institute's polyculture system
(Adapted from W.O. McLarney, 1970)

fish into believing themselves to be in roomier surroundings than they are. This has been achieved with *Tilapia* by Bill McLarney of the New Alchemy Institute, and with Rainbow Trout by Frank Mitchell of the Institute for Local Self-Reliance in Washington D.C. Dr. Mitchell's system works in an urban basement containing 500 gallon tank, artificial lighting and pumping equipment. 500 to 1,000 trout are maintained in tap water which is re-circulated every hour by a low-energy electric pump.

In the New Alchemists' system, solar-heated ponds are stocked with young *Tilapia* at densities of 3,000 per hectare and achieve a harvest of up to 3,000 kilogrammes per hectare. Food for the fish is almost totally provided by phytoplankton in the water. These organisms are in turn nourished by the manure of ducks which live on the same pond. The ducks are fed on fairly standard duck feed.

Similar polycultural systems in Malaya make use of several species co-existing on the same area to optimise local conditions. One example comprises a 4.4 hectare pond next to pigsties. Running water passes through the sties to carry their manure into the ponds where *Tilapia* and Chinese Carp are stocked. The fish thrive on fast-growing diatoms and crustacea produced by the pig dung. The ponds are also planted with a fast growing acquatic vegetable called *Ipomea Repens* which is harvested by hand at a rate of several hundred kilogrammes per day. These vegetable plants are fed to the pigs, thus completing the cycle. Overall, the farm produces 30,000 kilogrammes of pig-meat and 3,000 kilogrammes of fish each year.

John Wood

NEW ALCHEMY INSTITUTE

Bill McLarney in NewAlchemy *Tilapia* dome. The temperature of the dome is regulated by opening sections of its skin.

HYDROPONICS
the answer lies in solution

Hydroponics is the art and science of growing crops without using soil, by feeding them on solutions of water and nutrients which contain all the vital elements necessary for quick and healthy development. At first glance, such a method of cultivation might well strike the average householder or gardener as being directly opposed to traditional systems of tilling the ground, and indeed—following the views of some schools of thought—as unnatural.

Yet, if we will but take time to make just a brief study of the relevant facts we will soon see that although hydroponics is of course very different in practice to conventional farming and gardening, it is actually a completely natural technique, based on accepted ecological principles, and combining high productivity with several important environmental advantages for both plants and human beings.

In modern industrial societies, few persons, even if they are lucky enough to possess a plot of earth, have the opportunity—or the energy after a hard day's toil in factory or office—to dig, manure and weed the soil in order to produce green food for themselves and their families. In addition, the problem of space is fast becoming more serious and there are millions of people who would like to garden at weekends but who have not got any room to do so. Meanwhile, the prices of vegetables and fruits sold in shops and markets increase rapidly and constantly, putting ever greater strains on already hard-pressed household budgets and depriving men, women and children of the benefits of fresh produce, always essential for a balanced and healthy diet.

It is therefore not surprising that today more and more persons are turning towards hydroponics as a means of providing regular supplies of green foods and fruit in their homes. Gardening without soil can be very attractive to flat dwellers, people living in apartments or in tower blocks, in overcrowded cities and suburbs, or in other congested surroundings, whose resources are limited. Because hydroponic methods take up much less space than soil gardening would they are ideal for such situations. Moreover, soilless crop growing demands no hard manual work, and there are no jobs to perform comparable to those of digging, manuring and weeding the earth. Provided a few simple rules are adhered to, anyone can operate a hydroponic unit successfully in conditions where ordinary soil gardening would be impracticable.

The term 'hydroponics' means literally 'water working' and is derived from the Greek words *hudor,* water, and *ponos,* work. It was first used by Dr. William F. Guericke, of the University of California, in the mid-1930's. Since that time, of course, many advances have been made in soilless cultivation, so that we now find hydroponic techniques well established in many areas of the world. Numerous different methods of soilless crop growing have been developed, adapted to contrasting circumstances, such as climate, geography, finance and levels of technology. Thus there are hydroponic systems for large commercial farms, others for desert or barren regions, and still more for householders, amateur gardeners and those persons interested in self-sufficiency and diverse life-styles.

Plants need certain essential items to grow and produce harvests. These include: light, air, water, a support for their roots, and food. Air is a gift of nature; light may be too but it can also be provided by man in the form of electricity; water similarly can come from rainfall or by pipe and well; a support for the roots can be supplied through different devices; while food may be offered in convenient and ingenious ways, which are completely acceptable and satisfactory to the plants.

In hydroponics, we strive to create the best environmental conditions for crops. Instead of giving plants earth and manure to feed on or anchor their roots in, we provide them with certain types of substrates or growing media and nourish them on solutions of water and fertilizers. Various misleading statements are made from time to time asserting that hydroponic methods of culture are artificial and that the produce from soilless units is lacking in nutritional value. Now although it may well be that food produced in factory farms is tasteless and inferior, this is not the case with hydroponic produce. In fact, the flavour and palatability of fruits and vegetables grown without soil are excellent, because the plants receive maximum feeding with a well balanced range of nutrient elements. Extensive tests and analyses have indicated that the mineral and vitamin contents of hydroponic crops are fully up to highest quality standards. Flours from hydroponically grown wheat have proved better for bread making, while it has been possible to incorporate extra iron and calcium in tomatoes and other vegetables for feeding to babies and invalids. On farms, it is now possible to grow grass without soil in special hydroponic units, for feeding dairy cows and beef stock, which matures in seven days after sowing. This green forage is extremely high in protein and mineral content and greatly increases milk yields and the health and well-being of cattle or other livestock.

Agricultural scientists and farmers know very well that excessive artificial fertilizers, without the use of any humus, destroy the tilth of, and degrade, the land. But they continue to employ them alone or in unbalanced quantities for purely economic reasons to get money as quickly as possible, without thought for the future. This is the chief criticism that can be made of modern farming. Evils such as erosion, disease, and destruction of the environment follow upon this abuse of the good earth. But in hydroponics there is no land to destroy, so any such complaint cannot be made. On the contrary, by creating vegetation where there has been none, hydroponics performs a most valuable ecological function.

The hydroponic method, in practice, means that instead of applying organic or inorganic manures to land, where they have to be, in the first case, broken down by bacterial action before they can be assimilated by green plants, the fertilizers are given direct as solutions to the crops. Higher plants cannot absorb immediately organic materials. A considerable time must elapse before the necessary changes take place to make the nutrients present in such substances available to crops. What we are doing in hydroponics is simply to shorten this period dramatically, thus providing immediate nutriment in well balanced form to plants. This is why growth is so much more rapid in soilless cultures and the crops thrive so well. The process is perfectly natural and is in fact much safer and ecologically more sound than the current soil farming practice of spreading vast unbalanced quantities of chemicals over the countryside.

GROWING METHODS

Many different systems and methods of hydroponics are in use throughout the world today. Whilst some of these techniques are intended to serve the purposes of large commercial growers, quite a number are ideally suited to the needs of households, communities and families, for self-support and home production. Naturally, it is advisable to consider carefully the standard of education and the general social and technological development or condition of any community—those which exist or those which may be desired—when recommending a hydroponic technique for particular circumstances. It would be useless to introduce certain practices,

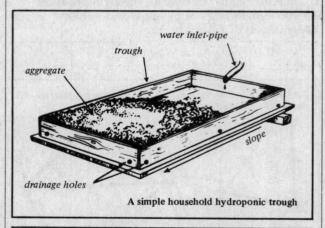

A simple household hydroponic trough

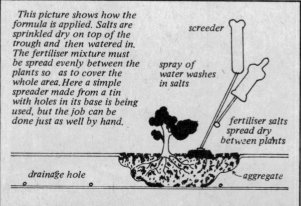

This picture shows how the formula is applied. Salts are sprinkled dry on top of the trough and then watered in. The fertiliser mixture must be spread evenly between the plants so as to cover the whole area. Here a simple spreader made from a tin with holes in its base is being used, but the job can be done just as well by hand.

The nutrients, once they are dissolved by the spray of water, go into solution and supply the plants roots with food. The cut-away section here shows what happens.

perhaps well suited to a peasant population living in under-developed surroundings, to a more intellectually advanced group in an industrial situation. Quite apart from differences in tastes and habits, there is a need to provide a viable level of operations for each case, or else skills present in the people concerned would be wasted. This is good ecology—to match the system to the subjects concerned, so that a satisfying and balanced life-style is secured.

Let us now consider a few methods of simple hydroponics for food production:

(a) Sand or aggregate culture. Very cheap hydroponic units can be made by lining wooden green-grocers' boxes or similar containers with polythene plastic sheeting or by using plant pots and plastic troughs. Normally, such receptacles should not be less than six inches deep and not over two feet wide, though they may be of any convenient length. For larger areas, beds or troughs, some eight inches deep by a yard wide and again of any appropriate longitudinal dimension, can be prepared by stretching the polythene sheeting over the ground or bare surface available, and supporting it at the sides and ends by bricks, stones, boards or other means. It is, however, possible to make almost any shape of trough or container to fit in with the circumstances of a backyard, kitchen, rooftop or other site. Many other good places exist for soilless gardens around the home, such as window sills, verandahs, the sides of pavements, and waste ground.

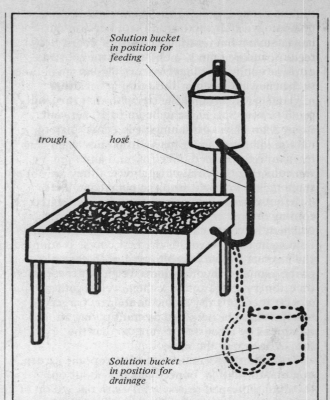

A small, easily made household unit. *The bucket is filled with nutrient solution which irrigates the growing container when placed in the elevated position. When lowered the bucket receives the drainage. The process can be continued indifinitely to maintain growth.*

Once the hydroponic container has been chosen and lined with polythene, if necessary, a small drainage hole should be made in the base, or if it is a very large and long trough then several holes must be made. In the case of pots, there will be no need to do this because apertures will already exist in their bottoms. Drainage holes are generally about ¼ inch in diameter and can be provided with removable plugs. The purpose of these is to allow excess moisture to seep from the troughs or pots. Gutters may be provided to catch this liquid, or saucers and trays can be placed underneath pots.

The next task is to fill the container with growing medium. This is the substrate which anchors the plants' roots in position and acts as a reservoir for the water and fertilizers. Sand, fine gravel, well-broken bricks, washed cinders and charcoal, vermiculite, and many other materials will make excellent growing media. Allow the substrate to come up to about ½ inch below the top of the sides of the container. Then smooth over the surface carefully. Some hydroponicists like to put an inch or two of pebbles or broken stones of larger size at the bottom of the troughs or pots beneath the main growing medium to ensure better drainage and aeration. Sands for hydroponics should be of medium and coarse grades, while the best sizes for gravels are 1/8th to ¼ inch.

The hydroponic trough or container will now be ready and should be watered with plain water to make the growing medium about as moist as a damp sponge that has been lightly wrung out. Excessive

Applying nutrients in a soilless bed formed of stones and sand.

watering is bad, the containers should not be kept flooded or water standing in them because this prevents air from reaching the plants' roots. Sow seeds not more than ½ inch deep in the substrate, or plant young seedlings by scooping out small holes in the growing medium and pushing back the material gently around the stems so that they will stand firmly. Spacing may be up to 50 per cent closer than in soil gardening. It is a good plan to raise seedlings at home for hydroponics by sowing the seed first in small boxes of sand and then transplanting the young plants, when they are about three inches in height into the main containers.

After sowing or planting have been completed, feeding or nutrient application must commence. Nutrient mixtures can be made up at home or may be bought ready-made. If the first course is adopted, the mixture shown in table 1 is a good general purpose one for hydroponics. Weigh out these salts on ordinary scales and mix them well together, storing them in a dry sealed container. Larger amounts may be prepared by multiplying all quantities by a constant figure, so that the proportions stay the same.

To apply the formula to the hydroponic garden, mix one-third of an ounce, which is about one standard unheaped teaspoonful, with one gallon of water and spray or pour as many gallons of this solution onto the surface of the growing medium as may be necessary to keep it continually moist, but not flooded or too wet. This should be done as often as necessary. In winter, application of nutrient solution once or twice weekly should suffice, but in warm, dry summer weather daily additions will probably be needed.

The solution can be applied in small units by watering can, but in larger troughs or beds it is easier to place it in an elevated tank or drum and allow it to run down through a hose pipe onto the growing medium. Whilst application is in progress, and for a short time after, keep the plugs in the drainage holes. Later, these apertures may be opened, to allow excess moisture to escape and air to be drawn into the substrate. The seepage can be collected in a bucket, tray or sump and returned to the tank.

Once weekly, open the drainage holes, to permit surplus liquid to run off, and every two or three months flush through the hydroponic containers with fresh plain water to remove any accumulated residues, and then start again with solution applications.

It is important to keep all hydroponic gardens clean and well cared for. During absences, for instance, on holidays, bowls, buckets or tanks of solution may be placed beside troughs or containers, and strips of cloth or wicks, with one end dipped into the nutrient liquid and the other inserted in the growing medium, to convey water and nutriment to the crops

◆ *(b) Bengal method* This is similar to the simple sand or aggregate culture already described, except that the growing medium or substrate is composed of a mixture of about two parts of coarse sand and three parts by volume of fine gravel, pebbles, broken bricks or other materials, all well blended together. The substrate is kept constantly moist, just like a damp sponge that has been lightly squeezed out. The method was devised in India, where great poverty exists, and because not many persons could afford solution tanks, the technique of dry application is employed. This means that after mixing up the formula the nutrients are scattered evenly over the surface of the growing medium at the rate of between one and two ounces of nutrient per square yard of trough space. Spreading of dry nutrients should be done on average weekly. Immediately after sprinkling the salts, they must be watered with plain water from a can or hosepipe, so that they dissolve and are washed down into the substrate in solution, to become available as plant food to the crops' roots. In between the times of nutrient spreading only plain water is given as irrigation to keep the troughs always damp.

The Sharder process. *Hydroponic rice in Bengal: the method is ideal for providing food for households. It is an organically based technique. (Note the manure shells or pots).*

Simple home hydroponics in Bengal.

A hydroponic garden. *In the first trough are beetroots and cauliflowers, one month after sowing. (Take our word for it).*

1	
Fertilizer	**Ounces**
Ammonium sulphate	15
Potassium sulphate	3½
Superphosphate	5
Magnesium sulphate	3
Ferrous sulphate—enough to cover the head of a match	

2	
Manure	**Ounces**
Hoof-and-horn meal	15
Bonemeal	8
Ground chalk	6
Ground magnesian limestone	18
Fresh wood ashes	20
Scrapings from a rusty iron nail—enough to cover half a teaspoon	

◆ *(c) Sharder process.* In order to help people who dislike using fertilizers, or those living in areas where local conditions make it difficult to obtain adequate supplies of inorganic nutrients, a process called the Sharder technique has been developed, also in Bengal. Normal beds or containers of aggregate are used, but to provide the crops with nourishment, manure shells or pots are placed at intervals along the troughs. These consist of earthenware vessels, lined with some kind of sieve or screen and pierced by a number of tiny holes in the bottom. The pots are filled with a nutrient sludge or semi-liquid manure, a typical formula for which is:

> *Fresh or dried dung . . 1 handful*
> *Matured oilcakes . . . 4 teaspoonfuls*

Alternatively, such materials as hoof-and-horn meal, bonemeal, shoddy, or similar plant foodstuffs can be utilised. Dried wood ashes are also fairly effective. To mature the oilcake (cotton, castor, groundnut or other feed cake or waste) knead it with a little water, add ground bones together with some potash (fresh wood ashes or saltpetre), then store in a closed container for about two months. This disposes of any odours.

When the manure shells are placed in the hydroponic troughs, and sunk a few inches into the aggregate, with only the upper portions remaining exposed, they slowly release their nutrient contents into the substrate. Covers should be put over the vessels, and from time to time they may be refilled with nutrient sludge or topped up. Every three months, flush through the beds or containers with plain water to cleanse them. Normal irrigation with water is provided to keep the substrate always moist. It should be noted that this process may be classed as organic feeding.

The formula shown in table 2 may be used in towns or industrial areas. *Mix well together and dilute to a thick sludge with water. Place in pots of about 2 lb capacity each, prepared as already described, and set them at intervals of up to one yard apart in the hydroponic units. The bottoms should be sunk three inches into the substrate. The sludge will slowly percolate into the growing medium, providing plant nutrients. See that it is not too thick and that the liquid strains slowly out of the vessels into the troughs or containers. It should not however run too rapidly. Top up with water and fresh formula monthly. Larger amounts can be made by increasing the total bulk, keeping the relative proportions constant.*

Self-sufficiency, eco-houses and various forms of alternative technology, are today of increasing importance. Several designs have been proposed, and used, which include the hydroponic production of green food based upon the adaptation of domestic waste matter for the nutrition of home grown crops. Waste and excreta, after processing by anaerobic digestion, algae farming, and other treatments, can be employed profitably, thus making for a self-contained life support system. When such organic nutrition is favoured, production of methane gas can be undertaken as well, so providing heat in cold periods.

Ingenuity and inventiveness, together with technological adaptations, have come to make hydroponics an ideal means of producing large amounts of foodstuffs very economically in quite simple ways, thus providing a significant contribution to ecological living. The field is open to further developments and we should see numerous such units in existence in the future.

by **James Sholto Douglas**

Hydroponic vegetable garden.

GREAT PIGS FROM LITTLE ACORNS GROW

Most people have a picture of traditional farming as animals grazing in flat pastures, or as golden wheat waving in the breeze. But we have not always used cereal husbandry as our primary source of food. In the Middle Ages, farmers of Western Europe used to herd livestock into the deciduous forests where they could feed themselves on seeds, nuts and berries from the trees. Larger trees such as Beech (*Fagus sp*), Oak (*Quercus sp*), Walnut (*Juglans regia*), and Sweet Chestnut (*Castanea sativa*) would often tolerate the growth of smaller food-bearing trees beneath their branches (for instance Hazel, *Corylus sp*, Cobnuts and Filberts etc.) making direct feeding easier for the animals (mostly pigs). This combination of several layers of vegetation represents the most productive use of available sunlight and soil in a given land-area. Manure from the animals would be dropped where it was most needed, automatically ensuring that the woodland floor remained rich and fertile. Any surplus food would be gathered by the farmer and stored as winter feed. Nutritionally, the feed from this system is of a surprisingly high quality (see table 1) and compares very favourably with the cereal feeds currently used on our farms. Shelled walnuts, for example, contain up to 16 per cent protein, in addition to fat, calcium, iron and vitamins B_1, Riboflavin and Niacin.

However, since the Middle Ages, the use of cereals as a main crop superceded tree-farming. As a result, farming became strictly governed by seasons, with a premium put on planning one year ahead. Farmers could now settle in one area but were committed to obeying the rigid cycle of a handful of annual crops. Modern agriculture now has these grasses trained to follow a simple uniform geometry, tailor-made for conveyor-belt machinery on our flat farms.

In the rain forests of New Guinea, nomadic tree-farmers still employ a system of cultivation which we call 'swiddening' (derived from an old Norse word meaning 'clearing'). Firstly, a clearing is made in the forest and the cuttings are either burned or composted to release their nutrients. A garden is planted with a varied arrangement of vegetables to ensure that variations in terrain are complemented by different plant heights etc. The crops are harvested sporadically, according to day-to-day needs, in order to maintain uninterrupted continuity of growth throughout the seasons. New tree shoots are carefully protected as they begin to grow amongst the vegetables, since they allow the garden to mature untended without undergoing a grassy stage. Because of their deep roots, the young trees (referred to by the New Guineans as 'Duk Mi' —or 'Mother of Gardens') absorb the nutrients which run away through the vegetable roots and which would otherwise be lost. On bare hills, by the introduction of trees, nutrient run-off can be reduced by a factor of up to 100. The New Guineans seldom keep their gardens for more than one year, moving to a new location while the forest reclaims the last one. Pigs are kept as a high protein investment for times of sickness or stress, and represent their only method of food storage. In this way, even though less than a tenth of the forest is 'used' at any one time, it will support 200 people per square mile in complete ecological stability.

It is well-known that the major deserts were produced by cereal farming on a large scale and consequent erosion of the soil. Some experimental work has been undertaken by James Sholto Douglas to re-introduce mixed economy tree-farming in the tropics. Certain drought-resistant trees such as Algaroba (*Prosopis juliflora*) and Carob (*Ceratonia siliqua*) have been used to upgrade poor soils and to provide food for livestock and people. Good varieties of Algaroba can produce up to 50 tonnes per hectare annually (see table 2) in addition to their long-term payoff in the form of timber. The Algaroba pods are nutritionally superior to maize and can easily be ground into meal for both human beings and for animals. Livestock may be supported in this way on indifferent soil at densities of 5 to 12 large animals per hectare (cattle etc.) or up to 62 small animals per hectare (sheep etc.).

Such abundance is not confined to tropical regions; one harvest from a single mature Portuguese Oak has been shown to equal the output from a whole acre of Maize, 1200 litres of Acorns.

Table 1. Cereals compared to tree products for nutritional content

Species	Protein (%)	Carbo-hydrate (%)	Fat (%)
Pine (*Pinus sp*)	31.0	13.0	47.5
Beechnuts (*Fagus Sylvatica*)	20.0	15.0	55.0
Almond (*Prunus amygdalus*)	19.0	20.0	54.5
Honeylocust (*Gleditsia sp*)	16.0	30.5	7.5
Walnut (*Juglans sp*)	16.0	15.5	64.0
Hazelnut (*Corylus sp*)	12.8	17.0	62.0
Chestnut (*Castanea sp*)	6.5	78.0	4.0
Acorn (*Quercus sp*)	5.0	60.0	20.0
Wheat	9.6	63.5	1.2
Oats	7.6	44.8	4.0
Barley	7.3	60.9	1.2

Table 2. Cereal compared to tree crop yields for UK conditions

Approximate annual cereal harvest	Approximate annual tree harvest (uncultivated mature trees)
4—6 tonnes/hectare	16 tonnes/hectare (edible crop and leaves)
	19 tonnes/hectare (timber and other products)

Table 3. Relative effects of different grasses on soil structure

	Soil loss (tons/acre/year)	Nutrient run-off (%)
Bare	41.0	30
Maize	19.7	29
Wheat	10.1	23
Maize/wheat/clover	2.7	14
Permanent grass	0.3	12

Since only eight per cent of the world's land surface is suitable for efficient cereal farming, it is difficult to see why Governments do not take a long-term view and reforest the land for food. The only unsuitable regions would be the ice-caps:— even Iceland has recently passed a bill in parliament for extensive tree-planting to reduce both land-erosion and the price of food.

In an intensive forest system, many by-products could be profitably adapted for industries parallel with agriculture. Research carried out by NW Pirie has shown that most leaves contain at least as much protein as most vegetables in common use (see table 4). It is a fairly simple process to remove the fibrous matter and to produce a high-grade curd for supplementing human or animal diet. This would provide an even greater food output per hectare than suggested by conventional figures. Subsidiary 'crops' such as timber, honey, milk, chemicals, wool and wild game are all benefits which would result naturally from a well-run tree-farm economy. Obviously, initial investment costs would be high for such a long-term farming cycle, but there are one or two short cuts possible. The *Juglans sieboldiana* species of Walnut is a quick-growing, high quality tree, and Carob trees can bear crops within two to three years from planting. Cereals and vegetables should grow adequately where trees are not fully established, provided the leaf-cover is thin.

With intensive horticultural research and development, it is feasible that Britain could become self-sufficient in food, whilst reducing its dependence on fertilizers, pesticides and fuel.

John Wood

Table 4. Some British tree products suitable for direct human consumption.

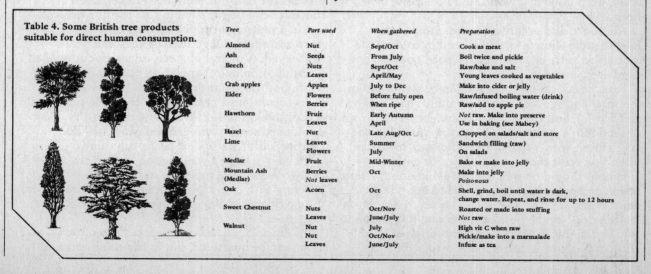

Tree	Part used	When gathered	Preparation
Almond	Nut	Sept/Oct	Cook as meat
Ash	Seeds	From July	Boil twice and pickle
Beech	Nuts	Sept/Oct	Raw/bake and salt
	Leaves	April/May	Young leaves cooked as vegetables
Crab apples	Apples	July to Dec	Make into cider or jelly
Elder	Flowers	Before fully open	Raw/infused boiling water (drink)
	Berries	When ripe	Raw/add to apple pie
Hawthorn	Fruit	Early Autumn	*Not raw.* Make into preserve
	Leaves	April	Use in baking (see Mabey)
Hazel	Nut	Late Aug/Oct	Chopped on salads/salt and store
Lime	Leaves	Summer	Sandwich filling (raw)
	Flowers	July	On salads
Medlar	Fruit	Mid-Winter	Bake or make into jelly
Mountain Ash	Berries	Oct	Make into jelly
(Medlar)	*Not* leaves		*Poisonous*
Oak	Acorn	Oct	Shell, grind, boil until water is dark, change water. Repeat, and rinse for up to 12 hours
Sweet Chestnut	Nuts	Oct/Nov	Roasted or made into stuffing
	Leaves	June/July	*Not* raw
Walnut	Nut	July	High vit C when raw
	Nut	Oct/Nov	Pickle/make into a marmalade
	Leaves	June/July	Infuse as tea

ACROSS THE HUNGRY GAP

Given a deep freeze, and a constant supply of electricity, any fool can preserve practically anything, and provided the maker's instructions are followed (ie air is excluded from the food and food is not kept too long) the food is nearly as good as new. But deep freezes are very expensive, and likely to get more so, and do not last for ever, and are a resource-consuming method of preserving food. They are, besides, unnecessary, and you can preserve all you need to preserve perfectly well without them, and it is far more fun.

VEGETABLES

In any climate between tropical and temperate you do not *need* to preserve many vegetables, because with good husbandry you can pick fresh vegetables all the year round, and the fact that you cannot have any one vegetable fresh every month of the year is a good fact. It is excellent, for example, to have to go without peas for seven or eight months, and then have the real gastronomic thrill of new peas in June when they arrive. Brussels sprouts, broccoli, cauliflower, hearted cabbage, 'roots' (turnips, swedes, beet), and above all celery can be made to last right through the winter and it is very nice not to have to eat them any more when the spring comes.

In cold climates people preserve cabbages by *clamping* them (putting in a heap outside, covering with straw or bracken and covering this with earth, but leaving air holes alow and aloft) or—colder still—keeping them in the root cellar. In North America the root cellar is universal, clamping not being sufficient against the intense cold. In Eastern Europe another method used is sauerkraut, which is not only a method of preserving cabbage but is very nice as an end in itself. Wash the inside of a wood or earthenware crock with vinegar, line it with cabbage leaves, shred 12 lbs of cabbage, mix with 8 oz salt, thump in tight, cover with whole cabbage leaves, stir occasionally for first three weeks, then leave covered until you want it. To use, drain, drop in boiling water, and boil for two hours.

All 'roots' and potatoes can be clamped in English-style climate—root cellared in colder. The root cellar must be frost-free, cleaned out well and aired every summer.

Peas, beans, pulses, soya etc can be well dried in the wind and sun when they are quite ripe (ie brown and brittle), and either hung in bunches from a roof (frost doesn't matter with them) or stacked in the dry. Thresh with a flail or over the back of a chair when you want them, store in bins or crocks.

Onions should be well sun-and-wind dried, strung and hung up, preferably in the wind but not too much rain.

Tomatoes can be bottled when ripe thus: wash in cold water, put in bottles, fill with brine of ½ oz salt to a quart of water, put screw-tops on *loose*,

Illustrations are from John and Sally Seymour's *Self-Sufficiency* (Faber and Faber, 1973).

SALLY SEYMOUR

place in large kettle of cold water covering tops and bring slowly to 190°F or 88°C. Keep at this for half an hour. Haul bottles out of water and screw tops tight immediately. Kilner Jars, designed for the purpose, are hard to get now, but OMCS (Old Mother Common Sense) will suggest other methods. Pouring molten wax or fat on top of food in a bottle seals the contents from bacteria for example. The principle of all bottling is to destroy the putrefactive bacteria of the food by heat—then prevent the entry of more by sealing. Green tomatoes can be wrapped in soft stuff or tissue and laid in a drawer not touching each other. Some will ripen and some will go bad. Or they can be chutneyed. A pound of green tomatoes cut up, half a pound of onions chopped, an ounce of salt, two teaspoonfuls cayenne pepper, 1¼ pints vinegar, ¾ lbs brown sugar or honey, ½ lb raisins, simmer till it goes thick, and bottle in hot sterilized jars. You don't need screw-tops—greased paper will do. Chutneys can be made of nearly anything.

Pickling is done by laying the stuff in salt for a day (to draw some moisture out), rinsing and covering with cold vinegar. Runner beans: shred and thump down tight in crock with plenty of dry salt.

FRUIT

Pears can be quartered, put in brine (an ounce of

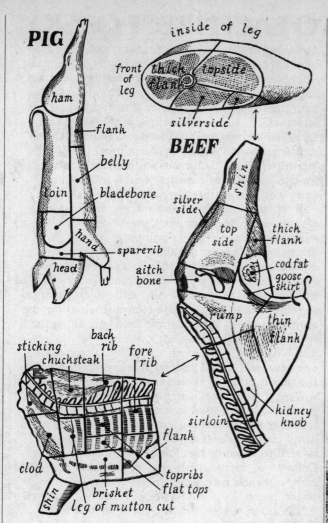

PIG

inside of leg

front of leg

thick flank

topside

silverside

ham

flank

belly

loin

bladebone

hand

sparerib

head

BEEF

shin

silver side

top side

thick flank

codfat goose skirt

aitch bone

rump

thin flank

back rib

sticking

chucksteak

fore rib

kidney knob

sirloin

flank

clod

topribs

flat tops

brisket

leg of mutton cut

shin

salt to one gallon of water) for a minute (stops them going brown) then dry on trays at 100°F (38°C) raising to 150°F (66°C) for five hours. Plums etc can be turned into prunes by dipping in lye made of one ounce caustic soda in one gallon of water for a few minutes—then washing very well and laying on trays over stove at 120°F (50°C) raising to 160°F (71°C) very slowly (or they'll burst). Keep in heat for two days. Soak for 12 hours before using. These are a rich source of vitamin A. Apples will keep if not bruised and laid on spore-free shelves not touching each other, well ventilated, away from frost and at an even temperature.

FISH

Salt herring, mackerel or pilchards by gutting and laying down in dry salt in barrel or crock. OMCS should tell how much salt. When required pull out and soak for twelve hours with changes of water if under two months in salt, progressively longer if salting has been longer. Soak at least 48 hours after six months' salting. Then cook, or pickle by putting in cold vinegar with onion and peppercorns etc for a week or two. Pickled fish, such as rollmops (pickled herrings), will keep a month or so—no longer. For thick white fish such as cod, split, rip out backbone, pile in dry salt and let brine run away (cf oily fish where you let the fish lie in its

own brine in a tub). After 15 days for a big cod, but less with smaller fish, pull out of heap and lay the fish in sun and wind (not rain) for a few days. Soak for at least 36 hours before you cook it.

MEAT

Bacon is the side of a pig, ham is its hind quarters. Rub in dry salt for three days, then leave bacon heaped in dry salt for two weeks, ham for three. Hang up. This sounds ridiculously simple but really is all you do. A tiny pinch of saltpetre sprinkled on the cut part before you salt helps keep the colour, and a handful of brown sugar rubbed on at that time gives sweetness. But care and OMCS must be used at all stages, otherwise disaster can ensue. You *can* hang in cool smoke for a week, if you want to, after salting.

Pickled pork, beef, mutton: cut meat up and put in brine (salt and water) which is strong enough to float a potato. Boil the brine to sterilize and dissolve all salt—then cool. Weigh meat down with a plank with a stone on it to keep from air. Soak well before cooking. Large hunks of beef (eg silverside) can be treated this way, then soaked and boiled.

MILK

Summer flush can be preserved for winter by making it into hard cheese, but you must get good advice or it will be uneatable. Butter can be well salted and flung *hard* into a sterilized (scalded then wind-dried) crock or tub, rammed in hard with the fist to exclude all air. Cover with greaseproof paper and leave. Wash by squodging in cold water to remove excess salt before eating. It will keep all through winter. In a hot climate make *ghee*. Simmer the butter gently for an hour, skim the scum off, pour into a sterilized container and cover. Cook with it.

CORN

(Wheat, barley, oats and rye in England). Either stack it in its straw and thresh when required, or thresh it in the field with combine harvester and then artificially dry, or do what the Ancient Britons did—keep it in air-tight containers, when its own carbon dioxide will preserve it from moulds.

And may you survive the Hungry Gap as our forefathers did of old.

John Seymour

FOOD

'EACH PIECE OF LAND TO EACH PIECE OF SKY'

Opportunist despots and capitalists are both creating and exploiting our precarious water situation. They intervene as custodians of the rain that falls out of the skies, attempting to 'supply' a resource which until their appearance was a natural dependence as free as the air.

The rain falls on every part of the Earth (well almost) *(1)*. Where, then, lies the logic in collecting rainfall in huge reservoirs and then returning it to its various points of origin? Evaporation losses are less in a small bore well or storage tank than in a large and relatively shallow reservoir, particularly if the well or tank can be partly sealed to retain a volume of semi-saturated cold air on the water-surface. Although the supply system of our munificent Authorities is undoubtedly big, it is unlikely that it is yet sufficiently vast to have any real effect in balancing out local differences between rainfall and demand *(2)*. Which leads us to the crucial question: at what scale does demand become 'unreasonable' in exceeding the natural supply of an area? Megatechnology knows no limits, and seeks out only the maxima in both supply and demand.

Rainfall farming, roof collection of water for home and industry, and all supplies of water from springs, lakes and similar sources *as found*, all represent a state of abundance and an enviably unhampered hydro-dependency akin to that of the primitive hunter-gatherer, to the small farmer of the humid regions, and now to the builders of 'autonomous' houses. Peoples of the tropical rainy and temperate rainy regions are in a more fortunate position to find or gather water and thus to subvert the hydrocrats. But in arid and semi-arid regions, water-supply is a factor in farming, living, and manufacture which has to be handled in league with many other people, because of scarcity of supply and bulkiness of need. Local tasks of digging,

damming, water-distribution, irrigation, and canal building can be undertaken by a family or group of neighbours 'each piece of land to each piece of sky' *(3)*, or (more frequently) they can be undertaken with the superfluous guidance of a hydro-bureaucracy. Kropotkin mentions the 'syndicats agricoles' or peasants' and farmers' associations of southern France, which were not until 1884 'permitted', as a 'dangerous experiment', to combine for the purposes of pumping water, inundating vineyards, and maintaining canals.

Integration of local water into an organic living system—with, for example, a greenhouse-cum-solar still; wind-powered water pumping; fans, or pumps driven by the power of falling water wherever available (from the roof?)—such a system forms a kind of benevolent water-works, and is a key part of the discorporate vision of AT, with which we hope to tempt you from the false convenience of buying municipal water 'on tap' and flushing it down the WC. See Fig 1 for ideas.

A divining rod, when used by a gifted operator, will locate underground sources of water for almost no cost. However the water is obtained it will most likely need some kind of purification if it is to be drunk or used in food preparation. A favourite solution is the solar still, Fig 2. This will distill even brackish water, seawater, or polluted rainfall to produce small quantities of pure water. Colin Moorcraft suggests that as plants are known to carry out their own water surveys, drill down to water, pump it up and purify it; it might be as well to ally ourselves with them. The solar still was developed from a cloche-like arrangement, Fig 3, and the use of the right plants as a kind of evapotranspirating wick may be the best solution. Lifting and moving of water from source to point of use may be most easily carried out if you have a

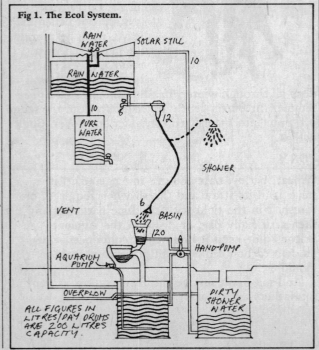

Fig 1. The Ecol System.

RAIN WATER
SOLAR STILL
RAIN WATER
10
PURE WATER
10
12
SHOWER
VENT
BASIN
120
HAND-PUMP
AQUARIUM PUMP
OVERFLOW
DIRTY SHOWER WATER

ALL FIGURES IN LITRES/DAY DRUMS ARE 200 LITRES CAPACITY.

Fig 2. Heat transfer and storage modes of air cooled solar still.

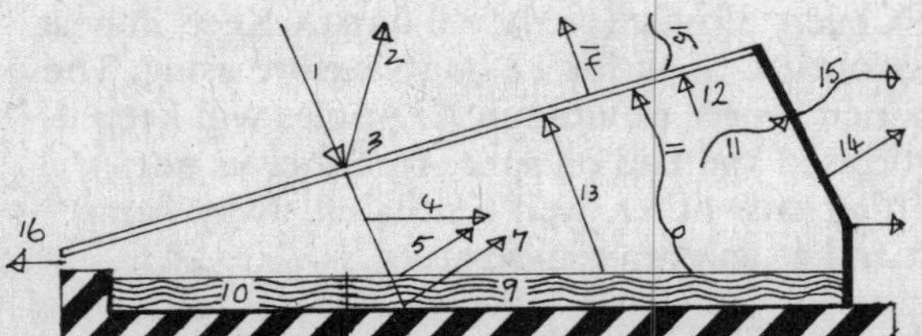

1 Solar radiation
2 Reflected from glass cover
3 Absorbed by glass cover
4 Absorbed by water vapour inside still
5 Reflected from water surface
6 Absorbed by salt water
7 Reflected from still bottom
8 Through insulation to outer ambient air
9 Absorbed by basin liner
10 Convected by basin liner to salt water
11 Air convection from vapour to glass and metallic cover
12 Latent heat
13 Thermal radiation on inner surfaces
14 Thermal radiation on outer surfaces
15 Air convection from outer glass and metallic cover to ambient air
16 Sensible heat condenser

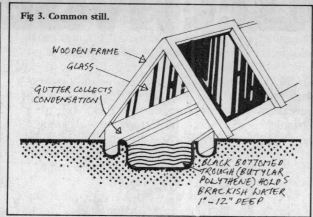

Fig 3. Common still.

WOODEN FRAME

GLASS

GUTTER COLLECTS
CONDENSATION

'BLACK BOTTOMED
TROUGH (BUTYLAR
POLYTHENE) HOLDS
BRACKISH WATER
1" – 12." DEEP

source with head above the pump location and/or flow. A hydraulic ram or a noria wheel, Figs 4 & 5, will raise water with its own power. Wind-powered pumps can be left permanently 'on' to raise water into a tank when the wind is sufficient. Self-regulating water-sprinklers or simple drip-feeds can also be let roll, supplying the greenhouse and garden.

Lest such a direct state of dependence upon nature be alarming, let us consider for a moment the ability of the big Water Authorities to provide an adequate supply of untainted water for developing industrialism. After the current wave of continental water engineering ends *(4)*, the transition to a gradually globally engineered climate will seem inevitable *(5)*. A possibly precarious water situation for some will have been turned into a perilous subordination to the artificial for all. Poison rain, putrefying rivers and lakes, and dying seas are inescapable effects and not 'by-products' of the systematic transformation of the material conditions of life. But they *are* at least temporary setbacks on the road to artificiality—which afford opportunities to big and small alike. In all States industrialists have the ambition (and in Communist countries even the ideological compulsion) to take over everything and invade every phase of life. The prerogative of the State's water authorities is everywhere guarded. There are now secrecy provisions in British law which make disclosure of details of water-polluting manufacturing processes unnecessary *(6)*. People are

Fig 5. The noria or peripheral pot wheel; a drawing from the Nung Cheng Chuan Shu. This traditional representation of the noria fails to do justice to the high lift available.

prosecuted for non-payment of fishing licences, but toxic effluent from factories accumulates and combines in unknown ways to kill the fish.

The majority of the world's hunters, gatherers, small fishermen, and rainfall farmers have found their proud self-sufficiency gradually eaten away. Pessimists will see no obvious reason why the Alternative Technologist's vision of 'autonomy' (not that 'autonomy' in its extreme forms is a particularly worthwhile ideal) should survive the coming onslaught of totalitarian technocracy, merely by boldly asserting its own separationism. But this book has not been written in the belief that Nothing Can Be Done.

REFERENCES

(1) A certain area of the Chilean desert has not received rain for over 400 years. The other global extreme in watery precipitation is over 23 metres annually. Evaporation exceeds rainfall only in midsummer in Britain, whereas in Algeria the evaporation:rainfall ratio is 59:1.
(2) With minor exceptions such as the towing of icebergs from Greenland into the Caribbean, the scale of Big supply systems for cities and industries is insignificant compared to climatic regions. 150 kilometres is a maximum distance for water supply of capital cities. The supply-demand argument doesn't hold water.
(3) This phrase is credited to the revisionist line of anarchist renegade Liu Shao-chi.
(4) There are Soviet proposals for damming and reversing the flow of some of their largest rivers, with consequent alteration in the Siberian climate. By comparison the British Water Resources Board's projects for barrages across the Wash and the Solway and the obliteration of the Lake District look quite mild.
(5) Borisov 'Can We Control the Arctic Climate', *Science and Public Affairs*, March 1969.
(6) Friends of the Earth column in the *Ecologist*, Feb. 1974.

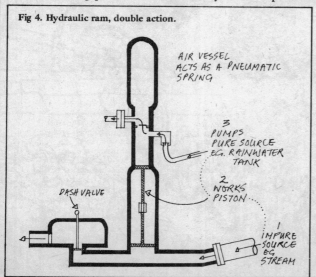

Fig 4. Hydraulic ram, double action.

AIR VESSEL
ACTS AS A PNEUMATIC
SPRING

3
PUMPS
PURE SOURCE
EG. RAINWATER
TANK

2
WORKS
PISTON

DASH VALVE

1
IMPURE
SOURCE
EG
STREAM

George Woolston

VISION 1/COLLECTIVISED

Where rows of houses share backyards, the land can be shared for better use and co-operative food production. The idea suggested here is to divide the area into that which remains private and that which is worked collectively. Other pooled yards could have different functions — for kids, light industry etc.

With such intensive cultivation, more food can be grown per acre in the towns than on farms.

1　Private space
2　Espalier fruit trees
3　Solar water heaters
4　Solar clothes drier
5　Vertical growing on nets
6　Shed
7　Chicken house
8　Compost heap
9　Pit greenhouse
10　Beehive
11　Cold frames
12　Glass cloches

GARDEN

INTERVIEW
JOHN TODD

Patrick Rivers

In California during the early sixties a small group of scientists, humanists and artists found that they shared a deep and growing concern about society's course of change and growth. They began meeting for earnest discussion, searching for ways in which a nucleus of disquieted people might help to create a saner world. Their basic premise was that science and technology generally were lulling people everywhere into a false sense of confidence about the future, and that one essential science—biology—was being neglected. To redress the balance, they aimed to switch attention to the need to reinstate social and biological diversity, which had become a casualty of Progress. After years of searching for a way to translate their concern into action, they

Around 1968 I was involved with a network of other people studying the direct effects of man's activities and the environment, he recalled. *We were looking at different forms of stress behaviour in aquatic animals. I had previously discovered hitherto unknown levels of social organisation in fishes, normally considered exclusive to mammals and birds.* The team with whom he was working made the significant discovery that extremely low levels of stress could upset key social signals, and that the effects became more marked among creatures with the highest forms of behaviour.

'You talk of stress—what kinds of stress?' I asked. *The effects of DDT, oil, thermal pollution,* he replied. *We began to see the insidious effects of man's depredation everywhere — and we weren't even beginning to study the synergistic effects of two or three different kinds of stress, yet we knew that in the real world there were hundreds of different kinds of stress affecting the system.* The discovery filled them with a sense of panic and an urge to do something rather than merely record the approach of doomsday. *Our first opportunity was to set up environmental studies in Southern California with a large budget from a couple of private Californian foundations; the National Science Foundation was also considering putting in a fairly hefty amount. It seemed a golden opportunity, but on intense probing we found that no assumptions were to be challenged or changed. For example, we were asked to do a multi-million dollar feasibility study on how to lower the impact of massive amounts of sewage on the Pacific Ocean. However, if one of us were to suggest that perhaps the way to deal with sewage would be to treat it at its source . . . use it as a resource rather than a pollutant, that kind of re-assumption was simply taboo.* 'We cannot change society, we can only make it better', the rationalists and pedants would quietly say.

We did have this one fantasy which was to create a small village, an academic community, primarily to try to restructure and recreate restorative approaches to living. It got academic approval from the University of California, and then I discovered that you're not allowed to live on University land— just a single little rule set up by the Governor

himself. *It was time to resign.*

He told how, with his wife Nancy, Bill O. McLarney—later to become a leading New Alchemist —and a group of students, he went to work with communards in the mountains near Mexico. The time spent there taught them how little they really knew. . . . *our so called modern education has estranged us from the living world,* he stressed. *We discovered that in spite of all the degrees and so-called knowledge we had, we knew no way of being able to tread lightly on those lands.* They realised suddenly that their activities had to be humble. They must learn how to make a microcosm which had all the restorative qualities that nature had in its own ecosystems; yet for this the modern science of ecology offered them no guidelines. *It was apparent that we would have to travel light and travel small,* he said, *working with groups of small farmers.* The few years of being diagnosticians had helped them learn how the world worked, but they still had seen only a narrow slice of it: inputs from artists and people in other walks of life were still to have their effect. In the end they found that their 'think small' philosophy came not out of someone's political rhetoric, but out of direct experience. *We can be criticised that this may not apply to the world at large, but a beginning has to be made somewhere. We shall always be small, but we want to demystify what we do. Hopefully the ideas will spread throughout the world with people like ourselves.*

Soon after the Institute came into being, John Todd and some of the other members moved east to Cape Cod and set up its first operational centre, on eleven acres of leased land, in a semi-rural setting surrounded by middleclass suburbia. There they rented homes close to the centre and began their practical experiments. These activities, important though they were, proved to be only part of the picture: the existence of a community was equally valid. I asked whether this 'community sense' was lessened by their being scattered, and I learned that it made little difference—in fact it allowed each family to live its own lifestyle, while still coming together for work and social visits. Nevertheless, the ten full-time members looked forward to the

NEW ALCHEMY INSTITUTE

formed, in 1969, the New Alchemy Institute, *with the far-reaching aim: 'to restore the lands, protect the seas and inform the Earth's stewards'.*

Foremost among its founders was John Todd, a

Canadian with degrees in parasitology, tropical medicine and oceanography, and a doctorate in psychology and ethnology. I met him in the autumn of 1973 at the Institute's eastern centre at Wood's Hole, Cape Cod, where the small community which comprised the Institute was experimenting in organic vegetable growing, aquaculture, solar and wind power, and waste-recycling. There, as we walked over the farm from one experiment to another, this energetic, fast talking pioneer, with a rare blend of practicality and prophetic vision, told me how the idea of the Institute developed, how its aims crystallised, explained its programme of experiments and the difficulties it faced. He also outlined his own philosophy.

day when they could be assured of greater permanence than a leased farm, as well as the chance to concentrate on reducing their inputs and outputs from and to the world outside. I was reminded of the Institute's declared aims: 'We seek solutions that can be used by individuals or small groups who are trying to create a greener, kinder world . . . Among our major tasks is the creation of ecologically derived forms of energy, agriculture, aquaculture, housing and landscapes, that will permit a revitalisation and re-population of the countryside.' Implicit in this declaration was the concept of relatively self-contained communities, capturing their own power, growing their own food and making use of their own wastes. The group longed for the day when they would be able to put all their aims into practice—not only at Woods Hole, but at other centres throughout the world, each revealing the special needs of the region in which it was located.

John Todd showed me the three main research activities under way, as well as a host of smaller ones. First of the three is the Backyard Fishfarm Project, directed by Bill O. McLarney, with the aim of producing nourishing, palatable protein for a community or family at zero cost (see page 36). The African *Tilapia* has been chosen—a fish which eats the algae at the bottom of the food chain, supplemented with vegetable waste and insect life. Two sources of insect life have been found: midges and gnats, attracted by light traps; and midge larvae breed on burlap curtains hung in manure-rich water. From Spring to late Autumn, solar energy maintains ponds at the 85°F water temperature which the tropical *Tilapia* requires; in winter the experiment ceases, surplus fish finishing up in the deep-freeze.

The second activity is a search for food crops with the genetic ability to resist insect pests. The group is concerned about over-extravagant claims made by organic growers, and they believe that most chemical-happy growers would only be converted when the crops most suited to ecological management had been identified.

The third activity, companion planting, is also concerned with pest resistance. Specific insects are repelled by the odours of certain crops, and these

crops are planted alongside those to be protected. To find the most effective combinations, the Institute had enlisted the co-operation of hundreds of collaborators across the country in a Science for the People programme. These groups and individuals conducted their own co-ordinated experiments to ensure that local variances were taken into account. The same collaborators also worked on other projects. Apart from these activities, John Todd showed me solar crop drying systems; worm-breeding in rabbit droppings for feeding to hens or fish; wind generators, large and small, a Savonius rotor water pump; and plot after plot of experimental vegetables and other crops.

Despite the familiar, recurring problems of lack of funds, coupled with the serious handicap of an impermanent site, Woods Hole has become a valuable source of new knowledge which must be made known. Under Nancy Todd's direction, the Institute publishes books, pamphlets and a regular Journal. The value of word of mouth, person-to-person dissemination is also recognised, and Saturdays are given over to visitors who work on the farm and share a picnic lunch. John Todd expressed the view of all the group, however, when he voiced to me his fear of over-exposure in the mass media. *This country has a habit of creating seven-day wonders: they get a lot of press and then die. We've found that our very best friends come through a process we call 'discovery'. Television is the worst of the popular media—it just gives you the latest thing. In contrast, if we are written about in a magazine where people are slightly pre-disposed, they discover us . . . make the connection on their own, 'from them to us', not 'us to them'.*

We need to know more of how change comes about. Our approach is to give all we can to a small and interested area which has fantastic spiritual and practical implications—which requires the kind of involvement people normally associate with religion. He paused, searching for the right words: *When you begin to work with nature, you realise the unknowingness of nature. You feel humble. You feel good about it all. You want to tell about it, because it is the most meaningful thing that is happening to you.*

KARL WEBER

Conventionally, articles on energy begin with a definition of what energy *is.*

'Energy,' they say, 'is the *ability to do work.*'

The ability to do *work.* Hmmm . . . The ability, in other words, to exert a force on a mass and push it over a distance. Now although this definition is perfectly valid — and indeed extremely useful, in that it leads to a quantitative method of measuring the magnitude of certain kinds of energy — its unconscious implications are starkly reductionistic.

Energy *could*, equally well, be defined as the ability to slap a friend on the back, to enjoy a glass of beer, or to make love, since everyone agrees that these activities require energy for their performance. But it is not. Instead, and significantly, energy is the name given to our ability to do *work* — to do our jobs properly, to fulfil our production quotas, to justify our existence in economic terms. It would be hard to think of a definition better suited to underpinning the puritanical, life-repressing, goal-seeking industrial civilisation in which so many millions of us are compelled to subsist today.

Consider an alternative definition of energy.

'Energy', said William Blake, 'is *eternal delight*'.

As Freeman Dyson points out: 'One need not be a poet or mystic to find Blake's definition of energy more satisfying than the definition given in textbooks on physics.' *(1)* Blake's phrase expresses with exquisite conciseness the non-utilitarian, joyful aspect of energy as we actually *feel* it in our lives. What we need, it seems to me, is a concept of energy which somehow achieves a fusion of the practical and the poetic aspects. A concept which reminds us that a solar collector, for instance, is not *only* an alternative way of heating water for showers or dish washing but also a constant reminder of our living dependence on the benevolence of the great Sun God.

In introducing the Energy section of this book, let me echo the words of Nancy Todd in her introduction to the Energy section of the *Journal of the New Alchemists:*

' We little thought, when we chose the title 'Energy' for this section of the Journal, of how many shadings of meaning the word could be understood to have. I have seen it used to describe

TONY DURHAM

ENERGY

Godfrey Boyle

the positive force that believers in a New Age feel is growing swiftly now and will take us forward in an Aquarian Era of serenity and heightened awareness.

Energy is spoken of to describe the impact of a personality or a group; of ones power to influence the people and events around one. It is still an apt term for what children have limitless amounts of.

We are using it, in this section of the Journal, in the more traditional sense of the capacity to do work. At the same time, in doing so, we are deep-

ly committed to working with as opposed to taking from Nature, and, as this implies a contemplative approach of learning to listen to the wind and sun and to growing things, then, perhaps when we chose 'Energy' to describe our work, we half-intended some of the more subtle meanings to be understood as well.'

Keeping the essential poetics of energy firmly fixed in our minds, then, let me turn back to the physics of the subject. One of the most important physical principles relating to energy is the **Law of Conservation of Energy**, alternatively known as the **First Law of Thermodynamics**.

The first law states that energy in the Universe is neither created nor destroyed. Energy may change in *form* — from gravitational energy and mechanical energy through electrical energy and chemical energy to light energy, heat energy and numerous other disguises — but the total *amount* of energy in the Universe stays the same.

Another key principle is the **Second Law of Thermodynamics**. According to the Second Law, each form of energy possesses a characteristic known as *entropy.* The entropy of an energy form is inversely proportional to the *temperature* associated with that form, and is a measure of its degree of *disorder.*

For example, hot water has a higher temperature than lukewarm water, so hot water has a lower entropy than lukewarm water and its energy is less disordered (or more ordered, if you prefer), than that of lukewarm water. (If you're confused by all these double negatives and inversions, don't blame me: blame Clausius — he invented entropy).

Generally speaking, the lower the entropy of a form of energy, the more *useful* it is. And the more 'useful' an energy source (ie, the lower its entropy) the greater the efficiency with which it can be converted into less-useful (higher entropy) forms.

For instance, gravitational energy has the lowest entropy of all and is the most useful. Gravitational energy, say in the form of falling water, can be converted into mechanical energy (say, the rotation of a turbine) with almost 100% efficiency, but the conversion of mechanical to gravitational energy is a less efficient process. Next to *gravitational energy* is mechanical energy, which in turn is more useful than electrical energy (and therefore has lower entropy), so the efficiency of conversion of mechanical to electrical energy (in a dynamo) is very high; but the efficiency of conversion of electrical to mechanical energy is somewhat lower.

Lower still on the scale of usefulness is heat energy. Although efficiency of conversion of most other energy forms to heat is very high, the efficiency with which heat can be used to generate these other forms is pretty low. Heat can be generated very efficiently from mechanical energy (in a friction brake, for example) or from electrical energy (in an immersion heater), but can only be converted back into these forms with relatively low efficiency — which is one reason why the generation of electricity in fuel-burning power stations is such a wasteful process.

The practical implication of the Second Law of Thermodynamics is that it's very important to match energy sources carefully to the tasks they are to perform. It's bad thermodynamics, for instance, to use high-grade (low entropy) electrical energy for providing low-grade (high entropy) home heating. And the high entropy heat of the sun is more effective when used directly as heat than when used to generate low-entropy electricity. Murray Bookchin puts it more gracefully *(3):*

'We should always have a diversified mosaic of energy sources — utilising, as it were all of the forces of Nature so that they interplay with our lives. In this way, we can develop a more respectful — even reverential — attitude towards Nature.'

Peter Harper deals in detail with the practicalities of tailoring demand to supply in the section on Autonomy.

Let's look instead at where all our energy comes from.

THE SUN KING (4)

The source of almost *all* the energy we use on earth is the Sun. The rate at which solar energy is intercepted by the Earth is about 170×10^{12} kilowatts, which is equivalent, if you like, to the power of 170 million million continuously-burning single-bar electric fires — or, to use a more personal metaphor, the flow of power which the 3,500 million people of the earth would be consuming if they *each* left more than 48,000 1kW electric fires burning continuously. Added up over a year of 8,760 hours, the total energy delivered by the sun to the Earth amounts to no less than 1.5×10^{18} kilowatt hours (kWh).

Compared to this enormous annual influx, the amount of energy we humans actually consume is extremely small. Our total world consumption of energy per year — in such forms as coal, gas, oil and electricity (but excluding food) — is about 60×10^{12} kWh. This is only one-25,000th of the annual solar energy input to our planet.

About 30% of the Sun's energy is reflected straight back into space. Another 47%, it has been calculated, goes to heating up the planet's land surface, its atmosphere and its oceans. This energy is re-radiated to space more slowly as low grade heat. And about 23% is used in evaporating, from our lakes and oceans, the water which eventually falls as rain and flows through our rivers back to the sea. It has been calculated that the total amount of hydro-power potentially available from this source is of the order of 26×10^{12} kWh per year. Eventually, this energy too is degraded to low temperature heat and re-radiated into space.

A little of the incoming energy, about 0.2%, causes pressure differences in the atmosphere and oceans, which in turn cause air and water to flow from areas of high pressure to areas of low pressure. These 'convection' flows manifest themselves in the air in the form of *winds,* and in the oceans in the form of *currents.* And when winds react with the ocean surface, they cause another indirect manifestation of solar energy — *waves.*

The total amount of energy contained in the Earth's winds, waves, and currents is estimated to be about 3.23×10^{15} kWh per year. It would be impossible to tap more than a fraction of this amount, of course. In practice, wind power for example is reckoned to be potentially capable of delivering something like 0.8×10^{12} kWh per year.

An even smaller amount of solar energy, only about 0.02% of the total, is absorbed in the vital process, photosynthesis, in which plants draw carbon dioxide and water from their surrounding environment and convert them into oxygen and carbohydrates such as starches and sugars.

The energy absorbed during this process, on which the whole of human, animal and plant life depends, is stored in the chemical bonds which hold the plant's carbohydrate molecules together. This chemical energy is released when an animal eats the plant as food; or it can be released simply by burning the plant, during which the plant's stored carbohydrate reacts with oxygen at high temperature and gives off its energy as heat.

When plants die, their leaves are normally decomposed by 'aerobic' (air breathing) bacteria, in the presence of oxygen, and some of the energy stored in their carbohydrates is released to the environment in the form of heat — which is why a compost heap becomes warm. But some dead organic matter is deposited at the bottom of lakes or in peat bogs, where there is little oxygen, and does not decay completely. When such partially-decayed matter, over millions of years, builds up and becomes buried under layers of sand, rock and sediment, it eventually turns into one or other of the 'fossil fuels' such as oil or coal, or the tar sands and oil shales now being heralded as the solution to the US 'energy crisis'. These deposits, while undergoing decomposition in the absence of air (*anaerobic* decomposition) give off large quantities of 'natural gas', which is another fossil fuel and is composed mainly of methane. (Methane can, of course, be generated by the anaerobic decomposition of ordinary organic matter).

The fossil fuels represent, in a very real way, the Earth's 'life savings' of energy: they amount to the planet's *non-renewable capital* because the geological and biological processes which formed them over the past 600 million years have proceeded so slowly that the deposits can be regarded as essentially fixed — at least in relation to any human time-scale.

By contrast, the energy flowing continuously to our planet from the Sun is *renewable,* or *income* energy, because it will keep flowing for as long as the Sun keeps shining, at a rate which exceeds by a factor of about 25,000 the world's rate of energy consumption.

Apart from the Sun, there are two other sources of income energy.

One is the gravitational pull of the Moon and Sun, which acts on the world's oceans and causes the tides. The total amount of energy stored in the Earth's tides has been estimated to be about 26×10^{12} kWh per year, or about 0.0017% of the total solar energy input. Some 0.56×10^{12} kWh of this energy is capable of being harnessed.

The other is 'geothermal' energy, heat generated deep in the Earth's core when radioactive substances decay. The total amount of geothermal energy flowing to the Earth's surface, either by direct conduction through the ground or by convection through volcanoes and hot springs, is estimated to be about 280×10^{12} kWh a year, of which 0.53×10^{12} kWh a year is estimated to be usable in practice. (Strictly speaking, geothermal energy is a non-renewable resource, but it has been calculated that even if so much heat were taken from the earth that its temperature cooled by one-tenth of a degree centigrade, the energy supplied would meet the world's present needs for four million years.)

Throughout history, mankind has found ways of tapping these renewable energy supplies — by building sailing ships and windmills to capture the energy of wind; by devising water mills to harness the rain that flows through rivers; by constructing houses with thick, south-facing walls to store the Sun's direct heat energy; and by burning trees and other plants to trigger the reaction with oxygen which liberates the energy stored in their carbohydrate bonds.

The energy stored in fossil fuels can also be liberated by reaction with oxygen, which is what we do every time we light a coal fire, start a car engine, switch on the oil-fired heating or light a gas stove. But every time we do so, we irreversibly deplete an energy supply that has taken millions of years to build up. Pre-industrial consumption rates were negligible, but at present consumption rates, we will have used up the Earth's entire supply or fossil fuels in a few hundred years from start to finish.

This reckless exploitation of our irreplaceable fossil resources has, however, been accompanied by exploitation of a different and more personal kind. Man's inhumanity to man has, of course, been a characteristic of all epochs, but the advent of easily-accessible concentrations of energy in the form of coal, and later oil, has amplified many times the power of the exploiter over the exploited, the tyranny of the oppressor over the oppressed. As Tolstoy observed more than seventy years ago *(5).*

'If the arrangement of society is bad (as our is), and if a small number of people have power over the majority and oppress it, every victory over Nature will inevitably serve only to increase that power and that oppression.'

The misery of the millions of labourers who worked in the Dark Satanic Mills of nineteenth Century England was made possible (although not *necessary)* by the coal that fuelled the steam engines which drove the primitive machinery of mass production. And the alienation of the car workers of Detroit and Dagenham today is made possible by the oil that powers both the sophisticated production lines and the chromium-plated end product.

Fossil fuels have unique characteristics which make them eminently suitable for exploitation by ruling oligarchies in the furtherance of their own interests. They are *concentrated* in discrete locations, on land that can be bought (or seized), unlike the renewable resources, which in general are pretty evenly distributed throughout the globe. Their extraction from the Earth requires large amounts of *capital* and a high degree of technical *expertise,* which means that only Governments and the largest corporations can afford to finance such undertakings.

Moreover, since deposits are usually located at a considerable *distance* from the consumer, vast amounts of profit and tax can be added to the cost throughout the various stages of transport and distribution without the customer normally being any the wiser.

So efficient, indeed, have the properties of non-renewable energy sources been in enabling the ruling minorities of society to preserve and extend their influence that when the exhaustion of the Earth's fossil fuel reserves recently appeared as a prospect on the horizon, the search immediately began for substitutes with similarly-obliging characteristics. The energy Czars of the world did not have far to look. Their friends in the military establishment had come up with just the answer, in the shape of nuclear fission.

When it comes to shoring up economic and political monopolies, nuclear fission is a well-nigh ideal energy source. Like coal and oil, it depends on digging up something solid and tangible, namely Uranium, from ground to which one can own the 'rights'. Better still, the refining and enrichment of Uranium requires even greater amounts of capital and technical know-how than are needed to process oil. Best of all, the technology involved in turning enriched Uranium into usable energy is so esoteric, so costly and so dangerous that the number of organisations in the world capable of performing the feat is probably only about a dozen at present.

The development of nuclear power will bring in its wake an increased death rate from cancer and leukaemia, and a higher incidence of genetic diseases in future generations, even if there are no catastrophic accidents, because 'small' quantities of 'low-level' radioactivity are routinely released to the environment by nuclear power stations and fuel processing plants.

And plutonium — a substance so toxic that just one kilogram of it could, if dispersed into the atmosphere, cause 2.7 million fatal lung cancer cases (6)— will be produced in vast quantities to fuel the highly-unstable breeder reactors needed to make atomic power an economic proposition.

But all that matters to the ruling oligarchy is that nuclear fission is potentially capable of providing a large proportion of the energy needed to sustain the status quo for a few more centuries.

When pressed, the exponents of nuclear fission admit that its exploitation implies serious problems, but they fall back on the lame justification that fission is just a 'stop gap' to tide us over until the scientists succeed in developing nuclear *fusion* which will, they say, enable vast amounts of energy to be created from the 'virtually-inexhaustible' reserves of deuterium in the world's oceans. Fusion reactors, they say, will be the 'ultimate answer'.

What they do not say is why it should be necessary for us to go to immense trouble to create our own fusion reactor when we receive one-and-a half million million million kilowatt hours of energy a year from the Great Fusion Reactor in the Sky known as the Sun. Could it be because no one has yet perfected a way to corner the market in sunshine? Is it because no one, so far, has been able to channel all the sun's energy into a small number of outlets from which it can be divided up into units and sold in packages, as has been done with virtually every other natural commodity?

Science is working on the problem, though. Peter Glaser, vice-president of Arthur D Little Inc, the international firm of management consultants, has since the late '60s been assiduously promoting a megalomaniac scheme for a huge solar power station in orbit round the Earth which would transmit its power back to ground level by microwave radio beam (7). Glaser suggests that an enormous panel of solar cells, 25 square kilometres in area, could generate electricity to power a battery of microwave generators. These in turn would feed their power to a one kilometre wide transmitting antenna, which would be focused on a 7km wide receiving antenna on Earth.

The microwave beam would pass straight through clouds with little absorption, and the receiving antenna would be connected, via suitable matching equipment, to the electricity grid system, to which it would supply something like 5,000 megawatts of power. The main advantage of the scheme, according to Glaser, is that the 'Satellite Solar Power Station' would be able to operate at full efficiency for 24 hours a day almost every day of the year, unlike terrestrial solar panels which cannot operate at night and work at reduced efficiency when there is cloud.

Among the disadvantages, however, are that the estimated capital cost of the SSPS (around £520/kW) £520/kW) is, even now, twice that of a conventional central power station and also greater than the capital cost of other large, but ground-based, solar energy collectors that have been proposed. And given that the whole project depends on the perfection of a number of technologies still at the development stage — such as the Space Shuttle, cheap mass-produced solar cells, and efficient, inexpensive microwave generators — it seems inevitable that the cost estimated at the moment are grossly over-optimistic. At the moment, development costs alone are reckoned to be around $20,000 million. And the problems involved in maintenance of an SSPS, assuming it can be stationed in orbit successfully, can at this stage only be guessed at.

More serious still are objections to the scheme on the grounds that the microwave beam, even if accurately pointed, is of sufficient intensity to cause concern about its possible effects on living tissue; and that the beam could accidentally (or deliberately, for military purposes) be deflected from its focusing

Energy: where it comes from & how it is used

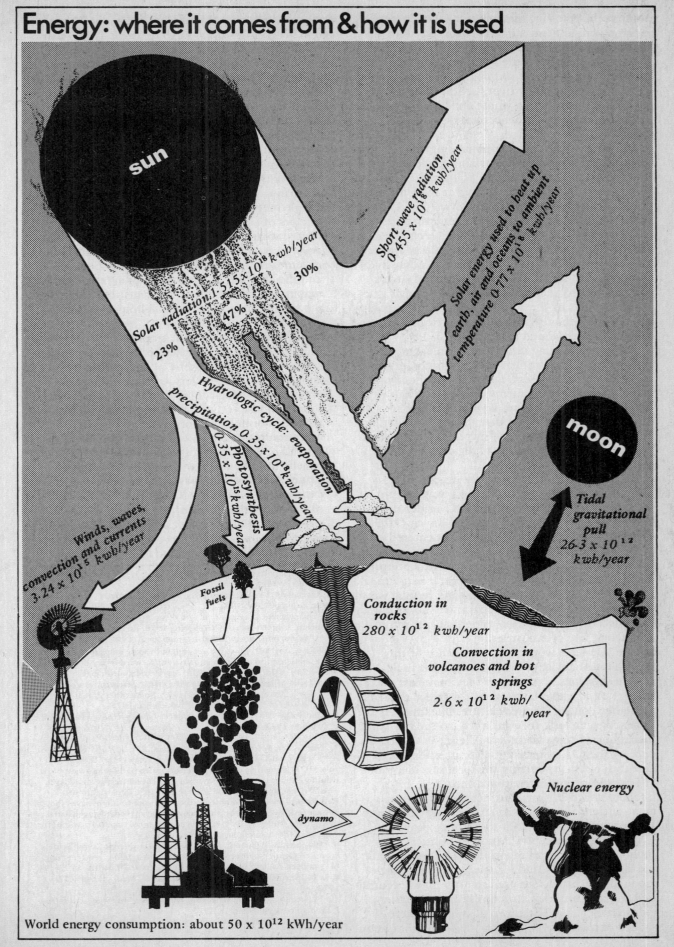

sun

Short wave radiation
0·455 x 10¹⁸ kwh/year

30%

Solar radiation 1·515 x 10¹⁸ kwh/year

47%

23%

Solar energy used to heat up
earth, air and oceans to ambient
temperature 0·77 x 10¹⁸ kwh/year

Hydrologic cycle: evaporation
precipitation 0·35 x 10¹⁸ kwh/year

Photosynthesis
0·35 x 10¹⁵ kwh/year

moon

Tidal
gravitational
pull
26·3 x 10¹²
kwh/year

Winds, waves,
convection and currents
3·24 x 10¹⁵ kwh/year

Fossil
fuels

Conduction in
rocks
280 x 10¹² kwh/year

Convection in
volcanoes and hot
springs
2·6 x 10¹² kwh/
year

dynamo

Nuclear energy

World energy consumption: about 50 x 10¹² kWh/year

point at the receiving antenna to a location where its radiation could harm human beings (8). But the biggest objection to the SSPS is that to an even greater extent than all the other high-technology megaprojects, such stations could only be constructed and operated by the richest corporations or nations of the world, in whose already over-powerful hands they would concentrate even more control.

Some recent schemes for harnessing wind power have displayed a similarly-alarming tendency towards centralised gigantism. William E.Heronemus, professor of electrical engineering at the University of Massachusetts, Amherst, put forward in 1972 a scheme for no less than 300,000 wind turbines to be erected on the Great Plains (9). The turbines, each 50ft in diameter, would be mounted 20 at a time atop enormous 850ft towers spaced at a density of about one per square mile. The output of such a complex would be equivalent to that of nuclear power stations of some 189,000 megawatt capacity, just over half the total installed electrical generating capacity of the United States in 1970.

But such a scheme, even if economically competitive with conventional energy sources, perpetuates the centralisation of energy in a manner which may protect the investments of the electrical Utilities but which ignores an essential characteristic of wind power — the fact that it needs no distribution system and is capable of increasing, rather than decreasing, the self-reliance of regions and small communities.

The centralisation of naturally-decentralised energy sources may not be the only way of turning them into commodities, however. Consider this quote from a recent article on wind power (10):

'Great corporations have not as yet entered into this field because wind energy has not seemed to be monopolisable over a pipe or wire. Enterprise can be rewarded, however, *in greater magnitude than ever before,* by producing and renting world-around wind-harnessing apparatus — following the models of the computer, telephone, car rental and hoteling service industries.'

In case you were wondering, the author of this shrewd bit of advice to our friends in the multi-national corporations on how they may best make a killing out of what Nature gives for free is that supposed hero of the counter-culture, Buckminster Fuller. We can look forward, then, to the day when the regime of some latter-day Allende is 'de-stabilised' by the CIA in retaliation for its attempts to take into public ownership the local subsidiary of ITT Wind Energy International Inc.

There are clearly two distinct modes of development of the naturally-distributed energy sources: a benevolent mode in which they are employed to facilitate the decentralisation of political and economic power, the redistribution of wealth and the liberation of the individual; and a malignant mode in which they are used to prop up the centralised and authoritarian structures of our existing industrial society. These two possibilities were spelled out with his customary clarity by that extra-

ordinary visionary, Aldous Huxley, nearly 30 years ago in his essay *Science, Liberty, Peace (11)*. I can do no better than to italicise the paragraph which seems to me the most important, and to point out that Huxley's comments, though originally addressed to the development of the 'tropical countries', apply with even greater force to the future of the more temperate regions of today's industrial world:

'Until recently, the direct use of solar power has been impracticable, owing to the technical difficulty of constructing suitable reflectors. A few months ago, however, it was announced that Russian engineers had developed a cheap and simple method for constructing paraboloid mirrors of large size, capable of producing superheated steam and even of melting iron. This discovery could be made to contribute greatly to the decentralisation of production and population and the creation of a new type of agrarian society making use of cheap and inexhaustible power for the benefit of individual small-holders or self-governing co-operative groups.

For the peoples of such tropical countries as India or Africa the new device for directly harnessing solar power should be of enormous and enduring benefit — unless, of course, those at present possessing economic and political power should choose to build mass-producing factories around enormous mirrors, thus perverting the invention to their own centralistic purposes, instead of encouraging its small-scale use for the benefit of individuals and village communities. *The technicians of solar power will be confronted with a clear-cut choice. They can work for the completer enslavement of the industrially-backward peoples of the tropics, or for their progressive liberation from the twin curses of poverty and servitude to political and economic bosses.'*

1. See 'Energy in the Universe', Freeman Dyson, *Scientific American*. September 1971.
2. *Journal of the New Alchemists*, PO Box 432, Woods Hole, Massachusetts 02543, USA
3. 'Environmentals versus Ecologists', an interview with Murray Bookchin, *Undercurrents* No 4, Spring 1973. Reprinted from *Alternative Sources of Energy* magazine, number 7, 1972
4. Some of what follows is a version, with some amplification and some condensation of arguments first put forward in my book *Living on the Sun*, Calder & Boyars, 1975. A great deal of the basic data on magnitudes of energy flows is from the classic *Scientific American* special issue on Energy, September 1971. Some other data is from *Energybook One*, Running Press, Philadelphia, 1975.
5. Quoted by Aldous Huxley in *Science, Liberty, Peace*, Chatto and Windus, 1947.
6. *Poisoned Power*, Gofman J. and Tamplin A. Chatto and Windus.
7. See Glaser, Peter, *Journal of Microwave Power*, Vol 5 No 4, 1970.
8. My own calculations (see *Undercurrents* newsletter 'Eddies', July 1973) show that the power density of an SSPS microwave beam would be about 26 milliwatts per square centimetre at ground level, The US Dept of Health, Education & Welfare's Department of Radiological Health recommends that exposure to microwaves should not exceed 5mW/cm^2, and the Russian safety standards, which are much more stringent, limit exposure to no more than 0.1mW/cm^2 for a day. See *Electronics* magazine, March 29, 1973.
9. Heronemus, William E., 'The United States Energy Crisis: Some Proposed Gentle Solutions'. A Paper presented before joint meeting of American Society of Mechanical Engineers and Institute of Electrical and Electronics Engineers, West Springfield, Mass., January 12, 1972.
10. Fuller, Buckminster, article on 'Wind Power' in *Energybook One*, Running Press, Philadelphia, 1975.
11. Huxley, Aldous,*Science, Liberty, Peace*. Chatto & Windus, London 1947.

PLANT YOUR OWN POWER

The world's largest industrial use of solar energy is in agriculture. This is due to the unique ability of plants to convert 0.02% of incident solar radiation into stored chemical energy by the process of photosynthesis. The plants absorb water and carbon dioxide from the soil and the air, and use sunlight to convert these materials into carbohydrates such as sugars and starches. The light energy is converted into the chemical energy bonding the carbohydrate molecules. Only the wavelengths of sunlight between 0.3 and 0.7 microns are used for photosynthesis, compared with the light from 0.3 to 1.1 microns wavelength which can be used by a silicon photoelectric cell. If the plant is eaten by an animal the chemical bonds of the molecules are broken by oxidation and energy is released to power the animal's body. The oxidation of plant matter in an animal is analogous to burning fuel, which is the simplest way to use the energy of plants to produce heat, drive machinery, etc. If a plant decays rather than being eaten, its stored energy is released largely as heat. An estimated thousandth part of total plant matter produced each year is deposited in conditions which do not favour decay or complete energy loss; and in these conditions the material undergoes the first stages of fossilization. When coal, oil or natural gas are burned the same chemical bonds are being broken as if the original plants had been burned, and the energy produced is originally the energy of photosynthesis.

WOOD

In 1950 wood fuel still contributed 4% of the total world energy supply. Of the earth's original 4.8 billion hectares of forest, 1.2 billion are now under management to produce a regular timber crop and another 2 billion are still virgin forest (the rest has been cleared for agriculture, cities, transport, etc). A hectare of mixed forest with trees of differing ages and varieties will supply about 7.4 tonnes of usable timber per year, a pine forest 10 tonnes per hectare per year, and a tropical rain forest 59 tonnes per hectare per year. If all the carbon in the 175×10^9 dry tons[1] of organic matter produced by the biosphere annually were burned as fuel at 75% efficiency, it would supply about 500×10^{12} kWh, roughly 10 times the world's energy consumption for 1970. As a fuel, wood has a calorific value of 4.2 kWh/kg.

The most effective way to use plants as a fuel is by burning them. Good combustion can release a greater proportion of the calorific value of plants than any other secondary conversion of their energy. Wood-burning appliances such as heating stoves and cookers can be obtained with efficiencies of at least 75% (Fig 1), although none are made in Britain because of our lack of forests, and traditional supplies of coal. The most efficient of these

1. See Bio-fuels section in *Energy Primer* (Portola Institute, 1974).

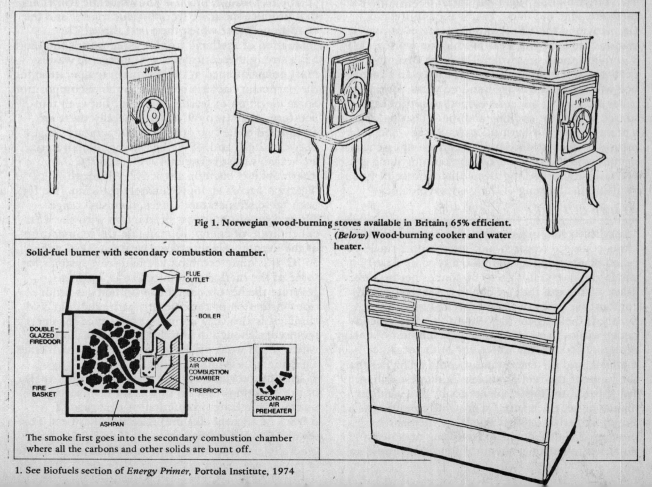

Fig 1. Norwegian wood-burning stoves available in Britain; 65% efficient. (*Below*) Wood-burning cooker and water heater.

Solid-fuel burner with secondary combustion chamber.

FLUE OUTLET

BOILER

DOUBLE-GLAZED FIREDOOR

SECONDARY AIR COMBUSTION CHAMBER

FIREBRICK

FIRE BASKET

SECONDARY AIR PREHEATER

ASHPAN

The smoke first goes into the secondary combustion chamber where all the carbons and other solids are burnt off.

1. See Biofuels section of *Energy Primer*, Portola Institute, 1974

appliances have secondary combustion chambers where the hydrogen and carbon monoxide released by the burning wood are burned to increase the total energy obtained. Wood can also be used to fire boilers for industrial use, as in a furniture factory in High Wycombe, Buckinghamshire, where a boiler is fuelled by wood offcuts and the steam drives a generator to run the machinery of the factory.

Wood and other plant materials can be converted into more conventional liquid and solid fuels such as ethyl alcohol and charcoal (usable as replacements for petrol and smokeless fuel respectively). These fuels were widely used during the war in timber-producing countries. During the Second World War the forester Edward Lundh doubled the effective annual wood fuel harvest in Sweden by improving forestry practices and eliminating waste. Buses, boats and tractors were fitted with wood gas generators which produced a mixture consisting largely of carbon monoxide, carbon dioxide, methane and hydrogen which was fed directly to the engine as a petrol substitute. Wood was also distilled to give motor lubricants, converted into cellulose cattle feed and, when fortified with soya flour and yeast, sold as a meat surrogate. These uses of wood ceased after the war because they were expensive compared with conventional sources of materials, but they showed how many of the requirements of a conventional energy-using system could be met by a renewable fuel.

PEAT AND DUNG

Two other fuels of vegetable origin deserve mention; these are peat and dung. Peat is used in Ireland, Germany and the USSR and there are even power stations fuelled by it. Peat production worldwide is 35 million tonnes per year. The great advantage of peat is that it is a renewable resource, and a managed bog will regenerate every hundred years. Dried dung cakes are used in underdeveloped countries as a source of fuel for cooking and space heating. This is a practice which is harmful agriculturally and medically because the land is deprived of essential manure and the smoke from the burning dung causes eye disease. But as long as no other source of fuel is available the burning of dung is unavoidable.

ALGAL CULTURE

The wish to gain higher yields per hectare of biomass has encouraged research into microscopic single-celled plants such as *Chlorella* (a type of algae) which can give yields up to 86 tonnes per hectare. These plants can then be converted into charcoal, combustible gases and combustible liquids by pyrolysis (heating to 500°-900° C in a closed container without air). A considerable amount of energy is required to dry the water out of the organic material, and the energy input could be higher than the value of the fuel produced. Some researchers suggest that the higher plants could give yields as high as algae, given suitable growing conditions. Reports of trials in West Bengal of the Sharder process of hydroponic culture (using organic nutrients rather than chemical solutions) quote an

annual yield per hectare per year of 2,000 tonnes, although the system has been tried only on a very small scale. This technique could be used with such high yielding crops as sugar beet to produce large quantities of fuel. Although beet could be converted into alcohol as a fuel it would also be ideally suited for conversion into methane gas by the method described in the following section of this chapter.

ANAEROBIC DECOMPOSITION AND METHANE GENERATION

When organic matter decomposes in the absence of oxygen (ie 'anaerobically'), as can sometimes happen in a poorly managed compost heap, incomplete oxidation takes place to give a mixture of ammonia, nitrogen, methane and carbon dioxide, and hence the characteristic smell of putrefaction. The cycle can be completed by the addition of more oxygen, the methane being oxidized to carbon dioxide and water. It is this property of anaerobic decomposition that could be exploited to yield another type of fuel from biomass.

Anaerobic decomposition was originally developed as a means of rendering harmless the sludge from the purification of sewage, and the methane produced was treated more less as a byproduct. However, where the sewage works is of sufficient size the gas has been exploited as a fuel for generating power in gas engines to serve the needs of light and heat at the sewage works (this happens at Mogden and Cambridge). Because of the research behind the process for the safe anaerobic decomposition of sludge, much is known of the bacteria that produce methane from organic matter and the conditions under which they best thrive. The generation of methane from organic wastes therefore has a strong theoretical basis. The organic wastes must be maintained at the optimum temperature for the particular bacteria involved in the decomposition. Some digestion of wastes will occur between temperatures of 0° C to 69° C but generally there are considered to be two optimum temperature ranges. Between 29° C and 41° C the 'mesophilic' bacteria are active, whilst between 49° C and 60° C the 'thermophilic' bacteria are active. Although digestion occurs at approximately the same rate for both these temperature ranges, the usual range allowed for optimum gas production with the least expenditure of energy to maintain the temperature of the decomposing wastes is between 32° C and 35° C. It is quite common in small-scale systems for some of the methane produced to be burnt to generate the heat required to maintain gas production. Insulation of the digester, particularly in cold climates, is also very important to reduce the energy required, although in hot climates such as India, where much work has been pioneered on small-scale digestion, this is not so critical.

It has also been recognized that the acidity (pH) of the digesting wastes is important in ensuring optimum methane production. A pH range of 6.8-8.5 (ie slightly alkaline) is accepted as best. For sewage sludge decomposition a pH of 7.0-7.5 is generally established but the New Alchemy Institute

VANNBAEREN

VANNBAEREN

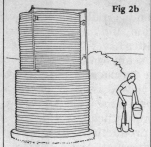

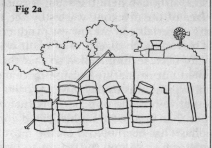

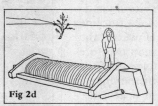

Fig 2. Methane digesters.
Fig 2a. Oil drum sump digesters;
Fig 2b. Variable volume methane holder; Fig 2c. Oil drum digester with inner tube as methane holder;
Fig 2d. Continuous production methane digester;
Fig 2e. Combined digester and gas holder.

found from experiments of digesting manure and plant wastes that a more alkaline mixture with a pH of 8.0-8.5 was better. The pH range is affected if raw organic material for digestion is added while digestion is taking place. The addition of excess raw wastes encourages acid conditions as the first stage of decomposition involves the production of volatile acids. If these are produced faster than the methane generating bacteria can break them down into the final products of anaerobic decomposition then the decomposition stops until sufficient methane-generating bacteria have grown and the balance is restored. It is possible to add lime or ammonium phosphate to restore the pH when it has become too acidic but alkaline sodium salts should not be added as these kill the bacteria. Raw wastes which are naturally more alkaline, such as horse and cow manures, can be composted aerobically to reduce the acids of the initial decomposition and hence keep the pH range at optimum for gas production.

The time allowed for gas production depends upon the type of digester and wastes being used. The original method was one of batch digestion where the wastes were put into a tank, sealed and left for a minimum period of one month, the actual time allowed for digestion depending on the size of the plant. During this time decomposition would be completed and all the gases given off and collected. Only when all the gas had been given off was the digester opened and the residual 'fertilizer' taken out (Fig2a,b,c). Alternatively, digesters have been operated where the raw wastes are ground up and added daily or weekly, with the completely digested slurry being expelled at the other end, gas production therefore being continuous (Fig 2d,e). For the recommended temperature range of 30°C to 35°C the normal period of decomposition is 1-2 months.

Once optimum conditions for digestion have been established, the yield of gas depends to some extent on the raw materials being digested. As mentioned, the main constituents of the gases of decomposition are methane (54-60%) and carbon dioxide (37-45%) with traces of hydrogen (0.3%), carbon monoxide

(0.1%), nitrogen (1.0%), oxygen (0.1%) and hydrogen sulphide (trace). This raw gas has a calorific value of 5.6-7.2 kWh/m^3. However, the gas can be scrubbed to remove the corrosive and non-combustible portions to give a product very similar to natural gas, consisting of 98% methane, 1% carbon dioxide and 1% nitrogen. The carbon dioxide and any ammonia present can be removed by bubbling the raw gas through lime water, and the hydrogen sulphide removed by passing it through iron filings. As the gas comes from the digester it also contains a considerable quantity of water vapour which should be removed by passing the gas through a desiccant to prevent subsequent condensation of water in the gas pipes causing corrosion.

Many different types of organic matter have been used in methane plants in an attempt to find the most efficient conversion of biomass, and hence solar energy, into methane. To some extent the materials used must be limited to those available. Thus in India digesters have been designed to use cow dung and some plant wastes as the raw material. The aim here was to supplant the use of dried cow dung as a direct fuel which involved the loss of manure to the soil. With the methane plant, although the initial capital investment is much higher, the cow dung is still used to produce a fuel but the slurry remaining once digestion is complete is a valuable fertilizer for the soil, only slightly less rich than a compost from aerobically decomposed wastes.

Digesters have also been run completely on plant wastes, although here the scum formed on the surface of the digesting wastes by the undigestible plant materials can inhibit gas production, and for this reason batch digestion of plant wastes has usually been recommended so that the scum can be cleaned out regularly. Because methane production from organic wastes has recently been viewed as an alternative method of producing fuel on a large scale rather than as a more sophisticated compost heap, emphasis has been placed on the most productive plant form to supply the wastes to be digested. Algae grown under optimum conditions can give a yield of 86 tonnes hectare compared to the 2.4-24.0 tonnes hectare of some of the higher plants. However, the algae must be harvested from the solution they are grown in before being digested and this requires energy. It has been argued that some of the high productivity higher plants such as sugar beet and sugar cane could probably achieve yields similar to those of the micro-organisms if grown in comparable optimum conditions and, with their stores of available sugars, may even contain more digestible material than the algae. There has so far been insufficient research to confirm either viewpoint.

FARMERS WEEKLY

In considering any wastes for digestion the quantities of available carbon and nitrogen in the material are important. In anaerobic decomposition the bacteria make use of the available carbon 30-35 times faster than the available nitrogen. If there is insufficient available nitrogen present, some of the bacteria die, thus releasing the nitrogen in their cells and restoring the balance. The digestion process is inhibited whilst this occurs. Once all the available carbon has been consumed fermentation stops and any excess available nitrogen remains in the final slurry. This will be lost to the atmosphere when the slurry fertilizer is spread on the ground. Table 1 shows the carbon:nitrogen ratios of various raw materials that might be used for digestion. However, the values for the C:N ratios in this table that have been measured in the laboratory may differ considerably from the actual C:N ratios of carbon and nitrogen available for digestion and for this reason they can only form a very approximate guide. From experiments in India, cow dung with a measured C:N of 25:1, richer than the recommended 30:1, was found to be an ideal waste for digestion and gas production. Water must also be included in the contents of the digester, which should be 7-9% total solids, so the ground raw wastes should be mixed to a slurry with water. Urine could also be used to mix the slurry but its high available nitrogen content should be included in the estimation of the C:N ratio. Table 2, which shows gas yields from specific wastes, measured empirically, may be a better guide to expected results.

The type of plant used for methane production can vary from the large-scale sewage works digester, plants that can now be purchased for converting intensive livestock wastes (pigs, hens) into enough fuel to run a farm (Fig 3), to a unit where a lorry inner tube is used as the digester and

Table 1

Material	N (% dry weight)	C/N
Urine	15-18	0.8
Blood	10-14	3.0
Bone meal	-	3.5
Right soil	5.5-6.5	6-10
Chicken manure	6.3	15
Sheep manure	3.8	-
Horse manure	2.3	25*
Cow manure	1.7	25 or 18*
Activated sludge	5	6
Fresh sewage	-	11*
Grass clippings	4	12
Cabbage	3.6	12
Tomatoes	3.3	128
Mixed grasses	2.4	19
Hay, young grass	4	12
Hay, alfalfa	2.8	17*
Hay, blue grass	2.5	19
Seaweed	1.9	19
Non-legume vegetables	2.5-4	11-19
Red clover	1.8	27
Bread	2.1	-
Mustard	1.5	26
Potato haulm	1.5	25
Wheat straw	0.5	150
Oat straw	1.1	48
Sawdust	0.1	200-500

non-lignin dry weight

Table 2

Type of waste	Gas production in m³/kg of dry matter	
Pig	0.39-0.54	
Cow (Indian)	0.21-0.31	from Fry & Merril
Chicken	0.39-0.88	
Conventional sewage	0.39-0.60	
Sewage sludge	0.33	from Cambridge City Council
Dung	0.24	
Vegetable waste	0.45-0.94	
Dry leaf powder	0.45	
Sugar cane thresh	0.75	from Singh
Maize straw	0.81	
Straw powder	0.94	
Activated sludge	0.62	

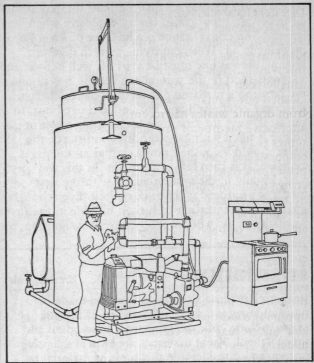

Fig 3. (*Above*) Mr F. Howarth's 'Biogas' digester system at his farm near Doncaster.

Fig 4 (*Right*) Mother Earth News Digester at Madison, Ohio. This is a special cold climate version of the models developed by Ram Bux Singh in India, see also Fig 2e.

Fig 5 (*Below*) Inner-tube continuous-process digester designed by L John Fry and Richard Merrill of New Alchemy Institute (West).

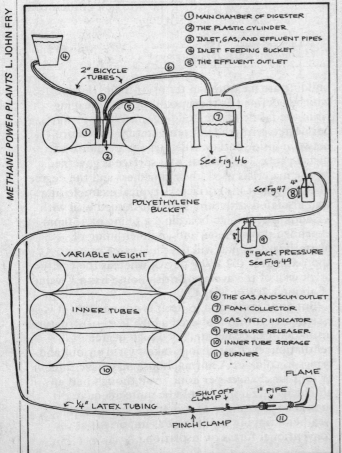

METHANE POWER PLANTS L. JOHN FRY

① MAIN CHAMBER OF DIGESTER
② THE PLASTIC CYLINDER
③ INLET, GAS, AND EFFLUENT PIPES
④ INLET FEEDING BUCKET
⑤ THE EFFLUENT OUTLET

2" BICYCLE TUBES

See Fig. 46

POLYETHYLENE BUCKET

See Fig 47

8" BACK PRESSURE See Fig. 49

VARIABLE WEIGHT

INNER TUBES

⑥ THE GAS AND SCUM OUTLET
⑦ FOAM COLLECTOR
⑧ GAS YIELD INDICATOR
⑨ PRESSURE RELEASER
⑩ INNER TUBE STORAGE
⑪ BURNER

FLAME

¼" LATEX TUBING

SHUT OFF CLAMP
1" PIPE

PINCH CLAMP

enough gas can be produced from two dozen back-yard hens to boil 2 litres of water in 20 minutes (enough to boil an egg but not enough to boil an old hen. Fig 5).

The digester designed for *The Mother Earth News* at Madison, Ohio, by Ram Bux Singh illustrates the typical features of most small-scale plants so far constructed (Fig 4). The digester is a metal drum 3,000 mm in height and 1,200 mm in diameter, surrounded by an outer drum which forms a water jacket through which water heated by some of the gas produced could be circulated to maintain the temperatures of 32° C-35° C for digestion. The digester can either be batch fed, being loaded, sealed and left for 30 days, during which time all the gas is given off, or it can be operated by feeding the wastes, chopped up and mixed to a slurry with water, at regular intervals. As each load of fresh slurry is added, an equal volume of the digested fertilizer is displaced, and gas production can therefore be continuous. A 1.5 kW pump is incorporated in the system both to pump the fresh slurry into the digester and the finished slurry from it. It also circulates the fermenting wastes within the digester. Although energy is needed to run the system, the plant is designed to produce 170 m³ of gas per month, whilst operating the pump for 20 minutes each day to stir the wastes uses the equivalent of 10.2 m³ methane per month and the gas required for burning to maintain the temperature would be slightly less than this amount. The gas is collected in the floating cover of the digester and the weight of this cover provides the gas pressure. From here it is led to the appliances. Other systems use separate gas storage equipment like very small gasometers but in all systems the weight of the cover either directly or counter-balanced is the means of pressurizing the gas.

Any discussion of actual digester systems must

take account of the fact that methane diluted in the air in certain proportions is very explosive when ignited. The critical range is a mixture of 4%-14% methane in air. When emptying a batch digester system, the gas line must be shut off well beforehand so any gas left in the system can vent to the air and the remaining methane can be fully diluted before the cover is removed and the sludge cleared out. In the same way, the first time the floating cover or gas holder is filled with gas after digestion starts, the cover should be pushed down so that all the gas is expelled. It is then left to fill again. In this way any air originally in the system mixed with the first methane produced will not be ignited. Even though the high concentration of carbon dioxide in the first discharge of gas will probably prevent its ignition, no attempt should be made to light it.

Apart from producing methane, the anaerobic digestion of biomass produces a valuable fertilizer for the garden or farm. It is best to let the final sludge stand for a while, so that any ammonia it contains can escape to the air as this would be harmful to plants. The sludge will be wetter than normal compost and also slightly more acidic so this must be considered when applying it to the soil. However, some experiments have shown that the nitrogen in the sludge in the form of ammonium bicarbonate may actually be more available to plants than the nitrates and nitrites produced by the aerobic composting of biomass.

Robert Vale

Insulation
Brenda Vale

Insulating materials can be either man-made or natural. Natural insulating materials of organic origin include cork, eel-grass mat, strawboard and sheep's wool. These materials are either expensive or require a considerable thickness of material to give a high degree of insulation. They are also adversely affected by damp and attractive to vermin. However, if a large amount of free or very cheap material can be obtained and suitable protection can be given from moisture, natural organic materials may be a good choice.

The main inorganic natural materials are mineral wool, which can be obtained in slabs or quilts and is made by extruding molten rock into fibres; and exfoliated vermiculture, which is made by heating a micaceous rock until it expands. These materials have an insulating value comparable to that of the man-made materials.

Apart from glass fibre, which is similar in form to mineral wool, most man-made insulants are made of oil-derived plastics. The most effective of these is expanded polyurethane, which has the advantage of resisting fire and moisture, but this is the most expensive material. Expanded polystyrene is cheaper and effective, but it burns fiercely, giving off poisonous fumes, unless a fire-retarding grade is obtained. The cheapest expanded plastic is foamed urea formaldehyde, but this has no mechanical strength and cannot be made into slabs or boards. It is this material that is pumped into cavity brick walls to add insulation. The walls provide a support for the weak foam.

When insulation, of whatever kind, has been installed, it must be protected against moisture vapour in the air. If vapour condenses in the thickness of the material it will be made useless, since the insulating effect depends on trapping dry air. To prevent condensation, a vapour barrier—such as polythene sheet (with joints folded and taped), vinyl wallpaper, or two coats of oil-based paint—must be fixed on the warm side of the insulation so that the vapour never condenses.

The insulating properties of the surfaces of a

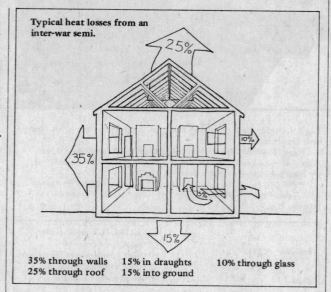

Typical heat losses from an inter-war semi.

25%

10%

35%

5%

15%

35% through walls   15% in draughts   10% through glass
25% through roof   15% into ground

building are measured in terms of their 'U-value', which is defined as the amount of heat escaping from the fabric of the building, measured in watts, per degree centigrade of temperature difference between inside and outside, per square metre of surface area. The U-value of a surface is governed by the materials used, their thickness and the degree of exposure of the surface. A typical example of a well insulated structure is timber-framed wall with a cladding of shiplap boarding, a filling of 150mm expanded polystyrene, and an inner lining of plasterboard, which will have a U-value of approximately 0.2 W/m^2 deg.C, whereas the cavity brick wall of the average British house has a U-value of about 1.7 W/m^2 deg.C.

But good insulation in itself is not enough. It is essential to realise that even a high level of structural insulation can be negated by a high degree of ventilation; each air change takes warm air out and brings in cold air. A normal house may have three or four air changes per hour, even though half an air change per hour would be quite adequate. It should be recognized that draught sealing and weather stripping are at least as important as the conventional forms of insulation.

SUNSHINE SUPERPOWER

Useful solar energy is collected simply and cheaply by plants, but the process is not very efficient in terms of the proportion of incoming energy converted. For many purposes it is more efficient or useful to apply solar energy directly as heat, or more rarely, by direct conversion to electricity. Solar heat is collected either at high temperatures by concentrating direct radiation from a large to a smaller area; or at low temperatures by allowing it to heat up materials exposed to it. The low-temperature processes are on the whole more efficient and permit the use of diffuse sky-radiation as well as direct sunlight.

HIGH TEMPERATURE SOLAR HEAT

The sun's energy can be used to produce heat at high or low temperatures. High temperature solar collectors are typified by the French solar furnace in the Pyrenees which uses an array of large moveable mirrors to produce temperatures in excess of 3,000° C (Fig 1). On a smaller scale there are many designs of solar cookers which will boil water, bake bread, etc, by focusing the solar radiation onto a small area by the use of reflectors (Fig 2). Similar devices have been built using curved reflectors to concentrate the radiation at a linear focus. A black pipe carrying water placed at this focus will be heated sufficiently to produce steam (Fig 3). The problem of concentrators is that they need direct sunlight and must be tracked to keep the sun on the required focus. The linear type lessens this problem and need only be adjusted in tilt once a week or less. The concentrating collectors

Fig 1. Solar furnace at Odeillo, Pyrenees, France.

are fairly complex in construction as the correct shape of the reflecting surface must be maintained, and their form means that they are very difficult to incorporate into the fabric of a building. If free-standing, they are liable to suffer damage from wind and exposure.

Fig 2. Parabolic solar cooker.

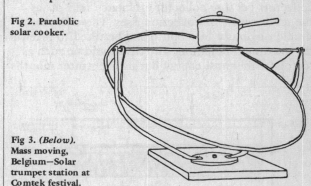

Fig 3. (Below). Mass moving, Belgium—Solar trumpet station at Comtek festival.

RAMPARTS

TONY DURHAM

LOW TEMPERATURE SOLAR HEAT

The commonest use of solar heat is in low temperature (up to 50°C) flat plate collectors. These have a black heat-absorbing surface which is in contact with the fluid to be heated (usually air or water) (Fig 4). The absorber has one or more transparent covering sheets. The solar radiation passes through the transparent cover and is absorbed by the black plate, which becomes heated. The infra-red radiation from the heated plate cannot re-radiate through the transparent cover to the outside so the temperature of the plate rises and the heat can be absorbed by a circulating fluid. The back of the plate must be insulated to prevent loss of heat. If the number of glass or plastic covers is increased the heat lost by convection and conduction through the face of the collector can be reduced, but the proportion of the solar energy reflected from or absorbed by the cover sheets also rises.

Flat plate collectors will collect indirect as well as direct radiation but useful temperatures are obtained only with direct radiation. It is not worth trying to achieve high temperatures with flat plate collectors because collector efficiency falls off as the temperature of collection rises. The collector should obviously face South and be tilted to receive the maximum radiation. The tilt should be such as to collect the most energy during the winter months when the heat is needed. The usual recommended tilt angle is the latitude of the site plus 15°, which, in Southern Britain, leads to an angle of 67°: difficult to incorporate into the fabric of a building. Fig 5 shows how, with a building of a given volume, a large collector can be built to replace the whole roof-covering at an angle of about 30°. If the collector is as cheap as the roofing it replaces, this design will give considerably more heat than the smaller area of optimum-angle collector that could be built within the same building volume.

THERMOSYPHON SYSTEMS

The collecting system can be either closed or open. In a closed system the fluid flows in tubes or ducts fixed to the black absorbing surface. Provided that all the pipes slope slightly upwards, and, more importantly, that the bottom of the hot-water tank or heat stove is above the top of the collector, the fluid will thermosyphon round the system without the need for a pump (see Fig 6). Early designs of closed collectors used copper tubing soldered to blackened copper absorber plates in order to achieve good thermal contact between the plate and the tube. Most recent designs in such collectors use pressed steel central heating radiators painted matt black. Points to note about thermosyphon systems are that the pipes must be of large diameter (for water systems, at least 28mm diameter) so that the flow is not reduced or stopped by friction. Because the system is always full, the water must contain anti-freeze to prevent trouble on winter nights, or it must be drained at night and refilled when the sun comes out.

PUMPED SYSTEMS

The main problem of a thermosyphon system is the siting of the tank or heat stove. In order for the system to work the tank must be higher than the collector, but the construction of a large tank above

Fig 4. Section through a 'closed' type of low-temperature collector with two covers and where the heat-collecting fluid flows behind the collector plate.

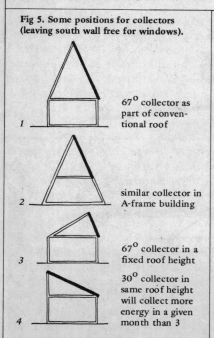

Fig 5. Some positions for collectors (leaving south wall free for windows).

1 67° collector as part of conventional roof

2 similar collector in A-frame building

3 67° collector in a fixed roof height

4 30° collector in same roof height will collect more energy in a given month than 3

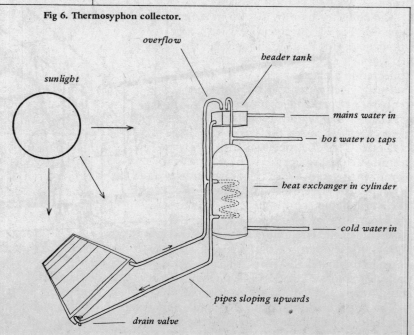

Fig 6. Thermosyphon collector.

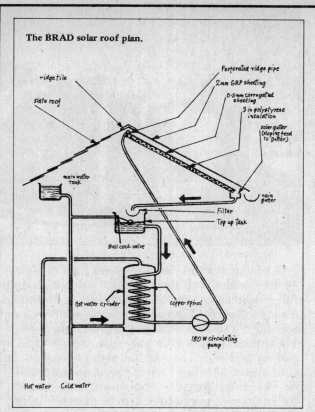

The BRAD solar roof plan.

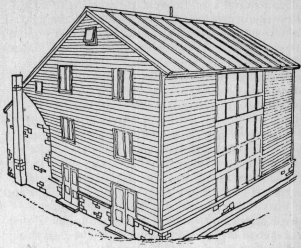

Fig 7. *In the solar collector used in the BRAD house (above) water is pumped up to a perforated pipe running along the ridge of the roof (left) and trickles over grey corrugated aluminium sheets where it is warmed by absorbed solar energy before being collected in a trough at the bottom.*

PATRICK RIVERS

one's roof presents considerable problems, and the system tends to be used only for collectors that supply domestic hot water to a conventionally sized hot water cylinder. If a pump is incorporated in the circuit the tank and collector can be sited independently of one another. At the same time the collector can be of the open type, where water is distributed along the top of the absorber plate, flows under gravity to the bottom and is collected and pumped through a heat exchanger to the top again.

The collector used by BRAD in Wales is of this type (see Fig 7); the absorber is dark grey anodized corrugated aluminium and the water is fed through a perforated pipe at the top and collected in a plastic gutter at the bottom. The collector gives water at 50° C in summer. One problem of open collectors, in theory if not in practice, is that water vapour will condense on the clear cover and lessen the amount of heat collected. This does occur at BRAD but does not seem to affect the operation of the collector significantly. Another problem is that as the system is not sealed, algae, fungi and other organisms that like warm damp conditions will tend to start growing. This can be stopped by putting a suitable fungicide in the circulating water. The fungicide should not contain any metallic salts that might corrode the metal absorber. Advantages of the open collector are its cheapness and the fact that it is self-draining and will therefore not freeze.

The need to add things to the circulating water (fungicide, black ink for increasing the heat absorbed, anti-freeze) means that the collector

circuit should be indirect, that the water flowing through the collector is not the same as the water which comes out of the taps. The collector water should flow through a coil of pipe in the cylinder containing the water to be heated. The same system is advisable for closed collectors to prevent any build-up of scale in the pipes.

COVERS

The choice of material for the clear covering sheets has an impact on the cost, efficiency and life of the collector. The usual number of sheets for year-round operation is two, although the computer programme of the solar energy research group at the Central London Polytechnic indicates that double glazing provides only a small increase in the heat that a collector will contribute. The BRAD collector mentioned above is single glazed but is designed only for summer use. Glass is the best material for covering in terms of transparency and, more importantly, long life, although it is relatively expensive, difficult to handle and breakable. The main disadvantage of glass is that it requires a supporting structure (such as glazing bars). The ideal material would appear at first sight to be a clear corrugated plastic because it would be light, easy to handle and being corrugated would require no glazing bars. The problem of transparent plastics is that they are almost all quickly degraded by sunlight and become brittle and opaque. The best plastics from a degradation viewpoint are polymethyl methacrylate ('Perspex') and polyvinylflouride (PVF). These are both more expensive than glass in rigid sheet form. PVF can be obtained bonded to clear corrugated glass fibre and this would be an effective collector cover were it not for the very high price. The degradation of plastics is caused by the ultra-violet content of sunlight and it may be worth using a layer of plastic under a single glass skin to achieve a cheaper double-glazed cover than if glass alone were used. The glass should help to cut out the ultra-violet light and therefore improve the life of the plastic. Care should be taken that the selected plastic does not melt or soften at the temperatures that may be reached in the collector.

PASSIVE SOLAR COLLECTORS

The simplest solar collectors are the 'passive' type where the structure of the building itself is used to collect heat without the need for pumps, fans, etc. Such collectors can generally be used only for space heating. A typical passive collector is that designed by Trombe and Michel in the Pyrenees (see Fig 8). It consists of a heavy (usually concrete) wall with horizontal slots at top and bottom. The outer south facing surface of the wall is painted black and double glazed, leaving a cavity between the wall and the glass. When the sun shines, the wall heats up, the air in the cavity is heated and rises, flowing into the building through the slot in the top of the wall and being replaced by cold air entering the cavity through the slot at the bottom. When the sun stops shining the heat stored in the massive wall continues to heat the air.

ALL PHOTOGRAPHS: STEVE BAER

A similar system is used by Steve Baer in New Mexico, with a wall made of black-painted oil drums full of water (see Fig 9). At night insulated shutters are closed over the outside of the oil drum wall and the warm water then radiates heat into the room. These systems have little long-term storage capacity and are best suited to climates with sunny days and cold nights, but they have the great advantage of no mechanical parts to break down, and no need for additional energy to run them. Water-heating passive collectors are on sale in Japan; these take the form of a black plastic pillow which is filled with water in the morning and left on the roof under a clear plastic cover. In the evening the heated water can be drained off for use.

STORAGE

A solar heating system requires a means of storing heat for overcast days. The commonest storage media are water or rocks. Water takes up less space for a given heat storage capacity but the container must be leakproof; rocks enable heat to be drawn off at the temperature it is put in without the temperature being reduced by mixing. Both require a large, highly insulated container, preferably inside the building to be heated so that the heat lost from the storage goes into the building. To keep the volume of storage as small as possible it is essential to reduce the heat requirement of the building by good insulation. Given a very large volume of storage it would be possible to store heat from summer to winter. This was tried successfully at MIT in the 1930s but is expensive. Chemicals have been used for storing heat—usually substances that melt when heated and give up heat on resolidifying, such as hydrated sodium sulphate. The problem is that after a number of heating/cooling cycles they cease to give up heat at the required temperature. All the chemicals so far tested for heat storage are more expensive than water or rocks. A further method of storing heat is in a two-vessel system rather than in a single container of one material. For instance, a solution of sulphuric acid and water may be heated by the sun and the resulting steam condensed in a separate vessel. When the remaining concentrated sulphuric acid cools and

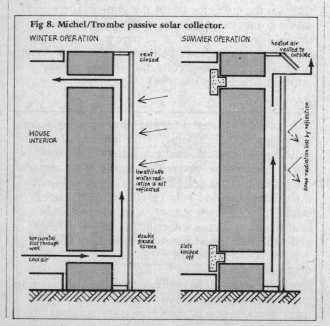

Fig 8. Michel/Trombe passive solar collector.

WINTER OPERATION   SUMMER OPERATION

vent closed   heated air vented to outside

HOUSE INTERIOR

low altitude winter radiation is not reflected

some radiation lost by reflection

horizontal slot through wall

double glazed screen

cool air

slots blocked off

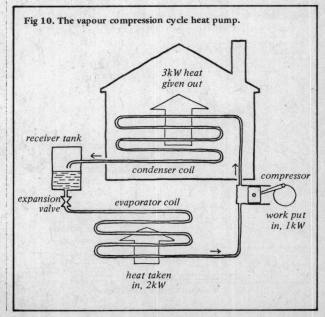

Fig 9. Steve Baer's oil-drum solar collector at Corrales, New Mexico. The first picture shows the shutter/reflector down to collect heat, the second shows it up to retain heat, and the third shows what the drums look like from inside.

the vapour pressure drops, the water in the other vessel will evaporate and re-enter the acid. When this happens the water gives up its heat of condensation and also the heat evolved when it mixes with the concentrated acid. If a valve is placed in the pipe connecting the two vessels, the heat may be stored indefinitely as the water will only recombine when the valve is opened. Such a system is obviously complex to build but could have the advantage of being smaller in volume than a water tank of the same storage capacity.

SOLAR PONDS

Heat may also be collected and stored in ponds. A pond is constructed with a black lining and filled with concentrated brine. A layer of fresh water is placed over the brine. The solar radiation passes through the water and heats the black bottom of the pond and hence the brine. As the brine is much heavier than water it cannot rise to the surface and evaporate. A coil of pipe in the brine conducts the heat away for use. This method has been tried in Israel by Tabor to provide low pressure steam to drive a turbine. The ponds must be very large in area to minimize heat losses around the edges.

TEMPERATURE AND EFFICIENCY

As flat plate collectors produce heat more efficiently at low temperatures there is a problem when this heat is required in a building. A conventional central heating system with radiators operates at 80°C whereas the collector will give heat at about 50°C. A warm air system will work at 50°C or less but the necessary ducts and fans take up considerable space, particularly in an existing building. The most effective use of 50°C heat is in large radiant ceiling panels containing water. Although these give the most comfortable conditions of any sort of heating, they are expensive.

HEAT PUMPS

The increased efficiency of low temperature heat collection and the possibility of simplifying the collector if it is not to collect at higher temperatures have led to the use of heat pumps with solar collectors. The heat pump works in the same way as

a domestic refrigerator by absorbing heat at a low temperature, doing work on it, and exhausting it at a higher temperature (see Fig 10). In the refrigerator heat is absorbed from the food, which is cooled and exhausted into the kitchen, which is (slightly) warmed. The quantity of high grade heat produced is greater than the amount of work put in. This apparently 'free' heat is gained at the expense of the temperature of the low grade heat source, which is reduced. Therefore, if one has a large volume of something which is at a fairly constant temperature, such as the earth, the air or a lake, heat can be extracted from it without reducing its temperature unduly. This is a method of using solar energy indirectly in that the low temperature heat source is initially warmed by the sun.

In the vapour compression heat pump (and the electric refrigerator) a suitable refrigerant such as Freon 12, at the temperature of the low grade heat source, is compressed as a gas to raise its boiling point to slightly more than the temperature required for space heating. The pressurized gas passes through condenser coils over which the air or water to be heated flows. This cools the gas to below its boiling

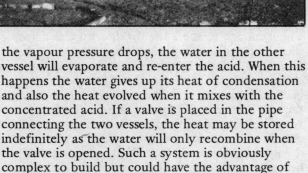

Fig 10. The vapour compression cycle heat pump.

point so it condenses and gives out heat. The liquid refrigerant is collected in a receiver and passed through an expansion valve which causes the pressure to drop and the temperature to fall. The cool liquid then passes through the evaporator coils, which are in contact with the low grade heat source. Heat is absorbed, evaporating the liquid which returns to the compressor.

The effectiveness of an ideal heat pump cycle is measured by its 'coefficient of performance' (COP). The higher the COP the more heat is upgraded to a higher temperature per unit of energy put into the system. Obviously if advantage is to be taken of the heat pump, the COP should be as high as possible so that the maximum amount of usable heat is provided for the expenditure of as little energy as possible. To achieve high values for the COP the difference in temperature between the low grade heat and the required high grade heat must be as small as possible. If a low grade source such as the soil or a river is being used, the temperature is fixed at roughly 50° C. This is about the lowest temperature the soil will reach at a depth of 1,200 mm in the southern part of Britain.

The effectiveness of a heat pump system is reduced by the fact that the circulating refrigerant needs to be cooler than the low grade source in order for heat transfer to take place to the refrigerant, and hotter than the required temperature in the building so that heat can be transferred to the heating medium. This can add 10—20° C to the temperature difference. It can be seen that the same problem of heat distribution arises as with solar collectors, for if hot water radiators are used the temperature difference will be high and the COP will be low. Further reductions in the theoretical efficiency occur because the compressor cannot be 100% efficient; because expansion and compression of a refrigerant

in a real installation never match its theoretically ideal behaviour; and because power is needed to drive fans, pumps, etc. For these reasons the overall effectiveness of a heat pump system is measured by its 'performance energy ratio' (PER), which is the ratio of the heat output to the input to the heat engine system. In practice the PER will be about 30% of the predicted COP. PERs of up to 6.0 have been achieved with units using waste heat from power stations at 25° C, and up to 5.0 using air or ground-water. However these were large installations; domestic scale installations can usually achieve 3.0 at the most.

In order to reduce the temperature difference, attempts have been made to use solar heated water as the low temperature source, and then to upgrade it. Because the solar heated water is not required at a high enough temperature for direct use as a heat source, the collector can be cheap and simple. A house was built in Tokyo using this system; the collector was not even glazed but merely painted black. The system in the house was complicated by the fact that heat was extracted from the mains water before it was pumped to the collector, and also from the house sewage caught in a tank before it passed to the sewer. In total, there were three heat pump systems. If a solar collector alone has to supply all the low grade heat input in such a system, it must have a very large area.

One point not often considered in relation to heat pumps is their efficiency in overall fuel terms. Most domestic installations are operated from mains electricity and may have a PER of 3.0, meaning that for each kilowatt-hour of electricity bought, 3kWh of heat are given out. However, the conversion of coal or oil to electricity in a power station is about 40% efficient, and losses in the transmission lines can reduce this to less than 25%. A solid fuel or gas boiler or closed room heater may be 70% efficient and therefore a heat pump with a PER of 3.0 is only the equivalent, with the expenditure of a lot of effort and complex machinery, of burning coal at home. A boiler could be used directly to boost the temperature of solar heated water to a usable level and would therefore be serving the same function as a heat pump plus solar collector installation at greatly reduced cost.

The heat pump comes into its own where it can be driven by a primary fuel or an ambient-energy source, rather than by mains electricity (see Fig 11). The high PERs obtained with large scale heat pump installations are often the result of driving the heat pump compressor with a diesel or gas engine, and using the cooling water as an additional source of heat. Here the energy of the gas (which could be methane if the installation were on a farm) is used directly to drive the engine and the heat produced by the inefficiency of internal combustion is also used, thus raising the efficiency of the total system. The heat pump is perhaps trebling the value of the fuel. Another possibility is to use a heat pump compressor to absorb the excess power produced by a large aerogenerator. Wind-powered generators must be governed to prevent over-running and

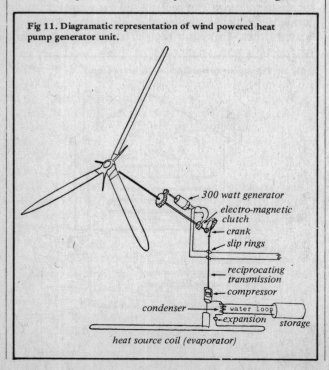

Fig 11. Diagramatic representation of wind powered heat pump generator unit.

300 watt generator

electro-magnetic clutch

crank

slip rings

reciprocating transmission

compressor

condenser

water loop

expansion

storage

heat source coil (evaporator)

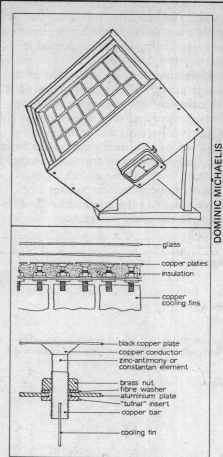

DOMINIC MICHAELIS

glass

copper plates
insulation

copper
cooling fins

black copper plate
copper conductor
zinc-antimony or
constantan element

brass nut
fibre washer
aluminium plate
"tufnal" insert
copper bar

cooling fin

solar cell / air heating panels

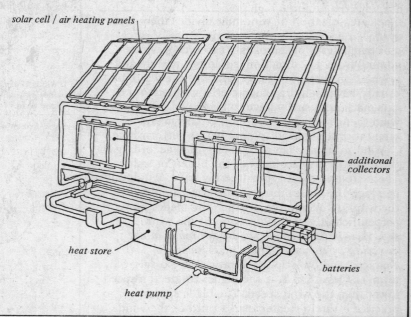

additional collectors

heat store

batteries

heat pump

Fig 12 (*Above*) **Solar thermoelectric generator (1955), output 1.3 watts/square metre. Fig 13** (*Above right*) **An experimental array of photoelectric cells used in conjunction with a flat-plate collector to operate pump switches, generating a few watts in direct light. Made by Solar Power Ltd. Fig 14** (*Right*) **Heating system for 'Solar One' house at the University of Delaware.**

subsequent damage, and much of the potential energy in winds of higher velocities is wasted. If the surplus energy could be taken up by a compressor the formerly wasted energy could be used and its value increased. Obviously heat storage would be required for windless days, and this could add considerably to the cost, but this and similar proposals (see Wind section) show a better use of the heat pump than simply as a means of using mains electricity as efficiently as a boiler uses coal.

DIRECT SOLAR GENERATION OF ELECTRICITY

Electricity can be produced directly from sunlight using devices with no moving parts.

◆ *Thermo couples* If alternate lengths of electrical conductors or semi-conductors of different kinds are joined together, and one set of junctions is heated while the other is cooled, an electric current is produced (see Fig 12). The heat could be applied by a concentrating collector of some sort to produce a solar thermoelectric generation.

◆ *Photoelectric devices* The problems of keeping the cold junctions cold while heat is applied to the hot side, of maintaining the sunlight focused on the

device, and the expense of the concentration have tended to favour research into 'photoelectric cells' where sunlight is turned directly into electricity (see Fig 13). The high cost of such cells, usually made of silicon crystals, has confined their use to space vehicles, but this cost is now falling with the development of cheaper materials such as cadmium sulphide, and simpler manufacturing techniques. It is now thought that cells could be produced for about £300 per kW (roughly comparable with the cost of wind generators). A house has been built at Delaware University (see Fig 14) using a $71m^2$ array of thin film CdS cells on a roof at a slope of 45° (with conversion efficiencies as low as 5% a $20m^2$ panel would be required to produce 1 kW). Air is blown through ducts behind the cells to cool them, and this air, heated to 24° C, is then used for space heating combined with a chemical heat storage bed. The cells are laboratory manufactured and no cost is given, but it can be assumed that at present the use of solar power to produce electricity is too expensive for general use, although new techniques for manufacturing cells may soon alter this situation.

Robert Vale

NATURAL, ENDLESS, FREE

The wind is a naturally-distributed, virtually untapped and non-polluting source of energy. As such, it offers many possibilities for the decentralization of power production, since the harnessing of wind can be easily controlled and maintained by the people who make use of its energy.

Everyone knows that wind was once used to push ships around the world—incidentally, some of the ocean crossing times of the old clippers were competitive with the crossing times achieved by modern freighters—and most people are familiar with the Dutch use of windmills to drain land reclaimed from the sea. But few know of the many other devices for harnessing the wind, developed over the centuries since the first windmills—evolved from sailing boats and animal mills—appeared in China and Persia around 2,000 BC.

A lot of work on wind has also been done in this century, but unfortunately a large proportion of it has consisted of research into large-scale machines, which are both expensive and very vulnerable in high winds. It is this preoccupation with *large* power stations which has stopped wind power from being fully exploited—quite apart from the essential foolishness of trying to centralize and charge for distributing a form of energy which Nature distributes for nothing. But there is another and more hopeful side to the wind power story.

WINDMILL TYPES

One categorization of windmills divides them into *vertical axis* or *horizontal axis* machines. Vertical axis machines ("panemones") can accept winds coming from any direction, so do not require any orientation system to turn them into the wind, but usually have high drag characteristics. Horizontal axis machines usually have to be turned into the wind (hence requiring special mechanisms for orientation), but tend to have better performance.

Wind machines can also be classified according to the mode of displacement of the blades or sails. There are two main types (see Fig 1): I. Windmills in which the blades move in the same direction as the wind; II. Windmills in which the blades move perpendicularly to the direction of the wind.

◆ *I. Windmills in which the blades move in the direction of the wind* These machines are characterized by a tip-speed ratio (see glossary of terms) of less than 1, ie the blades rotate at a speed lower than the wind speed. The blade speed in practice is rarely greater than a third of the wind speed which means that these are 'slow' machines.

The axis of the rotor in such machines is perpendicular to the wind direction and is usually vertical. Generally only one blade or sail is actively 'driving', while one or more of the blades is rotating against the wind—which retards the overall speed of the mill. The different methods employed to overcome this problem of retardation are what distinguish the different wind machines in this category.

a) Windmills with simple drag With these machines, the blade moving against the wind changes its position so that it offers minimal resistance to the wind, or is screened off on the windward side.

1. Screen wind machine (see Fig 2). A suitably-placed screen dispenses with the problem of retardation of the blades turning against the wind. The screen can either be fixed or moveable, the former obviously being only suitable when the wind direction is fairly constant. With a moveable screen, the machine can accept winds coming from any direction, although it can be a complicated process to move the screen. Screen machines can have a vertical axis (these are sometimes called

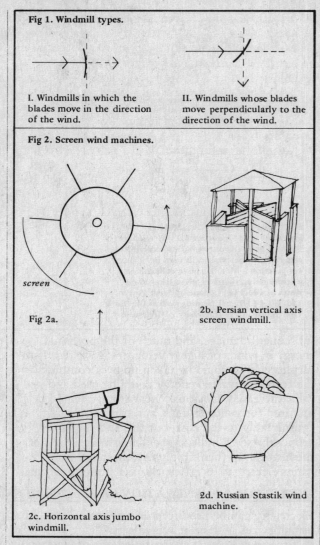

Fig 1. Windmill types.

I. Windmills in which the blades move in the direction of the wind.

II. Windmills whose blades move perpendicularly to the direction of the wind.

Fig 2. Screen wind machines.

screen

Fig 2a.

2b. Persian vertical axis screen windmill.

2c. Horizontal axis jumbo windmill.

2d. Russian Stastik wind machine.

'merry-go-round' windmills; see Fig 2b), or a horizontal axis (these are sometimes known as 'jumbo' windmills; see Fig 2c). The Russian Stastik windmill (Fig 2d), in which the whole machine was kept oriented into the wind was a horizontal-axis version.

2. 'Clapper' type wind machine (see Fig 3a). The blades or sails are hinged, and swing about a vertical axis. A stop situated near each blade holds it back

when it is in the drive arc of its cycle, yet leaves it free to feather in the wind for the rest of its cycle. This arrangement has the disadvantage of involving considerable machine maintenance because of the continual shocks received by the sails or blades when they bump up against the stops; it is this bumping action which gives the 'clapper' type its name. The clapper windmill is believed to have been one of the first windmills; there are some still in existence in China (Fig 3b).

3. Wind machine with cyclic variation in blade angle (see Fig 4). By means of an epicyclic mechanism or a system of belts or chains, the blades of such machines change their angle in relation to the wind, and turn round their vertical axes through half a revolution for each complete revolution of the rotor. The effect is similar to the clapper type without the shocks, but the complicated mechanism involved means that this machine loses one of the main advantages of the simple panemones, namely that of cheapness and simplicity of construction.

b) *Windmills with drag difference* With these machines the shape of the blade is streamlined so that the drag is less in that part of its cycle that opposes the wind. An important advantage of these machines is that they do not need a mechanism for orientation.

1. Cup-type wind machine (see Fig 5a). The "cup anemometer", used in meteorological stations for measuring wind speed, is the best example of this type of machine. The shape and number of cups may vary—as can be judged from Fig 5b. Such machines are not particularly useful for *harnessing* wind energy.

2. Transverse flow wind machine (see Fig 6a). These machines are analogous to the Banki water turbine, and are a transitional type between Type I and Type II machines, as the wind strikes the blade surface not perpendicularly, but at a small angle. The ingoing wind produces only a small part of the driving torque, the main power coming from the outgoing wind. Drag against the wind results in a loss in efficiency, and furthermore, with increasing speed of rotation, the braking torque increases more rapidly than the gross driving torque. There is however an advantage in this apparent inefficiency: no special devices are needed to limit the speed in high winds. This type of rotor also exhibits the 'Magnus effect'—a perpendicular force created by the airfoil-like properties of a cylinder spinning in the windstream. Its efficiency can be increased by the use of guide vanes, when high rotation speeds can be attained (see Fig 6b). This type of wind machine has not received the attention it appears to warrant.

3. Savonius Rotor (see Fig 7). This machine derives from the cup windmill, and bears a resemblance to the transverse flow machine. It consists of a vertical cylinder sliced in half along its vertical axis, the two halves so formed being pulled apart about 20% of the original diameter (there are some variations in this distance and in the shape of the curvature of the blades, from a fairly streamlined almost airfoil shape to a simple semi-circle). This

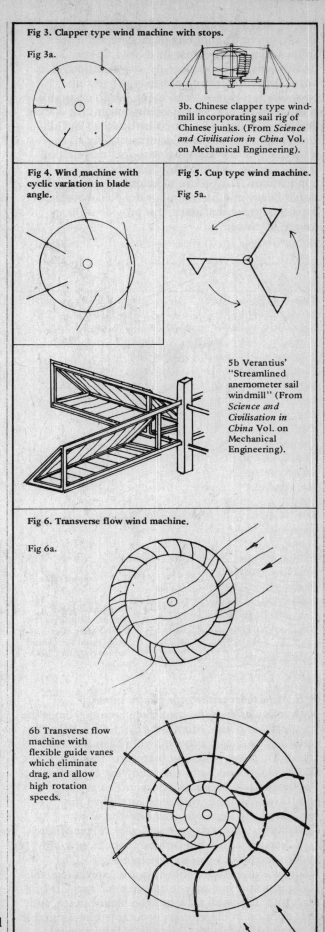

Fig 3. Clapper type wind machine with stops.

Fig 3a.

3b. Chinese clapper type windmill incorporating sail rig of Chinese junks. (From *Science and Civilisation in China* Vol. on Mechanical Engineering).

Fig 4. Wind machine with cyclic variation in blade angle.

Fig 5. Cup type wind machine.

Fig 5a.

5b Verantius' "Streamlined anemometer sail windmill" (From *Science and Civilisation in China* Vol. on Mechanical Engineering).

Fig 6. Transverse flow wind machine.

Fig 6a.

6b Transverse flow machine with flexible guide vanes which eliminate drag, and allow high rotation speeds.

type of machine operates in light winds and is ideally suited to pumping or mechanical drive applications, but because of its low tip-speed ratio (0.5 to 1.5), and therefore its slow rotation, it is not really suitable for electricity generation. Savonius rotors have been in use for some time as ventilators on vans and as ocean current measuring devices. The Brace Research Institute at McGill University in Montreal, Canada, catalysed a recent resurgence of the Savonius with its "recycled oil drum" design for Third World waterpumping applications. The oil drum Savonius, although it is rather heavy and has the poor drag characteristics typical of these machines, can provide a cheap source of power.

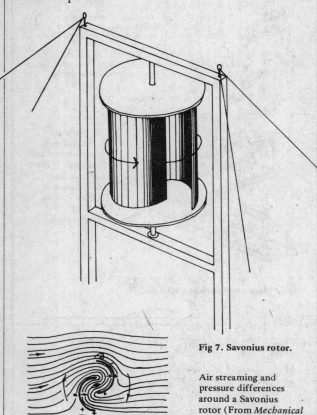

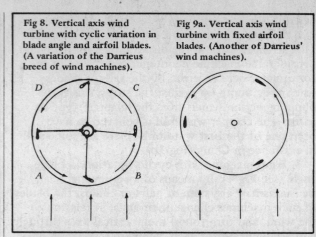

Fig 8. Vertical axis wind turbine with cyclic variation in blade angle and airfoil blades. (A variation of the Darrieus breed of wind machines).

Fig 9a. Vertical axis wind turbine with fixed airfoil blades. (Another of Darrieus' wind machines).

Fig 7. Savonius rotor.

Air streaming and pressure differences around a Savonius rotor (From *Mechanical Engineering*, May 1931 p.334).

◆ *II. Windmills with rotor blades moving perpendicularly to the wind* For these machines the tip-speed ratio may often be greater than 1—ie the blade tips rotate at a speed higher than the wind speed. They are, generally therefore 'fast' machines, and can be divided into the following categories: Machines having their axis perpendicular to windflow; Machines with axis parallel to the windflow, and kept oriented into the wind.
a) Machines with axis perpendicular to windflow
1. Vertical axis wind turbine (panemone) with cyclic variation in blade angle (see Fig 8). The blades are of airfoil sections. In these machines the blade is propulsive only in the arcs AB and CD (see diagram). The wind traverses the blades twice, and the variation in blade angle is obtained by a suitable rotation of the blades. Darrieus, a French wind

power engineer, patented a version of this machine in 1931.
2. Fixed-blade panemone (see Fig 9a and b). These machines only work when the tip-speed is much greater than the wind speed. It is necessary to start the machine in order to initiate self-sustaining operation, (for example by using a Savonius rotor to provide an initial torque). Such a machine, also covered in Darrieus' patent, is much simpler than the variable blade type, easy to construct, and appears to have many advantages and possibilities.
3. Vertical axis catenary wind machine (see Fig 9c). This is another variation of the No.II.2. type, and also covered by Darrieus' patent. The airfoil blades are bent into the form of a catenary (hoop shape) to avoid stresses and bracing. This type of machine has tip-speed ratios ranging from 4 to 7— almost as fast as a propeller type machine—but like No.II.2. it requires a starting device. A Savonius rotor at the centre can be used. Interest in this

Fig 9b. Fixed-blade panemone built by the author and John Shore.

DEREK TAYLOR

NASA

Fig 10. NASA vertical-axis catenary prototype.

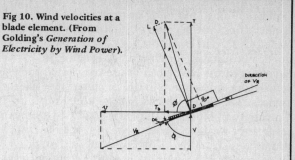

Fig 10. Wind velocities at a blade element. (From Golding's *Generation of Electricity by Wind Power*).

An active surface (flat or airfoil section) is placed so that it makes a large angle ($\phi + \alpha$) with the direction of the wind. V is the velocity of the wind when it approaches the surface. The forces thus result in the surface moving with velocity v perpendicularly to V. The relative wind velocity V_R is V- v. This V_R makes an angle α (angle of attack) with the surface. A force F acts on the surface and this has two components — lift force L perpendicular to the V_R and a drag force D parallel to V_R.

$$\text{Lift (L)} = C_L \cdot \tfrac{1}{2} \varrho \, A \cdot V_R^2 \quad \text{Drag (D)} = C_D \cdot \tfrac{1}{2} \varrho \, A \cdot V_R^2$$

Where A = area of surface ϱ = air density C_L = Lift component of the particular aerofoil used C_D = Drag component

Fig 11. Mediterranean type sail windmill.

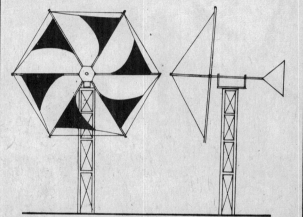

machine has recently been revitalized by work done at the National Research Council of Canada by two engineers, Raj Rangi and Peter South. They have carried out wind tunnel tests which show that a 5m. diameter turbine can produce 1 kW of electricity in a 20 km/h wind with blades turning at 170 rpm. They estimate that it would weigh 70 kg and cost around £20. This machine is one of the types being considered by NASA as part of its 100 kW windmill research programme, to help make the US independent in energy (!). This turbine has many advantages over conventional windmills, the main one being that it can receive winds from any direction without having to be oriented into the wind. This appears to make it suitable for use in urban situations where the wind direction is constantly changing and where a propeller type machine would spend a lot of its time chasing the wind rather than producing energy.

b) Machines with axis parallel to and oriented into the wind Wind machines of this category are: the Mediterranean-type sail windmill, English and Dutch windmills, propeller driven windmills, and multiblade fan-type windmills. These can further be sub-divided into high and low 'solidity' machines.

High Solidity Machines	Low Solidity Machines
●have a large area of blade proportionate to the total area swept by the wind	●have a small ratio of blade to swept area
●have a low tip-speed ratio	●have airfoil-section thin blades
●can start at low wind speeds	●have a high tip-speed ratio
●are less efficient converters of wind energy than propellor-type low solidity machines	●cannot normally utilize low wind speeds
●tend to be unsuitable for electricity unless high gearing is used	●convert energy more efficiently than high solidity types
	● are suitable for electricity generation

Because of their low rotation speed, their ability

to utilize low wind speeds down to about 2.5 m/s (6 mph), and their ability to start under load, high solidity machines are generally used for mechanical purposes—such as pumping and corn grinding.

Low solidity machines, which are more suitable for electricity generation, generally start to turn at wind speeds in excess of about 5 m/s (11 mph) though some machines with variable pitch blades will "cut in" at just over half this speed. They have a high tip-speed, often in excess of five times the wind speed.

In all machines with their axes oriented into the wind, the active surfaces of the blade are placed at a very small angle to the wind instead of being perpendicular to it, and the driving force, instead of being displaced in the direction of the relative velocity, makes an angle with it (see Fig 10).

The airfoil profile is placed so that it makes a large angle ($\phi + \alpha$) with the direction of the wind when it approaches the surface. The forces brought into play result in the surface moving, with velocity v in a direction perpendicular to the wind.

High solidity machines

a) Mediterranean-type sail windmills (see Fig 11). They consist traditionally of wooden blade arms triangulated with ropes and (usually triangular)

Fig 12. "Battle-Axe" windmill.

wooden blades

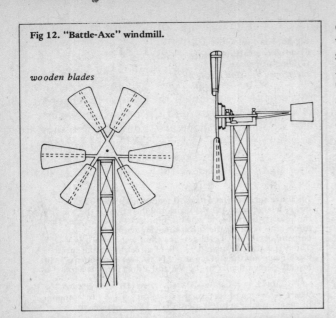

canvas sails. Of simple construction, these mills will work in slow winds, but have relatively low rotation speeds. Many are still in use around the Mediterranean notably on the Plain of Lassithi in Crete. The Brace Research Institute and Windworks, a research group based in Wisconsin, are cooperating to develop a machine of this type for use in the Third World to provide mechanical energy for pumping, irrigation and similar applications. Such mills rarely exceed a tip-speed ratio of 2, above which the curvature of the sails assumes an unfavourable profile and gives low torque.

b) 'Battle Axe' windmill (see Fig 12). This is similar to the previous type of machine, except that the sails tend to be wooden and can harness only low wind speeds. It is suitable for mechanical energy needs and is fairly simple to construct. VITA (Volunteers for International Technical Assistance of Maryland) have produced a set of plans for a version of this machine.

c) Traditional English (or Dutch) windmills (see Fig 13). There are many different types of the traditional windmills. They rotate slowly, though their large size gives a lot of power, utilizing up to 16% of the wind energy. Traditional uses include milling of grains and pumping, but these types are not really suitable for electricity production because of the large gearing ratios needed. The sails are of wood, covered with either canvas or with 'venetian blind' roller shutters. Traditional windmills can be useful if restored, but are expensive to build and complicated to operate.

Fig 13. Traditional Windmills. *(Upper left)* Great Chishill post-mill, Cambridgeshire, oriented by a fantail. *(Lower left)* Chesterton tower-mill: 19th century photograph of a unique structure, possibly designed by Inigo Jones: oriented by a winch inside the cap. *(Below)* Dutch 'Waterwipmolen': a drainage post-mill oriented by a capstan wheel. *(Top right)* 'Tjasker', smallest and simplest type of Dutch drainage mill lifting water by means of an Archimedian screw. *(Lower right)* A 'paltrok', a uniquely Dutch type, designed for sawing wood. The entire structure rotated on rollers on a brick base. *(Far right)* The most characteristic Dutch type, a thatched smock-mill oriented from the outside by a capstan wheel and spars attached to the cap.

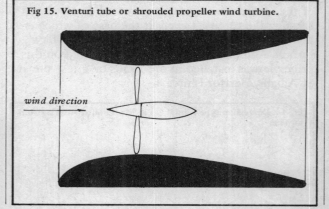

Fig 14. Multiblade, American or fan windmill. Mainly used for pumping.

d) Multiblade 'American' or fan-type windmill (see Fig 14). This machine has a good starting torque, and rotates at tip-speeds about equal to the wind speed. It is very suitable for use in locations with low wind speeds, and is typically used for pumping. This is the most common type of wind machine in production, in various forms, around the world.

Low solidity machines
Propeller-driven wind machines are the most efficient in terms of energy conversion at the present and are the most suitable for electricity production. They perform best at relatively high wind speeds, and can seldom make use of light winds. They have received the most attention in modern times because of their relatively high efficiency and because of the enormous amount of work done on airscrew propellers for aviation. They are, however, also the most complex, in view of the relative precision of the shape and curvature of the propeller blades, although once the shape has been designed, they are not too difficult to construct. If you do not feel that you can design the blades yourself there are various sets of plans (see Bibliography) available for small scale applications.

Some variations on the propeller-type and various methods of increasing its efficiency are now described.

a) Venturi tube (see Fig 15). An idea that has often been suggested is that of positioning the propeller (or indeed any other type of turbine) in the throat of a venturi tube. The tube increases the speed of the airflow, hence the rotation speed of the

Fig 15. Venturi tube or shrouded propeller wind turbine.

wind direction

rotor, the power and the aerodynamic efficiency. But this technique is generally considered uneconomic because the whole venturi-rotor assembly must be kept oriented into the wind, and it is usually easier to increase the rotor diameter instead to get the equivalent increase in power. Nonetheless, a fair amount of work on the subject has been done by the Electrical Research Association (see the ERA's publication no.C/T119, *A Preliminary Report on the Design and Performance of Ducted Windmills*, by G.M. Lilley and W.J. Rainbird) and by Windworks (see *Domebook Two*, p.121, 1971).

b) Depression-type wind turbine (see Fig 16). This consists of a hollow-bladed propeller with holes in the tips, which acts as a suction pump to draw air through an air turbine directly coupled to a generator. This is one method of increasing the effective rotation speed without gearing, but it has a low overall efficiency. When the rotor is turned by the wind, air is driven centrifugally out of the ends of the blades. The depression created draws air through the tubular tower, at the base of which is the turbine which drives the generator. A 100kw Enfield Andreau wind unit which operated on this principle was installed in the 1950s on a test site at St Albans, Hertfordshire.

Fig 17b. German NOAH wind generator.

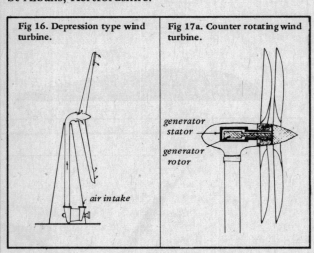

Fig 16. Depression type wind turbine.

Fig 17a. Counter rotating wind turbine.

generator stator
generator rotor
air intake

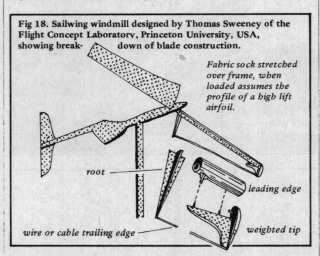

Fig 18. Sailwing windmill designed by Thomas Sweeney of the Flight Concept Laboratory, Princeton University, USA, showing break-down of blade construction.

Fabric sock stretched over frame, when loaded assumes the profile of a high lift airfoil.

root
leading edge
wire or cable trailing edge
weighted tip

c) Counter-rotating wind turbine (see Fig 17a). This type of machine has two propellers turning in opposite directions, placed one in front of the other. One of the propellers is connected to the rotor, and the other to the stator in a generator. The two opposing speeds of the propellers give an equivalent generator speed of up to double that of one propeller. But one drawback is the complex nature of the transmission mechanism. A version of this type, erected on the German island of Sylt, is the NOAH windmill (see Fig 17b).

d) Sailwing wind turbines (see Fig 18). This idea was evolved by Thomas Sweeney of the Flight Concepts Laboratory at Princeton University, USA, who developed the sailwing concept for the wings of gliders and lightweight aircraft. It consists of a propeller-type windmill (although the idea could also be applied to a Darrieus-type machine) in which the leading edge of each blade is an aluminium tube,

and the trailing edge is a tensioned cable. Over these is stretched a fabric sock which when loaded forms itself into a high-lift airfoil. This technique results in an extremely lightweight and efficient propeller. The first machine that Sweeney built had two 4 metre blades, each weighing only 6.5 kg. In a 32 km/h wind it produced seven kilowatts. The Grumman Aircraft Corporation in the US is to manufacture sailwing wind generators under licence, but plans for self-build models will be available shortly from William Flanagan, Flanagan's Plans, Box 5062, Long Island City, New York 11105, USA.

A low-technology version of this machine has been developed by Marcus Sherman of the New Alchemy Institute, using bamboo, string and canvas for the propeller. One of Sherman's mills has been used in India for water pumping, and another to drive a car alternator via a car differential!

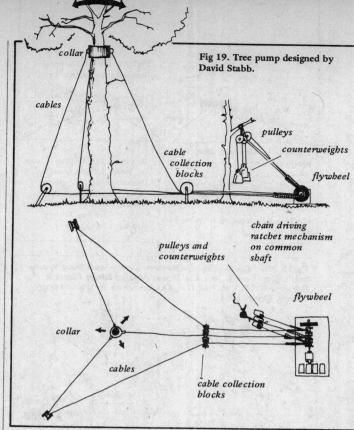

Fig 19. Tree pump designed by David Stabb.

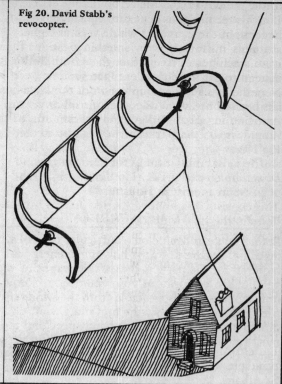

Fig 20. David Stabb's revocopter.

There are also several other wind energy conversion devices which do not fit into any of the previously-mentioned categories. Two that warrant a mention are tree pumps, and kites. Current interest in both of these is mainly due to David Stabb's research.

◆ *Tree Pumps* (see Fig 19). These are mechanical devices that harness wind energy via the intermittent movements of large branches and trees, which are triangulated by means of cables and pulleys to a chain-driven ratchet mechanism which rotates a shaft to supply mechanical power. This is quite an ingenious system, but it remains to be seen whether the idea will prove its worth. Also, extreme care should be taken to avoid damaging the tree, and advice from someone who knows about trees should be sought.

◆ *Kites* A kite has been developed that can climb and stall at a pre-set angle to the wind. It operates by means of a set of 'spoilers' on the nose, which open and drive the nose sharply downwards. During this downward motion a small counterweight rapidly winds in some of the tethering cable. During the lift motion that follows, the tethering cable is drawn out and rotates a ground-mounted ratchet mechanism. A major problem in the use of kites is the fact that they need to be launched whenever energy is required and that they require wind to stay up. This obviously limits any possibility of automatic operation. This limitation conceivably could be overcome by using an airfoil-shaped balloon filled with hydrogen or helium to keep the kite/balloon in the air during calm spells.

David Stabb has also been exploring various unorthodox types of kite, including a giant 'revo-copter' (a sort of flying Savonius rotor, see Fig 20) which would drive an endless tethering cable which in turn would drive a ground-mounted mechanism. Like the tree pump, the kite has yet to prove itself as an energy converter for static power supply. But it has at least one distinct advantage over conventional wind power plants, namely its ability to climb to relatively high altitudes, where wind velocities are much greater than they are near the ground.

HARNESSING THE WIND

Before installing a wind machine it is obviously important to know whether there will be enough wind to utilize. You will need to know:

a) The amount of energy expected annually;

b) The distribution in time—over the day, month, year or longer.

c) The probable duration of very high wind speeds, or of calm spells, during a given period.

The estimated energy available from the wind, globally, according to Golding, is approximately 13 million million kilowatt hours a year. The annual available energy per square metre of swept surface may vary between 100kWh for calm areas and 500kWh for very windy areas.

The annual average wind speed available at any site will depend on the following factors:

a) Its geographical position.

b) Its more detailed location, such as its altitude and its distance from the sea.

c) Its exposure—in particular, the distance away from any higher ground likely to give screening, especially in the direction of the prevailing wind.

d) The nature of the surrounding ground, even though it may not necessarily be high; for instance very broken ground, with rocks, woods or groups of trees, can seriously retard winds near the surface of the ground (Fig 21a).

e) The shape of land in the immediate vicinity. Because of the increased wind speed at higher altitudes, hilltops are very suitable locations for wind machines. A steep, though smooth, hill may accelerate the wind flow over the summit by 20% or more, by causing compression of the layers of air in much the same way as an airfoil or venturi tube (see Fig 21c). If the hill is not smooth, or the summit is too sharp, turbulence can be created (see Fig 18).

The most suitable areas for harnessing wind power are coastal areas, ridge lines of hills, and flat plains such as exist in Holland.

WIND DATA AND MEASUREMENT

Before you can decide on a particular type of wind machine, besides knowing how much energy is required for the particular task you want the windmill to perform for you, you need to know how much power is available from the wind on your site. You need to know the prevailing wind directions, the mean average wind speed and the most frequent wind speeds. It is possible to get a rough idea for the general area from windroses on Ordnance Survey maps (Fig 22) or from wind contour maps (Fig 23). But practically the only detailed data available in Britain is from a few meteorological stations and for a few sites that were surveyed by the ERA. So the only alternative to taking measurements for at least a year with an anemometer (see Fig 24), is to take a chance, and hope that the nearest available meteorological data does not differ too much from that for your site— or evolve a design by trial and error, trying out various models of different types to see how they perform over a period of time.

Some enterprising person should set up and co-ordinate a wind (and maybe also solar radiation) measurement programme to be carried out by schools, along the same lines as the recent, very useful, schools pollution monitoring programme.

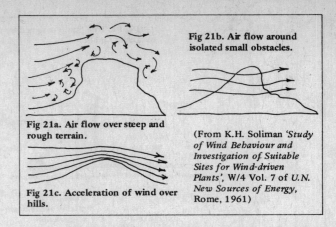

Fig 21b. Air flow around isolated small obstacles.

Fig 21a. Air flow over steep and rough terrain.

Fig 21c. Acceleration of wind over hills.

(From K.H. Soliman 'Study of Wind Behaviour and Investigation of Suitable Sites for Wind-driven Plants', W/4 Vol. 7 of U.N. New Sources of Energy, Rome, 1961)

Fig.23. Wind Contour Map of Western Europe with Wind Speeds & Energies (from J. Juul *The Design of Wind Power Plants in Denmark* W/17, Vol. 7 of U.N. Conference on New Sources of Energy, Rome, 1961).

The figures in circles indicate mean annual wind speeds. In the double figures, the first indicates the height of measurement, the 2nd the energy in kwh/m^2, measured in the vertical plane. The top of the map shows the scale together with the swept area required to produce 100,000 million kwh.

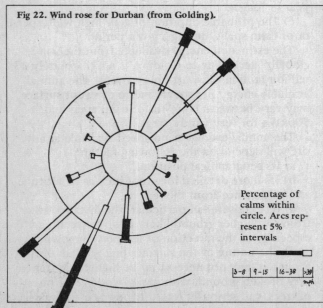

Fig 22. Wind rose for Durban (from Golding).

Percentage of calms within circle. Arcs represent 5% intervals

| 3-8 | 9-15 | 16-38 | >39 |
mph

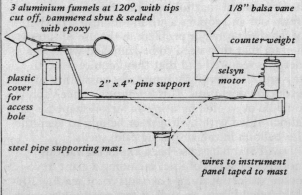

Fig.24. David A. Sankey's do-it-yourself anemometer & wind vane (*Scientific American*, June 1972).

3 aluminium funnels at 120°, with tips cut off, hammered shut & sealed with epoxy

1/8" balsa vane

counter-weight

plastic cover for access hole

2" x 4" pine support

selsyn motor

steel pipe supporting mast

wires to instrument panel taped to mast

Table 1. Beaufort Scale of Wind Forces
(from Golding *Generation of Electricity by Wind Power*)

Beaufort number (B)	Description of wind	Land observations	Equivalent mean velocity (knots)	Limit of mean speed at 33' above flat ground in open situations			Mean wind force in lb/ft² at standard density (P = 0.015B³)
				knots	mph	m/s	
0	Calm	Smoke rises vertically	0	under 1	under 1	under 0.3	0
1	Light air	Light drift of smoke	2	1 – 3	1 – 3	0.3 – 1.5	0.01
2	Light breeze	Wind felt in face, leaves rustle	5	4 – 6	4 – 7	1.6 – 3.3	0.08
3	Gentle breeze	Leaves in motion, light flag extended	9	7 – 10	8 – 12	3.4 – 5.4	0.28
4	Moderate breeze	Small branches move; litter, dust, leaves lifted	13	11 – 16	13 – 18	5.5 – 7.9	0.67
5	Fresh breeze	Small trees sway	19	17 – 21	19 – 24	8.0 – 10.7	1.31
6	Strong breeze	Large branches in motion; telegraph wires whistle	24	22 – 27	25 – 31	10.8 – 13.8	2.3
7	Moderate gale	Whole trees in motion, difficult to walk against wind	30	28 – 33	32 – 38	13.9 – 17.1	3.6
8	Fresh gale	Twigs break off trees	37	34 – 40	39 – 46	17.2 – 20.7	5.4
9	Strong gale	Chimney pots and slates blown off roofs	44	41 – 47	47 – 54	20.8 – 24.4	7.7
10	Whole gale	Trees uprooted, severe structural damage	52	48 – 55	55 – 63	24.5 – 28.4	10.5
11	Storm		60	56 – 63	64 – 72	28.5 – 32.6	14.0
12	Hurricane		68	64 – 71	73 – 82	32.7 – 36.9	18
13			76	72 – 80	83 – 92	37.0 – 41.4	23
14			85	81 – 89	93 – 103	41.5 – 46.1	29
15			94	90 – 99	104 – 114	46.2 – 50.9	35
16			104	100 – 108	115 – 125	51.0 – 56.0	43
17			114	109 – 118	125 – 136	56.1 – 61.2	52

Table 2. Theoretical maximum power extractible from the wind
$(P = 0.593kAV^3)$

Wind speed		Maximum power (kW) from various diameters of windmill				
(mph)	(m/s)	dia. 6ft 1.8m	dia. 10ft 3m	dia. 12.5ft 3.8m	dia. 25ft 7.6m	dia. 50ft 15.2m
10	4.4	0.078	0.121	0.38	1.5	6.0
20	8.9	0.637	0.984	3.08	12.3	49.2
30	13.4	2.223	3.454	10.4	41.6	166.4
40	17.8	4.960	7.638	24.6	98.4	393.6
50	22.3	10.160	15.710	48.2	192.8	771.2
60	26.8	17.220	26.550	83.2	332.8	1,331.2

For more detailed technical data see Golding's *Generation of Electricity by Wind Power*. See also the ERA publications, especially: *The Aerodynamics of Windmills Used For the Generation of Electricity* (No.IB/T4); *Windmills for Electricity Supply in Remote Areas* (No. C/T120); and *The Potentialities of Wind Power for Electricity Generation (with Special Reference to Small Scale Operations)* (No. W/T16). "Designing Windmill Blades" by Alan Altman in *Alternative Sources of Energy* (No.14), is also useful.

CALCULATION OF POWER

Power is equal to energy per unit time, and the energy available in wind is its kinetic energy. The kinetic energy of any particle is equal to one half of its mass times the square of its velocity, or $\frac{1}{2}MV^2$. Since the volume of air passing in unit time through an area A with velocity V is AV, the mass M of that air is equal to its volume multiplied by its density ρ or, $M = \rho AV$. Substituting this value of the mass in the expression for kinetic energy above, we obtain the formula:

Power = kinetic energy per unit time = $\frac{1}{2} \rho AV.V^2$ = $\frac{1}{2} \rho AV^3$.

Assuming that the swept area of the mill A is equal to $\pi D^2/4$, where D is the mill diameter, then the power = $\frac{1}{2} \rho \pi D^2/4 \, V^3$

Or, in general terms, Power (P) = $k A V^3$ where k is a constant (equal to $\frac{1}{2} \rho$).

In imperial units, the value of constant k is 53×10^{-7}, when the area of the turbine A is in sq ft,

the diameter D is in feet, the velocity V is in mph, and P is in kilowatts. In metric units, k is 64×10^{-7}, when the area A is in square metres, diameter D is in metres, velocity V is in metres per second, and P is in kilowatts.

Putnam gives a general formula which, when converted to metric units, becomes:

$P = 472. \, 10^{-6}. \, D^2. \, V^3$

Encyclopedia Britanica gives a slightly different formula, which, in metric units is:

$P = 484. \, 10^{-6}. \, D^2. \, V^3$

But the maximum amount of power that can in theory be extracted from an ideal windmill has been shown by Betz to be 0.593 times the theoretical power P in the wind, as given above. Hence, in theory, the maximum power extractible, P (max) = $0.593. \, 484. \, 10^{-6}. \, D^2. \, V^3$

But in practice this multiplying factor has been shown to be no greater than 0.4 or maybe less, ie the actual power P (act) $\leq 0.4. \, 484. \, 10^{-6}. \, D^2. \, V^3$

FURLING

The table relating wind speed and power from wind devices shows that there is, for example, more than a hundred times as much power available from a 50 mph wind as there is from a 10 mph wind. The tremendous energies of high winds can easily destroy a machine built to handle lower wind speeds unless special provisions are made for protection. Various devices for "furling" or bringing machines to a safe condition in high winds are illustrated in Fig 25.

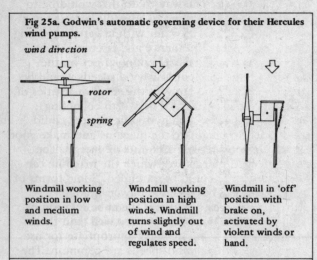

Fig 25a. Godwin's automatic governing device for their Hercules wind pumps.

wind direction

rotor

spring

Windmill working position in low and medium winds.

Windmill working position in high winds. Windmill turns slightly out of wind and regulates speed.

Windmill in 'off' position with brake on, activated by violent winds or hand.

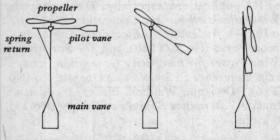

Fig 25b. Overspeed device used on many windmills including Kenwood's (1908), Jim Sencenbaugh's and Camm's amongst others.

propeller

spring return

pilot vane

main vane

Windmill in normal operating position.

Working position in high winds. Pressure on pilot vane pulls round propeller.

Windmill in 'off' position.

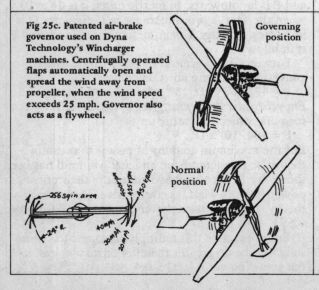

Fig 25c. Patented air-brake governor used on Dyna Technology's Wincharger machines. Centrifugally operated flaps automatically open and spread the wind away from propeller, when the wind speed exceeds 25 mph. Governor also acts as a flywheel.

Governing position

Normal position

ESTIMATION OF OUTPUT

To estimate a windmill's output you need to know its characteristics and the frequency of winds at various speeds. For each wind speed there is a corresponding amount of power per unit area, calculable from the formulae given earlier. Knowing the frequency of each wind speed you can calculate the theoretical amount of energy capable of being generated by a wind of that speed. The machine's efficiency will vary at different wind speeds and the total energy available for each wind speed must be altered accordingly. There is also a speed above which the machine must be furled to avoid damage, and this energy is therefore wasted. Below a certain wind speed the machine will not turn at all, so there is an energy loss at each end of the speed spectrum—though variable-pitch machines can sidestep this limitation to some extent.

The annual output of energy supplied depends on the actual wind behaviour, in detail, at the site and upon the design of the machine. These factors cannot be taken fully into account in energy estimations made from wind survey data giving only hourly wind speeds. But one procedure that can be followed, and that is not likely to lead to any misconceptions provided you realize its limitations, is recommended by Golding and is as follows:

  i) Relate the results of the wind speed measurements made during a relatively short period—one or two years—to the long-term wind regime at the site so that a velocity-duration curve can be drawn.

  ii) Cube the ordinates of this curve to give the power duration curve for the site (since power is proportional to wind speed cubed).

  iii) Estimate the specific output, T_s (expressed in kilowatt hours per annum per kilowatt of installed capacity) corresponding to a given 'rated' wind speed V_p. The rated wind speed is that at which the wind-driven generator gives its full rated power.

WINDMILL USES

◆ *Pumping and mechanical applications* For pumping, any type of wind machine is suitable. The specific type chosen depends upon whether the

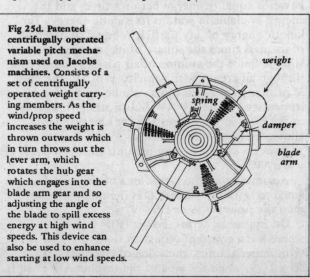

Fig 25d. Patented centrifugally operated variable pitch mechanism used on Jacobs machines. Consists of a set of centrifugally operated weight carrying members. As the wind/prop speed increases the weight is thrown outwards which in turn throws out the lever arm, which rotates the hub gear which engages into the blade arm gear and so adjusting the angle of the blade to spill excess energy at high wind speeds. This device can also be used to enhance starting at low wind speeds.

weight

spring

damper

blade arm

most frequent wind speeds are low or high, and the skills, material and money available.

If simplicity of construction is required and the wind regime is mainly one of steady, low wind speeds, then go for a Savonius rotor, Greek-type sail mill, or one of the battle axe or multiblade types. If the wind direction is constantly changing with low wind speeds, then a vertical axis machine that can make use of winds from any direction, such as (again) a Savonius, a simple panemone (II.a.2), or a transverse flow machine (I.b.2) may be more suitable.

If more money is available and steady, relatively high speed winds are experienced then propeller-driven machines will be more suitable. If the wind speed is high, yet the direction of windflow is constantly changing, then the Darrieus vertical-axis turbine, or possibly transverse-flow machine, may be the most satisfactory. For mechanical purposes—such as driving machine tools, milling, compressing air and so on, the same basic criteria as for water pumping apply.

◆ *Electricity generation* Because of the high rotation speed of most normally available generators, and to avoid very high gear ratios, the preferred types of wind machines are limited at the present time to the propeller and Darrieus types—and possibly transverse-flow machines. But these machines do not normally cut-in at low wind speeds, so light winds are effectively wasted. This situation is unlikely to change until some clever electrical engineer comes up with a slow-speed generator which is not of prohibitive size and weight (preferably self-built). This could allow slow winds to be harnessed for electricity production by slow but high-torque machines like the multiblade, Savonius, or Greek-type sail mill.

◆ *Vapour compression* Another use to which a wind machine can be put is to drive the compressor of a heat pump (see Fig 26). This overcomes one of the disadvantages of the heat pump, namely that of dependence on the National Grid for electricity to drive the compressor: the efficiency of power generation on the National Grid is so low that it is probably more efficient to use the fuel which

produced the electricity directly for heating on the premises.

One problem with using wind machines to drive heat pumps is that compressors usually have to be driven at a constant speed, whereas a windmill's rotation is irregular—but this problem is probably surmountable.

◆ *Heating water by hydraulic braking* A more direct way of turning wind energy into heat is by creating turbulence in a fluid—a wind-driven version of Joule's classic mechanical equivalent of heat experiment. A simple way to do this would be to couple the wind machine to a paddle rotating in a well-insulated tank of water with inward-projecting vanes to generate turbulence and frictional heat (Fig 27). This will have a braking effect on the wind machine which at low wind speeds would be a disadvantage (and anyway the small quantities of heat developed would not be worth collecting); but at high speeds, such hydraulic devices could simultaneously regulate the machine and make good use of the considerable amounts of energy. The range of wind speeds over which the machine can usefully operate could be extended. Some forms of hydraulic brake have a cube power braking characteristic which matches the cube relation of wind speed and wind energy very well, and these would seem to be particularly appropriate for use in areas where high wind speeds are common. The idea is being explored by David Stabb, Simon Longland and others.

Fig 26. Windmill used in conjunction with a heat pump cycle having as its heat source solar heated water.
Because of the compressor's particular characteristics it may be necessary to substitute a wind generator and electric compressor and pump. One advantage of this heat pump system is that it gets over one of the main disadvantages of solar heaters, namely that they do not produce hot water in the winter.

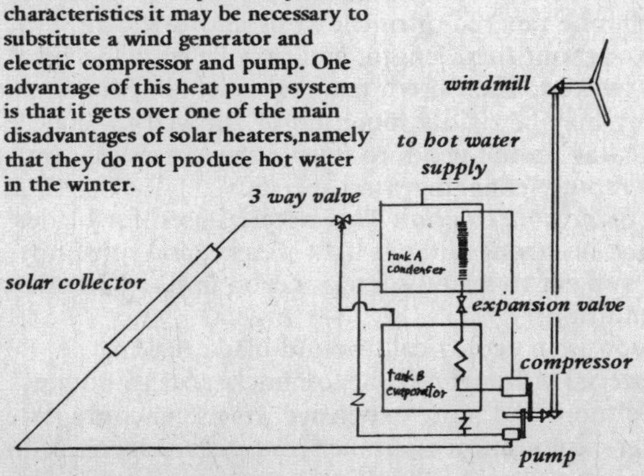

solar collector

3 way valve

windmill

to hot water supply

tank A condenser

expansion valve

compressor

tank B evaporator

pump

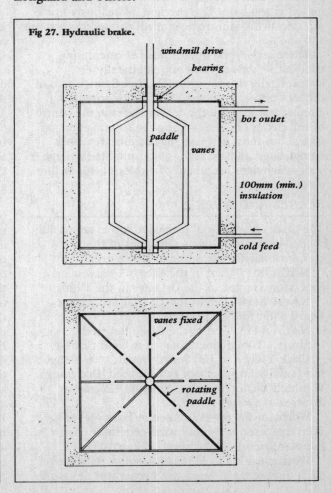

Fig 27. Hydraulic brake.

windmill drive

bearing

hot outlet

paddle

vanes

100mm (min.) insulation

cold feed

vanes fixed

rotating paddle

ORIENTATION SYSTEMS

Horizontal-axis machines need to be kept facing into the wind. Some of the possible orientation systems are as follows:

a) A tail vane mounted downwind from the rotor, which keeps the rotor facing into the wind by an action similar to a rudder on a boat (see for example Figs 11, 12 and 14). Most small wind power plants are oriented by this mechanism.

b) If the blades are angled to point slightly downwind of the mast or tower, the wind pressure on them makes the machine self-orientating. This principle is used in two of the wind generators designed by Windworks, and on the wind generators and wind pumps produced by Lubing (see Fig 28).

c) Fantails. These are mounted on a plane perpendicular to the main rotor, and are in effect small windmills, usually of the multiblade type. They are rotated by any cross wind and drive a reduction gear which orientates the main rotor into the wind. This was one of the main orientation systems of the traditional tower mill (Fig 29), and is still used on some large modern wind generators.

d) Rotating mast. Instead of just pointing the machinery at the top of the mast into the wind, the whole mast can be rotated. The Brace Research Institute's 32 ft diameter airscrew windmill is oriented in this way (see Fig 33). But it does not turn automatically, and has to be moved by means of a hand crank driving a truck crown wheel and pinion at the base. This method is obviously not as suitable as the automatic control offered by systems a, b and c.

There are several other ideas for orientating windmills—'yawing' motors, electrically or hydraulically driven; rotatable tripods with two of the legs carried on bogeys which run around a circular track, while the third rotates in the centre of the circle; or even floating the rotating part on water. But most of these suggestions are rather complicated and are really only suitable for large scale machines—which are of dubious value in any case.

BLADES AND SAILS

The blades of windmill propeller rotors are usually shaped in the form of one or other of the conventional airfoils, some of which are:

NACA 0015 Used in the ERA's 100kw wind generator, erected in the Orkneys in the 1950s.

NACA 2418 Used in the US War Production Board wind turbine project.

NACA 4415 Used in the Brace Research Institute's 10m diameter airscrew wind turbine.

Clark Y Used in Jim Sencenbaugh's 'O$_2$ Delight' self-build wind generator design. (See 'Designing Windmill Blades' by Alan Altman, *Alternative Sources of Energy* no.14.)

Wortman FX 60−126 Used in Hans Meyer's 10 ft diameter, self-build wind generator design (see *Popular Science*, November 1972, p.103).

Wortman FX 72−MS150B Used in Hans Meyer's 12 ft diameter self-build wind generator design.

Fig 28.

LUBING MASCHINENFABRIK

Juul (Gedser Mill) Airfoil (similar to Clark Y) Used on Gedser mill in Denmark in 1958 (the profile is given in Vol.7 of the *Proceedings of the UN Conference on New Sources of Energy*, 1961, p.233.)

Data about NACA and Clark Y airfoils can be obtained from *Theory of Wing Sections* by Ira Abbott and Albert von Doenhoff (Dover, New York, 1959) and data about the Wortman airfoils from *Stuttgarter Profilkatalog I* by D. Althaus (Institut fur Aerodynamik und Gasdynamik der Universitat Stuttgart, 1972). Details of the Lejay Manufacturing Co.'s designs for 6 to 10 ft windmill propellers are given in Fig 24.

The blades themselves may be solid; fabricated (skin covering a skeletal framework); or of the sailwing type described previously. They may vary in number from two to twelve or more but the optimum number of blades is three. They may either be tapered or of the same chord-width throughout their length, and may be of plane form or twisted. Their pitch may be variable or fixed, and they may be rigidly mounted or allowed to 'cone' or 'drag' in the wind, to relieve the stresses set up by rapidly changing wind speeds.

◆ *Blade construction* The material used for blades must be strong and yet light weight, and must not be subject to serious deterioration in bad climatic conditions.

Wood is an ecologically-sound blade making material although it is becoming harder to obtain, and more and more expensive. Its use encourages over-exploitation of timber resources—especially in the Third World, where little replenishment is

Fig 29.

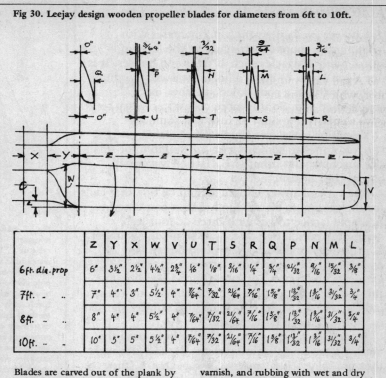

Fig 30. Leejay design wooden propeller blades for diameters from 6ft to 10ft.

	Z	Y	X	W	V	U	T	S	R	Q	P	N	M	L
6ft. dia. prop	6"	3½"	2½"	4½"	2¾"	1/16"	1/8"	3/16"	1/4"	3/4"	2¹/₃₂"	9/16"	15/32"	3/8"
7ft. ″	7"	4"	3"	5½"	4"	7/64"	7/32"	2⁵/₆₄"	7/16"	1⅝"	1¹³/₃₂"	1⁹/₁₆"	3¹/₃₂"	3/4"
8ft. ″	8"	4"	4"	5½"	4"	7/64"	7/32"	2¹/₆₄"	7/16"	1⅝"	1¹³/₃₂"	1³/₁₆"	3¹/₃₂"	3/4"
10ft. ″	10"	5"	5"	5½"	4"	7/64"	7/32"	2¹/₆₄"	7/16"	1⅝"	1¹³/₃₂"	1³/₁₆"	3¹/₃₂"	3/4"

Blades are carved out of the plank by means of plane, saw, spokeshave and sand paper. The blades should be protected by sealing against moisture with about five coats of enamel or varnish, and rubbing with wet and dry emery paper between each coat. The tips also have to be protected by means of metal foil or a standard metal tip designed for aircraft propellers.

DEREK TAYLOR

taking place and soil erosion is the consequence. Why not plant some trees and put some wood back?

Timbers approved for aircraft propellers are: walnut; some mahogany; Queensland silk wood; ash; iroko; and silver spruce. As a general rule, timber used for propeller construction should not weigh more than 40 lbs per cu ft. Specifications for walnut, mahogany, ash and spruce, together with details of methods for testing timbers, may be obtained from the British Engineering Standards Association. Wooden blades need protection at the tips, due to the high tip rotation speed, and there are several sizes of standard brass tip available.

Wooden blades can be made by anyone with a plane, spokeshave and patience, and are very suitable for small wind machines (see Fig 30). But various other materials and systems have been developed to reduce the weight.

Fabricated blades The process of making this type of blade will be familiar to any model aircraft builder. It consists of covering a skeletal framework with a fabric which is then toughened by aircraft dope, plywood—or even paper, if a tough enough grade is found. Great care is needed for this method of construction and it is generally not worthwhile for propellers under 2 metres in diameter.

Fibreglass blades Fibreglass is a relatively light, fairly easily manipulable and mouldable material, and fibreglass skills are nowadays quite well distributed throughout the population, thanks to do-it-yourself car-body repairing and boat-building. Such blades are weather-resistant and light in weight.

Expanded paper blades In this method of construction, honeycomb paper is cut with a bandsaw to the required shape, then the honeycomb is expanded along the length of the blade shaft (usually a metal tube), and 'jigged' to give the blade the desired angle of attack. When the honeycomb is in the required position, the blade is covered with a fine-weave fibreglass cloth, followed by fibreglass resin. This simple and cheap method of constructing precision airfoils was developed by Hans Meyer and Ben Wolff of Windworks.

Expanded polystyrene and urethane core blades This method is similar to the previous one, and consists of cutting the core into the required profile (this can be done with a hot wire), and then covering it with fibreglass cloth and resin. The process is similar to that used for surf-board construction.

Metal blades Metal blades are not really suitable for self-build, small-scale propeller-type wind machines. But simple, bent-metal blades can be used in multiblade designs. Metals and plastics are not only large consumers of energy in their production, but the processes involved tend to be very polluting, so these materials should be avoided as far as possible. Otherwise, only recycled scrap metal should be used.

◆ *Sails* Sails usually consist of a sheet of canvas—as employed, for instance, in Greek-type sail mills, the sails of traditional English mills, and sail panemones of the Chinese type. But they can be of the 'Venetian Blind' type; or with roller shutter sails (some of the later traditional mills and early electric mills were of this type); or with wooden sheets, as on the 'battle axe' or 'Jumbo' mills.

ENERGY

TOWERS

The power available from wind increases with height and is more constant above the level of surrounding obstacles such as trees and houses. It is not a good idea to install a horizontal-axis windmill permanently on a roof unless the roof has a streamlined top. So it is more-or-less necessary to have a supporting mast or tower of some sort.

Telegraph poles (see Fig 31) if available, and scaffold tubes to some extent, are suitable for small-size machines but otherwise a lattice tower will have to be constructed.

The type of tower chosen should be one that calls for the minimum of technical skill in construction. A simple lattice tower with three or four legs, depending on relative costs, can be made of timber, as in Jim Sencenbaugh's self-build design (Fig 32), or one of the Brace timber lattice masts (Fig 33). Or, more commonly, of steel (Fig 34)—although this is not so suitable for the self-builder, unless an old electricity pylon or a floodlight, railway signals or radio mast can be scrounged.

Monolithic concrete towers have been used for many of the Danish wind generators, and although they are relatively attractive in appearance (they resemble somewhat the old traditional windmills) they are rather expensive and suffer from vibration problems (at least when constructed on a large scale).

The Brace Research Institute has done some work on concrete *block* towers, which worked out cheaper than steel towers, but like masonry towers they may suffer from vibration problems, and obviously they are more permanent and less portable than lattice masts.

Hans Meyer has designed an attractive 30 ft tall octahedron module tower made of 250 ft of one inch electrical conduit tubing (see Fig 35); it could also be made of bamboo struts.

Another useful tower idea is to use a telescopic mast, as Villinger in Germany have done. Brace have also explored the possibilities of these masts.

The actual erection of a mast can be made much easier by the use of a 'gin pole', as shown in Fig 36.

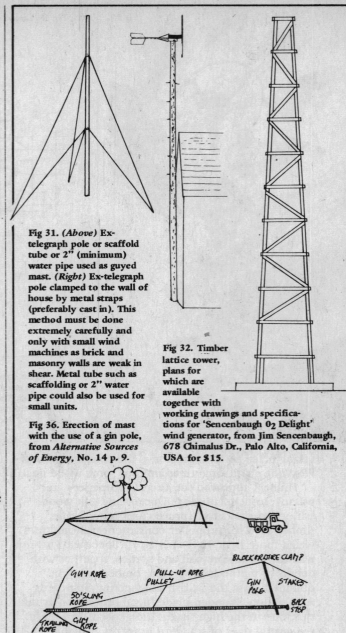

Fig 31. (*Above*) Ex-telegraph pole or scaffold tube or 2" (minimum) water pipe used as guyed mast. (*Right*) Ex-telegraph pole clamped to the wall of house by metal straps (preferably cast in). This method must be done extremely carefully and only with small wind machines as brick and masonry walls are weak in shear. Metal tube such as scaffolding or 2" water pipe could also be used for small units.

Fig 32. Timber lattice tower, plans for which are available together with working drawings and specifications for 'Sencenbaugh 0₂ Delight' wind generator, from Jim Sencenbaugh, 678 Chimalus Dr., Palo Alto, California, USA for $15.

Fig 36. Erection of mast with the use of a gin pole, from *Alternative Sources of Energy*, No. 14 p. 9.

GENERATORS

For small scale wind machines the most popular generators are car alternators or dynamos, both of which are widely available from car breakers. Another useful idea is to run electric motors in reverse as generators.

◆ *Car alternators* Car *alternators* have several advantages over *dynamos* for use with wind turbines. They start producing an electrical charge at low revs, they are lighter, generally have higher outputs, and offer less rotational resistance than dynamos.

They consist, basically, of a magnet within a coil of wire. When the magnet is rotated by the rotor, an alternating current (AC) is produced which is then rectified to direct current (DC), electronically, by diodes.

Alternators should not be used without a battery in circuit, otherwise they may burn themselves out. Some types of alternators need to be 'energized', before they will start to charge, so the battery used will have to have some charge in it; in such cases a wind pressure operated micro switch must also be in circuit, which will energize the field coils from the battery.

Because of their greater sophistication and their use of electronic components, alternators tend to be rather more expensive than car dynamos—although I bought a brand new Prestolite 35amp alternator for £15 and a second-hand Lucas 11AC 45amp alternator for £8.

Types of car alternator available in the UK Lucas: 10AC—35amps; 11AC—45amps; 11AC—60 amps (uprated version). All work at 12 volts and are battery-excited. Lucas: 15ACR—28amp; 16ACR—

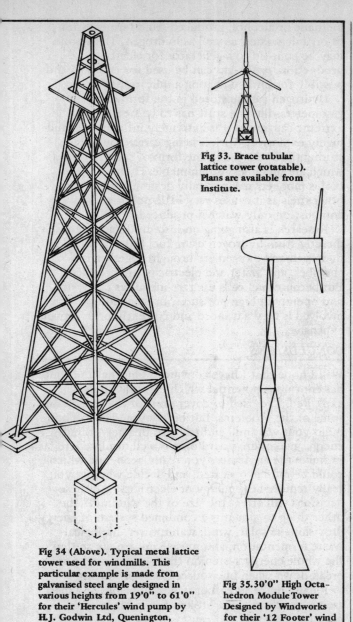

Fig 33. Brace tubular lattice tower (rotatable). Plans are available from Institute.

Fig 34 (Above). Typical metal lattice tower used for windmills. This particular example is made from galvanised steel angle designed in various heights from 19'0" to 61'0" for their 'Hercules' wind pump by H.J. Godwin Ltd, Quenington, Gloucestershire.

Fig 35. 30'0" High Octa-hedron Module Tower Designed by Windworks for their '12 Footer' wind generator plans, and made from 250'0" of 1" electrical conduit tubing.

circuits are simpler, but they 'cut in' at a higher rpm than do alternators, so higher gear ratios are required. Their output is much lower (the maximum output for most car dynamos is around 22amps at 12 volts), they tend to be much heavier than alternators, and they offer more resistance to the rotor. But they have often been used successfully —it really depends on how much power you want, what's available and how much you have to spend. Dynamos are also suitable for reversing and running as 12 volt DC motors, which could be useful for providing 12 volt power tools.

The most common car dynamos in Britain are the Lucas C40 range.

Another possibility is to cannibalize a petrol or diesel generating set and use the generator, geared-up sufficiently, coupled to the windmill. But unless you happen to find a dumped one, such generators are not cheap, and they usually produce 240 volts AC, which is difficult to store in batteries.

Although scrapped cars are a good source of alternators and dynamos, and although they are put to better use on a user-controlled non-polluting wind machine than on a polluting and energy-consuming motor car, the concept of autonomy in wind-produced electricity is undermined by this dependence on high technology industry for electrical components. Until some progress is made towards the construction of slow-speed alternators and dynamos from scratch, wind generator builders are not going to make much of a dent in the capital-intensive industries, however much they pretend they are independent of them.

ENERGY STORAGE

◆ *Batteries* At the moment, the main type of storage available is the electric battery; and the choice is more-or-less limited to batteries of the lead-acid or alkaline (nickel-cadmium or nickel-iron) type. Lead-acid batteries have the shorter life but alkaline types are more expensive.

The lead-acid battery *can* be designed to be recycled easily. This still cannot be done with most of the present designs of car battery, where the cases have to be axed apart, then thrown away, and only the lead reclaimed. Several lead-acid types are available—to suit every application, from cars to tractors, lorries, buses and industrial emergency power supplies.

The capacity of batteries is measured in ampere hours (AH). A 300AH, 12 volt battery can supply 300 amperes at 12 volts for an hour, that is 3.6kWh (12 x 300) of energy. The battery's life will depend not only on the sort of battery but also on the discharge rate. If a battery has to supply a heavy load, it discharges rapidly and it will have a short life. The life of a battery is usually measured by the number of charge-discharge cycles it can cope with. If a battery has a lifetime of approximately 1,000 cycles (car batteries have a typical life of 750–1,200 cycles) and each cycle takes four days, then the battery will last for about 4,000 days. For maximum life, the lead-acid battery should never be more than half discharged.

34amp; 17ACR—36amp; 18ACR—43amp; 20ACR—66amps. These work at 12 volts, are self exciting. Refer to Lucas manual on *Alternators* for details (Joseph Lucas Ltd, Birmingham B18 6AU, England). Prestolite (Smiths): 1235—35amps; 1245—45amps; 1260—60amps; all work at 12 volts and are battery excited. Dodge Dart: 45 amp (max) at 12 volts, battery excited. Motorola: 85A2004R—85amp at 12 volts, battery excited.

For outputs greater than one alternator can produce, you can couple several to the windmill. This approach has a certain advantage over the use of larger generators—namely that you can run just one alternator when the wind speed is low, which offers less resistance to the windmill.

◆ *Car dynamos* Car dynamos are more widely available and cheaper than alternators (you can pick up a reconditioned dynamo for £5) and the

◆ *Pumping water uphill* Because of its fairly low efficiency and the relatively large volume of water needed to store a given amount of energy, this system seems to be suitable only for use in conjunction with a small-scale water power installation, or on sites near to large volumes of water, such as lakes, rivers and reservoirs, or sites where there is a large difference in height, such as wells, mine shafts, or quarry pits. Basically, a pumped storage system works by raising water from one level to another by means of a wind driven pump, and then, when electricity is required, letting it drop to the original level through a water turbine connected to a generator. The technology required is relatively simple and fairly well developed, but overall storage costs may be high.

◆ *Compressed air* This method depends on storing the wind's potential as compressed air, retaining it in a gasometer, and, when energy is required, releasing it to drive air turbines, coupled to a generator for electricity production or integral with the appliance for which energy is required. The technology of air turbines is quite advanced, especially in dental and mining equipment. The main problem is the prohibitive volume of the storage and the need for a robust pressure-vessel.

◆ *Fly-wheels* Fly-wheels are a method of storing potential energy mechanically, in the momentum built up by a spinning mass. There have been several developments in fly-wheels in recent years, mainly on a high-technology level. High-speed fly-wheels need stringent quality control in manufacture to avoid the risk of failure, which can be catastrophic. Some work has been done on running fly-wheels in a vacuum, which improves the efficiency considerably by eliminating air resistance. But fly-wheels are still uneconomic for most applications at the moment.

◆ *Hydrogen* If the electricity produced from a wind generator is used to break down water by electrolysis, hydrogen is produced. This can be used as fuel to drive engines (and if these are fitted with water jackets to reclaim waste heat, their efficiency is improved). Hydrogen-powered engines may be designed for dual-fuel use, to operate with methane or alcohol, produced from fermentation of organic wastes, as well as hydrogen. The engine may be coupled to a generator for electricity production; or the gas can be used for cooking, and possibly for limited heating applications.

Hydrogen can be stored in the form of gas in gasometers. But the stuff has to be treated with extreme caution as it is extremely inflammable and highly explosive. Work is being carried out into storing the hydrogen in the form of solid hydrides, which are much less inflammable. Hydrogen as a fuel is more environmentally desirable than most other fuels as it causes very little pollution: on combustion only water is produced.

Research is also going on into producing electricity directly from hydrogen using fuel cells, in which hydrogen and oxygen are brought together in a chamber, and water and electricity are produced. But because fuel cells use rare metals as catalysts and operate at high pressures, the technology involved is very advanced and currently prohibitively expensive.

CONCLUSIONS

Well I hope that I have convinced you that the wind has enormous potential which is totally under-exploited. I've tried to cover most of the aspects and some of the problems. But before you dash off and build your windmill and tap into this new-found energy, make sure your home is well insulated, re-examine the appliances you really need, and which could be muscle operated, and decide whether you really require heat energy or electricity. All these decisions will affect the size of the windmill. The other thing to aim at is a combined system of energy provision—ie solar, wind, waterpower, biological waste fermentation, and muscle power, etc so that the whole energy system in the dwelling does not break down when one source is not producing.

Finally make sure your windmill blades and mast are well anchored as a broken flying blade or falling mast can be lethal and cause a lot of damage.

Happy windmilling.

Derek Taylor

GLOSSARY OF WIND POWER TERMS
Aerofoils (or Airfoil)
Wing, sail or blade which is shaped to produce lift at right angles to the direction of airflow. In cross section the upper surface is curved in a convex camber, while the lower surface usually has either a concave camber or flat surface, unless it is a symmetrical aerofoil, in which case it has a convex camber on both surfaces.
Anemometer
A device used for measuring the speed of the wind.
Chord (or Chordwidth or Chordlength)
The distance from the leading edge to the trailing edge of the aerofoil, ie the width of the blade. A constant chord width is a blade whose width is constant from root (or hub) to the tip.
Horizontal Axis Windmill
A windmill whose drive shaft is horizontal as in traditional European windmills.
Inverter
An electronic device for converting direct current to alternating current.
Power Coefficient
The ratio of the power output from the windmill to the power available from the upwind of the windmill. It can be construed as a measure of the efficiency of the windmill. It will vary from windmill to windmill but is unlikely to exceed 0.63.
Golding gives this expression

$$c_p = \frac{\rho \frac{A}{4} V_1^3 \left[(1 + \frac{V_2}{V_1}) (1 - (\frac{V_2}{V_1})^2) \right]}{\rho \frac{A}{2} V_1^3}$$

$$= \frac{(1 + \frac{V_2}{V_1}) (1 - \frac{V_2}{V_1})^2}{2}$$

Where ρ = density of air
V_1 = velocity of wind upwind of windmill
V_2 = velocity of wind downwind of windmill

Overall power coefficient = electrical power output ÷ power in the wind for swept area

Rated Wind Speed
The lowest windspeed at which full power is produced. At higher windspeeds this output is limited by the controlling mechanism to this full rated windspeed. The outputs of small wind units vary depending on the rated windspeed for which they are designed, and this rarely exceeds 30 mph.
Rectifier
An electronic device which converts alternating current into direct current.
Tip Speed Ratio

$$\frac{\text{speed of rotation of blade tip}}{\text{windspeed}}$$

Vertical Axis Windmill
A windmill whose drive shaft is vertical.
Watts
A unit of power equal in electrical terms to Volts x Amps:
1 kW = 1,000 watts = 1.34 horse power; (the power given out by a one-bar electric fire).
1 horse power = 0.746 kW;
1 kWh = 1 kW consumed for 1 hour.

ESSENTIALLY CO-OPERATIVE ENERGY

Biocosmeticians and ecologists, are currently busy recommending 'safe' solutions for the abiding energy crisis, and hydro-electric projects are frequently put forward as an environmentally-inoffensive answer. Although it is true that the power which can be obtained almost everywhere from falling water is gained not from polluting and limited resources of fossil fuels, but from the combination of the earth's gravitation and the evaporation power of the sun, artless large dam engineers have insisted that only *large* impounded volumes of water can be economic.

This is not only inaccurate, but brings with it all the calamitous environmental effects which only large scale projects can bring. The Akosombo dam in Ghana illustrates the impotence of ecologists. They warned of the danger of the dam spreading the chronic disease 'schistosomiasis', but were ignored. This project was advertised as accelerating the economic development of Ghana, but in reality it has increased Ghana's dependence on the World Bank, the US government, and US private enterprise. Kaiser Aluminium now obtains cheap electricity, the World Bank collects its 6% interest, and the Ghanaian people suffer the outbreak of schistosomiasis.[1]

Flood and famine, contrary to the extravagant publicity claims of large dam builders, are also often increased rather than decreased.[2] Since at least 1936, artificial earthquake tremors have occurred near dams, and there has been a full scale dam-induced disaster with force 6.4 earthquake and at least 200 deaths.[3]

Transcendance of this gloomy legacy of hydropower will obviously be a traumatic experience, or an exhilarating one — depending on your point-of-view. Neither collective control nor biotechnic machinery alone seem at all likely to be sufficient to overcome the generations of removal from nature and mutual dependencies which we have suffered. There is a continuous line to be drawn from the feudal lord's or abbot's privileged control over water milling, through the capitalists' early realisation that control over natural dependencies (such as water) *was* control over people, to the neo-colonialist Mekong and Cunene (Angola—Namibia) projects.

What to do? 'Alternatologists', with characteristic moderation, tend to prefer to challenge Big Power's use of the less ownable and weaker *wind.* There are, of course, a few country communes fortunate (and affluent) enough to actually own a source of water-power. But can this count as a genuine threat to megatechnology's Big Power Systems, even if it should become possible to demonstrate total self-sufficiency? To stage real confrontations in this area a leaf must be borrowed from the squatters' handbook.

A possible hit-and-run squatter-power technology is represented by all those means of tapping water-power which *do not* require extensive construction or excavation works. Power can be obtained from small sources without dam-building. The devices have to be light, quickly removable and very simple to build.

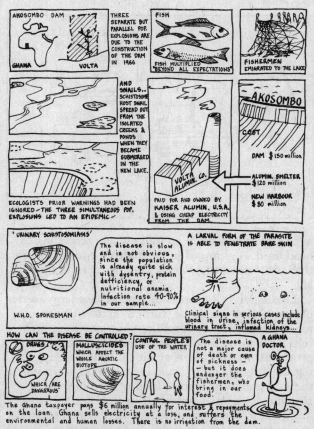

A ship mill. *(corn-mill, laundry, paper- or saw-mill).*

A floating pier or small anchored or moored raft can be built to support a wheel or a turbine—on the principle of the Roman or Hungarian ship-mill. The

---

1   Compare for example the 'World Bank Report' by the International Information Centre, Grønnegade 37, Copenhagen, 1970 and 'Health and Planning' by Dr. Guy Lavoipierre in *Africa* magazine No. 16, December 1972.

2   At the Kariba (Zambesi river) dam regulation of the discharge was carried out according to the owner's requirements for power generation, and totally without regard to the attempts of the now ' refugee ' farmers to support themselves. This is typical.

3   'Fill a Lake, Start an Earthquake' by Prof. J.P. Rothe, in *New Scientist*, 11 July 1968.

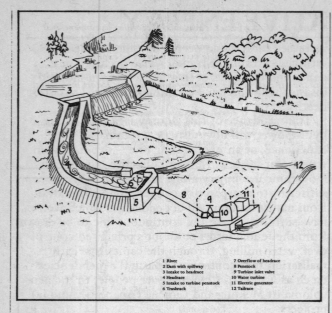

1 River	7 Overflow of headrace
2 Dam with spillway	8 Penstock
3 Intake to headrace	9 Turbine inlet valve
4 Headrace	10 Water turbine
5 Intake to turbine penstock	11 Electric generator
6 Trashrack	12 Tailrace

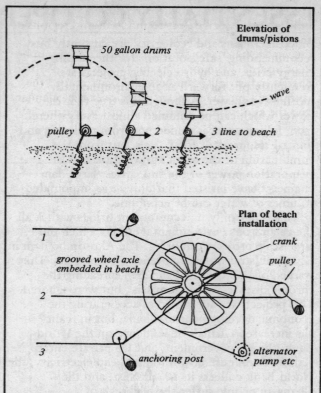

Above left: **Author's drawing of a typical intermediate output water power plant, after Hamm.** *Above:* **Plan and elevation of a system designed to utilise the power in the sea's motion.** *Below:* **A home-made Pelton.**

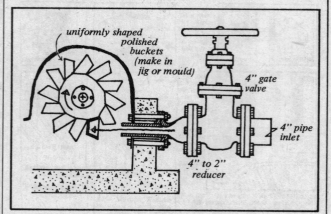

wheel drives machinery carried aboard, to which work may be brought and the product in due time carried off. A floating 'Noria' wheel could form the water supply equipment of an itinerant community.

A spoon-tilt hammer would provide a crushing, beating or pumping action from the redirected flow of a convenient small stream. It works like a Scandinavian well-counterpoise or Persian hand shaduf, but in reverse. The weight of a bucket of water, constantly filled and automatically emptied, drives a hammer or a pump.

Wave power can be tapped with a series of floats linked via cables and pulleys to a flywheel.[4] Another method is by means of a Savonius rotor.

In the cities the water mains tap should be used as an adopted source of water power. A small Pelton wheel can be fashioned out of sheet metal (eg. tin cans). This might save your electricity bills whilst perhaps simultaneously hastening the crisis of capitalism—an advantage not shared by most of the 'ecological' alternatives.

Under ancient law throughout the world "he who owns the land owns the water". Monopoly rights over power sources can be challenged, just as much as the more easily recognised rights over land and property. Water power is the archetypal free, endless, essentially co-operative energy resource. It certainly says something of the compelling nature of the forces concerned that even the normally competitive small mill owners of the nineteenth century would co-operate to obtain the maximum power from shared streams. The operators of a succession of mills, making use of almost every inch of available head (as in Sheffield, England), were forced to acknowledge the limits of 'backing-up' between the millpond and the upstream neighbour's dam. Closing of a sluice-gate at a mill not only starved the supply to all mills downstream, but was also liable to operation of the upstream neighbour's mill, by reducing or eliminating his available head of water. Maintenance works after storm damage were

normally shared between mill owners according to head used. A group of individualistic entrepreneurs thus was forced to evolve a kind of coercive mutual aid.

Like almost all sources of renewable energy, water power cannot simply be 'turned on' to suit our requirements (eg. corn milling) but may have little relationship to complex year-round industrial processes. Working days at the mill were rarely regular, it being quite usual to knock off work when the mill pond was empty, leaving the sluice-gates closed overnight to collect the supply for the next day's work. Water must be regarded as an alchemical power source, unpredictable but not quite as notoriously fickle as for example the wind. Few mills can get water, and hence work, on a regular 12 month 24 hour basis. Depending on rainfall, season, and the wisdom of the operators in sharing available

4 *Alternative Sources of Energy* Nos. 10 & 11, for details.

power with up—and down—stream neighbours, a mill can be operable year-round in humid regions of the globe, and seasonally in other regions. Even during the hard Scandinavian winters a flow can be kept up under the ice. It is only the advent of fossil energy industrialisation which has introduced the complete supremacy of the clock over the calendar, and the abolition of the rhythm of the seasons.

George Woolston

How much water power is available? According to conventional economic assessments total world installed (large scale) water power is some 5% of the potential. The remaining 95% of large scale water power available may now never be exploited. Intermediate scale projects (c. 100-250 kW) are increasingly being reconsidered, particularly in Finland and Russia, thus giving the lie to the official resource estimates which used to distort the natural distribution of water power and omit all the smaller hydropower sites.

Incidentally, if you develop a new water device you might consider patenting it to prevent its co-option. But remember that the purpose is to redistribute the powers and skills of the Earth amongst the whole of humanity — and give your patent freely to non-profit groups.

Applications of water power

Type of motion in machine	Type of prime mover in water	Work done	Process, eg.
Reciprocating: cam or piston	Horizontal axis wheel	Sawing	Timber reduction
		Air bellows	Blast-furnance in iron or glass works.
		Water pumping	Mining, land drainage and irrigation; industrial processes involving cleaning or cooling
		Trip hammer	Forge; crushing ore, clay
		Power shears	Trimming metal tools
Rotary with direct horizontal drive	Horizontal axis wheel	Tumbling	Tumbler-mixing of eg. concrete; stone polishing; laundry
		Raising water ('Noria')	Water supply for irrigation or manufacture
Rotary with gearing to horizontal axis drive *(a)*	Horizontal axis wheel	Roller milling	Paper manufacture; metal rolling mills
		Grinding	Tool manufacture; Wire drawing Textile weaving; fulling cloth
		Turning	Metal and wood lathes
		Boring	Pipe and tube making
		Dynamo	Electricity generation
		Winding	Wire coil and rope making
Rotary with right-angle gearing to vertical drive *(b)(e)*	Horizontal axis wheel	'Turntable'	Potter's wheel; wood turning
		Grinding 'Mortar and Pestle'	Corn-grinding; flour mill; crushing aggregate Grinding powders
'Intermittent counterpoise'	Tilt-hammer		Forge; crushing ore, clay Beating out metals Pumping
Vertical axis rotation *(c)(f)*	Submerged 'panemone' or reaction turbine	Direct or geared drive for most of the above purposes	
Vertical axis rotation *(d)*	'Norse mill' type		Corn-grinding, etc. in small amounts

(a)

(b)

(c)

(d)

(e)

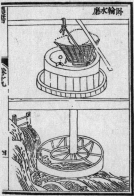

(f)

ENERGY

CAST IRON POWER

A *prime mover* is simply a machine which consumes fuel and puts out work in the form of rotational or reciprocating motion. Most prime movers are *heat engines.* A car engine, a jet, a rocket and a turbine are all heat engines.

A block diagram of the simplest heat engine cycle is in Fig 1, showing that fuel is the source of high temperature heat energy (A) and that when it is supplied and burnt, the engine (B) does work either turning a shaft, pushing a piston up and down, or pushing something along. But then there is heat rejected from the system(C), often spoken as *low grade* heat, which is at such a low temperature relative to the inside of the burning part of the engine that it cannot be made to do any more useful work. This heat is normally wasted to the air. Obviously it would be ideal if this rejected heat could be made to travel along path (D) to the heat store (A) to be re-used, but broadly speaking this means that low grade heat would have to be 'pumped up' to a higher temperature to enter the heat store (A), and this would require more work.

The simplest practical heat engine is shown in Fig 2. A piston (B) is sliding fit in cylinder (A) and beneath the cylinder, which is a good conductor of heat, is a gas flame and a block of ice. There is also an arrangement for moving the flame and the block of ice to and fro under the cylinder. When the flame heats the cylinder, the air trapped by the piston expands and pushes the piston upwards and so does work by raising the weights (W). When the block of ice is shifted into position, the heated air in the cylinder loses heat to the ice and contracts, so the weight comes back down again. But pushing weights up and down is not very useful, so substitute a crankshaft for the weight platform and you have an engine which will turn a shaft and do useful work.

In an actual engine, the heat supply could equally as well be burning petrol inside the cylinder or heat applied to the outside of the cylinder. The first type is called an *internal combustion engine,* and the second an *external combustion engine.*

Unfortunately, as with almost every other really good idea, the heat engine got into the hands of the voracious high technologists. It soon became much more efficient in terms of the energy extractable from the fuel to do work, but at the same time it became much more difficult to make and had a very much shorter lifetime.

Two of my own engines illustrate this point. One is a small air-cooled twin cylinder machine from a motor bike and the other is an old single cylinder gas engine built about 1927. Both engines develop about the same power.

The small twin is a masterpiece of high technological skill. It is made up of high pressure aluminium alloy castings, specialised lead-indium materials and weighs about 50 pounds. The speed at which it develops maximum power is about 5000 RPM. The gas engine, on the other hand, is nearly all cast iron, its construction is as simple as it is possible to be, it weighs about 240 pounds, and develops its maximum power at about 800 RPM. So we have a small, light, high speed, efficient engine and a large, heavy, low speed, relatively inefficient engine.

If it possible to talk about 'good' and 'bad' engines, I hold that the small twin is a 'bad' engine because it is made of sophisticated, expensive and energy-intensive materials, it will only run on high octane fuels at a high speed—making a lot of noise. It is impossible for a small workshop to duplicate and its maximum life is only a few years. Conversely, the gas engine is a 'good' engine because it is made of simple, non-energy intensive material, it will run on almost any inflammable gas (propane, methane, hydrogen). It runs very slowly, making only a slight

---

Fig 1. Principle of operation of a heat engine.

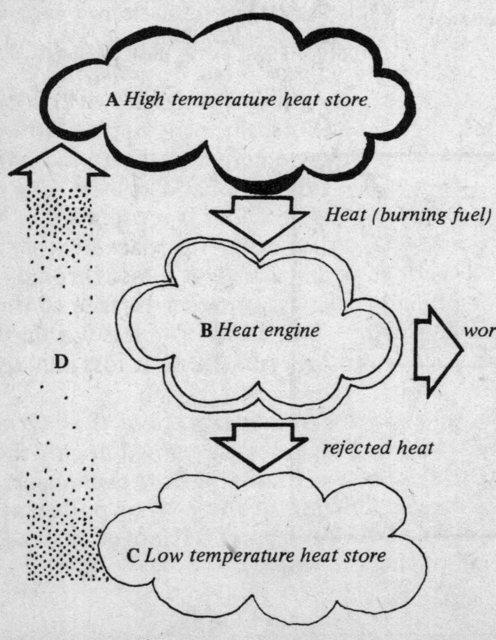

A *High temperature heat store*

Heat (burning fuel)

D

B *Heat engine*   work

rejected heat

C *Low temperature heat store*

Fig 2. The simplest practical heat engine.

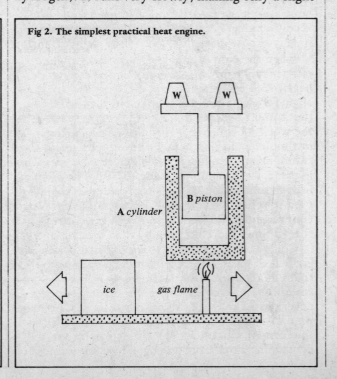

W   W

A *cylinder*   B *piston*

ice   gas flame

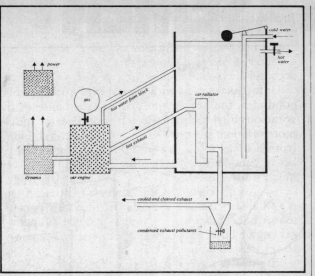

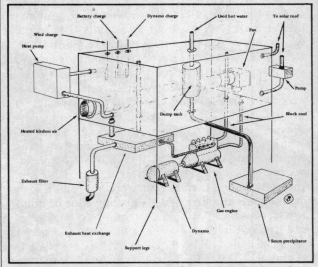

Fig 3. *Above:* Drawing and schematic diagram of the simple total energy system.

This is a small 'total energy' system for a house. It is a very well insulated water tank on legs, and the space under the legs is occupied by a small prime mover; in this case, a gas powered car engine driving a dynamo. The waste heat from the engine block passes into the water. The hot exhaust gases are cooled through a heat exchanger, again connected to the main volume of water.

Used hot water from the house is held in the dump tank until its heat has been lost, and is then passed through a scum precipitator and back through filters into store for re-use.

Waste kitchen heat is drawn through a corrugated aluminium tube, losing heat to the water in transit and the stored water can be pumped over the solar roof panels when the sun is shining.

The space under the tank is also closed off by insulation panels to ensure that heat lost by radiation from the engine will percolate through the base of the tank into the water store.

Immersion resistance heaters are connected to a wind charger the battery store and the dynamo, when there is an energy surplus in any of these three locations.

noise, and it is easy to duplicate, given some iron, a small foundry, a lathe and a drill. Its maximum lifetime is almost indefinite, given only slight attention.

When the conventional engineer talks about efficiency, he refers to the amount of calories or heat which can be extracted from the fuel by the engine to do useful work, and says that efficiency is the amount of work done by the engine while it did the work. I believe that this idea of efficiency is incomplete and that any definition relevant to the future must include factors which represent machine lifetime, design simplicity and the amount of energy used in fabrication, as well as the amount of energy used to refine the raw materials used in construction. (For example, aluminium production requires fifteen times more fuel energy than steel).

Going back now to Fig 1, we saw that waste low grade heat given out by a heat engine cannot be used to do more work, so the efficiency—in the *conventional* sense—of any contemporary engine never rises above 40%. In other words, 60% of the potential energy of the fuel is voided to the air in the form of waste heat. But, if instead of just demanding *work* from an engine, we say we need

heat as well, then we can begin to design very simple arrangements which supply both.

These are sometimes called total energy systems. I have built a very simple version (Fig 3) which anyone can copy and which has been happily generating electricity and hot water for over a year. Its efficiency is over 80%, since the normal 40% of the original fuel energy emerges as rotational power and is used to drive a dynamo, and at least 40% of the normally-wasted remainder is recaptured as heat and is used to make hot water for space heating or washing. The remaining 20% is still lost through conduction and radiation from the surface of the engine and dynamo, but if the system is within the envelope of a dwelling, even this heat loss can also be used.

One quite unsuspected advantage of this setting is that since the exhaust gases are cooled during their passage through the car radiator heat exchanger, a considerable proportion of the gaseous pollutants condense to a liquid and can be removed instead of voiding into the atmosphere.

Kit Pedler

Designed for the basic maintenance of a large urban house with up to 20 occupants. This example includes facilities for clothesmaking and shoe repair, pottery, household decoration and repairs, and poster making. The equipment could all run on low supplies of energy except the kiln. Although the scene is imagined as a basement, it could equally well be part of the Centre House workshop of Vision No 4.

1 Silk-screen posters
2 Water
3 Finished pots
4 Painting equipment
5 Kiln
6 Clay bin
7 Kick wheel
8 Cobbling equipment
9 Loom
10 Silk-screen frame
11 Treadle lathe
12 Power drill
13 Vice

ORKSHOP

INTERVIEW
SIETZ LEEFLANG

After ten years of writing about the deepening environmental crisis as science correspondent of Algemeen Handelsblad, one of Holland's major daily papers, Sietz Leeflang felt he had had enough. It was time to do something practical. He had become convinced that centralised, large-scale, high-energy technology, with its enormous demand for capital and raw materials, lay at the root of our civilisation's troubles. It was time to start developing a new, decentralised, small-scale technology, a technology based not upon the rape of the Earth but on the energies and materials which mother nature provides freely for us all.

Oddly enough, Sietz says it was not until much later that he became aware of the very similar ideas being voiced around the same time, the late sixties, by people like Robin Clarke and John Todd — though he did have some contact with Robert Jungk.

Anyway, in 1969 he began to put his ideas into action. Ironically, realising that he himself would need to contribute a fair amount of money to set the ball rolling, he decided to leave Algemeen Handelsblad and take a well-paid job as Press Officer to the giant multi-national Philips electrical conglomerate — an organisation which, though it professes a strong environmental awareness and manifests many of the more acceptable attributes of modern capitalism, nevertheless represents in many ways the very antithesis of his ideals.

Nearly four more years passed until in 1972, after selling his house to raise some more cash, Sietz made an end to compromise, left the Philips headquarters at Eindhoven, and moved about thirty miles down the road to do his thing at the small farm at Boxtel where his now-celebrated Projekt de Kleine Aarde — the Small Earth Project — began.

De Kleine Aarde (DKA) is now a flourishing centre where visitors of all ages come to learn about windmills and solar collectors, organic farming and wholesome foods, methane digesters and heat pumps and geodesic domes and bee keeping — all of it infused with a characteristic brand of Schumacher-esque political economy.

In parallel with the centre's educational role, a great deal of practical research work is now afoot. A large multi-bladed aerogenerator, specially adapted to the intermittent, low-speed winds of the region, has been built successfully; an insulated solar-heated dome, complete with working methane digester, has been constructed by DKA's technical wizard, Jaap t'Hoft; and the fields produce a fine crop of healthy food for sale to food cooperatives in surrounding towns and villages.

The De Kleine Aarde project has now put itself firmly on the map. Quite apart from the enthusiastic support of thousands of associate members and benefactors throughout the Netherlands, the Dutch government is now providing some financial backing — a fact which makes some radicals pause. Perhaps the project has been a bit too successful? Perhaps it has compromised a little too much with traditional Dutch conservatism? Maybe the solutions Sietz and his fellow workers are proposing will fail to weed out the root causes of the problems they have so accurately diagnosed, and will simply be co-opted by the wily old Dutch capitalists?

When I talked to Sietz Leeflang, he was taking his first holiday for several years; his project was now established and its future to some extent secure — though by no means assured. It was a good time to discuss where De Kleine Aarde was going, what it stood for, its successes, its failings.

In your project you seem to have already done immensely more than anyone in Britain to develop and promote alternative technologies.
Yes, well perhaps we have been a little too daring, tried to do a little too much. Our future is still in the balance. We have the feeling that we have just made it, perhaps. But I am still not sure — it still gives me sleepless nights. We have had a great deal of luck, of course. We have had huge bills, thousands and thousands of Guilders, and no money to pay them, and I have often thought, well, now everything must come to an end and we will be bankrupt. But then, suddenly, new money has come in.

How much money do you need to keep the project going?
Roughly about 150,000 Guilders a year, which is equivalent to about £20,000 in British terms. That is just the educational part. The other activities we can finance ourselves by publishing our paper *De Kleine Aarde*, by selling produce, by giving lectures, and so on.

The Government of Holland gives the impression of being very sympathetic towards ecology and conservation. Your project is getting some Government money, isn't it?
Yes, partly. The ministry of culture, recreation and social work is now financing our educational programme, and there is also a possibility that the ministry for health and environmental problems will also help us.

What about the agricultural side of your work. I believe you've been doing some interesting things.
Well, our latest — and our most risky — activity is that we have set up a small food wholesale venture. We have had to buy a big four ton lorry and to pay someone a salary to do the job.

You distribute the food to groups of consumers?
Yes. We are getting more and more of these "consumer circles" in Holland. They are something I strongly believe in, because they could be a first step away from supermarkets and back to normal small shops giving personal service.

How many of these consumer circles do you supply?
About five or six, but it is growing slowly. You can compare each circle with a small shop — it has about the same turnover. We have a shop at the farm which has a very big turnover — about 150,000 Guilders at least. If we could have more shops like that things would be wonderful. But I don't believe that consumer circles will last very long, because it is always a few people in the circle that have to do the work. It is a very big problem to get these people to sell produce on a regular basis.

Have the actual agricultural techniques used on your farm been totally organic — have you used any artificial fertilisers or insecticides?
No.

And you have found that the soil still maintains its fertility?

Yes. I must say that the results are very convincing and really give us hope. We can see a kind of natural balance coming back.

What exact system of agriculture do you practice?

We are following at least three methods. We have a partially bio-dynamic system . . .

Planting with the phases of the moon, and so on?

Yes . . . and also we do companion planting. And the third system is mulching — but we do not have much confidence in the mulching technique because we have had so much trouble with it.

How do you see the project affecting the life of Holland in the short term and in the long term . . . ? Is there any chance that Holland may in the near future start to become more self-sufficient, along the lines which your project would advocate?

Yes, I would think so. Because of over-population, the Dutch are probably a bit more interested in these things than other people — it's something to do with a feeling that something is about to happen.

A feeling that the Dykes will break . . . a sort of crisis mentality?

I don't know. They are interested, anyway. You can feel it.

If there is a chance of Holland rejecting the technological society and centralism, how would it come about politically?

Well, we do get some help from certain political parties. The "radical" party — the former Dutch Catholic "Folks Party" — is now a very "progressive" small party. They have one or two people in Government who are really interested in the things we do. A lot of the support we get is from them. On the other hand, the Socialist party . . . I don't believe they really want to help us because they are more centralist in their way of thinking. Of course, some of the things we are propagating with the Small Earth are, in a sense, very conservative.

In the strict sense of the word.

Yes. We want craftsmanship coming back, we want small shops giving personal service to people — we want all sorts of things which I imagine a conservative would like.

On the other hand, aren't these things which various utopian socialists have advocated as well? — the older kind of socialists, William Morris types. And anarchists — Kropotkin for instance?

Yes, of course. I myself am not against socialism, but I am against the centralised variety of it. I am opposed to the present capitalist system, but I am not against honest and simple business.

How will you stop the changes you want being coopted by the system that already exists? How will you stop firms like Royal Dutch Shell and Unilever and Philips starting to turn out windmills on a production line, or starting organic farms on millions of acres . . . that sort of thing?

I cannot believe that big firms like Philips will start making windmills.

But they are already making them. They own Dunlite, for instance.

Yes, but are Dunlite mills really a consumer product?

No. But what about heat pumps, then — they may eventually become a consumer product.

Well if Philips makes heat pumps or Stirling engines which can be used on farms and communities like the one we are building, then I would say okay, make them, then we can use them: why not?

But how will you then stop them from making these devices in such a way that they will not last quite as long as they should, so that Philips can sell a new model in five years time? How will you stop all the familiar capitalist consumer syndromes being repeated?

Of course we cannot stop them. There is only one thing that can stop them — and that is that it is not feasible. Things may have to be made to last longer because of resource exhaustion.

But is it not very possible for a firm to fly in the face of ecological and resource necessity in the interests of short-term profit?

Yes, it could be. But in the long term, they will have to bow to the natural law.

Do you see firms like Philips and Royal Dutch Shell and Unilever actually going out of business, or changing radically?

They may lose a lot of money on techniques which are not of real value. For example, Philips are building a "recycling house", and they are using high-temperature heat storage systems. This, developed by Schroeder, uses salts, and it is a very nice system, but I don't believe that it is feasible. But they are making it, and it is costing them a lot of money. On the other hand, the work Philips did on the Stirling engine was very courageous. I think it's a mistake to see companies like Philips as great nasty conspiracies. In great companies like Philips there are lots of individuals pursuing their own hobbies . . . But I do not believe in huge international conspiracies. They simply do not exist. We have the existing system, that's true, and I know that huge concerns like Philips try to have a consistent policy. But they are completely dependent on all kinds of individuals, giving them right or wrong advice.

If companies like Philips and Unilever don't go out of business, then, how do you feel about the problem of alienation? Do you go along with the socialist ideal to the extent that you feel that workers in factories should have control over their working conditions and ownership of their industries . . . ?

Well, that would happen automatically if you had more decentralisation. To force it upon the existing factories would be very difficult because you couldn't control these huge systems.

That may be so, but surely it would still be possible to have authoritarian businesses, even if they were decentralised?

Yes, but workers' control is much more capable of being practiced when you have decentralisation, when you have small firms.

Godfrey Boyle

There are few climates so benign that occasional protection is not needed from what they throw at the people who live in them. There are two ways of gaining this protection. One is to create a small, personal portable microclimate. This is called clothing. The other is to create a larger, generally stationary microclimate. This is called building.

These two are to some extent alternatives — the more of one, the less of the other, but this does not seem to be widely recognised. In affluent societies the sheer functional necessities diminish and clothes and buildings come to have other functions — display, containers for possessions, expressions of craft skill and so on. People tend to have as much of both as they can afford.

But as inflation bites deeper, and the non-renewable resources get scarce, the attraction of basic functional design and basic materials increases. It becomes rational to use more clothes and less heat, to make ones own clothes, build ones own home, and to create them from traditional materials as far as possible, aided by judicious inputs of modern technology.

In this section there are two articles on clothing. One is a plain and simple 'recipe' for making shoes out of a traditional material — leather — and a modern waste material — old car tyres. Easy. Cheap. Anyone could do it — and should. The other clothing article is about textiles, spinning, weaving and dyeing. Apart from more recipes (some very nice ones on natural dyes) the author uses the subject to show how technology and politics interacted with each other over textiles in the early days of capitalism. New techniques were not introduced merely to increase productivity, but to increase control over the workers. And if this happened in textiles in the 19th century, where else in the 20th? *Circumspice.*

In building, the assumption is made that present patterns of industrial building are inadequate. They are expensive to to build, and more so to run. They demand large supplies of scarce material and energy resources. They do not lend themselves to maintenance by the users. They become territorial enclaves in which private life turns into pathetic isolation.

Three approaches have been made to the problem of creating cheap, user-involved, pleasing dwellings. The first concentrates on the *organisation* of building and maintenance, and discusses self-build projects and tenant-control in urban areas, particularly focusing on *rehabilitation* of existing buildings. The second is essentially a state of mind and a way of life, and lyrically records the delights of 'living lightly' in flexible, quickly-built, temporary shelters, which are perhaps the missing link between clothes and houses. The third approach is to 'return' (but with modifications) to traditional building practices and local materials: abundant, renewable, low-energy, beautiful. There are two articles on this. One surveys typical examples of vernacular building in Britain, and the other looks more thoroughly at one important method, the use of subsoil — an abundant and cheap resource if ever there was one.

The unorthodox but sound functional rationality of these building principles should not allow us to overlook their sensuous poetics. Lloyd Kahn, champion of traditional methods, and craftsmanly impresario of alternative shelter, expresses the sensibility in the following remarks:*(1)*

'It took me a long time to realize the formula:
Economy/Beauty/Durability: Time

TONY DURHAM

MAGNUM/CONSERVATION FOUNDATION/UN.

You've got to take *time* to make a good shelter. Manual human energy. For example, used lumber looks better than new lumber, but you've got to pull the nails, clean it, work with its irregularities. A rock wall takes far more time to build than a sprayed foam wall.

The best materials are those that come from close by, with the least processing possible. Wood is good in damp climates, which is where trees grow. In the desert where it is hot and you need good insulation there is no wood, but plenty of dirt, adobe. Thatch can be obtained in many places, and the only processing required is cutting it.

Plastics and computers are far overrated in their possible applications to housing...

Walking amidst magnificence of Indian craftsmen with MIT dimly in mind, I realized that there may not be any wondrous new solution to housing at all. That there is far more to learn from wisdom of the past and from materials appearing naturally on the earth, than from any further extension of whiteman technoplastic prowess...

In times past, people built their own homes, grew their own food, made their own clothes. Knowledge of the building crafts and other skills of providing life's basic needs were generally passed along from father to son, mother to daughter, master to apprentice.

Then with industrialisation and the population shift from country to cities, this knowledge was put aside and much of it has now been lost. We have seen an era of unprecedented prosperity in America based upon huge amounts of foreign and domestic resources and fueled by finite reserves of stored energy.

And as we have come to realize in recent years, we are running out. Materials are scarce, fuel is in short supply, and prices are escalating. To survive, one is going to have to be either rich or resourceful. Either more dependent upon, or freer from centralized production and controls. The choices are not clear cut, for these are complex times. But it is obvious that the more we can do for ourselves, the greater will our individual freedom and independence be.'

1. Kahn, Lloyd, *Shelter*, Shelter Publications, PO Box 279, Bolinas, California 94924.

LIGHTWEIGHT / TEMPORARY / LOWCOST / QUICK / MOBILE
by Stefan Szczelkun

Alternative? Only in possibility of usage.

There is often a certain threshold above which, or faster than which the cultural enforcements that limit our activity cannot be effective. Temporary dwellings can allow some kinds of no-compromise in the face of consumer culture, a fluidity that law despairs at. For instance, if you can get your hippyhappy lifestyle into the back of a commercial van and don't mind being a little bit secretive, you can live in the heart of areas that would otherwise be *forbidden* (or too expensive, which amounts to the same thing). This can be useful in investigating and revealing . . . A homebuilt canvas tipi can give you a dwelling that is noble and yet can avoid the prohibitive rates, mortgages, rents and other restrictions of a standard heavy property.

"A primitive people is not a backward or retarded people; indeed it may possess in one realm or another, a genius for invention or action that leaves the achievements of civilised peoples far behind."
        —Levi-strauss

Why panic if you gotta move homes or jobs? Don't be rushed into something that is not right. Take time off to think. Build a dome in a friend's back garden. You'll probably find you can live in it for several weeks. Building a dome with friends can be quick but at the same time rewarding experience; being a mathematical form, the emphasis is between individuals working together (basic politics) rather than other more personal modes of structure where mutual agreements over style need to be made. This can be a long process if the fullest creative involvement of each person is to be achieved.

This use of domes as social pivots, and their symbolic newness and geometrical simplicity is more important to us than their advantages as a mass produced lightweight modular-component efficient hitek commodity *a la* B. Fuller.

Tech. Note. Homebuilt domes have been notoriously leaky and generally uncomfortable to live in over long periods. All those criss crossing diametric joints just don't make sense when the weather gets going. The best domes are seamless. For temporary usage choose plastic or fabric cap over stick frame; for a more permanent job use monocoque construction of ferrocement or glassfibre or shingles. The best cheap shingles are probably pieces of roofing felt with a drop of cold bitumen on all the awkward bits. This technique is used on standard housing all over the USA.

Council tenants in my area of South Wales stay together whilst their houses are being modernised. It is an extraordinary sight, the people live in caravans in their front gardens and their furniture is stored in old pantechnicons (cheaply obtained once they fail the MoT plating test). The householders are minimally displaced and are in a good position to monitor their own conversion job, making sure standards of construction and finish are to their satisfaction.

Gypsy lifestyle has been increasingly outlawed in Britain and most parts of Europe in the last decade. Gypsies are a big embarrassment to the neat suburbanisation of the Western world and its cherished ideals of convenience and comfort. Much of the opposition to them has come from *local organisations* rather than central government. What is happening is the gradual destruction of minority lifestyle, different from genocide only in that individual lives are spared. At first sight it seems strange because gypsies aspire to modern commodities of their own. A slick chromy caravan full of vinyl upholstered, curved and folding furniture and cut glass mirrors will cost up to £12,000 new and a cheap version secondhand is still £4,000; but its still a challenge to the Ideal Home as a commodity showcase.

Fairground peoples are another group with an embarrassingly out of line style of life. The old four-wheel heavy living-wagon that developed with this lifestyle is one of the best (most enjoyable, comfortable, functional, flexible, vibrant, rich, etc.) small living spaces ever designed for taking advantage of the modern Western world's fantastic road system. Fairground culture has a complex servicing system of wintering grounds, repairers and component-dealers, stores and manufacturers. If they didn't have this separate realm to wander about in they would, no doubt, also be destroyed. These wagons may occasionally be obtained cheaply in a poor state of repair and it is worth the labour of love necessary to restore them as near to their former glory as you can afford (mahogany panelling and cut glass not being amenable to five year obsolescence and investment return). An interesting thing about these wagons is the way they quickly deteriorate if they are not lived in. Used regularly they last remarkably well, but left unused, even over one winter, the deterioration due to damp and condensation will be severe.

It is important to the making of non-hierarchical networks that all those involved in creating alternatives to consumer relationships, and that are 'lucky' enough to have property, make facilities on that land available for nomads to stay, and also to have an open enough economy to enable the visitors to support themselves at least to some extent (for example an exchange of labour on land for food). Such arrangements could lead to an exciting diversity of meetings and exchanges of skills and information. People dropping in could live in all kinds of temporary or mobile houses, including sheds, caravans, buses, vans, boats, tipis, domes, attics, greenhouses, dairies, barns, caves . . . Also useful for worksharing exchanges.

Liberate land; don't let it possess *you*. Clear distinctions need to be drawn between territoriality and arbitrary ownership. Tough nut here. Crack it now folks.

Tramps have the simplest and arguably most 'flexible' tent, the long mackintosh. You have to be a very dedicated non-consumer to live well with this little equipment; but remember it is skill with simple equipment that counts as much as the doubtful comfort and

convenience of the usual carful of heavy and expensive bright orange camping gear.

Time is money nowadays—you can't have it both ways.

The only way that camping and survival stuff relates to alternatives in this day and age of the urban guerilla is as an experience of what life is like without all the modern paraphernalia; commonly convincing those that go on such holidays that primitive life must have been a fiction or at least dreary, damp and dismal, but you can't expect to go camping once a year in a continental chalet tent and get any notion of what life was like for the North American Indian. My point, amongst all this banter, is that our knowledge of life's basics is so confused by obtuse commercial criteria that perhaps we should examine it all from scratch.

The move from conventional forms into new spaces that relate to ideas of broader alternatives is best illustrated from current events. The pictures on pages 102—3 that accompany this section were taken at the **Windsor Free Festival** August 1974 on Wednesday when the festival had been running successfully for five days. When the festival started the previous weekend there were about 20,000 people present, but by midweek numbers had dropped to several thousand as people returned home or to work, or went off to get supplies in readiness for the next weekend, when large numbers were again expected. The next morning we woke up to a military style police eviction by 600 constables in active service backed up by the rest of Thames Valley Police and the local army barracks. 300 people were arrested defending their right to live as they chose.

MERCATOR

Left, from the top: **Ashphalt shingled dome; home in transit; lightweight tent in use on a roof in South London; house truck made from junk; a bit of suburbia floats on the Thames.** *Above:* **Winter tent; ferro-cement dome.**

All except the London photos courtesy Lloyd Kahn's *Shelter*.

For more information on all this stuff and the following pages, see Stefan's *Survival Scrapbook No. 1: Shelter*; Unicorn Books 1972.

billowing parachute.

no comment.

hessian tree tent.

undyed tipi

no comment.

leafy thatch courtyard and fire place.

leafy thatched hut.

no comment.

no comment.

bedouin type.

geodesic with tunnel extension.

LIGHT

free food twice a day.

spontaneous demonstration against police harassment.

WINDSOR FREE FESTIVAL

ancient showmans wagon

neat caravan

coach

ex-Army tug.

for sale

biggest domes

shop out of pantechnicon.

kentish town.

wally's food.

bus.

HEAVY

pyramid tent

ELECTRIC MUSIC

8am thursday

SHELTER

Tree houses

STEFAN SZCZELKUN

This section has been chosen to be extended to include some practical details because tree houses seem to have a specially favoured place in lists of idealised or fantasy houses. There is also a feeling of working and living closely with one of the most remarkable and agreeable structures of nature in all its seasonally changing aspects. On top of all this romantic slosh you also get a better view (?), are away from ground damp, protected from marauders, use little space; and if you pick a reliable tree, have a solid foundation. And anyway I had this photostat of a secret government paper on *The Arborialisation of Emergency Offices in Times of Cultural Regression* hanging around for ages, so let me leak a little of it, just in case . . .

When setting out to build a tree house in earnest, selecting a particular tree or trees is the first consideration. The choice may be influenced by numerous criteria (or the 'criteria' might be influenced by the choice!). However you go about it there are certain trees such as Elm that should be avoided, and certain situations such as lone trees on high ground (lightning risk?) that might have unexpected disadvantages. Oak is very often a good tree offering natural platforms. Pine growing close together allow several trees to be used as supporting pillars. Probably the most important consideration will be the amount of cover or camouflage available to the structure, especially in wintertime.

Having selected a tree, the platform is the first part to be constructed. Lashing is better than spikes or nails, which might damage the tree. Other possibilities are various clamps using perhaps nuts and bolts but the choice can be made on what is available. Start off by lashing two poles to the trunk, either together or one at a time. (Fig 1). Do this just above some projection or bulge in the trunk, if possible, to make certain that the platform cannot slip down the tree. If the trunk is smooth at the height you require the platform to be at, then you must finish the lashing by going around the trunk several times below the poles. A second pair of poles are then lashed above and at right angles to the first pair. (Fig 2). Eight more shorter poles are then lashed from the end of these 'joists' to the trunk. Ideally these bracing pieces could be rested onto lower branches of the tree so as to give them more purchase. Other poles may be laid across as joists, and braced in a similar fashion. This is then the foundation for the floor which may be made of more poles or boards if they are available.

When the basic platform is finished *test it* thoroughly. The superstructure can be made of almost anything that you could make a shed out of on the ground. Slabbing, the name given to the outer off-cuts made when sawing up natural 'round' timber, can be bought very cheaply as 'fire wood' by the lorryload, and makes good cladding material. With a bit of care you could choose slabbing of the same wood as your tree. Other good choices to blend with the surroundings are wooden shingles or shakes, wattle screens, (wickerwork could weave right into the structure of the tree itself), paper mache, thatching, canvas or bark, especially birchbark.

A roof framework can be made in a similar way to the floorframe but this time the structure is braced from above with poles and/or ropes. Uprights for the walls are lashed between roof and floor frames. Wall sections will probably be best constructed on the ground and hoisted up unless your platform is spacious enough to contain a workshop.

A good hoist will be the most essential piece of equipment that isn't found in every common-or-garden toolkit. A single block will suffice, suspended well above the required height and worked from ground level. A light guy onto the load should be used to guide it up.

In summary, what you need to build a tree house is . . . A knowledge of trees generally, and of trees in your locality by observation (sketching is a useful technique for making revealing observations), and climbing; a knowledge of knots (practice); rope, lashing cord, axe (felling axe and hand axe), hoist.

So once again it all comes down to ingenuity with what you've got around, a few good tools and getting started.

Fig. 1

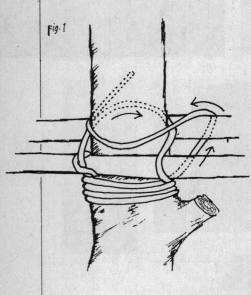

Fig 2.

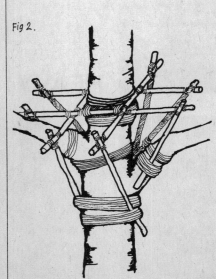

ANDREW TWEEDIE

Inflatables

Inflatables are simple enough to make but
require much more togetherness, with power
source and fans to keep them blown up.
When you want to make an inflatable that is
to be used many times or over a longish
period as a dwelling, then the design needs
some expertise. It is best to start off with
something simple.

Most exciting use of inflatables (eg Action
Space) is not as dwellings but as people-
mixers and mindblowers. These may consist
of huge zippered bags filled with air, sealed.
The effect these have rolling on crowds is
dynamic to say the least. Or large tarpaulins
sealed around the edges and continuously
filled with air. People attempt to walk,
slither, crawl, bounce, float, roll, sink into
and over them. Or inflated tubes coiled
about, or weirder and weirder amoeboid
fantasies with people inside them, walk on
waters, hot air trips, street barricades, giant
phalluses, air rafts and island kites, solar
powered airships, big sex dolls, helium UFOs,
you name it.

GRAHAM STEVENS

Shanty settlements in Britain

A dominant culture ensures its continued survival by reinforcing the aesthetic value of its essential artifacts and devaluing or ignoring aesthetic notions that relate to ideas that, if developed, would undermine it. It is in this way that the modern movement of the early twentieth century, which tended to search for fundamental principles and achieve a purity and clarity of expression, was quickly utilised as a means (an excuse) of increasing the efficiency of accumulation by cutting out craft work, decorative detail and anything superfluous to measurable or commercial criteria (function is here very close to being 'commodity'). The contemporary commercial image attempts to become all-pervasive, giving to culture as a whole the smooth, sleek modern look of dramatic banality; but in this milieu there are cracks that give us an inkling of better times.

The shanty settlements scattered about Britain demonstrate (albeit to a very limited degree) a situation in which people build homes for themselves with the least restrictions. In peculiar circumstances the tether on people's building-capacity has slipped a little. Not much, but enough to give us a taste of a creative sphere disallowed by our present customs but dear to all our hearts. Our Homes.

The same aesthetic may be observed in people's mature back gardens, ideally observed from a slow train, and again in old allotments. To appreciate these slight structures as beautiful you must make an effort to re-educate your eyes to the aesthetic criteria of chaos. When a building or garden has been worked on intimately and completely over a longish period of several years by an individual or group, without thought for a conscious visual effect, but with love and care, then the character and idiosyncrasies of the workers interweave and modulate the fabric so thoroughly that it reflects the dweller's inner head. That's where these places make it—they've got soul.

As people demand more and more from the contemporary productive potential and gain potential power through their familiarity with it, laws increase the realm of the impersonal, global image of compliance.

Shanties are replaced with standardised chalets, solely for holiday use, or simply erased; allotments are given neat concrete sheds and concrete paths, and renamed Leisure Gardens. Things are either a mess or tidy. There is no discussion of meaningfully interconnected chaos (although people still seem to like nature) or of the limiting rigidity of an ordered tidiness imposed by those who do not touch or feel.

Most of the shanties have been remodelled extensively since the original design and it is one of the great advantages of the sort of ultra-cheap ticky-tacky higgledy-piggledy hotch-potch that many of the houses are made of, that it is relatively simple to add and subtract from them. The capacity for growth is particularly important as it allows someone to start with a very small, cheap, easy to erect hut, and gradually extend it as they beg, steal or borrow materials until they have a magnificent villa! It is interesting to note that most of the shanties do not reach this stage before the inertia of construction and the satisfaction of spatial needs stabilises the process at a surprisingly compact size.

STEFAN SZCZELKUN

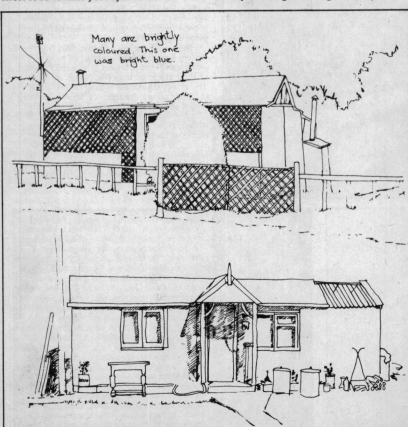

Many are brightly coloured. This one was bright blue.

Observations as above are often made with reference to the Third World, that suggest in a paternal tone that the lessons are not for the tired and retired empire builders back home. Perhaps they are, though in the past few years I have come across five localities with lively shanty settlements, scattered throughout Britain in the Gower peninsular, Edinburgh, the Sussex coast, Newcastle and Middlesex Thameside.

As far as I know from my casual investigations, the shanties all date from before the 1947 Planning Acts which changed the nature of building permission and made it a much tighter financial game. A man with a beautifully kept shanty on the Gower peninsular in South Wales, with many extensions, two chimneys, and a large conservatory full of flowers told me he had been there 32 years and was one of the last to arrive. (Getting a difficult site on which he had to cut a level out of the hillside). Many people had followed an early plan that had been 'approved' by the council, but he hadn't. He had built his own ideas and never got inspected or hassled. He paid a small ground

rent and didn't seem to be worried about a lack of security of tenure or investment value. He lived there all the year around, as did many occupants (though not the majority, I would guess). He thought it was great to be in such a nice site near to the sea. The shacks or chalets are low lying and set in sandy hills, so they don't affect the scenery much. This seems to represent a typical pattern throughout the country although there has been great variation. The shanties

on the banks of the Thames, for instance, were all permanently occupied.

Many of the shanties follow a similar design pattern which seems to derive from pioneer homesteads. A simple 4 by 2 frame is clad with boarding. The chimney is brick or stone and there is a covered verandah to the front. The first extensions are usually to make larger kitchen and bathroom and toilet facilities, or sometimes the verandah is enclosed. Around and about ones like this are an enormous variety of other types: all stone, bus without wheels, based on wagon with mollycroft roof but almost unrecognisably covered in extensions and structural changes, rickety sheet steel system pre-fabs, railway coach, and so on. Nearly all are brightly coloured; they have to be regularly painted and tended or they soon deteriorate.

When people are at least allowed to build a house for themselves as they please and from what they can get hold of, traditional techniques using local materials having been lost or disallowed on the grounds of being too permanent, then it is often a carpentry technology that lingers on. This is perhaps because it is of more ubiquitous use. Whatever the reason, most of the structures are wooden. They sell for around £500 to £1,500 which is often the price of the materials and fittings alone. The site, being theoretically insecure and liable to rent, is of negligible market worth. These conditions ensure that shanties do not figure as properties in the same way as normal houses.

Whether dwellings would become similar to these structures if we got rid of the present restrictions on our activity remains to be seen. However they are not to be looked at as utopian models or sacred ideals, but are merely practical indications that possibilities of self control that we are led to believe would have ugly and undesirable results could in fact be a start in the process of individually directed creative activity that will lead to better times.

FOLK BUILDING

The cheapness of transport and raw materials, and the high cost of labour (and especially skilled labour) have combined to make traditional building practices and materials hopelessly uneconomic. But times are changing. Sharply rising costs of fuels and industrial raw materials on the one hand, and a variety of social, aesthetic and environmental factors on the other, now point to a time not far distant when traditional methods—almost certainly hybridized with suitable modern techniques—may once more play a significant role in construction. In this article Brenda Vale reviews the main vernacular building methods, relating them to the local materials on which they usually depend. In the subsequent article, Colin Taylor describes one of the methods— rammed earth construction—in greater detail.

Vernacular building methods are often associated with the use of on-site materials. These methods of building were originally based on the use of immediately-available, low-cost materials, exploited during periods when labour on the land was not required: most families in a village would co-operate to build or maintain their own houses, sometimes under the direction of one or two skilled people.

SCARCITY OF TIMBER

Timber was once used to build the majority of houses in Britain, but as the forests were gradually cleared to make way for agriculture, other materials came into use. America, with a proportionally larger area of forest, has a greater tradition of timber building than Britain. The scarcity of timber for building is also due to the fact that it is in demand for pit-props, paper-making, chip-board and box-making. To supply the carcassing timber for one house each year would require between 1.2 Ha and 2.3 Ha of European Larch, worked on an eighty-year rotation.

It is therefore not surprising that the vernacular traditions of this country cover a wide range of all construction materials with timber framing reserved for the roof structure (although timber-framed walls, infilled with bricks or clay plaster on lathes or straw, do survive).

STONE CONSTRUCTION

The methods of stone walling in different parts of the country reflect the type and size of stone quarried in the area. The granite in the houses of Devon, Cornwall, Cumberland and Wales was laid in unequal sizes and heights of courses, just as the stone came from the quarry, to avoid the extra work involved in cutting it, since the stone is very hard and expensive to quarry. In smaller houses and cottages the courses, normally less than 380mm high, were normally laid without mortar. Cornish granite walls, usually 610-760mm, had the stones laid more-or-less at random. These cottages were frequently white-washed.

Fig 1
Almshouses at Chipping Campden, Gloucestershire, built of Cotswold limestone.

All other stones used for building are sedimentary rocks. The walls of Cotswold cottages, never less than 500mm thick, were generally built of stone throughout (Fig 1). The method of walling depended on the way the stone came from the quarry and varied from rubblestone, laid in thin layers, to thicker courses of roughly squared and dressed 'ashlar'. The window jambs and quoins were built of dressed stone. The seemingly solid walls were often formed of an inner and outer skin of stone filled with small stones and other rubbish, such walls naturally suffering from frost damage and any settlement of the building. The typical roof had a pitch of 55 degrees and was covered with local stone slates, graduating from the larger, thicker slates placed on the eaves, to the thinnest and smallest at the ridge. The upper-floor rooms were made in the roof with dormer windows forming a characteristic feature. Northamptonshire limestone walling was constructed in a similar way with a variety of colour introduced by interspersing alternate layers of red ironstone with grey limestone. The roof pitches were also often lower, as the stone slates quarried in Northamptonshire were generally larger than those of the Cotswold area.

The limestone walls of the houses of York and Tadcaster were made of large stones, usually placed in regular courses. In the Dales, the stones were rough-faced and small, and built into courses with wide mortar joints. The typical building form was single-storey, long and low, and covered with a plain roof of low pitch. This was hung with large stone slates between 25mm-37.5mm thick. Rye-straw was

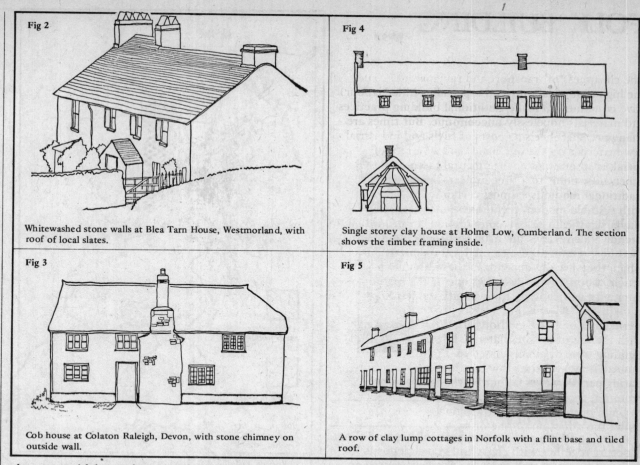

Fig 2

Whitewashed stone walls at Blea Tarn House, Westmorland, with roof of local slates.

Fig 4

Single storey clay house at Holme Low, Cumberland. The section shows the timber framing inside.

Fig 3

Cob house at Colaton Raleigh, Devon, with stone chimney on outside wall.

Fig 5

A row of clay lump cottages in Norfolk with a flint base and tiled roof.

also once widely used as a roof covering for these houses. The houses of the local grey limestone of the Peak District of Derbyshire are very similar, with the roof pitch sometimes as low as 24 degrees. These roofs were hung with heavy sandstone slates. Unlike the Cotswold roofs, these low-pitched roofs were cut as little as possible by dormers or gables, resulting in the characteristic long lines of ridge and eaves.

In the Lake District a hard, shaley, slate-like stone was used in a characteristic pattern. The grey-green slates were laid 'water-shot' or sloping outwards. Mortar was placed in the wall 50mm back from the face in a 125mm wide layer. Stones placed at the face and back of the wall were interwoven as much as possible and any rubble filling in the middle was built in without mortar. Through-stones were placed laterally the full length of the wall at 1,000mm height intervals. The Lake District also possessed slate, used for roofing, which looked like stone-slate and was grey-green or rust in colour (Fig 2).

SUB-SOIL CONSTRUCTION

In some areas where there was no available local stone, the sub-soil was found to be suitable for building walls. 'Cob', made by treading straw into wet mud, is found in Devon and Dorset. When thoroughly mixed, the mud was laid diagonally in courses of 475-600mm wide on a rubble or brick upper foundation wall. The walls had to be left for one to two years to dry out before applying the protective exterior coating necessary to prevent the wall disintegrating when rain wetted the surface. Wide eaves were also needed to throw the water off

the external walls. The roof was often thatched as the walls were not heavily load-bearing and the thatch formed a light roof covering (Fig 3).

Around Wiltshire the chalk below the topsoil was dug out and straw and water added, the whole mass being well trodden to form a chalk mud. The form of the house using this 'Winterslow' method was similar to the cob houses except that the chimney was traditionally built up through the middle of the house, whereas in cob houses the chimney was built on the outside wall. Another similar method using a type of white clay called 'Witchert', found approximately 450mm below ground level, was used in a limited area of Buckinghamshire around Aylesbury. Related methods for forming monolithic walls of sub-soil are found in the East Riding of Yorkshire near Hornsea, in Cumberland (see Fig 4), around Northamptonshire and in Moray and Banffshire in Scotland. Local variations in method are found including alternating layers of mud and straw and mud and stones.

The other major area of soil building is East Anglia. 'Clay lump' construction is found in Norfolk and Suffolk and differs from the other methods as the mud was first mixed and then pressed into moulds without top or base. They were turned out after two or three days and then stacked diagonally on edge for a further month, after which they were ready for use. The blocks were laid like bricks, using a thin mixture of earth or a weak lime mortar (Fig 5). 'Marl lump' is a similar construction method, using the marly clay found in South Cambridgeshire.

Fig 6.

Flint pebble at Morston, Norfolk with brick reinforcing

FLINT CONSTRUCTION

In the Southern and Eastern parts of England flint occurs together with chalk and gravel deposits. In the commonest wall form the flints were used at random and laid in lime mortar stiffened with cement. A random flint wall was built up with a large external facing-flint on both sides, the smaller flints being used for 'harling'—flinging the chips against the wet mortar. The use of complete transverse brick courses as well as brick linings to windows, corners, etc, gave additional stability. Sharp corners were always difficult when using flint and before the widespread use of brick a tradition of rounded corners and curves grew up. Squared flints were also used, laid in courses with very thin mortar joints or as a dressing for rubble walls. Pebble and cobble walling was built in the same way as random flint (Fig 6).

LOCAL BRICKS AND TILES

Before the mass-production of bricks, local brick-earth pits, combined with small facilities for making baked bricks, meant that the houses again had an immediate link with the soil they stood on. In the same way, hand-made tiles and pantiles were distinctive to each region. The major brick-earth deposits in Britain are found in the Midlands and South England as well as small local deposits.

THATCH

Apart from hand-made tiles and before the railways could bring cheap Welsh slates to the rest of the country, the only alternative in areas where there was no stone was thatch in the varying forms of reed, straw, heather, furze, etc, according to what was available. Of these, only reed and straw thatch-

Areas where earth walling survives.

Pebble is found in the N. The long belt of flint occurs in the E and SE. Cobble walling is found along E Norfolk and E Sussex coast.

Map showing areas where earth walling was used and where flint, pebble and cobble walls are found. Taken from Brunskill, R.W. *Illustrated Handbook of Vernacular Architecture;* 1970.

ing is still practiced. 'Long-straw' thatching is found in all major corn-growing areas and requires careful threshing to avoid damaging the straw. The length of the straw can be seen running parallel to the slope of the roof and such thatch has been described as appearing to have been poured over the roof. The technique known as 'combined wheat reed' is widely used in Devon and Dorset, although found elsewhere. The straw is put on the roof with the butt ends exposed on the surface, giving a neat, close-cropped appearance. Norfolk reed is found growing in the marshes and tidal estuaries of Suffolk,

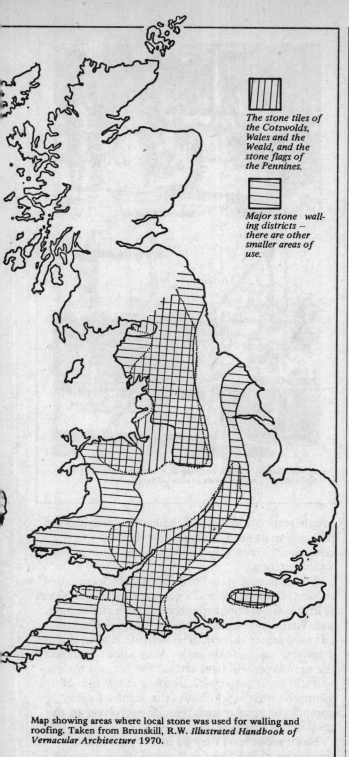

The stone tiles of the Cotswolds, Wales and the Weald, and the stone flags of the Pennines.

Major stone walling districts — there are other smaller areas of use.

Map showing areas where local stone was used for walling and roofing. Taken from Brunskill, R.W. *Illustrated Handbook of Vernacular Architecture* 1970.

Norfolk, Essex, Dorset, Hampshire and Glamorganshire, the best reed being obtained from beds that are cut regularly. The reed is laid in a similar manner to combed wheat reed and has a similar appearance. The ridges of Norfolk reed roofs are nearly always thatched with sedge as the reed is too stiff to bend across the ridge.

Any return to such traditional methods, although they can be used perhaps with some modification, is of course limited to the amount of material available.

To envisage thatch as a universal roofing material as it once was in the varying forms of reed, straw, heather, furze, etc, over the whole of England would be impractical. However, to use thatch roofs near the reed beds where the material and expertise are situated might prove practical, as a well executed roof of Norfolk Reed should last from 50-60 years with proper maintenance, before the top layer is stripped down and rethatched. Even longer time periods have been recorded. The ecological impact of a thatched roof is negligible since the reed beds occur naturally in suitable estuaries, and although mechanical harvesters have been introduced, the whole of the process is essentially one of harvesting and using the materials by man-power only. Even when the thatch is finally rejected there are no problems of disposal as it is simply organic matter and can be composted.

To build in materials that it is simple to recycle is another possible approach, together with the use of waste materials where there is a ready source of these. Just as brick and concrete are reused as hardcore and there are proposals for making building products out of crushed compressed refuse (Japan) and glass (America), it may be profitable to use materials either similar to thatch and earth which present little problem of disposal, or to use materials like timber and stone in such a way that they are preserved in good condition and can still be used when no longer required in their existing form. Before 1939 small houses continued to be built in Yorkshire using wall stones taken from demolished buildings, particularly old mills.

Were 'autonomous houses' to be built on unserviced land, which would probably be relatively inaccessible, a return to using regional materials might find economic justification, especially if we are designing these houses for use in the future when the demand for energy may have exceeded the supply. Where clay suitable for firing for bricks occurred, at one time it was automatically assumed that one built a clamp on site and produced the bricks to meet the immediate building requirements. Centralization, very broadly speaking, came only with the cheap transportation that we still have but which will almost certainly account for a growing proportion of the costs of building in the future. Nevertheless, even if this economic argument is not acceptable there still exists a case for designing houses that can be built by their owners and this situation readily fits with some of the traditions behind vernacular building methods. Reconsideration of our use of building materials should lead to the design of low-energy buildings with perhaps more thought going into the materials and constructional methods used so that it is possible to use parts of the building again, or at least remove the need for costly disposal.

If houses were built in Great Britain to fit all site conditions there might even re-emerge vernacular architecture which, judging by the current interest in nostalgia, many people would welcome.

Brenda Vale

THE GROUND OVER OUR HEADS

Earth, in one form or another, has been used for centuries to erect buildings in all parts of the globe. Earth walls were common all over Europe, including Britain, until the end of the last century. Earth wall traditions declined as a result of economic pressure to produce more profitable materials, such as brick or concrete. But many fine old earth buildings still exist in this country. Some are around 400 years old, which illustrates just how durable properly constructed earth walls can be.

It requires very simple skills and equipment to transform raw soil into a wall of very high constructional performance with virtually no capital cost. Building walls of soil has many other points in its favour; as a building material it is rot-proof, fire-proof, sound insulating and has notable thermal characteristics. It is also independent of the restrictions of centralisation since soil requires little transportation and processing.

Why then, with these obvious merits, has the earth wall ceased to be one of the most widely used indigenous materials in this country? Much of its downfall is due to unwarranted prejudice and the opinion that earth building is primitive, but it is true that earth walls built using traditional 'unstabilised' techniques in many cases cannot compete with conventional materials because of their weakness to water penetration and instability; they must be well protected and require a fairly high degree of maintenance.

Attention, however, has in recent years been concentrated on techniques for eliminating these weaknesses by the addition of 'stabilising' agents. It is now possible, using these additives with a wide range of otherwise unsuitable soils, to produce walls which can compete with many modern materials.

Earth used for building purposes is taken from below the topsoil layer, generally 2-3 feet (0.6-0.9m) below ground level, so as to exclude organic matter from the soil, as this may seriously affect the durability of the finished wall, particularly where stabilisers are used. The subsoil is then subjected to one of two basic procedures depending upon the proportion of sand, silt and clay in the soil and its general characteristics:

◆ **(a) Puddling.** The soil is mixed with a sufficient quantity of water (16-20%) to distribute the particles uniformly throughout the material, so creating a homogenous mass of graded particles.

◆ **(b) Ramming.** The soil is beaten or compressed to compact the soil particles tightly together, forcing out excess water and increasing their natural attraction. The soil is moist but the moisture content should not exceed 12%.

Soil may be considered as a compound of solid matter (silt, clay and sand), water and air; the solid matter is rock at various stages of decomposition. A

Above: **Rammed chalk building at Amesbury—Ministry of Agriculture. Chalk cement blocks at Amesbury.**

simple test on a sample of the earth will reveal the proportion of each of these differing soil components (silt, clay and sand) and is known as the *Sediment Test.*

A transparent glass bottle with a constant cross-section, flat bottom and a capacity for not less than ½ litre is filled about quarter full with the sample soil. Water is then added up to ¾ capacity and is left to saturate the soil. The mixture is then shaken vigorously and left to settle. After about 45 minutes the sand layer will have settled the silt and the clay will still be in suspension, settling at the rate of 12mm/hr. After eight hours the depth of each component is measured, relating each layer to the total depth (100%).

Many other tests may be used to assess the properties of the fine fractions of the soil, which in most cases have very active characteristics. Fine clay is smooth to touch, but silt—and to a greater extent sand—is gritty, especially when gnashed between the teeth. After assessing the relative properties of clay, silt and sand the soil may be classified broadly as belonging to a certain soil type.

MONOLITHIC PUDDLED WALLS

The exact composition of traditionally built puddled monolithic walls varied slightly with locality, as adjustments were made to suit local soil characteristics. A clayey or chalky mud mixed with straw was trodden into position, laid diagonally in

12in (300mm) courses or scars. The first layer or 'course' was built on top of a 24in (600mm) high basewall of burnt brick or stone, so that it overhung an inch or two either side. Successive courses were built with the diagonal layers inclined in opposite directions to those of preceding courses. The base is a weak point in any earth wall and should be well protected from any rain splashes and knocks. A damp proof course, consisting of two courses of slates, was also later adopted to prevent rising damp entering the base of the wall. Each course was allowed to dry out for 2-3 weeks before it was built on, and the wall was smoothed (pared) down flush with the base wall.

The term ' cob ' is now used to describe puddled monolithic mud walling. Three-storied buildings have been constructed with 'cob' walls ranging from 18in (450mm) thickness upwards, but 24in (600mm) is general for two-storey work. Hipped roofs, well tied, were preferred to the gable ended type, which results in large awkwardly shaped areas of exposed wall. Openings could be cut in 'cob' walls for windows and doors, or were formed as the work proceeded using timber lintels with a minimum of 18in (450mm) bearing. Four men can generally only build about 70ft (22m) run of 24in (600mm) thick 'cob' walling per day. It is therefore a slow process with drying periods of about a year after completion. When thoroughly dry the walls were rendered with lime 'rough cast' or 'slap dash'. This consisted of a ¾in (37mm) undercoat of lime and sand with a top-coat of crushed aggregate, slaked lime and sand.

Rendering is difficult to apply to 'mud' walls, so

horse hair was added to the mix as reinforcement. Traditionally the base wall was finished with two coats of pitch to make it impervious to moisture. Occasionally the puddled walls were cast in shuttering in the same way as concrete but this was not common in Britain—apart from certain types of chalk wallings—as the shutters tended to retard the drying-out process: although in some cases the 'cob' was laid against the boards to provide a smooth finish on the internal face of the wall. 'Cob' walls tend to suffer severe shrinkage, cracking and require a large wall thickness to be stable during erection. They might therefore be better used as an insulating infill material to a structural frame, because of their inferior strength.

An improvement on monolithic puddled walls is to form blocks, generally known as 'adobe', or in this country, 'clay lump'. Blocks have many advantages over monolithic walls:

◆ (a) Drying shrinkage takes place in the blocks before they are built into the wall, reducing cracking and eliminating long drying periods.

◆ (b) Blocks are easier to handle than 'cob' and the thickness required for stability is substantially reduced.

◆ (c) Relatively smooth wall surfaces are formed using blockwork and no smoothing (paring) of the walls is necessary before plastering.

◆ (d) Discontinuities in the material can be spotted early by running tests on specimen blocks to be used in the wall.

◆ (e) Production of blocks allows walls to be built in cavity form, increasing its insulation properties (leading to improved 'U' values).

The mixture is trodden together in the same way as 'cob'—although puddle mixers have been used, but mixing frequently has to be stopped for cleaning.

The quantity of straw to be added depends on the amount of clay in the soil. The higher the clay content, the more straw that is required, although a maximum of 20% by volume is generally recommended, as a larger percentage is liable to reduce the strength of the blocks. Clods of soil should be avoided in all earth building as they produce differential drying, shrinkage and cracking. Water is mixed gradually to give even distribution; loss of moisture after mixing should be avoided. The mixture is shovelled into moulds placed on the ground and is kneaded into corners. A straight edged piece of wood, dipped in water is used to smooth the block, and the block is left until dry enough to retain its shape. Moulds are generally made of timber but with multi-block moulds should be lined with metal for easy block removal. The blocks are left on the ground in a shaded site, after the moulds are removed, to prevent rapid drying. They are then cured for 2-3 weeks well protected from rain. Adobe blocks can be moulded in many shapes and sizes; wedge shaped bricks or 'tubali' (inter-locking, base-to-point) are a form from West Africa but the most common are rectangular— generally 18in x 9in x 9in, 18in x 9in x 6in and 18in x 6in x 6in. The compressive strength of Adobe blocks varies between 10-40 kg/cm² and they

Puddled Monolithic Walls :

thatched roof

plate

large overhang.

timber lintel with 18" bearing

strong lengths of wire embedded in rendering to provide key.

slate cills.

joists creosoted at their ends.

finish of lime wash over rough-cast rendering

plate.

COB BUILDING :

2 c.s. slates as d.p.c.

broken glass embedded in base of wall to prevent rodent attack.

pitch plinth

g.l.

wall built of brick or masonry base-wall

foundation of cyclopean concrete (large stones bedden in concrete.)

SECTION :

have an approximate unit weight of 1,920kg/m^3
Similar principles to brickwork are employed for
laying Adobe blocks. They are bedded in a soft
mortar of lime and clay, or of the soil used for
blocks mixed with sand. The blocks are wetted
slightly to prevent absorption of moisture from the
mortar and ensure good bonding.

The wall is then rendered or painted with
solutions which have a stabilizing effect, such as
boiled linseed oil, sodium silicate and casein whitewash. Stabilizers, though, are not generally effective
for puddled mixtures, with the exception of
Bituminous Emulsions, and to some extent lime.
Bituminous Emulsions consist of about 55%
bitumen, 43-44% water and 1-2% emulsifying agent;
the water is released upon exposure to the air,
leaving the bituminous bond. Solutions can be
'early' or 'late' breaking, the latter being retarded to
allow time for mixing before the water is released.
The percentage of emulsion added depends on the
proportion of sand in the soil: 4-6% for soils with
over 50% sand; 7-12% for 50% sand; and 13-20% for
under 50% sand. Lime can be used for soils with high
clay content, but additions of cement are not
generally too effective.

RAMMED EARTH (Pise de Terre)

Rammed monolithic walls are formed by pounding
the soil between shutters in 4in (100mm) layers.
Traditionally buildings constructed from *Pise de
Terre* are abundant in the province of Lyon, France

Rammed earth building.

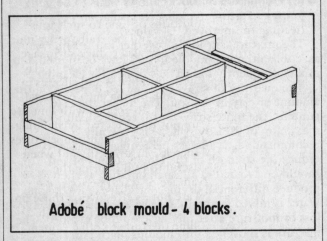

Adobé block mould - 4 blocks.

Traditional mud walling methods in Britain

Name	Locality	Composition
Cob or Clom or Clob	Devon	3 parts of clay shale to 5 parts straw
	Cornwall	3 parts of 1:2 mixture of clay and broken slate to 5 parts of straw
	Hampshire and Dorset	3 parts of 3:1 mixture of chalk and clay to 5 parts of straw
Marl Mud	Hertfordshire	
Wichert	Buckinghamshire	3 parts of a mixture of clay sand and chalk to 5 parts of straw
Chalk Mud or Clunch	Wiltshire Berkshire Hampshire and Surrey	Mixture of graded chalk and straw (sometimes built in shuttering).

and parts of Spain, Belgium, and Germany. Most
soils between 40-75% sand and gravel together and
18-24% clay may be used for ramming. Rammed
walls can, however, be built with 24-39% clay, but
these will be inferior and require a larger amount of
maintenance. An ideal soil would be sandy clay
loam containing 40% rounded pebbles passing a
25mm sieve, 18% clay, 7% silt and 35% sand. Up to
45% gravel content gives a marked increase in
strength for rammed walls, but strength is reduced
with greater percentages.

The ease with which rammed earth shuttering can
be taken down and reset in position largely governs
the speed of erection. There has been much
improvement in this direction, particularly in the US.
Traditional wall forms have been heavy and
cumbersome, requiring a lot of bracing and
alignment. But at Texas Agriculture and Mechanical
College lighter-weight plywood has been substituted
for the heavy planking usually adopted, and at the
Commonwealth Experimental Building Station in
Australia, roller forms with detachable wooden
clamps have been developed. A combination of
these techniques are shown—with the additional
improvement of metal hinges which allow the
construction of corners, at any angle, using only one
shutter. Dan and John Magdiel in the US have
developed an all-metal form where the sides are
released by a lever at the completion of a course.
They also eliminate the need for a corner form by
ramming one course over and at right angles to
another—similar to a quoin of brickwork.

Rammed walls are built off basewalls in the same
way as 'cob' and 'adobe'. Soil with 12% cement has
been used to form the basewall in low rainfall areas,
in place of burnt brickwork. On well drained sites
the soil cement mixture is rammed against the sides
of the trench on top of a bed of consolidated rubble,
or a strip foundation of cyclopean concrete. In
Britain, however, these base walls would remain
almost permanently damp and soil cement might not
stand up to frost attack, under such conditions.
Various treatments have been used to form a barrier
to rising damp, but conventional membranes will
probably give the best results. With the shutters in
position soil is rammed in successive layers until the
section of wall reaches the height of the shutters 24in
(600mm) - 36in (900mm). The shape of the ramming

COLIN TAYLOR

COLIN TAYLOR

CLOUGH WILLIAMS ELLIS

Rammed chalk-cement house at Amesbury.

Chalk cement block house at Amesbury.

Clay lump workshop, Norfolk.

iron varies with the type of soil but flat rammers weighing 5-12lbs are most common, lifted about 18in (450mm) with each stroke to provide an even intensity. No imprint of the rammer should be left when the soil is properly compacted. Although stability can be achieved with relatively thin walls, 14in (350mm) is the minimum practical width for a man to work between the shutters, which limits the minimum width for monolithic walls. Chicken wire or barbed wire laid zig zag fashion is sometimes used as reinforcement, embedded in every other course. The ramming of each course is done in an opposite direction to that of the preceding courses. The reinforcement also restrains shrinkage in a manner similar to that effected by the planks of timber embedded in traditional *pise* walls.

The moisture content of soil mixes governs drying shrinkage and the durability of the finished walls. When soil is compacted, and increasing proportions of water are added, the unit weight of the soil increases. Eventually a point is reached where the unit weight goes down. This is known as the 'optimum moisture content'. A soil compacted at this moisture content will possess astonishing durability and have maximum density. As much as a storey height may be erected safely in one day and courses may be built upon as soon as they are completed. One man working between the shutters can erect about 6ft (1800mm) square of *pise* per day and it is therefore a much quicker process than puddled walling.

Cement is the most popular stabilizer for rammed work, and has in the past been used extensively to form road bases. Cement forms a rigid skeleton without chemical reaction from the soil, and generally yields much higher strengths than other stabilizers. It is most effective for soils with high sand content, which in many cases are mechanically unstable. Soil cement mixtures should not be allowed to stand for more than 10-15 minutes as drying sets in, and they are kept moist after compaction to allow the cement to hydrate and gain strength. Addition of 5% cement to the soil is usual for building blocks. This produces strengths between 600-1000lbs/in² and stability even when saturated for long periods.

But most stabilizers, including cement, are difficult to mix with heavy clay soils, and have little

stabilizing effect. Additions of lime to such soils make them more workable and generally prove more effective than cement. They also reduce shrinkage. Lime is increasingly effective with increase in clay content as it reacts with aluminates and silcates in the clay portion of the soil, producing a chemical bond (pozzolanic reaction). Reactions with lime are slow and mixtures are not too affected by standing time—usually 24 hours. Curing at high temperatures produces a marked increase in strength, and when using lime soil it is useful to build during the summer to take advantage of warm periods. Additions above 5% are not as effective as those up to this point and there is a limit to the strength attainable with soil-lime mixtures—unlike cement, where larger proportions of cement correspond to greater increases in strength. The chemical reaction may be increased with the addition of other pozzolanic materials such as fly-ash but not enough is known yet to manipulate soil-lime mixes in the same way as soil-cement.

Other materials such as resins, waste sump oil, and water proofing chemical solutions have been used with limited success but they require much more study before their behaviour can be thoroughly assessed.

These stabilizers may be added to the soil mix for rammed walls but they may in many cases prove too expensive to incorporate into the whole wall, and a 4in (100mm) - 6in (150mm) surfacing of the stabilized soil mixture may be rammed with unstabilized earth used for the main portion of the

SHELTER

wall. This process is known as 'plating' and in many cases has proved satisfactory.

Big business has already shown itself to be interested in stabilized building materials, following the development of a petroleum-based stabilizer known as BMX, which was developed by Esso for the industrialised production of earth blocks using a complicated processing plant, so illustrating a total disregard for the almost unique qualities of earth. As yet BMX blocks have not been produced commercially, however.

Building walls in monolithic, rather than block form has a certain advantage in that the best *pise* is formed with the soil incorporating pebbles which make it unsuitable for block production. Generally, though, pressed blocks are a better proposition than monolithic walls and machines have been developed to provide high-compaction, constant-volume blocks. Hand operated machines such as the Cinva and Landcrete presses compress the soil to 500-600lbs/in^2 and some hydraulic machines apply between 1000 and 1200lbs/in^2. Blocks of soil-cement are the

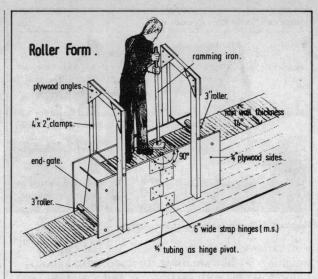

Roller Form.

plywood angles.

4"x 2" clamps.

end-gate.

3" roller.

ramming iron.

3" roller.

rain wall thickness 7½"

90°

¾" plywood sides.

6" wide strap hinges (m.s.)

¾" tubing as hinge pivot.

most commonly produced. Permutations of the moulding boxes have produced other soil-cement materials, such as floor tiles and 'U' shaped, precast lintel sections. Soil cement tiles are rammed with 16% cement and bedded in mortar of a similar mix to the tile, with tile edges touching. The joints are then stopped up with a neat cement slurry and the excess wiped off a few hours later. 100-150 blocks per hour have been produced with Landcrete machines and Cinva claim 200-300. All soil-cement products should be kept under cover after production, watered for the first 24 hours, and kept damp for a further seven days. They may be used after 21 days. The blocks built up with a soft mortar of 1:7 to 1:10 soil-and-cement, or a 1:2:8/9 mixture of cement, lime and sand, to reduce shrinkage at the joints.

Many finishes have developed to protect and stabilize wall surfaces. Rendering is the traditional finish but it is difficult to apply to earth walls and in many cases requires a mechanical key to prevent it coming away from the backing. Cement render is too short (brittle) and a mixture of 1 lime : 3 sand, one cement or lime 'roughcast' are probably the best rendering, but inevitably requires high maintenance. Slurries and paints are therefore preferred for

Thermal conductivity of walling materials

Material	'k' (B. Th. U. per sq ft per hr per deg F difference, per inch thickness)	w/mdegC	Authority
Rammed Earth	4.7	0.675	University of Saskatchewan
Pressed bricks or blocks	4.7	0.675	Assumed
Adobe blocks	3.50	0.5	University of California
Adobe: sun-dried brick	3.58	0.52	as above
Stabilized adobe brick	4.00	0.58	as above
Common clay brick	8.00	1.15	Building Research Station UK
Limestone	10.60	1.53	National Physical Laboratory UK
Dense concrete	7.00	1.01	as above

(Taken from *A Manual of Stabilized Soil Construction for Housing* by R. Fitzmaurice.)

Compressive strength of typical earth types (rammed)

Mix	Compressive strength lbs/in^2	N/mm^2
3 sand 2 clay 1 shale	685	4.78
3 sand 2 clay 1½ shale	543	3.82
6 sand 4 clay 1 shale	498	3.50
1 sand 1 clay 0 shale	196	1.37

Tests at 30 days on soil specimens of various composition to be used in rammed earth construction mixed with 11% water content by weight. A minimum working strength for soil to be used for rammed earth work containing a liberal factor of safety is 1.97 N/mm^2 (358 lbs/in^2).

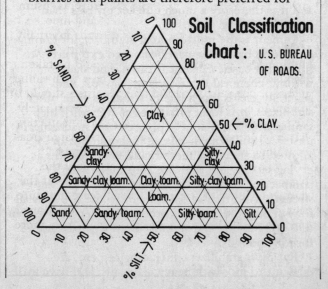

Soil Classification Chart : U.S. BUREAU OF ROADS.

% SAND

% CLAY.

% SILT

Clay
Sandy clay
Silty clay
Sandy-clay loam
Clay loam
Silty-clay loam
Loam
Sand
Sandy loam
Silty loam
Silt

W.H. RANSOM

CLOUGH WILLIAMS ELLIS

CLOUGH WILLIAMS ELLIS

COUNTRY LIFE

Some exterior finishes to earth walls

Finish	Composition	Application
Rendering	1 lime: 3 sand: 1 cement	Tyrolean finish for easier application will require regular maintenance
Roughcast	¾ in undercoat lime and sand, top coat crushed aggregate, slaked lime and sand	Traditional finish for 'Cob' walls forms good protection to the wall but also requires regular maintenance
Slurry	Cement and lime	Rammed walls wetted 24 hours before application
Water proofers	2 coats of hot applied tar with finish of sand thrown over each coat	Traditional finish to Norfolk Clay Lump provides good low maintenance finish but is expensive and messy to apply
	Sodium silicate solution sprayed onto wall surface or added to the mix	Has been used successfully in this country for chalk walling
	Boiled linseed oil painted onto the surface of the wall	Used in low rainfall areas such as Israel, Africa and South America
Norfolk Colour Wash	Mixture of hot lime and water with a lump of tallow stirred hot into each batch	Generally applied over tar finish to Clay Lump cottages, the tallow acts as an adhesive
Casein Whitewash	5lbs casein, 3 lbs trisodium phosphate, 1 sack Hydrated lime, 3 pints formaldehyde, 13 gallons water	Brush applied
Paints	50 cement; 25 fine gritty sand; 36 Calcium stearate; 2 Calcium chloride; 50 water	Water added after ingredients mixed dry

rammed walls although rendering is advised for 'Cob' or 'Adobe' walls. Certain creepers also serve to protect earth walls from severe exposure. Gypsum plasters will not adhere to the earth, and lime plasters are generally used to finish walls internally.

All techniques require simple plans with a minimum of projections and care should be taken to evenly distribute loads over a large area with timber plates or concrete pads. No lateral thrusts should be tolerated and 'pitched' roofs should be adequately tied, providing large overhangs for good protection. Earth buildings should be designed with large areas of walling unbroken by windows and doors.

Public resistance to the idea is probably the biggest obstacle to the revival of earth walls at the moment, but with the inevitable increase in future energy costs earth walls will, if properly developed, provide a valid alternative to walls built from more conventional materials.

Colin Taylor

From the top: Adobe block production. Fine example of Devonian cob farmhouse. Cob farmhouse, Budleigh Salterton. Cob building at Amesbury.

SHELTER

SELF HELP HOUSING

Housing is essentially a social and political process, but most innovation concentrates on technological and design questions, pushing the problems of the *users* into the background. It is easier to deal with the technical questions than with people: models can be made of technical solutions and prototypes built, but such 'solutions' to housing treat homes as *objects*. This reflects a world-wide tendency to see problems solved through production — the creation of objects to be sold. The users of such objects become consumers whose only activity is to buy and passively accept what they are given. Housing is usually seen as a problem of the production of objects.

We may hope that heavy-system building was the ultimate in production biased housing . . . every city has its high flats and deck access tenements, architectural forms developed to justify the enormous capital cost of system building. This was to be the answer to the housing problem — fast, efficient production — but the efficiency proved to be an illusion and we are now left with a legacy of buildings that can only be demolished with explosions. As a reaction more radical innovators have come up with technologies with a lower impact, flexible, adaptable and lightweight houses. They are still concerned with solving the product-ion questions first . . . they see houses as objects divorced from their social context. We aren't short of ideas about how to build houses. What we must turn our attention to is who is in control of the resources by which they can be built.

Housing isn't primarily about the production of objects: it is a complex net of activities and processes in which people interact, social institutions are created and forces of social injustice and oppression operate. It is only by changing these factors that housing may be organised satisfactorily. And, it can be argued, only then can the approximate technology satisfy needs. Autonomous or flexible house technologies may then come in useful, but unless they are appropriate to the way housing is organised, they cannot possibly be developed to their full potential.

Even people who claim to be concerned about the 'housing problem' — homelessness and so on — tend to see housing in terms of production. Slogans such as "We need a crash programme of house building" are used by politicians and others of all hues who somehow assume that all housing problems will be solved by building more units. This tends to put into second place questions of management, organisation, finance and dwelling needs when these are the main issues. As a result more housing is produced that is rigidly designed for the stereotype standard nuclear family. Those who fall outside that category find it harder and harder to house themselves.

Housing tends to reflect the nature of capitalist society: it is unequally distributed, it tends to reinforce social divisions and conformity, and it

The end of a disastrous failure in public housing policy. Hailed as a brilliant contribution to 'urban renewal' in 1954, the Pruitt-Igoe project in St Louis, Missouri became virtually uninhabitable through chronic vandalism, violence and neglect, and was largely demolished in 1972.

UNITED PRESS INTERNATIONAL

provides ample scope for investment, profits and production.

While many continue to call for more houses, some people are beginning to understand that the other questions are more important. Surprisingly it is often those people most in need or most involved in the process — the users or the homeless — who realise the futility of appeals for more production and instead appreciate the need to get the process and the activities right first. Homeless families are beginning to realise that it is the way houses are under-used or left empty that brings about the crises; those in substandard houses or clearance areas may begin to refuse the newly produced housing the council offers them and insist on rehabilitation or changes in the procedures of rehousing. People are beginning to question the abilities of the main agencies in housing to get the process right: and this may bring them to a confrontation with the established forces in society. No longer are the local authorities, spec builders and housing associations criticised only by 'experts', but by the people themselves who want more control over the housing process.

In the last two or three years groups have emerged who are trying to control their own housing, and there is a wide range of community action campaigns, 'user controlled' projects, self-help and squatting activities that represent a movement of sorts. The idea of users controlling housing isn't a utopian vision, therefore, but a practical objective of a significant and growing number of people. The rest of this article looks briefly at some examples of attempts to assert more control and the political potential and drawbacks of such a movement.

One way in which people can get more control over their housing is through 'self-help'. Self-help usually implies that people work on the construction of the houses themselves. By doing so they cut costs and provide themselves with better housing at a lower price than similar housing on the market.

Self-build housing associations have been functioning for a number of years. No one has a clear picture of how many exist in Britain, as many have registered but, because of the massive bureaucratic problems they face, have failed to get as far as building. There are quite a few that have successfully built houses, in Yorkshire and the South of England for example. Using rules set out by the National Federation of Housing Societies they buy land, borrow money and do the building work on a spare time basis, often with very rigid rules, imposing fines on members who don't do their full share of the work. When their houses are complete they buy them on a mortgage in the usual way through building societies, but maybe getting a house worth, say, £12,000 at today's prices for only £6,000. Architects may find the work of such groups disappointing because the houses rarely look different from the average spec built 'semi', but of course the self-builders are anxious that their houses shouldn't differ from the conventional norm because of problems of resale.

Being a member of a self-build association is not always easy, and few would be prepared to put in the work demanded for the dubious 'security' of a mortgage and middle-class status. What these associations can teach us, however, is that people with limited knowledge of building work can soon acquire the expertise to participate in building. There is no great mystery about the skills of building.

BLACK ROAD

Self-help building work has also emerged out of a community action struggle over a 'rehabilitation versus redevelopment' issue. In Black Road, Macclesfield (Cheshire), the residents of 34 houses waged a two year battle with the council to prevent their early nineteenth-century terraced houses being demolished as unfit for human habitation. Instead they got an improvement area declared and undertook to improve the houses themselves. Initially they had the work priced by contractors, but then the residents saved money by doing many of the jobs themselves in the evenings or at weekends. Through this kind of self-help they were able to save on average about £1,500 a house

The terrace in Black Road, Macclesfield, after co-operative rehabilitation by the tenants.

and thus make optimum use of the improvement grants available from the council. They were also able to save a large amount by working on external environmental improvements.

The success of the Black Road project depended a great deal on co-operation from the local council, the builders involved, the role of the architect, who lived in one of the houses, and the commitment of the residents — conditions that might be hard to reproduce elsewhere. But as a precedent they are providing inspiration for local groups from all over Britain. The Black Road Residents' Association is continually hosting coach loads of visitors from other working-class areas.

At Black Road the self-help work was done on an informal basis — they didn't fine each other as in the self-build housing associations. Many of the residents were old people and tenants, and to facilitate the scheme they worked out novel forms of mortgage so that the old people could buy their houses. Also the back garden areas were taken into a form of common ownership and a trust set up to administer them. Persuading the council of the feasibility of the scheme and setting up these organisational questions were far more difficult than the actual building work. The rehabilitation was done in a year, whereas the campaign and negotiations took over two years.

The difficulties of setting up such a project are daunting. The system just isn't geared to letting people help themselves. It would be possible to get enmeshed hopelessly in red tape and the organisational and financial commitment may seem unnecessary and frightening. For most working-class people whose housing future seems limited to the paternalistic provisions of a local authority, to get involved in self-help housing is a big step, but some people seem prepared to make it in order to achieve a measure of control over their lives and housing.

INNER CITY AREAS

In many inner city districts community action groups are following the Macclesfield example and developing new forms of organisation to control the renovation of properties. Many of the big cities like Manchester, Birmingham and Glasgow had embarked on massive slum-clearance programmes and replaced old working-class communities with huge housing schemes whose faults have been only too well documented. But these programmes have ground to a halt partly because of government pressure and partly because of opposition from residents and professionals to the local authorities for example or at public enquiries. In Manchester, areas like Chorlton, Longsight and Ladybarn — scheduled for clearance — are now spawning locally controlled housing associations, building co-operatives and other groups determined to implement rehabilitation themselves. Similarly in Saltley in Birmingham and Govanhill in Glasgow local groups have been formed to organise improvements.

In Saltley the residents, many of them immigrants, came together to fight the councils' condemnation of their houses and have now set up a self-help building group and a tenants' co-operative. They made an *Open Door* television programme and were inundated with requests for assistance.

It is possible to see these developments as mainly for the better-off members of the working class. Home-owners tend to form the core of any campaign to save houses from demolition. In some cases not everyone favours rehabilitation. In Manchester for instance many residents in Longsight felt they had lost the chance to be rehoused because of the 'saving' of their houses. They attacked the 'students' and young professionals who had come in to organise the opposition to the council plans. Yet in some of Manchester's newest council housing schemes (like Moss Side District Centre) the new tenants are clamouring to get out of them, and back to the old-style terraces.

TENANTS TAKE OVER

The initiative for users' control in the field of public and housing-association housing tends to come from progressive thinkers rather than tenants themselves. Various people have come up with proposals for involving people in the management and organisation of their housing (rather than direct involvement in building and maintenance work). Some experiments have begun, particularly in the housing-association world.

◆ *The Holloway tenants co-operative* is an example of this.[1] The tenants/members of a co-operative organisation negotiate with a housing association to buy on their behalf and improve houses for people in serious housing need. The ownership of the houses remains with the housing association but the tenants are in charge of management, heavily bolstered by paid professional community workers and the like. It is questionable whether such a scheme actually saves money, but it does give the tenants some say in what happens to their housing.

◆ *The Granby tenants co-operative* in Liverpool claims to be a step further on from this because the co-operative actually owns the housing it manages. Several tenant co-operatives have been set up within this area of Liverpool and they are able to organise their own professional help through a Neighbourhood Housing Service which they also manage.

The argument has been put forward for many years by the Co-operative party and various writers like Colin Ward[2] that tenant management is applicable to council housing also. The most common model suggested is based on Scandinavian experience where the local authority *sells* housing schemes to tenant-managed co-operatives. There is no doubt that this idea is being considered by a number of local authorities, and the Minister of Housing, Reg Freeson, has recently set up a working

1 *A Better Place*: story of the Holloway Tenants Co-operative (Shelter 35p).
2 Colin Ward, *Tenants Take Over* (Architectural Press £3.95).

TOM WOOLLEY

party to report on the feasibility or otherwise of this idea. Significantly there are no representatives of tenants' organisations on this working party! The G.L.C. is also considering proposals for a different kind of scheme — a form of extended participation — for Thamesmead, the 'new town' to the south-east of London.

What is important is that pressure for this sort of scheme isn't coming from tenants, though there is massive criticism of the inefficiency and poor management of local authorities. The principle of tenant management is that tenants, organised locally, can provide a better and more sensitive service than centralised and clumsy bureaucracies. Some local authorities offer tenants rent 'holidays' and grants if they will repair and redecorate a house when they move into it because otherwise the re-letting delays can be four or five months every time a house falls vacant. But this is only O.K. for tenants if it is worth their while financially; at present housing finance is locked into such a rigid system that it is hard for local authorities to, say, lower rents in return for tenants taking over certain management responsibilities. Many schemes are decaying rapidly and tenants may be unwilling to take responsibility for housing that the council can't cope with.

SUMNER HOUSE

But in areas of housing crisis ordinary working-class families may adopt the ideas of tenant

(Opposite and Above) **Street demonstration by Tenants.** *(Below)* **Ernest Mills, secretary of the Summer House tenants group.**

management and self-help as an answer to their housing problems. Sumner House in Tower Hamlets East London, is an example of this approach.

In the summer of 1974 an organisation of homeless families on the council waiting list were frustrated at the council's lack of interest in their plight. They moved into an empty council block

D. MORRIS

(called Sumner House) and set up a tenants' co-operative. They said they would manage and improve the block instead of the council. The block had been emptied for a very extensive and costly rehabilitation scheme, and when the council found that 'squatters' had moved in they set about smashing up the remaining empty flats to make them uninhabitable. Gradually the numbers occupying the block have grown until there are now over fifty families there. The co-op has been negotiating with the council to legitimise their position, claiming that it can carry out improvements, to the tenants' satisfaction, at a much lower cost using self-help work. Many members of the co-op are skilled tradesmen and they reckoned they could take on a great deal of the improvement work. In return they want the council to recognise them and leave them in *control* of the block, paying reduced rents. At the time of writing the situation is very much in the balance as the council is still holding the threat of eviction over the group. Whatever the immediate result, however, the impact of Sumner House will be far reaching. The group has brought together the squatting idea, tenant management and the use of self-help building work to cut costs. It is sufficiently credible to make the council seriously consider its case. This could be a model for similar action elsewhere, which would reduce the enormous housing loss of empty properties awaiting re-letting and repairs or improvement.

There is no clear movement emerging from all this activity. Many of the groups mentioned above have come together at various points to compare notes, but there are many different ideas about objectives and strategies and there are many who are critical of the ideas of user control and self-help.

There are the usual criticisms from the Right that reflect the authoritarian unwillingness to accept that ordinary people can do anything for themselves without the control of experts and central bureaucracies. For all the Tory rhetoric about self-help, the capitalist institutions (the banks, building societies, building firms, etc) will do little to help working-class people organise their own housing.

From the Left is the fear that many socialists have of community action, in general, that it is part of the old fashioned voluntary movement, papering over the cracks and letting the system off the hook by doing jobs the system ought to do . . . a weakening of the Welfare State. The correct tactic is to *demand* a better and extended Welfare State. Public housing, for instance, was the result of decades of struggle by the labour movement . . . the thought of selling it off to tenant managed co-ops is horrifying to them. A more sophisticated criticism realises that the Welfare State involves a complex network of state *and* voluntary agencies that seek to dissipate and control working-class discontent. Organisations thrown up by the working-class from trade unions to retail co-operatives to tenants' associations can become

agents of social control, holding back the very people they were supposed to liberate.

In a similar way tenant participation or management may be offered in carefully controlled doses where the tenants have no control over wider policy decisions or finance, but are tied down with time-consuming administrative and committee responsibilities which prevent them from taking a more political path.

It is the economic question which is the most serious, however. The use of time or labour by working-class people to organise or build their own housing may be a form of double exploitation. Some of the surplus generated at work by their labour is invested in housing. This housing is then sold or rented back to the working-class and there have been many bitter struggles over the level of rents that have been charged. If a worker has also to work on the building or maintenance of his housing, then he is paying twice over for someone to lend him the wealth that he produced in the first place.

In the short term it can be financially advantageous for *some* people to become involved in self-help and user controlled schemes, but in the longer term any movement for more control in housing must confront the question of economic and social justice and see their struggle in terms of achieving a just distribution of wealth. However, the many experiments in organising housing that community action is generating must not be dismissed on the grounds that, like many other programmes for change, they are reformist. The lessons that can be learnt from tenants' co-operatives are that it is questions of organisation, activities and structures that must be got right first, with production and technology developing in the most appropriate way.

Such a movement also helps to demystify the role of the 'expert'. Housing is no longer seen as a complex and difficult task that only architects and housing managers and others can tackle, but a simple process from management to building that anyone with a modicum of common sense can take on. Such projects serve as models for the devolution of power and responsibility within society and they also educate the participants in the realities of urban politics and processes. If the lessons are learnt, those involved will become aware of the need for wider change and of the objective of control over institutions rather than merely demanding that those in power do things better.

Tom Woolley

For more information about self-help and user-control housing:
The author works at the Architectural Association School of Architecture (36 Bedford Square, London WC1B 3ES). Some students and staff there are involved in research or practical activity in this field and are in touch with a number of action groups. To facilitate communication between these groups and help people who want more information, they are building up a 'communications network' to circulate documents and put activists and practitioners in touch with each other. If you would like more information about this, please write to Tom Woolley at the above address enclosing a large stamped addressed envelope.

MAN MAKETH THE CLOTHES

MARION L. CHANNING

In these days when clothing, yarn and cordage are becoming just another route from the oil-wells to the pockets of the capitalists, it's almost as subversive to mention the 'natural' fibres, such as wool, flax, sisal, jute and cotton as it is to mention their important companion, cannabis or hemp. (It's even more subversive to examine closely the development of the technology of fabric production; it's hard to touch on a single area within the criticism of modern industrial technology and the interests it serves without turning to some phase within the evolution of spinning, weaving and the production of fibre, to illustrate one's case). We thus dedicate this section "A subversive coverage of the covering of man", to all those who may be in danger of forgetting that wool grows on sheep and that cotton is now almost a synthetic fibre, considering the amount of pesticide and fertilizer that is used to keep it as a commercial monoculture.

'Natural' fibres fall into four categories: animal fur (including wool, horse-hair, human hair, goat hair and rabbit fur, etc.); fibres in the stems of plants (jute, etc.); fibres from the leaves of plants (sisal, etc.); and seed or flower fibre such as cotton. This section will deal only with the cultivation of fibres which are suited to a temperate climate and which have disappeared from common use under the pressure of 'progress'.

◆ *Stem or 'bast' fibres* Hemp, flax, nettle and hibiscus all give fibres from their stems. In each case these are located running length-ways along the stem underneath what could be called the 'bark' and surrounding the central 'woody' core.

FLAX (Linum usitatissimum)

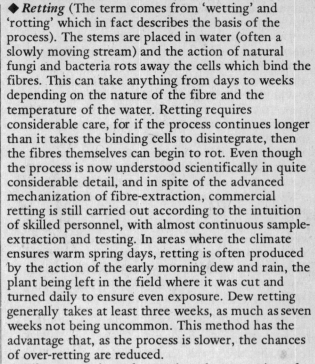

There are about 150 species of this plant widely distributed throughout the world. The species suitable to temperate climates has a greenish-grey stem growing to about three to four feet before branching at the top to produce pale-blue flowers. The seeds are crushed to produce linseed-oil, but the extraction of fibre generally requires the plant to be lifted before the seeds ripen. The plant requires fertile soil, weedless and well worked, under which conditions it will take about three months from the sowing of the seed till the yellowing of the leaves indicates readiness for cutting. A moist summer is said to give the softest linen—hot, dry weather being required for cord fibre. Once cut, the stems are stripped of their leaves and seeds, and left to dry. When dry, the crop is ready for the process which is common to the extraction of most stem fibres.

◆ *Retting* (The term comes from 'wetting' and 'rotting' which in fact describes the basis of the process). The stems are placed in water (often a slowly moving stream) and the action of natural fungi and bacteria rots away the cells which bind the fibres. This can take anything from days to weeks depending on the nature of the fibre and the temperature of the water. Retting requires considerable care, for if the process continues longer than it takes the binding cells to disintegrate, then the fibres themselves can begin to rot. Even though the process is now understood scientifically in quite considerable detail, and in spite of the advanced mechanization of fibre-extraction, commercial retting is still carried out according to the intuition of skilled personnel, with almost continuous sample-extraction and testing. In areas where the climate ensures warm spring days, retting is often produced by the action of the early morning dew and rain, the plant being left in the field where it was cut and turned daily to ensure even exposure. Dew retting generally takes at least three weeks, as much as seven weeks not being uncommon. This method has the advantage that, as the process is slower, the chances of over-retting are reduced.

◆ *Fibre extraction* After retting, the extraction of the fibre from the stalks differs slightly from crop to crop; generally, however, the procedure involves drying the stalks and then breaking or crushing the cores which should have become brittle. The broken stem is then drawn under a scraper or 'scutch' to separate the wood from the fibre. In most cases, however, the fibre can be stripped straight off the stem by hand.

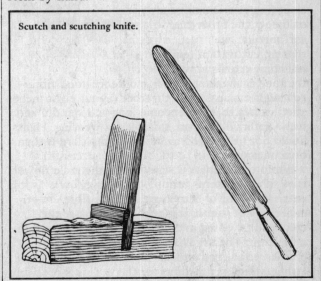

Scutch and scutching knife.

NETTLES (Urticaceae)

The main commercial fibre from the nettle family comes unfortunately from a species quite removed from the stinging nettle. "Ramie" as it is called (from *Boehmeria Nivea*) can only be cultivated successfully in tropical climates, although *Laportia canadensis*, which gives a slightly coarser and stronger fibre has reportedly been grown in the

South of France with some success. The nettle family produces fibre that is particularly resistant to bacterial action, ensuring a very high wet strength and making it ideal for fishing-net cord.

The common stinging nettle *(Urtica dioica)* is reputed to have produced very high quality cloth, although there is only one reference that I have ever come across that mentions any details about extracting the fibre (N.B. Dutt 'Neglected Fibres', *Indian Text,* 1937). Apparently boiling the dried nettle in 'water and ash' allows it to be stripped from the stem. (This seems to agree with the description of the normal procedure for the production of ramie which apparently has to be de-gummed chemically because the normal retting process is ineffective).

My own attempts to produce fibre from the stinging nettle have never resulted in a product suitable for cloth; scraping the dried nettle stems with a sharp knife removes the fibrous layer but boiling this with ash does not seem to break this down to any substantial degree. However, carding of the products after boiling and drying does give coarse but spinnable cord fibres.

HEMP (Cannabis delecticus)

It's probably unnecessary to say that this grows quite successfully in a temperate climate. (My volume of *The Vegetable Kingdom* 1890—a source of much forgotten wisdom— says that cannabis once grew wild in parts of England; but if anyone should offer you a map to the secret forgotten hemp-land, remember the proverbial '*pot* of gold'.

Hemp cultivation requires well-composted soil to give good high stem growth and hence good fibre— growing the plants close together (about eight inches apart) causes them to become long and spindly and gives a softer fibre more suitable for weaving. Plants should not be allowed to 'ripen' as the fibre is then too tenaciously held to the stem for successful extraction. (Ripeness is signified by the male flowers fading and the stems turning slightly yellow). As it is better—in terms of the fineness of the fibre—to err on the side of youth, it is reasonable to use the ripening of the first male plant as a signal to pull the entire crop. The heads and the roots should be returned to the soil and the stems left to dry before retting (which proceeds as for flax). This is probably the right time to warn you that "Honestly, Officer, I was only growing it for making rope" may not be sufficient defence against the plant's most implacable enemy.

Talking of enemies, *The Vegetable Kingdom* notes that hemp-growers never have to worry about noxious weeds, for which the plant has a 'natural repulsion'; ground over-run by particularly 'virile weeds or grasses' can be reclaimed ('cleansed') for use by a season's planting with hemp, which is then ploughed back into the soil.

The book also mentions that hemp has 'the peculiar property of destroying caterpillars and other insects which prey upon vegetables' and recommends the planting of hemp borders around the vegetable beds. I've never seen that mentioned in a gardening book. (Parenthetically, if you note that as well as all these remarkable properties, hemp makes better quality and longer lasting paper than wood-pulp, *and* yields more per acre than forest, it's hard to avoid the conclusion that the plant is one of God's great gifts to humankind. It would seem that its suppression is not merely a terrible waste, but Agin the Natural Law. Eds.).

LEAF FIBRE

There is really only one leaf fibre suitable for production in temperate climates: New Zealand flax *(Phorium Tenax).* This is a plant with long, flat leaves encircling the base of a straight stem several feet high. It propagates both by seed and by the production of creeping rhizomes (suckers) which branch out in a circle around the plant. Although leaves may be picked after the first year the plant actually takes about three to four years to mature and it seems wise to keep the rhizomes attached until it is three years old. In 1890 the Botanic Garden at Chelsea in London reported that some thirty-six leaves were produced on average in those first three years, each leaf giving approximately one ounce of fibre after extraction.

A few days' retting in stagnant water breaks down the leaf cells sufficiently for an older mangle or wringer to 'squeeze' out the non-fibrous matter. Washing in running water and bleaching in the sun gives a fibre fit for weaving and excellent for cordage and rope. Cultivation requires good soil and protection from frost.

FROM FIBRE TO CLOTH

Turning your mountain of fibre into cloth or cord will generally require it to be spun, although in the case of wool, and other hairs, very warm and pleasant rugs can be woven with unspun fibre.

The usual step preparatory to spinning is *carding* when the fibres are combed to make them parallel and overlapping. 'Carding' is often referred to as 'teasing', after the dried flower of the teazle which

Carding. The two carding combs are drawn across each other.

formed the earliest carding comb. Modern (hand) carders consist of two flat pieces of wood with handles, covered on one side with leather into which rows of thin nails have been inserted and bent towards the handle. They are used above and below the fibres to pull them into line. Unless really fine yarn is required or the fibre is particularly short, carding—particularly in the case of wool—is almost unnecessary once you have mastered the technique of spinning.

◆ *Spinning* This is just as it sounds—the fibres are twisted together so the microscopic protruberances on their surface become interlocked to produce a yarn. The simplest technique for spinning 'mechanically' involves the use of a rotating shaft on to which the yarn is fixed. When the yarn is in line with the shaft (slipping off the end) it is twisted and unspun fibre can be added in as the yarn extends. In its simplest form this 'rotating shaft' can be the vertical axle of a 'drop spindle' consisting of a length of wooden dowel inserted through the middle of a flat

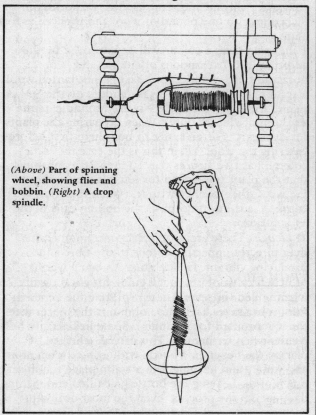

(*Above*) **Part of spinning wheel, showing flier and bobbin.** (*Right*) **A drop spindle.**

wooden disc (see above). The spindle is spun with the thread looped around the top of the shaft, the thread being drawn out as the device is allowed to fall towards the ground. When one section of thread is finished it is then wound on the spindle and the procedure repeated. These two separate actions occur simultaneously in the 'modern' spinning wheel; the 'flier' rotates to give the twist, whilst the bobbin, which is also rotating in the same direction but at a slightly greater speed owing to the relatively smaller diameter of its pulley, takes up the spun thread. The process of spinning really requires two hands, one in front 'pinching' off the already twisted yarn while the other is used to draw out a short

length of the unspun fibre into the thickness required. The front 'pinch' is then released so that the new length twists, the rear hand now performing the 'pinching' function. It's then only a matter of getting your foot to work (to turn the wheel) in an even rhythm independently of the movement of your hands.

The spinning wheel system with its flier and bobbin is only one of two basic techniques used in industrial spinning. The other system derives from the 'spinning jenny' in which the action of the drop spindle is preserved in a mechanized form, the thread moving back and forth between being in line with a rotating shaft and therefore twisting, and being perpendicular to the shaft and hence being wound on. Three famous names from the industrial revolution are associated with the progressive development of spinning based on the latter system: James Hargreaves, Samuel Crompton and Richard Roberts (so the uncritical history books tell) improved mechanical spinning so that the output of

Hargreave's spinning jenny.

yarn was able to meet the needs of the cloth mills. A closer analysis however, shows that the motivation for the mechanization of the spinning process cannot be explained simply by the shortage of yarn. Hargreaves and Crompton both produced machines initially which increased the output of yarn sixteen to twenty-fold yet remained 'skilled' hand-operated, wooden devices, suited to home use. There is ample evidence to suggest that had the home spinners used these machines in place of the normal spinning wheel there would have been an overproduction of yarn. Yet copies made 'illegally' by home spinners were confiscated under the law when large patent royalties were not forthcoming from their owners. The machines installed in the factories were 'second generation' versions, much too heavy and expensive for home use, and requiring no *skilled* operators. Roberts produced a fully 'automated' water driven machine which *needed "no operators at all"*. The process of mechanical evolution has clearly more motives than simple *efficiency* or *productivity*. This was openly stated in advertisements for the Roberts machine and in Andrew Ure's weighty review of the *History of the Cotton Manufacture of Great Britain* (1830). In fact Ure went on to elaborate what he saw as the 'Philosophy of Manufacture' in which he extols the virtues of technological progress because: "Whenever a process requires particular dexterity it can be withdrawn from the *cunning* workman, who is prone to irregularities of all kinds, and placed in charge of a peculiar mechanism, so self-regulating that a *child* may superintend it". He goes on to explain that considerations of this sort have given *"extraordinary stimulus to mechanical science"* and concludes that when "capital enlists science in her service, the refractory hand of labour will always be taught docility". One could easily re-name Ure's *Philosophy of Manufactures* (1835) 'Arguments for an Alternative Technology'.

◆ *Weaving*
'Weaving is the interlacing of two threads, the active *weft* crossing the passive *warp* at right angles. For easy manipulation of the warp and beating-down of the weft, it is essential that the warp threads be kept under tension. All the complexities that have been added to the loom are only to save time or make intricate weaves possible. They do not alter the fundamental function of a loom as a warp-stretcher.'
That beautifully simple description of the elements of weaving comes from *The Techniques of Rug Weaving* by Peter Collingwood (Faber and Faber, London 1968) which justly deserves the cult rating it is achieving. It is an indispensable element in any serious attempt at weaving. For the less serious, the price (around £8 UK) probably prohibits purchase but it's certainly worth a trip to the nearest library.

There are myriads of texts on weaving and it would be ridiculous to attempt to summarize the detailed information contained in them. However, even the best books do have a tendency to assume that equipment is merely a problem of ascertaining the type of weaving desired, and notifying the nearest loom supplier. It *is* possible to be more resourceful. Any rigid frame can serve the purpose of stretching the warp. An old bed frame, a large picture frame, even an old deck chair, would suffice. Try using existing furniture; for almost a year I wove on the underneath of a couch using two sticks placed across opposite pairs of legs to give me the frame, raising the couch end-on gave a good vertical 'fold-away' loom—a simple answer to the problem of fitting a loom into a small room. A 'frame' loom is excellent for making rugs; you can use twine for the warp and almost any thick yarn for the weft (old rags cut into endless strips make very warm and hard-wearing rugs when used as weft).

The only other tip worth mentioning (because most books don't) is that you will be extremely unlucky if you live in an area without a local *Guild of Weavers, Spinners and Dyers,* full of people who live, eat and sleep, weaving and spinning, have lanolin in their blood and skeins of information at their fingertips. Do not move without contacting their secretary or attending one of their (usually frequent) meetings. Write to the *Association of Guilds of Weavers, Spinners and Dyers,* c/o Mrs M.J. Emery, 64 Holly Hill, Bassett, Southampton, Hants, UK, for the address of your local branch.

DYEING

Now lastly for a little colour (naturally). Table 1 gives a list of the more common plants (and one insect—cochineal) which can be used to dye wool. Unlike 'chemical' dyes most of the 'natural' dyes will not directly colour the fibre, it being necessary first to *mordant* the fibre. In this process some intermediate chemical is introduced, which has the dual properties of combining with the dye colour and adhering to the fibres. Mordanting is as important as dyeing: a badly mordanted skein will dye badly.

In table 1 only two mordants are referred to, alum and chrome. To mordant with alum use 3oz of alum and 1oz of cream of tartar to one pound of wool. Dissolve the alum and the cream of tartar in cold water and place it on a slow fire. When the liquid is warm add the wool, bringing it slowly to the boil. Simmer for an hour and then lift out the wool. It can now be used immediately for dyeing, but it is often better if the wet wool is left for a day or so.

For the chrome mordant use ¼oz of potassium bichromate to one pound of wool and proceed as for alum.

In some cases a colour will be improved by the addition of 6-7 teaspoons of vinegar and 1/6 oz of potassium dichromate, to the alum-mordanted wool after it has been dyed. This is denoted by the '++' sign in the table. (A single + is used to indicate the addition of vinegar only). When preparing the plants for dyeing it is often easier to boil them first before entering the wool. When this is the case the 'time' column has two figures (eg '10 then 20'), meaning that the plant was boiled for ten minutes without the wool, then twenty with it. (When there is 'alum++' a third 'time' gives the boiling time in the ++ solution).

◆ *Lichens* These are *substantive* or non-mordant dyes directly imparting colour to the fibre and producing vibrant, fast colours. An equal weight of lichen to wool is a rough guide for good results when boiled for several hours (placing the lichen in a muslin bag saves having to comb out the pieces when the wool is used for spinning). Some lichens give best results when fermented. This can be acheived by placing the lichen in a bottle with urine (or ammonia and water) and keeping it in a warm place for about one month. Leaving the bottle half-filled and shaking daily assists the process. Even the most ordinary rock-covering grey lichen (which gives a brown colour when boiled) can produce a beautifully vivid magenta or puce when it has been fermented. It is generally the crustaceous lichens (commonly found on rocks at about 1,000 feet) which respond to fermentation. Even for simple non-fermented dyeing the colour of the dye will often bear little resemblance to the colour of the lichen. For instance *Parmelia omphalodes,* which is a tight green leafy-looking lichen which grows on rocks above 2,000 feet, gives a rust red when boiled for two hours. Experiment with your local lichens. Try it, you'll lichen it.

Chris Ryan

Table 1 (for 1lb of wool)

Material F = flowers L = leaves	Colour	Mordant	Volume or weight material	Time boiled (approximate)
Bedstraw roots	Crimson	chrome	1 lb	1 hr
Birch L	Yellow-tan	alum	2 galls	soak 12 hrs then 1 hr 30 mins
Bracken buds	Green	alum	1 lb	2 hrs simmer
Camomile F	Buff	alum	7 quarts dry	30 mins
	Gold	chrome	" " "	30 mins
	Khaki	alum++	" " "	30 mins then 10 mins
Goldenrod F	Brass	chrome	2 galls	15 mins then 20 mins
	Yellow Brown	alum++	" "	15 mins then 20 mins then 10 mins++
Marigold F	Brass	chrome	1½ galls dry	15 mins then 20 mins
	Yellow tan	alum++	" " "	15 mins then 20 mins
Onion skins	Gold	alum	10 ozs	10 mins then 1 hr
Pine cones	Red-yellow	alum	1½ lbs	3 hrs
Privet L	Gold	chrome	2½ galls dry	soak 12 hrs boil 20 mins then 30 mins
Ragwort F	Yellow	alum	1 lb	15 mins then 1 hr
Sunflower F	Gold	alum++	1½ quarts dry	20 mins then 30 mins then 10 mins++
Weld	Bright Yellow	alum	10 ozs	1 hr then 1½ hrs (salt added to bath enriches colour)
(Whole plant except root)	Mustard	chrome	10 ozs	1 hr then 1½ hrs

Imported Dyestuffs

Walnut husks	Brown	none	2 galls	soak 1 hr boil 50 mins then 30 mins
	Dark-brown	alum	" "	soak 1 hr boil 50 mins
	Even darker	alum++	" "	soak 1 hr boil 50 mins then 10 mins
Tea L	Rose tan	alum	8 ozs	15 mins then 30 mins
	Light brown	chrome	8 ozs	15 mins then 30 mins
Coffee beans	Brown	alum	1¾ lbs	20 mins then 30 mins
	Yellow tan	chrome	" "	20 mins then 30 mins
Cochineal (extract)	Rose pink to red	alum	1 oz powder	soak 1 hr boil 15 mins then 1½ hrs
	Purple	chrome+	2½ ozs powder	soak 1 hr boil 15 mins then 1½ hrs
	Flag red	See note	3½ ozs powder	*Note* Soak cochineal in 3½ ozs of cream of tartar; boil 10 mins, strain, add to one cup water ¼ oz stannous chloride and 2 ozs nitric acid. Put in wool, boil 1½ hrs. Stir constantly.
Fustic	Gold	chrome	½ oz	30 mins only
	Yellow	alum++	½ oz	30 mins then 10 mins++
Indigo	Dark Blue	See note		*Note* Indigo does not require a mordant. It has to be purchased from a stockist and the directions for the particular type of indigo should be followed. Powdered indigo is not soluble in water and treatment used to get into a soluble solution is the secret of obtaining good colour. Look for old recipes in books and libraries. The recipe for the royal blue/purple colour that led to indigo replacing woad is a forgotten secret!
Madder root	Lacquer red	alum	8 ozs	soak 12 mins boil 45 mins
	Orange red	chrome	8 ozs	soak 12 mins
Logwood	Purple/blue	alum	3 ozs chips or 6 ozs extract	1 hr

Brief notes
(those marked * fade. Amounts and times need experimentation)

Dockroot*	Yellow/brown	alum
	Chestnut	chrome
Elderberries***	Soft purple	alum
	" "	chrome
Tomatoes**	Grey	alum
	Blue/grey	chrome
Foxglove (flower tops)	Lemon	alum
	Gold	chrome
Flax flowers (in bud)	Beige	alum
	Chestnut	chrome
Hop leaves	Cream	alum
	Green beige	chrome
Acorns (stand in water several days)	Buff	alum
	Olive	chrome

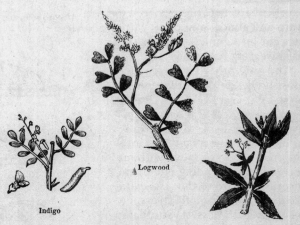

Logwood

Indigo

Madder

Tyre shoes

The properties needed for shoes are: durability, pliability, waterproofness, with a certain amount of breathing. Leather and rubber tyres fulfill these demands adequately. For self-made shoes, it is vital to have simplicity of design, availability of materials, and basic tools.

Tools: sharp knife, scissors, hammer, pliers, nails — brass (not escutcheon pins) or carpet tacks (best coated) non-water-soluble glue, heavy-duty needles, thread (waxed), eyelet hole puncher — size 5, waterproofing wax.

Materials: leather (15p-20p per sq ft at the moment), alternatively synthetic leather from car dumps, tyre treads from car dumps/garages.

Boot eyelets, ¼'' rivets, buckles and laces are all useful.

The cost of a pair of shoes should range from nothing to 70p.

TYRE CUTTING

Choose a tyre with a wide tread to avoid the problems of corners. Using a sharp knife, cut the sides off the tyre close to the tread, and then across it, leaving you with a long strip of tread, enough for 3 pairs of shoes.

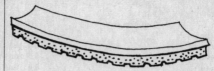

It is easier to cut through the surface by degrees rather than trying to saw through it. The discarded sides can be used to resole bought shoes.

Mark around each foot in turn and add ¼'' to the perimeter to account for width of nail heads and leather uppers. Cut out the shapes, closing in at the instep. For better comfort glue a piece of leather to the upper side and trim close.

The sole is now prepared.

CUT CLOSE TO INSTEP FOR BETTER HOLD

UPPERS PATTERNS

Sample description of one-piece uppers (always add ¼'' to perimeter for fixing to soles).

Mark only the unwanted side of a skin, using your foot as a model, cut a narrow ankle slot out from an edge of a skin, unwanted side up. Slip your right foot in, pat the leather down and mark around your foot. Add ¼'' perimeter for the thickness of nail heads and cut out. Turn over the leather pattern and it will fit the left foot, right side up. Copy a reverse facsimile for the right foot. Decorate with pieces of leather or with leather dye.

EXTRA OVERLAP AROUND HEEL

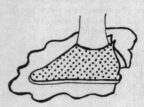

LEFT FOOT UPPERS. AT THIS STAGE DECORATE ACROSS WITH THIN STRIPS, SHAPES OF LEATHER GLUED DOWN. (LATER NAILED STITCHED WITH UPPERS TO SOLES).

(c) One-piece, front-seam shoe.

RIGHT FOOT

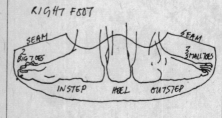

SEAM   SEAM
BIG TOES   3 SMALL TOES
INSTEP   HEEL   OUTSTEP

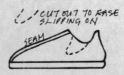

CUT OUT TO EASE SLIPPING ON

SEAM

Other Pattern Ideas
(a) Basic pattern

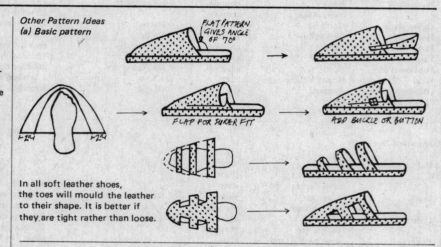

FLAT PATTERN GIVES ANGLE OF 70°

FLAP FOR SURER FIT   ADD BUCKLE OR BUTTON

In all soft leather shoes, the toes will mould the leather to their shape. It is better if they are tight rather than loose.

(b) Measure perimeter around sole of foot, desired height of heel, and length from toe to ankle.

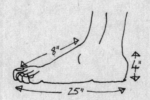

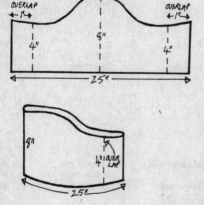

OVERLAP 1''   OVERLAP 1''
4''   8''   4''
25''

8''   4'' OVERLAP
25''

Mark out this general shape, with ¼'' added along the perimeter, cut out and bring the two 4'' edges together, overlapping so they meet, and stitch. Perimeter should still be 25''.

Affix to sole, and fold either of these two ways:

TAKE IN AT HEEL

STRAP AND BUCKLE AROUND HEEL

STRAP AND BUCKLE OVER BOOT

FOR THIS TYPE THE SOLE SHOULD BE LONGER/ POINTED TO ACCOMODATE FOLDS

FIXING UPPERS TO SOLES

Before fixing the uppers to the soles, the uppers should be in the flat state, with a ¼" perimeter, with any desired decoration (dye can be applied after). In most cases, seams should not be stitched until toward the end of the operation, for last minute adjustments.

First check that the uppers only give about ¼" overlap below the tyre sole when your foot is in position. Nail around the outstep, away from the seam, in most cases the seam is at the back, therefore nail until the toes are reached. Check fitting again, cutting off excess. Nail around the toes and down the instep (remember to glue as you go to keep water out), drawing close in at the instep for hold. Fit for the seam and stitch up with or without overlap, at exaggerated angle for grip, approx. 75°. Nail down around heels.

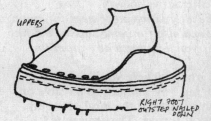

UPPERS

RIGHT FOOT OUTSTEP NAILED DOWN

Nails must be longer than the width of the tyre and leathers. At intervals the shoe is turned over, and the excess nail is hammered into the tyre, thereby acting as a hook, and deep enough to be protected from the ground.

SOLE-LEATHER
MESH
TYRE

The same procedure is taken for stitching, but through the side of the tyre, hitching beneath the mesh. Stitching through rubber tyres is labourious and slow.

Other methods

Note sandal suggestions above. Fixing uppers without other materials. Using a chisel cut slits in appropriate places through tyre, and then cut out edges to sink straps in (protection). Insert all the straps, pull tight over foot, bring ends up to meet, and cut off ¼" longer. This ¼" is cut into a button, and slipped through a small slit in its own strap. The same procedure can be used with long straps to make cross-over sandals, the buttons being used to secure the ends.

The weakest part of these shoes/treads are the leather uppers. Otherwise I could guarantee them for tens of thousands of miles before you needed a retread. Good luck with your treads . . . man.

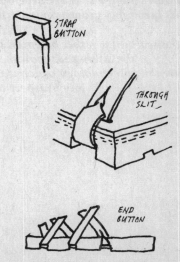

STRAP BUTTON

THROUGH SLIT

END BUTTON

NICK MELLOR

Nick Mellor

INTERVIEW
Peter van Dresser

*When I called on Peter van Dresser late in 1973, the
energy crisis had just penetrated public
consciousness. Throughout the United States the
word 'energy' was on everyone's lips, and the
bandwagon of alternative energy sources was filling
up with a motley crowd of 'eco-freaks', university
departments, small-time entrepreneurs and spies
from the oil companies and other big corporations.
But in the thirties, when Peter made solar-heated
domestic water heaters, and even just after the war,
when he built solar-heated houses and equipped
them with wind-driven generators, he was a lone
and often criticised pioneer: no one had given
thought to the prospect of oil wells drying up or
the demand for energy increasing exponentially.
Thermal pollution would have sounded like science
fiction. Van Dresser's pioneering efforts to use the
sun's energy were part of a transcending vision and
philosophy: he saw naturally-defined geographic
regions which might become self-sufficient through
the skills and intelligence of their people, grouped
into communities on a human scale. He perceived
his own country's 'under-developed' areas absorbing
its inevitably growing population as an alternative
to ever-bigger cities.
I asked him whether he entertained any hope that
the alternative movement, particularly the
alternative technology which was part of it, offered
any prospect of changing society.*

Not at its present level of intensity; I live in hope
that a genuine psychic change may be operating
seriously on society as a whole, and that the present
gropings towards an alternative society are the
forerunners of a serious movement. But from my
experience with it I find it confused, fragmented
and self-defeating. I'm talking about the communes
and drop outs. They're not genuine. They are
pseudo, still linked with the establishment in ways
which pretty well neutralise their pretentions to be
exponents of the alternative society.

◆ *You criticise the alternative movement for aiming
at self-sufficiency and also for being too locked into
the system. Aren't you denying it any room for
manoeuvre?*

There is a middle ground where you don't pretend
at self-sufficiency, but rely as much as possible on
the resources and products of the local economy.
That's the distinction I make. The drop outs I
criticise most are the ones that *pretend* at self-
sufficiency—living in a wigwam and all the rest of it-
yet going to Safeways once a month for their
proteins. This is just a destructive fantasy. The viable
middle ground is a slow evolutionary process in
which each year you try to reduce your dependence
on a greater economy and try to utilise the products
of your region more effectively. You try to integrate.
You try to strengthen the village community and the
regional economy. Phoney self-sufficiency gets in the
way of evolving this *localised* self-sufficiency, so
important for a viable future.

◆ *Would you rule out the use of, say, windmills, or
piping, or other products which might have been
produced several hundred miles away?*

Certainly not. Even the most fanatical self-
sufficiency addict uses an axe and a shovel, and they
are both products of highly technological linkages.
What I object to are the linkages to supermarkets for
protein—which incidentally involves the constant
use of the automobile. You know, we are obsessed
with the need for mobility, not for functional
reasons, but psychologically we just can't stay in one
place. It's ridiculous to use this most destructive and
complicated of modern industrial products for
inadequate reasons. But most minimally, if there's
no other means of transport, it is all right. A carefully
rationed old 'pick-up', kept in reasonably good
shape and used infrequently, is better than the drop
out's fantasy of a horse which eats as much as five
or six cows, and in this country is very ecologically
destructive.

◆ *You've put the case for decentralisation as one
remedy for the sickness of society. Do you envisage
an eventual migration from cities to the
countryside?*

Some time ago I became dissatisfied with
'decentralisation' as a description of this philosophy;
'*recentralisation*' may be better, for we need to form

and recentralise life around urban centres and communities on a more human scale. The way out of the problem of the existing huge urban conglomerates seem to me to be an evolutionary process over a period of decades which would not be a physical moving of people from big cities out to the country, but would change the institutional environment which moulds our society. This would mean that the whole hierarchy of smaller communities would regain their economic viability and begin to re-habilitate themselves in economic terms. So at first there would be a halting of the exodus from provincial and rural areas to the great cities, and a relative shifting of growth rate in favour of smaller centres. After several decades the relative magnitude of the great centres would diminish in favour of a fully developed 'hinterland'—as it is erroneously called—we'd see a recolonisation of country districts so that they could be reclaimed gradually and gently, skilfully and artistically.

However, the chances of our society being able to conceive of such a programme and carry it through systematically over a period of decades are very slight. It is a utopian hope, but I still feel it's the only way out of the terrible impasse our civilization is getting into. But any notion of *wholesale* resettlement of people from New York and Chicago to satellite towns is total fantasy.

Another alternative of course—and what a lot of people secretly hope for—is a rapid breakdown of the whole system and total chaos to solve the problem. But it wouldn't *solve* the problem—simply alter conditions in a violent way.

◆ *How long do you think the system can survive without collapse?*
Now there's a question—I'd say thirty years , for fun! I think the system will make constant adjustments—all kinds of 'ersatz' ways of making people do with less and crowding them into less space. They will keep us going for a long time, despite a gradual deterioration in the condition of life. One hopes that by taking thought and statesmanship we could avoid that kind of solution, and for that reason it is very precious. But it still is only a germ—not even an embryo.

The particular strategy I'm interested in is concerned with relating this undercurrent of feeling to logical thought, bringing it to the surface in rational terms as being a scientific and sound solution of our problems. I want to make the whole subject understandable, rather than a mystique.

I don't like the term 'alternative technology' very much: it reflects the American hope that gadgets will solve problems. Much more is needed—the whole alternative rationale for restructuring society. Technology is only a portion of this, and to emphasise it misses a very large part of what has to be thought about and done. I feel that to speak as if technology has a drive of its own is not defensible. Technology has been moulded very much by *human* institutions and drives, and I would argue that we have to change our motivations and our social and economic relationships, and that in the process technology will be evolved to satisfy real human needs. If you throw the burden on technology as an imaginary entity on its own, as I say, you run the danger of the good old American habit of trying to solve problems with gadgets—even though the gadgets may be solar energy and wind generators. We must be wary of leaping on the bandwagon of alternative technology as a panacea: I know of wealthy drop outs who have bought an expensive wind generator and set it up on top of a dome while still running enormous four-wheel drive vehicles which use a hundred times more energy every day than the wind generator delivers. The wind generator is then purely a symbol: the lifestyle that goes with it has not changed to validate it.

◆ *What do you see as standing in the way of desirable social change?*
We have built a Frankenstein monster of industrial and commercial relationships which is almost totally running our lives. It derives its motivation from our acceptance of it and our failure to conceptualise any other value system. A very subtle subject. The change I'm talking about—I don't know how to describe it—a psycho-cultural change? I wouldn't call it just a spiritual change, but it would certainly have to include what are called spiritual values.

◆ *Do you think that the change we are talking about is possible within a capitalist system?*
The typical modern Liberal is inclined to think that the alternative to capitalism is an enlightened Marxist or communist system, and this I don't believe. I think that the change is no more or less possible under a capitalist system than under bureaucratic communism. Yes, I think that a new type of economic relationship is necessary. I incline towards mutual libertarian or anarchistic political solutions as the nearest to opening up the possibility of achieving this creative, free society. Capitalism, as I see it, is the monopoly of the monetisation of credit—a highly efficient mechanism for concentrating power and wealth, and one which has to be abandoned in favour of monetary relationships that don't have this built-in monopolistic power.

Experiments in community are possible under the kind of government we have now: the greatest obstacles to them are not capitalism but the internal psychology of ourselves. To blame failure entirely on capitalism is kind of 'copping out' and dodging the real issue. This is not a defence of monopoly capitalism, but I can't visualise how the difficulties would be less with any of the other existing systems.

Patrick Rivers

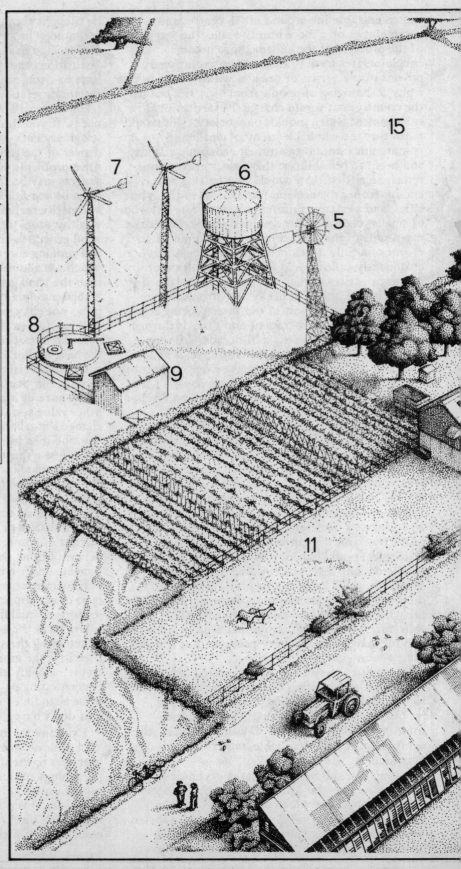

VISION 3/AUTONOMOU

Intended for rural or semi-rural areas. These dwellings would be independent of grid services. Some services (waste treatment, some food, space and water heating) would be provided at the household level, others (electricity, water, cooking gas, some food) at the community level, where economies of scale make shared facilities cheaper. The houses are based on Brenda Vale's 'Autonomous House' design, described further in part IV of the Autonomy section.

1 Solar roof
2 Conservatory
3 Vegetables
4 Savonius rotor (pumping)
5 Windpump
6 Water tower
7 Wind-generators
8 Methane digestor
9 Power-regulation, battery store
10 Byre and equipment — store
11 Animal pasture
12 Pond
13 Garage
14 Fruit bushes
15 Collective services paddock.

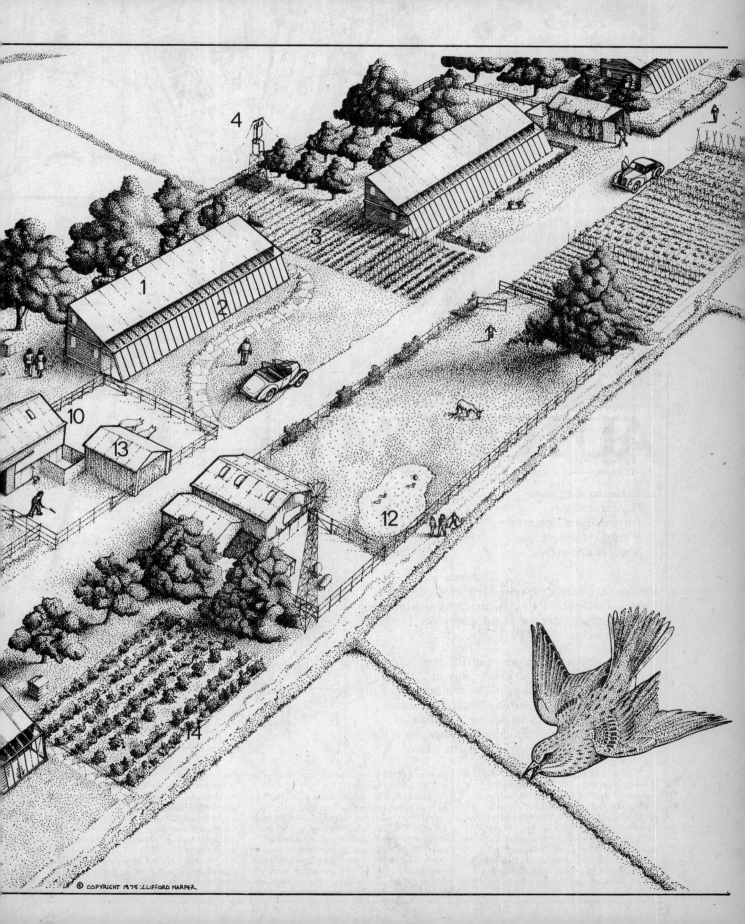

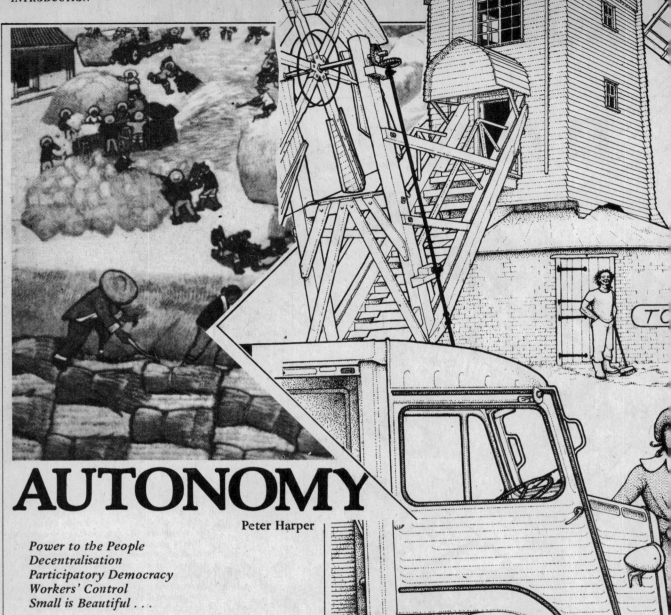

AUTONOMY

Peter Harper

Power to the People
Decentralisation
Participatory Democracy
Workers' Control
Small is Beautiful . . .

. . . between
the lines are values expressed repeatedly in this
book: of self-generated activity, distributed responsibility, control from the bottom upwards. In short,
of *autonomy*.

Autonomy is a vague and fruitful idea. It has
many ambiguities — it can too easily hide 'I'm all
right, Jack' escapism and deliberate disregard of the
public good — but something like it is necessary
to counterbalance the insensitive gigantism of
modern societies and rekindle the sense of ability
to initiate, create, control, and participate.

How far can autonomy be taken? Perhaps
if we could achieve the kind of political
autonomy implied in the phrase 'workers'
self-management', that would be enough to
be getting on with? But this may need to be
complemented by some kind of economic
autonomy, such as that implied by the phrase,
much used in China and Tanzania, 'Self-
reliance'. For some, even this is not enough,
and they seek to underpin political and economic autonomy by seeking autonomy in the

basic resources needed for survival. That is to
say, in 'self-sufficiency'.

The notion of self-sufficiency and the idea
of resource-autonomous economic units may
seem naive, but it has had a special attraction
for critics of industrial technology, because
it seems to solve a number of problems at
once. The use of local and renewable resources
in a cyclical rather than linear-flow economy
reduces depletion of non-renewable resources
and environmental impact. There would be no

need to exploit others, nor would such a unit
be susceptible to economic exploitation or
interference. The alienation caused by remote,
fragmented, inhuman production systems
would be overcome by the involvement and
direct participation of both producers and
consumers, using 'convivial', human-scale
technologies.

Unfortunately the very ambitiousness of
such schemes leads to their dilution. In the
19th century, the spirit of thoroughgoing

业 学 大 寨

MORROW

autonomy aimed at networks of utopian communities, but in spite of occasional successes resolved itself ultimately in the homestead and 'five acres and a cow'. Things have not changed much. While many dream that sophisticated but responsive and humane technology could now allow us to realise the ideal of collective autonomy, what is now taking shape on the drawing boards, in sub-urban backyards, Welsh valleys and the hills of New Mexico, is the autonomous house, 3 bedr., all mod. con., built to reduce dependency on external supplies of energy, utility services, and to a lesser extent, food.

Autonomous houses have become one of the most conspicuous symbols of 'alternative technology'. As virtual zoos of alternative gadgetry, they provide a convenient summary of the state of the art, and they show how different small-scale technologies can operate more-or-less elegantly together in an integrated system. For these reasons, autonomous houses are the focal point for this section of the book. They are not to be dismissed out of hand; the first steps have to be taken, and we may have much to learn from these experi-

ments. On the other hand, autonomous houses may be the first steps of a false trail. They need some kind of critical assessment. The non-technical questions need to be asked that so rarely find their way into print:

How far can economic and resource autonomy practically be taken on a small scale?

Could it ever become widespread — without, on the one hand, subsisting on potatoes and welfare payments in autonomous caves, or on the other hand, being subsidised by research grants or the private incomes of gentleman conservationists?

What about production? Who makes all the autonomous equipment in the first place? Can there be such things as 'autonomous factories'?

Should autonomy be simple and frugal, like a peasant smallholding (which is highly autonomous) or costly and complex, like a manned space-station (which is also highly 'autonomous')?

Does autonomy merely pander to individualism and competitiveness, leading to 'Private affluence and public squalor'?

Does autonomy benefit only those who undertake it, or could it benefit society as a whole? What if everybody did it?

These questions crop up throughout the

fairly lengthy text which follows. There are eight parts. The first examines the possible scope of resource autonomy, and places the autonomous dwelling-unit in its proper (and limited) context. Parts II and III are mainly technical and describe various features of autonomous units. Part IV presents a number of proposed designs, (referred to throughout the text by numbers preceded by a letter: B3, D2 etc). Part V concerns the economics of autonomous units, and ends with a discussion of economies of scale. This introduces the last part of the section which focuses on communal-scale units. Part VI contains designs and Part VII puts forward two proposals for semi-autonomous communities, one rural, one urban.

The section is therefore a mixture of description, analysis, polemic and fantasy. Attempts to keep these decently apart have failed. That is the way the subject seems to be. Reality Rules OK.

AUTONOMY

I   THE LIMITS OF MATERIAL AUTONOMY

Consider Figure 1: a house which generates its own energy, collects its own water, treats its own wastes and grows its own food. The idea of such 'autonomous servicing' for houses first started in response to 'ecological' problems of resource depletion and environmental damage associated with providing household services in more conventional ways. But there were other implications too. For many people, autonomous houses represented the technical realisation of the political or existential autonomy that is one of the basic themes of this book: not just having legal or social control over one's destiny but having one's hands directly on the hardware. Some went even further and embraced autonomous servicing as a means of total self-sufficiency that absolved them from any obligation to the rest of society. Such notions still persist, and it is important to make clear just how autonomous servicing fits into wider concepts of autonomy, and in which aspects of our daily lives autonomy is technically feasible, economically rational, and socially desirable.

Different levels of autonomy and collectivity must be distinguished. A group may be collective with respect to an individual yet autonomous with respect to a larger group. Autonomy does not necessarily mean *private.* What we really need is a new pattern of autonomy/collectivity that counters the separation of public production and private consumption into completely distinct aspects of life done at different times and in different places. Obviously there are many other preconditions for solving the problems of post-industrial capitalism, but of all the 57 varieties of socialism that might replace it, radical 'autonomists' (let us call them that) would aim for those in which collectivity incorporates involvement and control from the bottom up; and autonomy implies also responsibility, solidarity, and belonging. A crucial part of this new pattern would be the revival of economic activity at the level of the *local community,* which has been bled dry during the course of industrial development. Certain aspects of consumption would be made more collective, certain aspects of production would be made more autonomous, and a far greater economic role would be played by the community. The idea is one of *co-operative autonomy.*

How would this affect economic life? Which spheres of productive activity might be better autonomised, which collectivised, and which left as they are? Consider five categories of basic requirements:
Communications services: roads, mails, telephones, TV etc.
Social services: medicine, education, legal aid, repairs etc.
Domestic goods: (a) large capital kind: house, furniture, car, cooker, sewing machine etc; (b) smaller day-to-day kind: utensils, washing powder, clothes, books, plaster ducks etc.
Utility services: fuels, electricity, gas, water, waste disposal.
Food: as basic stuffs or processed (bread, canned food, TV dinners etc).

Typically, these are all produced centrally. Could it be changed? Communications for a start are intrinsically shared, and make no sense at the private level, although community transport, information and entertainment media could meet a great part of the needs (see **Vision** No 6). Social services could be (and are) organised at the community level (eg free schools, creches, libraries, medical centres, advice, repairs etc). In all these cases, equipment and supplies would come from the public sector. 'Private' autonomy here is out of the question.

Turning to domestic goods, there is considerable scope for community, or even household, autonomy in finishing or assembling, given the basic equipment and materials. Autonomy can be taken quite a long way back along the trail of added value, but the trail leads ultimately to the public sector. A community may for example do its own baking and become 'autonomous' with respect to bread. It could go further and grind its own flour, but could hardly produce its own wheat. It might do its own building, furniture-making, printing, weaving; have its own foundry, dairy, garage, kiln, tannery and glass workshop. These would permit autonomy with respect to *processing,* and hence to control of work, but even apart from the initial capital stock, would need continual supplies of sand, cement, wood, steel, non-ferrous metals, glass, inks, paper, clay, leather, fibres and so on. Furthermore there are certain basic consumer goods that it would be absurd to make by any other method than mass production. They are all around us:

pencil	screws
thermometer	paint
bottle teat	window glass
light bulb	polystyrene insulation
matches	clock
string	tampon
sewing machine	disinfectant
spectacles	preserving jar
needles	. . . etc

The pattern of demand made on centralised production might be very different, but basic dependency on it would remain.

Consider now utility services and food. Here the possibilities for household and community autonomy are stronger. It seems to be far easier to conjure them 'out of the air' (in some cases literally) than is the case with durable goods, once the initial capital is provided, which of course must again be brought in from outside at the beginning. The rationality of massive investment in alternative servicing and food obviously depends on opinions about future supplies — particularly in a vulnerable trading economy such as Britain's, — but if the gloomier scenarios prove close to the truth, greater autonomy at various levels may be inevitable, and could have profound consequences for social life. The argument goes like this:

High food yields are maintained only by declining supplies of fossil fuels and fertilisers; by imported feedstuffs; and at some cost in environmental deter-

Fig 1. An archetype: A miniature ecosystem in the country, sustained by sun, wind, rain, muck and muscle.

1 Solar roof captures sunlight to heat water
2 Rain water collected for home use. Wind powers windmill
3 Water purified and stored
4 Decomposition of wastes produces methane gas for stove in house
5 Water from treatment systems flows to fish pond and vegetable garden
6 Vegetable garden
7 Animals provide nourishment

ioration. Even then output does not meet the demand. But continued imports of food cannot be guaranteed indefinitely. In Britain at least, greater yields per acre need to be achieved, by methods which do not require high inputs of energy and artificial fertilisers. This can only be done by relatively labour-intensive methods, and favours a gradual redistribution of population into rural areas. Meanwhile, to meet long-term energy needs (unless the nuclear gamble comes off better than expected) we should plan to meet a growing proportion of our energy demands from renewable sources such as sun, wind and biofuels. These are diffuse and distribute themselves. On the whole it makes no sense to elaborately concentrate them and distribute them all over again. They are not much use for industrial purposes, or for domestic use in cities, but are ideal for rural dwellings. Once again a major shift to these alternative sources favours redistribution of population. Similar arguments apply to water supply, waste treatment, and nitrogen recycling.

This general conclusion about redistribution of population is reinforced by the possibilities of small-scale production and social services discussed earlier. There should be many more factories and workshops in the countryside, serving the needs of the local population and making use of agricultural by-products. Back in the cities, possibilities for increasing food production are considerable (see **Vision Nos 1 and 4**).

There are, then, severe limits to the possibilities of autonomy in basic material needs. Given post-neolithic habits of consumption, attempts to achieve total autonomy are misconceived. In many areas less rather than more autonomy is desirable. Yet the overwhelming dominance of centralised production can only be countered by extremely practical — as well as ideological — forms of autonomy. These are to be achieved, not just by defiant acts of individual DIY, but by the growth of community production wherever it is feasible. At the moment the growing-point in technical autonomy is in the utility services, and for the purposes of this section of the book, they constitute a case-study for basic autonomy which can later be expanded to other spheres. The discussion starts off with the case of servicing for the rural or semi-rural house-and-garden; then extends the principles to rural and urban communities, and suggests ways in which, far from the separatism of some of its adherents, technical autonomy can contribute to the well-being of the wider society: Co-operative autonomy.

II MEANS OF AUTONOMY

There are logically three ways of reducing dependency on external sources of supply. Perhaps the most obvious is simply reducing personal consumption, or lowering standards of comfort, convenience, amenity, etc. I shall call this *Making Do*. The second is to make better use of what is available, getting an equal benefit for less input, for example by using fluorescent instead of incandescent lamps. I shall call this category *Clever Ideas*. The third way is to find *Alternative Resources*, for example wind energy to drive a generator and produce electricity. Typically, autonomous units reduce dependency by a mixture of all three. Each has both *technical* and *social* aspects, although naturally social ones dominate the first category and technical ones the last category. They are categories of convenience and not always easy to separate in practice.

ALTERNATIVE RESOURCES

This is the largest and most conspicuous category of 'means'. It involves mostly technical issues and comprises most of the cliches of alternative technology gadgetry. Before I describe the various systems themselves I must define a number of terms and introduce some notations which I will use throughout this section.

An autonomous unit is the basic system under consideration, and different parts of it, for example

the electricity system, the waste-treatment system and so on, are called *sub-systems*. In any autonomous unit there tend to be three kinds of elements: *collectors*, for example wind generators, roofs for rainwater; *stores*, for example, heat storage tanks, batteries; and *converters*, for example methane digestors or water-recycling systems. Sometimes a sub-system may have all three kinds of element, but this is unusual. *Appliances* such as light bulbs or gas stoves constitute a fourth kind of element, but these are the same as in a conventional system.

Total autonomy in all services, food and energy is unusual. Units are usually supplied by a mixture of four types of source (or, in the case of waste disposal, sinks). These four, gradually approximating 'pure autonomy' are:

Mains: supplied more or less continuously from large-scale central plant (electricity, gas, water, sewerage)

Stored: supplied intermittently, ultimately again from central plant (fuel oil, paraffin, bottled gas, refuse collection, bought food)

Local: supplied from on-site or within walking distance of the unit using resources characteristic of the locality rather than universally available (wood, peat, small-scale hydropower; spring or well water; septic tank, earth closet, land drain, garden produce, wild foods)

Ambient: in principle universally available (sun, low-grade heat from air, soil or water, wind, precipitation, water vapour, greenhouse and hydroponic produce).

ELECTRICITY

Electricity, unlike food or sanitation, is not a fundamental need, but it has become a kind of *lingua franca* for energy, allowing one form to be conveniently converted into others. Many functions which are normally performed by electricity could be handled in other ways (lighting, refrigeration, tools, washing machines, mixers, sewing machines) or in many cases dispensed with altogether. Only certain rather small loads actually *need* electricity (radio, TV, record player) and these can be run off accumulators or dry cells if necessary. However, many of these appliances have become part of the standard way of life in industrial societies, and most of them are specifically built for electrical operation. For these reasons, designers of autonomous units rarely feel they can ignore electricity altogether. Either they make provision for generating it on-site, or else they specify (or assume) mains connection, especially where other parts of the system themselves depend on electricity.

Electricity can be generated by direct conversion of fuels via the fuel cell, or direct from sunlight by photoelectric devices, but these are not yet economic for use on a large scale (see 'Sunshine Superpower' by Robert Vale). The only practical method at the moment is by kinetic energy driving a generator or alternator. This energy may in rare cases be derived from water power (see 'Essentially Co-operative Energy' by George Woolston) or from a stationary heat-engine (see 'Cast Iron Power' by Kit Pedler), but the overwhelming choice in autonomous units is a wind-driven rotor. An encyclopaedic typology

of rotors is given in Derek Taylor's article, 'Natural, Endless, Free'. The typical basic circuit for the electrical sub-system of an autonomous unit is shown in Fig 4.

Output varies a great deal with different windspeeds, and a voltage regulator is used to make the best use of this variable supply. At average windspeeds, the loads are supplied directly from the generator. When output exceeds demand, the batteries are charged, or when it greatly exceeds demand and the batteries are full, it can be used for larger loads which are normally not feasible, the commonest being a resistance heater in the solar heat-storage tank. When the output of the generator falls below the level of demand, current is drawn from the batteries. 'Normal' domestic consumption would require an extremely large rotor and a great deal of storage capacity, which would be difficult and expensive on a domestic scale. Uses of electricity are therefore usually restricted in autonomous units to essentials such as lighting, small appliances and pumps: an annual demand of about 1200 kWh, with a wind generator of under 2kW capacity. Such a small system generally produces low-voltage direct current, and extra equipment is needed to convert to high-voltage AC.

Costs vary in different circumstances, but wind-generated electricity with battery storage is likely to cost over five times as much per kilowatt-hour as grid electricity. This may change as grid prices rise, or if rotor, generator or battery costs fall. Nevertheless an economical and reliable wind-electric system needs a good windy site, low demand, careful use, occasional maintenance, considerable storage capacity or some kind of back-up

system. In a sheltered site, a high tower will be necessary. The cost of this may be reduced somewhat by building it on to the structure of the unit (eg Figs A2, A3, A4, D1, E4) but there are potential problems of vibration and noise. These have yet to be properly assessed, as has the matter of rotor blades shattering in a storm and slicing through the lover and his lass in the bedroom below.

SPACE HEATING

In cold or temperate climates, space heating accounts for the largest amount of energy consumed over a year in a typical house, but the *density* of heat needed is low compared with other energy needs — about 100 watts per square metre. This is about the same density as solar energy, on average, so there is some logic in trying to bring the two together. A large solar collector and heat store are usually the core of the heating system in an autonomous unit, supplemented by heat pumps, excess wind energy, wood, or bought fuel as a back-up, together with very high standards of insulation.

Solar heating systems can be either *passive* or *active*. In the passive types the collector and the store are the same, usually a massive glazed wall (see 'Sunshine Superpower' by Robert Vale). Essentially they even-out heat variations over short periods and are ideal for heating in climates with cold but clear winters. Elsewhere they are relatively ineffective. Active solar systems collect heat by passing water or air over a blackened, glazed surface, then store it in carefully insulated tanks, from which it can be withdrawn in controlled quantities. The size of the collector and store relative to the building to be heated naturally

The precise mixture of these types of source in a given unit, over seven sub-systems which I shall examine (electricity, space heating, water heating, cooking, waste disposal, water supply and food) specifies what I shall call the *pattern of autonomy*, indicating both the degree and nature of autonomy realised in that unit. Almost any conceivable combination is possible and the variety is great.

The physical aspects of the pattern of autonomy are often expressed by a flow--chart showing the flow of energy and materials through and around the system. Fig 1 represents a simplified version of such a flow-chart. A more precise case is shown in Fig 2, which expresses an ambitious pattern of autonomy that is both *comprehensive,* covering all the subsystems; and within each subsystem virtually complete, meeting all the demand from ambient resources. Fig 3 shows, by way of contrast, a flow-chart for a typical mains-serviced dwelling. Most autonomous units described in this article fall somewhere between these two cases, showing *selective* autonomy, and within each subsystem, only *partial* autonomy.

A third, if somewhat deviant, general type is represented by simple unserviced rural dwellings running chiefly off local resources. They are by definition highly autonomous, but in a completely different style which might be dubbed 'plain' autonomy in contrast to the 'fancy' variety most in evidence in these pages. These basic tupes, and a notational alternative to the flow-chart, are discussed further in Box 1 in Section IV.

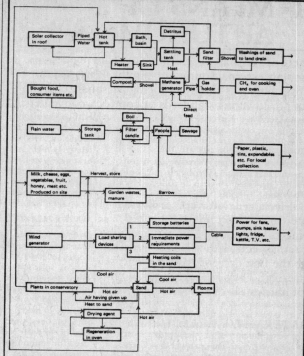

Fig 2. Services flowchart for an autonomous house. It describes the service system for Brenda Vale's house, Fig A5 [from Vale (i)]

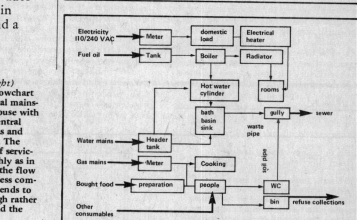

depends very much on the climate. Where there is plenty of winter sun, both can be modestly sized, but in climates like that of Britain which are exceptionally ill-favoured in this respect, very large collectors are needed to catch what little there is, and very large stores to bridge the long sunless periods. In fact, in such cases, either storage has to be large enough for summer sun to be used for the winter, or auxiliary systems must be used. Fig 5 shows a typical pattern of heat withdrawal from an interseasonal storage tank. Further details of solar heating systems may be found in Robert Vale's article 'Sunshine Superpower'.

Some idea of the variety which solar collectors and heat-stores take can be gained by comparing cases in section IV.

Fig 3. *(Right)* Services flowchart for a typical mains-serviced house with oil-fired central heating, gas and electricity. The standard of servicing is roughly as in Fig 2, but the flow pattern is less complex, and tends to pass through rather than around the system.

Fig 5. *(Left, below)* Hypothetical pattern of heat withdrawal from an interseasonal heat-storage tank. During the winter, inputs from the solar collector to the tank fall short of withdrawals for space heating, and the temperature slowly falls. In the summer, the temperature builds up again, reaching a maximum in October. In practice, temperatures as high as this are unlikely to be reached, and larger stores of lower temperature would be necessary. (From Longland).

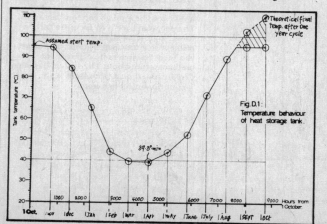

Fig.D.1: Temperature behaviour of heat storage tank.

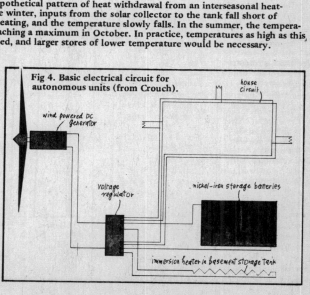

Fig 4. Basic electrical circuit for autonomous units (from Crouch).

(IV). Where the collector is integrated into the building it can exert a strong influence on shape and orientation (Figs A1 — A6, and Fig 5 of 'Sunshine Superpower').

Greenhouses attached to the building are also used to collect certain amounts of solar energy. They are relatively cheap enclosures to create, can be shut off by insulated shutters if necessary, and have a number of other advantages that have made them common features of autonomous unit designs. They may be embedded in the structure (Fig E1), form extensions on the south side (Fig A5), or constitute a major part of the living space (Figs A3, C1, C2, Figs 20 and 21).

Another ambient source of low-density heat is that contained in the air, soil, or in bodies of water. This can be collected by a heat pump, a device which, rather like a sponge might do with water, can mop up dilute external heat and squeeze it out in a more concentrated form inside, where it is needed. The operation of the heat-pump is described in 'Sunshine Superpower' by Robert Vale. Examples of their use in autonomous units are the BRAD house (Fig E1) and Miller and Gilchrist's Orkney design (Fig 6). In these two cases, power for the compressor comes from mains electricity, and since electricity is generated at only 30% efficiency at the power station from the overall energy-use point of view, the output of a heat pump must exceed the input energy by at least three times if it is to be better than burning the fuel direct. This is a great disadvantage of current heat-pump schemes, and it would be better to try and drive the compressors directly by wind, (see Fig 26 of 'Natural, Endless, Free' by Derek Taylor). The braking effect of the compressor would help prevent the rotor over-revving in very high winds and allow the use of occasional high wind-energies which would otherwise be wasted because the rotor would have to be shut down to avoid damage. The main difficulty with this elegant scheme is that the compressor would not operate when the wind wasn't blowing, and the use of battery storage would be hopelessly uneconomic. Probably the best use for excess wind

energy in space heating is to use a Callender friction device which converts fluid turbulence into heat. This again acts as a brake which does useful work, and has been proposed in Thring and Smith's octagonal house (Fig A4) and in Simon Longland's design (Fig A2).

The chief *local* source for space heating is wood, which can be managed as a fuel crop (see 'Plant Your Own Power' by Robert Vale). Trees are combined solar collectors and stores which work at lower average efficiencies than heat-collectors, but are relatively cheap and can be operated under very difficult conditions. On burning they provide heat at relatively high density that can serve for space-heating, water-heating or cooking. The work required to prepare them for burning can be an economic benefit or disbenefit, depending on how you look at it, but I am with Thoreau, who said, "Wood warms you twice."

WATER HEATING

Over the year, less energy is needed for water than for space-heating, but water has to be hotter (over 40°C). In many autonomous unit designs, solar space and water heating are combined, the hot-water tank being fed from the heat-store and boosted to higher temperatures if necessary by immersion heater, methane gas, etc. In many schemes, particularly the low-cost ones, water-heating is the sole function of the solar collector. Since there is no need for enormous storage tanks or heat-distribution systems, these systems can be quite inexpensive. The BRAD roof, for example (Fig E1), is a simple construction of anodised corrugated aluminium, covered with glass-reinforced plastic, with a total area of 60 square metres. It is optimised for summer hot water, and provides adequate amounts for at least eight months of the year. Its cost of about £8 per square metre, compares with about £20 a square metre for systems with adequate storage for space-heating.

Other hot-water systems are optimised for the winter, and are mounted vertically (eg Fig C1). A collector of 40 square metres is said to be adequate to provide for 'normal consumption' of hot water all year round in a family

dwelling, but in climates such as Britain's it is risky to put all one's eggs in the solar basket. A more practical scheme would be to use the solar collector to preheat water to feed a stored-fuel boiler. This would save fuel and guarantee *hot* hot water.

In some designs there are unusual quantities of methane gas available as a fuel (Figs B1, B3 and 20), and this may be used for heating water. In the simpler, low-cost units, hot water is freely used when available, and simply foregone when it is not. Where wood is available, it can obviously be used to supplement other sources.

COOKING

Cooking requires relatively small quantities of high-density heat. In a large number of autonomous unit designs, methane gas is specified for cooking, produced by anaerobic fermentation of organic wastes (usually sewage, kitchen and garden waste, or manure from any animals kept on the site). Other units use wood, wind electricity or solar cookers but in many designs no special provision is made for autonomous energy for cooking, and in these cases bottled gas or a solid-fuelled range is generally used.

A discussion of methane generation can be found in 'Plant Your own Power'. The gas is produced in an airtight container called a *digestor*. In many as-yet unbuilt designs, digestors are dutifully and hopefully incorporated, but on a family scale in cool climates their efficacy is rather doubtful. Unless supplemented by some (usually off-site) source of waste they will not produce enough for 'normal' cooking demands. In temperate climates they need to be kept at optimum temperatures for the methane-producing bacteria to function (about 40°C) and this can use as much energy as the digestor produces. Building the digestor inside the house would help to keep it warm, but this is rarely done because there are inevitably odour problems and a certain risk of explosion.

The kind of elaborate design needed is shown by Jaap 't Hooft's digestor (see Fig B1). This is a sealed tank of 3 cubic metres capacity, with a double brick skin, heavily insulated and with a heating coil. It is fed with manure from a neighbouring hog farm, and provides gas for cooking and washing, via a small geyser, for at most two people. Some designers have proposed trying to boost methane yields by first using the sewage to grow algae, which are themselves digested. This has been demonstrated in the laboratory, and a system applying it was designed by Graham Caine for use in Street Farm House (Fig 7). In the end it was not built, and is probably more trouble than it's worth.

Fig 6. Orkneys House designed by John Miller and Allan Gilchrist. (a) Plan. A heat-pump withdraws air from the large window spaces, extracts the low-grade heat, and distributes it to storage in the hollow walls via a trench running under the house. (b) Section of the heat-storage walls. Heated air (at about 50°C) flows up from the lower duct and transfers its heat to pebbles or aggregate filling the wall cavity. Heat is transferred to the rooms by opening louvres set at intervals along the inside face of the walls. (After Miller and Gilchrist, see also Fig 25) 1 Storage wall; 2 Trench; 3 Heat-pump; 4 'Solar' windows; 5 Foundation slab; 6 Circulation duct; 7 Insulation; 8 Concrete; 9 Aggregate.

(b)

(a)

Fig 7. Algae-boosted methane-production system. Methane gas produced only from the waste products of a single family is unlikely to be enough for cooking needs. The proposal here is to fix extra carbon through growing algae on the sewage effluent in a transparent tank. The algae can then themselves be digested for methane production. The system has been demonstrated on a laboratory scale, but it is not practical in a home.

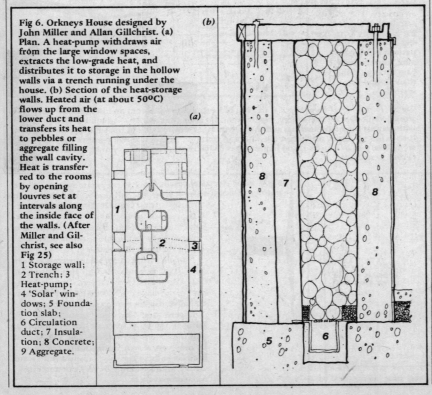

Fig 8. 'Solar kitchen, designed by J. Swet for Community Technology, Inc., Washington, D.C., developed to show that high temperature heat from the sun can be used indoors even when the sun is not shining. 'The glass-enclosed pipe is heated by solar radiation concentrated onto it by the trough-shaped reflector. An insulated extension (hidden by the enclosure far end) delivers the heat to the hotplate (partially hidden) on which the coffee pot and an as yet unbuilt thermal storage mass sit. The collector tracks the sun automatically. Larger versions could be developed for community-scale food processing or local light industries.' (From Hess).

Fig 9. Solar cooking system proposed by John Shore. A concentrating trough collector focuses onto a steam pipe which passes into a vacuum flask containing food [from Shore (i)]

(a)

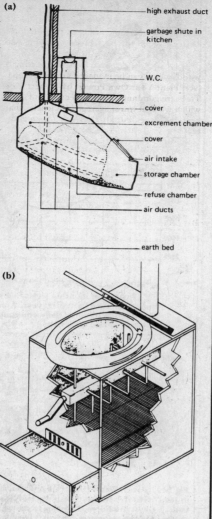

- high exhaust duct
- garbage shute in kitchen
- W.C.
- cover
- excrement chamber
- cover
- air intake
- storage chamber
- refuse chamber
- air ducts
- earth bed

(b)

Fig 10. Two aerobic composting toilets. (a) 'Clivus' designed by Rikard Lindstrom. This is a large fibreglass box which is 'seeded' with ordinary soil, and composts sewage and organic kitchen wastes. At ordinary household temperatures, the heat generated is enough to keep air flowing in at the bottom and up the 'chimney', to prevent odours.. The resulting soil-like compost can be used on the garden [From Vale (ii)] (b) Experimental composter designed and built by John Shore. Sewage matter drops through a series of batten screens into a drawer from which it can be removed when fully composted. Probably best situated in an outhouse [from Shore (i)].

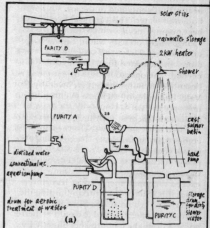

(a)

Fig 11. 'Ecol' water collection, purification and waste-treatment system. See also Fig C3. (a) The system, showing daily flows in litres. There are four levels of water purity. Apart from the water heater, an optional extra that would operate on windy days, the system needs only the negligible amount of energy required for the aquarium pump. Solar water heating could be incorporated with only minor modifications [from Vale (ii) after Ortega et al]. (b) The outbuilding which houses the system. The solar still forms the roof (from Ortega et al).

(b)

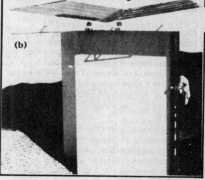

The use of solar energy in cooking is rather rare, but is occasionally attempted with concentrating solar collectors. Generally these can only be used in direct sunlight (Fig C3), but Community Technology, a group in Washington, D.C., have designed a self-tracking concentrator that stores heat in a mass of lithium nitrate, useful for several hours (Fig 8). Another ingenious solar cooking method has been proposed by John Shore for his autonomous unit design (Fig C2). A parabolic-section collector has a steam-pipe at the focus, which passes through a vacuum flask (Fig 9). This might seem a precarious method of cooking, but would be useful in economising on methane, performing the same slow-cooking functions as 'hay boxes', or 'fireless cookers'.

WASTE TREATMENT

Several kinds of wastes are generated by households, and, in autonomous units, different methods may be called for to deal with them in the most effective way. Normal urban households dispose of all solid waste via refuse collection, and all liquid wastes via the mains sewers. In the country solid waste is usually burned and/or buried; sewage wastes are led to septic tanks or cesspits; and other liquid wastes to 'soakaway' land drains. The aim in an autonomous unit is not merely to get rid of the stuff, but to use it in the most efficient way possible.

There is little to be done with non-organic refuse such as tins and bottles except to use them as little as possible and recycle them.

Organic solid waste from kitchen and garden is usually *composted* in order to return the nutrients to the soil whence they came. The same holds for sewage wastes, which are particularly rich in nitrogen. They constitute the most 'dangerous' wastes from the point of view of health risks and must receive some kind of treatment to render them harmless. In contrast, dirty water from washing and laundry is relatively safe and can be put to various other uses, or, where water is scarce, recycled. Although there are a large number of elaborate garbage and waste-disposal systems which in theory might find a place in autonomous units, most of them are costly, require chemicals or extra energy for operation, may need periodic removal of products for treatment elsewhere, and completely waste the valuable materials which an autonomous unit should be carefully husbanding. One proprietary brand of sanitation hardware is called the 'Destroilet'. That says it all.

Composting of both liquid and solid organic wastes can be either aerobic or anaerobic. Aerobic composting of sewage wastes is usually accomplished indoors in large containers such as those shown in Fig 10. They are in effect, indoor compost heaps and yield a hygienic soil-like substance suitable for use as fertiliser. Sewage is mostly water, and what is left behind after the composting process is surprisingly little, so these devices need emptying only perhaps once or twice a year. It is sometimes a disadvantage of these systems that they do not deal with waste ('grey')

water, which needs a separate system. Where there is a garden, this can be used there (unless it contains toxic wastes). Even if grey water is disposed of through the mains sewers, the reduction of contamination and the saving of nitrogen is, from the public point of view, a step in the right direction.

Another form of aerobic system has been built in the Ecol house (Fig 11; see also C3). Waste from a flush toilet passes into a drum through which air is continuously bubbled by a small aquarium pump (powered from the wind-generator).This rapidly purifies the water to the point where it can be pumped up into the cistern for flushing. The solids build up only very slowly in the drum. The close association between waste disposal and water supply in this example is very common in autonomous units.

Anaerobic composting in methane digestors, apart from yielding a certain amount of energy, as discussed under 'Cooking', produces a rich effluent which can be used in hydroponic food-growing, as in Street Farm House (Fig 18), or directly on to garden soil, where it makes an excellent conditioner. Methane digestors, even where gas production is not feasible, may often be cheaper to build than the more conventional septic tanks, because they do not need the 'absorption field' to handle overflow which is often the greater part of septic tank costs.

In theory, there is further scope for improving the quality of use of sewage wastes. Since humans extract only part of the potential nutritional value of the food, the most efficient use of human sewage, as with vegetable wastes, is not to feed them to bacteria, but to animals for protein production. It has been claimed that dewatered human faeces, mixed with straw and grit, make a perfectly balanced diet for laying chickens, and could provide adequate amounts of the kind of space-intensive primary protein ideal for autonomous units. Hopefully the taste of the chickens would not be affected by the feed. The chicken manure could then be used for methane generation, and the effluent for fertilizer in the usual way. This is in fact an extension of a very old principle (Fig 12).

WATER SUPPLY

In rural areas where a supply of pure ground water is available from a spring or well, elaborate water systems are not necessary, although 'fancy' techniques such as windpumps might be used to bring the water to where it is needed. Otherwise an autonomous unit must rely on precipitation, and/or recycling. Further discussion of water supply problems can be found in George Woolston's 'Each Piece of Land to Each Piece of Sky'.

Precipitation patterns vary greatly from one area to another and may require quite different systems of water supply. In very rainy areas roof-collection may alone be enough to meet the typical Euro-American demand of 100-200 litres per person per day. More usually, a very large collecting surface would be needed, and it is generally more expedient to recycle the water, even though technically speaking this can complicate the system quite a lot. Also, rain may arrive in large quantities in a short time, and large storage tanks are needed if this is not to be wasted, typically having a capacity of a quarter of the annual yield. Calculated levels in such a tank for a typical year are given in Fig 13.

Mains water is usually purified uniformly up to drinking standards, but in a small unit it is slow and ultimately uneconomic to bring all water up to this level. It is usual to partition the water into 2, 3 or even 4 distinct levels of purity according to the job it has to do. These levels are: A, drinking water; B rainwater; C, 'grey' water (eg soapy water); D, 'black' water (sewage). A fairly simple application of this is in Jaap 't Hooft's house (Fig 14, see also B1). Rainwater is collected from the surface of the dome via a gutter round the base, and is stored in an outside settling tank. Water is hand-pumped to a header tank inside the house, and used without further treatment for washing, laundry, etc. A small quantity is filtered to drinking and cooking standards. Waste water (purity C) is stored in a holding tank and used for flushing the toilet. This is simple and effective. Strictly, there is no 'recycling', just sensible re-use. The Ecol house (see Fig 3C) uses a similar system, but with refinements (Fig 11). Apart from re-using black water purified by aeration, grey water is used to feed a solar still for drinking water.

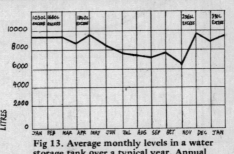

Fig 12. Pig privy. Pete Russell writes: 'Methane tanks and clivus units are still pretty sophisticated pieces of technology compared with the privies I encountered in south India. These masterpieces of ecological sanitation have two entrances: the normal one in the front and a second one at the rear for pigs. Each time you make for the privy the nearest pig heads for the rear entrance and, before you've had time to settle down the pig is grunting expectantly from its own half. At first it may be a little disturbing sitting there with nothing but a hole in a plank separating your more delicate parts from several hundred pounds of hungry bacon. bacon. Any apprehensions are, however, quickly dispelled as you realise that the fruits of your efforts are being fully appreciated and you can sit back and ponder the beauty of nature's own recycling systems that require no technology, orthodox or alternative.'

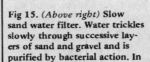

Fig 13. Average monthly levels in a water storage tank over a typical year. Annual precipitation 530mm, daily consumption 90 litres. [From Vale (i)]

(a)

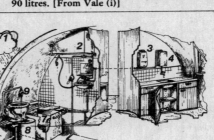

Fig 14 (Above). Water collection and re-use system in Jaap 't Hooft's house. 1 Rainwater; 2 Header tank; 3 Geyser; 4 Filter; 5 Gutter to rainwater cistern; 6 From rainwater cistern; 7 Grey water store, for flushing; 8 Septic tank; 9 Hand pumps.

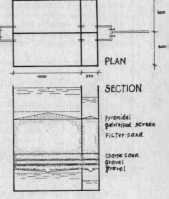

PLAN

SECTION

pyramidal
galvinised screen
FILTER sand

coarse sand
gravel
gravel

Fig 15. (Above right) Slow sand water filter. Water trickles slowly through successive layers of sand and gravel and is purified by bacterial action. In this system part of the filter is divided off for separate treatment of drinking water, the main part being fed with recycled water for washing etc.

The whole thing is doubled to avoid interruptions of supply during cleaning and maintenance.
[From Vale (i)]

Solar stills can be effective in certain climates, but for most of the year in climates like Britain's other means of purifying water are necessary if 'normal' demand is to be met from ambient sources. Slightly dirty rainwater can readily be treated in a slow sand filter (Fig 15), but water that has too much fatty material in it will quickly clog the filter. For recycling grey water it is usually necessary to precipitate the fats with agents such as sulphuric acid or ferrous sulphate (Fig 16). The scum of fatty acids produced can be fed to the methane digestor or aerobically composted.

A very reliable water system may involve a number of the methods discussed here, and may be complex and costly, relying on an elaborate system of pipes and electrically-switched pumps and valves (for example, Fig 17). Probably in most cases it is more rational to reduce demand to the level where it can be met by simpler systems.

FOOD

Provision of food is always a special case in autonomous units because it requires such a lot of space. Many designs omit food altogether as being an insoluble problem for a site-free design. Others assume a site that could provide a certain amount of food, or treat the whole site as a single unit, specifying crop layouts and housing for animals. Complete specifications of the yields and diet as part of the formal system is unusual, although many designs incorporate food-producing elements into the building structure in one way or another. The 'average site' is expected to provide vegetables and dairy products. Grain, meat, condiments, fruit and other items are assumed bought in from outside.

The kind of on-site husbandry usually envisaged is illustrated in **Vision** No 3. Vegetable-growing is predominant, with chickens, goat, perhaps a cow or pig. Lacto-vegetarianism is obviously favoured as a basic type of diet because it makes more efficient use of the land (see 'Cut Out the Tripe') but scavengers such as pigs or geese can make good use of high grade waste and help speed up the decay cycles (Fig 12 is perhaps rather an extreme case but catches the spirit of the thing). Fertility is maintained by composting and suitable use of legume crops, thus avoiding the need for bought fertilizers, although

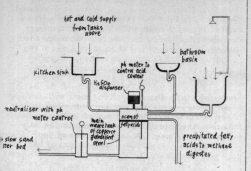

(b)

1 Living unit and hydroponicum; 2 Barn and livestock sheds; 3 Methane digestors; 4 Water-powered generator.

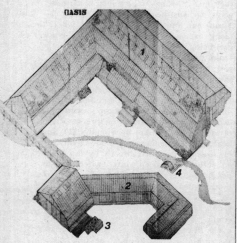

OASIS

Fig 16. *(Above left)* **Waste water pretreatment system.** Where 'grey' water needs to be recycled to meet water demand, the heavier contaminants (fats etc.) are precipitated first (from Crouch).

Fig 17. *(Right)* **A comprehensive water-system incorporating waste-treatment, water-supply and water-heating subsystems. Drinking water is derived only from rain water, is treated separately from recycled water in the slow filter, and is further purified by a silver-impregnated filter-candle.** [From Vale (i)].

Fig 18. *(Left centre)* **Hydroponics in Street Farm House (a) before (b) after.**

Fig 19. *(Below left)* **Oasis. An autonomous greenhouse proposed by Mick Bedford, incorporating livestock and hydroponic produce.**

Fig 20. *(Below right)* **'Ark' designed by New Alchemy Insitute for Prince Edward Island, Canada.**
1 Living unit; 2 Solar Collectors; 3 Fish tanks; 4 Greenhouse.

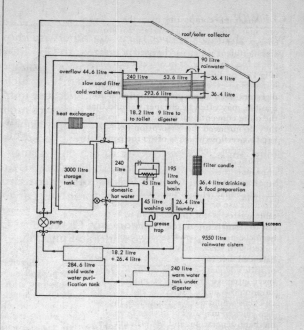

Below left: Pattern of autonomy for Oasis and *Right:* for Ark.

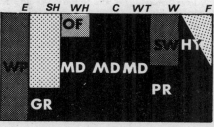

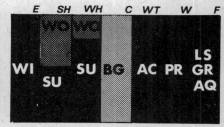

certain dressings such as lime, slag or bone meal will be needed from outside from time to time. The general bias is 'organic husbandry' (see 'Animal Farm' by John Seymour and 'Compost Culture' by Lawrence Hills).

Greenhouses are extremely useful aids to autonomy in food production, and are often incorporated into the dwelling structure. Some units virtually *are* greenhouses. An integrated greenhouse has a number of advantages. It lengthens the growing season and can provide exotic crops which add variety to temperate produce, especially in the winter when the occupants are down to kale and potatoes. It also provides a cheap, light, spacious and sheltered extension to the house, and traps solar energy. The plants purify the air, permitting lower ventilation rates and hence lower heat losses. Examples of such integrated greenhouses are found in Figs A3, A4, A5, C1, C2, E2, E3.

These greenhouses are not invariably used for food, but when they are they generally have growing-beds of normal soil. Yields under these conditions are high, but of course the space is limited. Greater efficiency can be achieved by hydroponics (see 'The answer Lies in Solution' by Sholto Douglas). A semi-hydroponic system was successfully used in Street Farm House (Fig C1). Beds of soil and aggregate or vermiculite were laid out in bays over plastic sheeting, and fertilised with effluent from the methane digestor (Fig 18a). This produced excellent yields of peppers, tomatoes, sweetcorn and other crops (including tobacco), which, together with the usual temperate crops grown outside the house, made the unit self-sufficient in vegetables for most of the year (Fig 18b). A vastly more ambitious speculation is Mick Bedford's 'Oasis' (Fig 19), a giant greenhouse/hydroponicum/ barn/dwelling unit designed for total self-sufficiency in food, with hydroponics as a basis. Hydroponics has certain disadvantages. Chemical nutrients generally need to be brought in from outside, although careful recycling of nutrients (as in the Street Farm case) can reduce the demand. A purely hydro-ponic diet may be systematically short of certain minerals and vitamins, but this is over-come by combining it with other sources of food.

Another unorthodox greenhouse structure is the New Alchemy Institute's 'Ark' proposal, which is founded on their experiments in aquaculture (Fig 20). A dwelling unit is sand-wiched between two glasshouses, one for vegetables, the other for intensive rearing of fish, and also containing banks of solar collectors. Golueke and Oswald's cylindrical design is functionally similar, but very different in appearance. It aims at a surplus in food, and incorporates a cow, chickens and people into a single compact structure (Fig B3). The animals are fed with algae grown in tanks on the roof, and the human inhabitants consume some of the milk and eggs, plus vegetables assumed grown on an adjacent plot. Surplus milk, eggs and algae feed are sold, and in favourable conditions are claimed to be able to cover the running costs of the unit.

This concludes discussion of the alternative resources which autonomous systems generally seek to tap. The range of possibilities for each sub-system and for integrated systems, can, however, only be fully encompassed by all three of the logical 'means' taken together. The other two, 'Clever Ideas' and 'Making Do' are discussed next.

AUTONOMY

CLEVER IDEAS

What I shall call 'Clever Ideas' are otherwise known as Doing More With Less, and boil down ultimately to Good Design. Economically speaking, they are ways of increasing performance for a given cost (at least in the long run), or equivalently, reducing cost for a given performance. I say 'in the long run' because in many cases a Clever Idea costs something at the outset but saves more later.

A lot of the examples here could apply equally well in ordinary mains-serviced units, but in an affluent society where (for the time being, anyway) service costs absorb only a small fraction of income, it is hardly worth the bother. An autonomous unit is much nearer the margins, and Clever Ideas are often necessary just to ensure minimal supplies. The pressures for intelligent and careful design are much more intense.

I distinguish three categories of Clever Idea: Leak-Plugging; Partition of Function; and Multiple Function.

LEAK-PLUGGING

I have borrowed this term from Philip Steadman (*Energy, Environment and Building*) to indicate strictly technical methods of increasing the efficiency of the resources available, usually involving a special device or design choice and applying particularly to energy use. The most important form is insulation, achieved generally by linings of glass wool, wood wool, or polystyrene foam inside or outside roofs, walls and floors (see also the article on insulation by Brenda Vale).

Together with double or triple-glazed windows, weather-stripping, and insulated shutters, designers generally try to get the 'U-value' (heat-loss) down to 0.3 $W/m^2/^0K$. Heat-loss can also be reduced in the general design of the building by recessed windows; porches or air-locks; orientation away from prevailing winds; underground building. Roof overhangs may prevent excessive heat gain in the summer, and yet allow access of low-angle winter sunshine in south-facing windows. Ouroboros (Fig A1) illustrates a number of such general design features. The north side is covered by an earth bank (berm) which deflects the wind, insulates, and raises the frostline. The shallow roof is covered with sods for summer cooling. In winter a deep layer of snow builds up which is highly insulating (Fig A1 c). The plan form is trapezoidal, maximizing solar receipts on the south, minimizing heat losses on the north.

A more elaborate method of saving energy is by using heat exchangers or 'thermal wheels' to recover heat from stale air or waste water. More common is the choice of equipment which is less prodigal in its use of energy, such as fluorescent instead of incandescent lamps; self-regulating closed stoves instead of open fires; pressure cookers or 'fireless cookers'; and radiant heating rather than air-heating, which gives the same subjective effect but is not lost in ventilation. Similar principles apply to water saving: showers rather than baths; mist rather than spray showers; foot-operated taps; non-flushing toilets; front rather than top-loading washing machines.

Often the inhabitants of an autonomous dwelling cannot (or will not) adjust the equipment so that it performs optimally. The fix for this is in automatic control devices. Solar-collectors for example can be activated by thermistors or by photoelectrically-operated pumps, and shutters may also be controlled by the heat balance.

PARTITION OF FUNCTION

The principle here is to match the available resources as closely as possible to the jobs they have to do, both qualitatively and quantitatively. Services such as space-heating, water supply and electricity are normally provided uniformly at the highest standard needed. This is in principle wasteful, but is justified by current economics on the large scale. In a small unit the pressures are strongly against such waste, generally in a fairly obvious way. Attempting, for example, to use methane for space heating would exhaust the supply rapidly, to little effect; or conversely, using diffuse solar energy for cooking would do little more than make a good junket. The case of water purification has already been discussed (Figs 11, 14), where up to four different purities may be maintained, only to the degree required for the purpose. Similarly, the electrical sub-system voltage regulator channels the current to various loads depending on the level of supply (Fig 4).

In space heating, temperatures may vary in different spaces for different uses at different times. Night temperatures can be lower than day. Workrooms and bedrooms can be cooler than sitting rooms. In the larger autonomous units it is usual to divide the living-space up into sections separated by insulating partitions or shutters to avoid the need for heating it all. The upper storey of Brenda Vale's design for example (Fig A5) and the 'greenhouse' half of Alex Pike's design (Fig A3) are closed off in the winter. John Shore's design (Fig C2 b) has the same idea, but carried a step further. Not only is the greenhouse section shut off, but a very small extra insulated 'warm, cosy area' is provided, into which the inhabitants can retreat on exceptionally cold days. Herbert Girardet's 'Radial House' uses the same idea on a collective level (Fig E5). A large central room surrounding a furnace is itself surrounded and surmounted by other rooms, thus well-insulated. This is used as a communal room which most of the inhabitants will use in the winter, the other rooms being used only for sleeping, physical work, etc. This is of course a resurrection of an ancient pattern of life; and shows how technical and social aspects of design may be difficult to keep apart.

MULTIPLE FUNCTION

In this category of Clever Ideas, economics are achieved either by making the output of one system the input of another, or by making a single component do a number of different jobs. Many of the standard cases have been encountered already. A methane digestor treats sewage, generates gas and provides fertilizer; a greenhouse extension provides food, traps heat, creates a sense of space, and purifies the air; building structures can serve as windmill towers or as heat stores (Fig 6); solar collectors can double as roofs, walls (or both, Fig A6) or insulators (Fig A3, A4).

These multiple functions are generally achieved through close integration of all the components in the unit (as in Figs A1–6, E2 and E3), in contrast to more dispersed systems such as B1, B2 or C3. On the whole spatially integrated systems are probably more efficient, but they have certain disadvantages that have to be overcome, because the demands of different sub-systems may conflict, as well as complement one another. Vibration and noise from windmills has already been mentioned. With solar collectors the problem is blocking of natural light from the south. This has to be solved in various ways, perhaps the most ingenious being in Thring and Smith's design (Fig A4), where the living-space is raised off the ground, the lower part being used for service elements, storage tanks, garaging and livestock. At night the solar panels cover the living-space as insulated shuttering, while in the day they are lowered, revealing the windows and greenhouse.

Another idea of Thring and Smith's is an integrated sun-wind-heat pump system which takes advantage of the seasonal reciprocity of the sun and wind in Britain (Fig 21). Space heating at the beginning and end of the heating season is provided directly by the solar collector. In the deep winter (when average wind speeds are higher) the load is taken over by the wind-driven heat pump, using the solar collector as a heat exchanger. In principle such a system could also be used for summer cooling, simply by reversing the heat-pump cycle. In countries with continental climates, systems which perform both heating and cooling functions are obviously rational, although they need not always involve sophisticated gadgets like heat pumps. Steve Baer's 'Drumwall' system (illustrated in Robert Vale's 'Sunshine Superpower', Fig 9) achieves the same effect rather more simply.

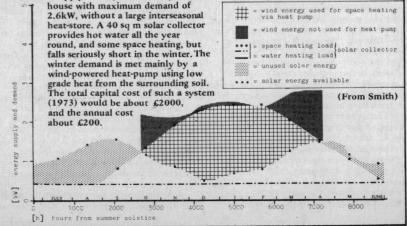

Fig 21. Mixed solar and wind-driven heat-pump space- and water-heating system. Pattern of demand and supply. The system is designed to meet all heating needs for a well-insulated house with maximum demand of 2.6kW, without a large interseasonal heat-store. A 40 sq m solar collector provides hot water all the year round, and some space heating, but falls seriously short in the winter. The winter demand is met mainly by a wind-powered heat-pump using low grade heat from the surrounding soil. The total capital cost of such a system (1973) would be about £2000, and the annual cost about £200.

= wind energy used for space heating via heat pump

= wind energy not used for heat pump

= space heating load / water heating load } solar collector

= unused solar energy

= solar energy available

(From Smith)

energy supply and demand [kW]

JULY   A   S   O   N   D   J   F   M   A   M   JUNE

1000   2000   3000   4000   5000   6000   7000   8000

[h] hours from summer solstice

MAKING DO

In this third class of 'means' to autonomy I include mostly social or psychological adaptations to autonomous life which entail at least nominal sacrifices of comfort/convenience/time/consumption levels, a group of concepts for which no single word will quite do, but which I shall call 'amenity' for short. I say 'nominal' because they are essentially subjective, and although such sacrifices may seem utterly real and equally intolerable to some people, to others they are barely noticeable, and to yet others they are positive benefits. This class of 'means' differs from the others in that the social aspects predominate over the technical, and the costs incurred are 'amenity costs' rather than money costs. But, as always, the distinctions are blurred. Earth berms are an economical and effective idea, but there comes a point when underground living is not everybody's ideal home. Keeping different purity levels of water segregated may become a source of anxiety with children around. Charging and discharging a methane digestor can make demands on the temper. And so on.

There is, however, one distinction which becomes clearer in this category: that between the *nouveaux pauvres* for whom anything goes because Making Do is a way of life, and those who aim to produce exactly matching autonomous substitutes for all that underpins the high bourgeois style.

BELT-TIGHTENING

Although Making Do is mainly social or psychological in character, the technical aspect is not left behind altogether. Certain technical choices made for other reasons may inevitably involve amenity costs, like the earth berm, water system or digestor instanced just now. When sub-systems or components are reduced in size, quality or reliability, they may be a lot cheaper and be more sparing of resources, but naturally their performance is poorer and this must be counted an 'amenity cost'. Examples include lower light wattages; lower thermostat settings and ventilation rates; hand- rather than electric-pumps; fans rather than air conditioning; small window ratio; low-rated appliances (fridges, etc); smaller house-volume.

The term 'Belt-Tightening' is again borrowed from Philip Steadman, and designates technical choices that impose relatively light amenity costs; reduce demand individually by a few percent and collectively up to 50 per cent; and are applicable in normal dwellings as well as autonomous units. Even these light amenity costs can be mollified by second-order Clever Ideas which might well be called 'slimming aids'. Low light-levels, for example, can be made more effective by focusing the light where it is needed. Low ventilation rates can be sustained better if the air is freshened by charcoal filters or ultraviolet lamps — although this kind of thing makes one start to think of the old woman who swallowed a fly.

Lowering the whole size of dwelling relative to the capacity of the service systems is perhaps the most drastic form of Belt Tightening. It makes pretty well everything cheaper because less materials are used, and less heat is required, but of course there is a tendency for it to feel cramped. This can be alleviated by various 'psychological' design features, such as Alex Pike's view over the greenhouse (Fig A3 b). Jaap 't Hooft's house (Fig B1) is deliberately compact to retain heat, but the designer claims that the dome form feels more roomy than a cuboid of the same volume. Although there is only one main room, the bed is raised to leave the floor free, and the furniture stacks or folds away (Fig 22). Also the window area, although triple-glazed, is very small (about 2%), but the seven triangular windows are carefully sited for maximum effect: one at the head of the bed in the east, two above the work space on the south, and one by the kitchenette at the west, and the other three placed high for sky lighting.

SHARING

Efficiency in the use of resources can be multiplied by sharing space, materials and facilities. Examples include communal laundry, cooking (especially baking), saunas, heating and waste-treatment. In a fixed space, sharing necessarily implies increased density, but savings can still accrue with normal densities in larger buildings (see discussion of 'Size' below) or in groups of buildings, with shared facilities. The nominal costs are in the resolution of conflicts over access to facilities; overcoming the sense of infringed privacy, or of absolute convenience and possession; or just personality conflicts. Sorting these out by group discussions, rotations, co-ordination, and strict allocation of responsibilities would seem intolerably irksome to most people: it's bad enough even for experienced communards. But sharing has its social benefits as well (Fig 23) which I shall not go into now. Many of these points are developed further in 'Local Economies of Scale' in section V, and also in section VII.

ADAPTATION TO AMBIENT CONDITIONS

In sophisticated autonomous units, internal conditions are more or less 'normal', but less plutocratic units are often at the mercy of the elements, and the occupants either acclimatise themselves or modulate their activities to suit the conditions. Water hot enough for baths or showers, for example, will not be available every day. On sunny days one must seize the time — and perhaps use the solar cooker to economise on methane. At other times, raw food is certainly good for you, and one can get used to it surprisingly quickly. On cold days one may need to put extra clothes on, as our ancestors did. It is amazing how effective this is. Again, adaptation can be remarkably rapid, and one even comes to enjoy the cold season as a special kind of atmosphere. It makes the kids tough as well, providing they have plenty to wear. As for electricity, a prolonged calm spell may necessitate reliance on natural daylight or candlelight, but this again can make a pleasant change — remember the power cuts?

EFFORT AND CARING

Again, the sophisticated autonomous unit can provide fairly normal services without much maintenance, by using good-quality components and automating many of the sub-systems. Simpler units have probably been self-built, with a lot of bodging, and may need constant attention. Blinds and shutters may need to be adjusted, and collector angles shifted, plants and animals attended to, food prepared carefully (eg fine chopping to save heat), wood cut, repairs carried out, digestors fed and emptied, water quality monitored, generators oiled and adjusted, batteries topped up, discussions engaged in. All this requires skill and effort (although again, not that much when you're used to it) and the necessary tools and materials. Failure of effort and caring will result in deterioration performance, costly remedial measures, and health risks. These are potentially tough sanctions and demand an unusual measure of commitment to the unit.

Fig 22. Interior of Jaap 't Hooft's house (see Fig B1) during construction.

Fig 23. Communality v. Separateness: the Red Rockers' dome. A dozen adults living together in a giant self-built dome for three years. It has many advantages:

So: "After three years of living in a heap, most of us have decided that in order to keep becoming new people, to keep growing and changing, we need more privacy. We are still a communal family that wishes to hold together but we need a new kind of shelter for this period in our growth — shelters that will be places to make love in, argue in, to play music and write and worry and think and decide what the next step is to be. So we plan on building four small houses this summer. These will be sleeping spaces — small shelters designed for one, two or three people, probably without kitchen facilities."

AUTONOMY

CHANGING HABITS OF LIFE

It may be that, for economic reasons beyond anybody's control, such changes of taste, habit and social life as are discussed under this category 'Making Do' will be forced on the population as a whole. The value of fancy autonomous houses that provide nearly normal service standards is that they could break people in gently, while a new fund of social knowledge about frugal living accumulated — as it did during the war. Certainly, habits are hard to change: washing, diet, overall consumption patterns, and particularly work.

Partial transfer of work from outside to inside the unit (perhaps with shorter hours in the day, or fewer days a week) is rarely feasible with present employment practices. And the pattern of fulfilment in the lives of most involves a level of consumtion and money transaction that makes the penny-pinching style of *nouveau-pauvre* autonomy look ridiculous. Autonomy only really makes sense in a non-consumer setting, but it is worth pointing out that, given the basic resources (land, tools, etc), the basic effort needed to grow a years vegetables, build a house, knit a sweater, cut wood, pump water, and compost the sewage, is pretty well constant, or if anything declines gently as new methods are worked out.

Meanwhile the cost of buying such goods or their equivalents rises continually, often faster than typical wage-rates for work which is exchanged for the money which is exchanged for the goods. The point is that if doing all these productive tasks directly is enjoyable, which it is for many and could be for others, and if working 'outside' is not, it is quite irrational to go through a charade of exchanges, except to obtain the basic materials. Inflation may bring a lot of people to this point, and what at first seems an intolerable cost may eventually come to be seen as an agreeable, and obvious, pattern of production.

Another difficult hurdle might be the erratic pattern of life in autonomous units vulnerable to the weather and seasons — in such stark contrast to the comfortable uniformity of suburban existence. Here again there are hidden delights. Every day is good for *something*. On calm sunny days one eats solar-cooked food, has a bath and enjoys the weather. On windy days one notes with relief that the batteries are being charged. When it rains one is delighted that the tank is being filled and the plants watered. Every season has its food, and winter is a time of collective life and festivals. Am I being over-lyrical? Yes, but there is certainly a positive side to Making Do, which for many autonomists is the *raison d'etre* for the whole thing.

III VARIATIONS IN AUTONOMY

This section concerns other 'secondary' aspects of autonomy which condition, and are conditioned by, the primary choice of means. They are also conditioned by the purposes of the autonomists, the circumstances in which units are built, fashions, social hang-ups, half-baked theories, accidents, windfalls and so on.

FUNCTION

Most autonomous units are intended to be just *homes*, although inevitably they have some experimental character. Sometimes the experimentation is formal, as is proposed in Pike's design, or Thring and Smith's, backed up by computer simulation studies, etc (Fig A3 and A4). Jaap 't Hooft's house is also experimental and is carefully monitored (Fig B1). Although 'self-sufficiency' is a slogan often brandished, few units come close to providing their occupants with a complete living. For this, some kind of surplus must be produced for sale, the most convenient being food, as proposed in the New Alchemy Ark (Fig 21), Oasis (Fig 20) and Golueke and Oswald's design (Fig B3). However, a moderately autonomous homestead-type unit producing most of its own food should be able to reduce necessary external work by at least half, depending on the standard of living of its occupants.

SIZE

There are two aspects to the question of size. Firstly, how physically large a unit is, and secondly, how many people are supposed to live in it. The two are related as density of occupation. The examples given in section . IV show that the nuclear family yardstick is most common — 3 or 4 occupants, with a normal floor area giving houses about the usual size. The practical lower limit is probably represented in Jaap 't Hooft's autonomous bedsit (Fig B1) although John Shore has pushed miniaturisation to its physical limit (Fig 24). On the other side of the family norm, Figs E1-E3 and Fig 19 are large and meant for collective occupation. Where the limits are in this direction is hard to say. Soleri's 'arcologies', with millions of inhabitants in a single structure, indicate the grotesque possibilities of further extrapolation. Probably above 10-20, even in determinedly communal groups (Fig 23), social and other forces will favour breakdown into clusters of buildings, giving 'autonomous villages' such as E5. The economies of such communal units are discussed later under 'Local Economies of Scale', and technical aspects in section VII.

FORM

Theoretically the basic unit of autonomy is the *site* — an area of land. This is obvious in the 'village' case just discussed. Generally, however, the design focuses on a *building* and does not specify the nature of the whole site. The overall form of the building is determined by a large number of factors, for example, pre-existing structures, the pattern of autonomy, climate, availability of certain local materials, aesthetic preferences, and so on. These tend to conflict with each other and the designer has to find suitable compromises.

A compact form is favoured by many designers because it is best for retaining heat. In theory the best shape is the sphere, but this is hardly practical, and reverts to the dome (Figs B1 and B2), the cylinder (Fig B3) or some approximation of these (Figs A4, E5). A compact form has the advantage that service elements can be concentrated in a

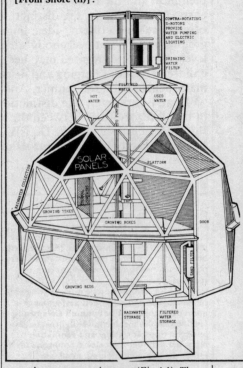

Fig 24. **Solo dome designed by John Shore. The smallest autonomous unit ever conceived?** [From Shore (ii)] .

central core to save pipe runs (Fig A4). The dispersed systems of B1 and B2 leave the structure free to assume the optimum shape, but take up more ground space and miss the benefits of 'double function'.

Integration of a solar collector into the structure exerts a profound influence on shape because now it is desirable to *maximise* part of the external area. Robert Vale has argued for a 'long, low, south-facing' form, which in the houses designed by him and his wife Brenda takes a characteristic wedge shape (Figs A5, E2, E3). Ouroboros (Fig A1) is also wedge-shaped, but slopes the opposite way from the Vale designs. Its trapezoidal plan is a clever way of increasing collector area to volume ratio. Other Cambridge designs have adopted quite different solutions to the problem of form (Fig A3, A4, A6), whereas the BRAD house (Fig E1) is conditioned by the stone cottage of which it is an extension, even though it completely dwarfs the original. Such conditioning by a pre-existing structure is almost total in an urban conversion (Fig D1).

SITE SPECIFICITY

Some units are designed for a specific location; others for a specific *kind* of location (eg city or country); others for a specific climate. Most of those discussed here are intended for temperate climates without any particular location in mind, but a rural or semi-rural setting is usually implied.

In the city, autonomous units may hardly work at all, and are almost obliged to start with an existing structure. Aside from the

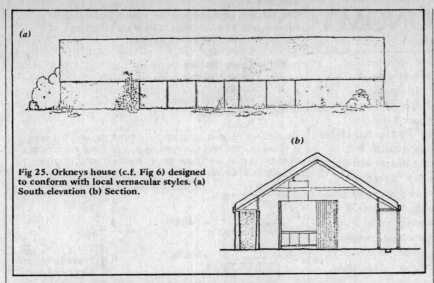

Fig 25. Orkneys house (c.f. Fig 6) designed to conform with local vernacular styles. (a) South elevation (b) Section.

SOURCES & THANKS

The Berkeley Tribe. 'Blueprint for a Communal Environment', in T. Roszak, (Ed). *Sources,* Harper Colophon, 1972.

Brown, R, and P. Stellon. 'The Energy Cost of a House', Architecutral Association Rational Technology Unit, 1974.

Caine, Graham. 'A Revolutionary Structure', *Oz*, Nov. 1972.

Crouch, Gerrard. 'The Autonomous Servicing of Dwellings: Dept. Architecture, U. of Cambridge, 1972.

Energy Primer, Portola Institute, 1974.

Girardet, Herbert. 'New Villages Now', *Undercurrents* No 10, 1975.

Golueke, G. C., and W. J. Oswald. 'An Algal Regenerative System', *Compost Science* Vol 14 No 3, 1973.

Hess, Karl. 'Community Technology', *Spark* Vol 4, No 2, 1974.

Longland, Simon. *Possibilities for Autonomous Servicing,* 5th Year Thesis submitted to Dept of Architecture, U. of Edinburgh, 1974.

Merrill, Richard. 'Integrated Systems', in *Energy Primer,* Portola Institute, 1974.

Minimum Cost Housing Group, McGill University. *Stop The Five Gallon Flush.* School of Architecture, McGill University, 1973.

New Alchemy Institute (East). 'An Ark for Prince Edward Island', NAI, Box 432, Woods Hole, MA 02543, USA.

Ortega, A., *et al The Ecol Operation,* Minimum Cost Housing Group, Dept. of Architecture, McGill University, 1972.

Pike, Alexander. 'The Autonomous House', *Architectural Design* 11/75, 1974.

(i) Shore, John, 'Organic Living', *Undercurrents* No 8, 1974.

(ii) Shore, John. 'Organic Living Experiment', *Undercurrents* No 6, 1974.

Smith, Gerry. 'Economics of Solar Collectors, Heat Pumps and Wind Generators', Autonomous Housing Study, Cambridge, 1974.

Steadman, Philip. *Energy, Environment and Building.* Cambridge U. P., 1975.

't Hooft, Jaap. *Het Kringloophuis,* De Kleine Aavde, Munsel 17, Boxtel, N. B. The Netherlands, 1974.

Thring, J. 'Threshold Analysis of Services', Autonomous Housing Study, Cambridge, 1973.

Thring, J. and Smith, G. 'An Integrated Heating, Power, Water and Waste Treatment System', Autonomous Housing Study, Cambridge, 1974.

(i) Vale, Brenda. 'The Autonomous House', Autonomous Housing Study, Cambridge, 1974.

(ii) Vale, Robert, and Brenda Vale. *The Autonomous House,* Thames and Hudson, 1975.

I would like to thank also the following people who gave me unpublished material, advice and information: Mick Bedford, Philip Brachi, Gerry Foley, Alan Gillchrist, Bruce Haggart, Ian Hogan, John Miller, Patrick Rivers, John Shore, Gerry Smith, Martin Spring, Phil Steadman, Jaap 't Hooft, James Thring, and Robert and Brenda Vale.

opposition of health authorites to D.I.Y. sewage treatment, and the planning officer to rooftop wind generators, the pollution levels (lead, etc) make rainwater a poor source and reduce solar receipts, buildings disrupt the flow of wind and shadow solar collectors, and auxiliary resources such as wood are scarce although the resource of scrap exists in abundance . Probably it is not worth ripping out the existing services, and sweet compromise is best, discussed further in section VII.

Most designs would work better in rural areas, although the Street Farm House (Fig C1) is a celebrated case of an autonomous unit on unserviced city land (a playing field), and Mick Bedford's Bracknell housing estate (Fig E4) is an idea for a formerly agricultural site on the outskirts of a stockbroker-belt town. More strictly site-specific are Ouroboros (Fig A1), designed for very harsh winters and to use local wood as an auxiliary fuel; Ecol

(Fig C3), designed for the tropics (it was built in Canada, occupied for a summer and abandoned in October); and Miller and Gilchrist's design (Figs 6, and 25) adapted to the sunless but relatively warm winters of the Orkneys.

NEW OR EXISTING STRUCTURES?

Any widespread development of autonomous servicing must surely depend to a large extent on the conversion of existing buildings. This, however, has been very rare among autonomous unit designs because starting from scratch is technically cleaner and more generalisable. Two exceptions are designs by Ian Hogan, one for a suburban house (Fig D1) and the other realised in his own house on a rural hillside (Fig 22). Another dream for the city is discussed in section VII and depicted in **Vision No 4.**

LIGHTWEIGHT/NOMADIC OR SOLID/ LONG LIFE?

Arguments about 'ecological building' rage between advocates of lightweight temporary recyclable structures, such as the dome or yurt (see 'Lightweight, Temporary, Quick, Mobile' by Stefan Szczelkun) on the one hand; and those who favour building more carefully for much longer life-spans on the other. Light structures can be put up quickly, easily and cheaply, and be well adapted to the needs of the occupants. They can also be dismantled and moved, or rebuilt in a different form. Yet they are difficult to service properly and tend to be very poorly insulated. And they usually leak. These difficulties can be overcome with careful design, as shown by Street Farm House (Fig C1), which, although roughly built, has withstood severe winters with a bit of patching. John Shore's design (Fig C2) is made chiefly of wood, glass and cardboard, but problems of insulation have been carefully considered, so it should not have the fearsome heat-loss problems that Ark (Fig 21) and Oasis (Fig 20) might have were they ever built. Robert Reines's 'Integrated Living System' is also a lightweight structure, but very heavily insulated with polyurethane foam (Fig B2).

Long-life building is in principle more economical of resources over its life-span, but poses the problem of changing uses. Alex Gordon's slogan 'Long Life, Loose Fit, Low Energy' suggests the solution of a general-purpose structure in which sensible initial investment in insulation and low-energy services can pay for themselves over and over again during their multi-purpose life-spans. There is no doubt that temporary structures are a lot of fun, but this long-term approach must obviously be the fundamental strategy.

TRADITIONAL OR INDUSTRIAL MATERIALS?

Although most autonomous units are designed to be built with standard industrial materials, some autonomists have tried to carry the principle of autonomy to the construction itself, and use on-site or local materials. Such local resources (wood, stone, subsoil, slate, reed, straw, etc.) are those used traditionally in building, and it has been observed that a suitable mixture of these and certain modern tools and techniques could lead to an economical and attractive 'new regionalism' in building (see 'Folk Building' by Brenda Vale, and 'The Earth Above Our Heads' by Colin Taylor). The use of local materials can require unusual skills, but these are not impossible to learn, and potentially there are good opportunities for cost savings in materials, transport and labour. Traditional materials may be necessary in some areas to fit in with planning regulations or local tastes (Fig 25 & Fig D2). Elsewhere they are just good sense, like the sod roofs of Ouroboros (Fig A1) and Street Farm House (Fig C1).

Where more conventional materials are used, most units are custom-built to a unique design, but others, with mass-production in mind, have proposed modular constructions. In Simon Longland's design, octagonal units can be assembled to give any size desired (Fig A2). Robert Reines's systems involve standard steel sections for the dome, and separate solar and wind units, which can be arranged in any convenient way (Fig B2).

The diversity of means, and the ways they are realised, allows a wide range of possibilities in the design of autonomous units. Some examples from this range, and the 'types' that tend to emerge, are described in section IV.

AUTONOMY

IV FAMILY AUTONOMY
Designs for Autonomous Houses

This part presents fourteen designs for family-sized autonomous units. The full specifications would require almost a book for every case, and only the barest bones can be given. I have tried to give an impression of the form and layout of each design, summarizing the pattern of autonomy by the bar-chart notation described in Box 1. The classification into four groups is perhaps a bit forced, but draws attention to certain features which tend to cluster together.

Few of these designs have been built, and most of them will probably never get beyond the drawing-board. But they are serious attempts to create minimal scale autonomous units. I picked these because they are representative, and illustrate various points in the text. Designs for units above the family scale are described in part VI.

A Integrated/spacious

This category contains designs that approximate the space and service standards of normal mains-serviced dwellings. The subsystems are closely integrated into the structure. They tend to be highly autonomous, sophisticated, and very expensive.

A1 *'Ouroboros'. Built by students at University of Minnesota School of Architecture. Trapezoidal plan to minimise heat loss on north side, which is also banked up by an earth berm to raise the frostline. A sod roof is used for summer cooling and winter insulation.*

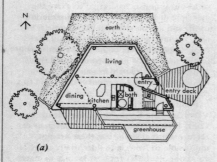

(a) Plan ground floor
(b) Section
(c) View from the north side in winter.
(d) Pattern of Autonomy

(a)

BOX 1.

The 'pattern of autonomy' of an autonomous unit is summarized in a bar chart. There are seven bars, representing the following services

E	Electricity
SH	Space Heating
WH	Water Heating
C	Cooking
WT	Waste Treatment
W	Water Supply
F	Food

Each bar is divided (arbitrarily) into four, and the way it is filled in indicates the type of source from which the demand is met, and how far it approximates 'normal' standards of consumption.

Key	Type of source	
☐	Absent	
░	Mains	These terms are explained, with examples, in the text on page 138
▒	Stored	
▓	Local	
■	Ambient	

Further information about each subsystem is given by letters on the bars as follows:

AC	Aerobic composter	OF	Other fuels (coal, paraffin, etc)
BG	Bottled gas	PR	Precipitation
CT	Chemical toilet	RE	Recycled
FC	Fireless Cooker or hay box	RU	Re-used
		SL	Still
GA	Garden produce	ST	Septic tank
GR	Greenhouse	SU	Sun
HP	Heat Pump	SW	Spring or well
HY	Hydroponics	WI	Wind
LS	Livestock	WO	Wood
MD	Methane Digestor	WP	Water power

The interpretation of these charts should be fairly straightforward.

(b)

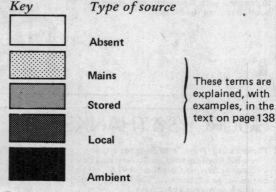

5kW DC aerogenerator

vent — sod roof — solar absorber — shading overhang (summer only)

vent — sleeping loft — natural venting

insulating berm — living — dining — low energy kitchen — greenhouse — garden

higher frostline

solar storage (all heat) — sewage composter for garden

constant 50°F

(c)

(d)

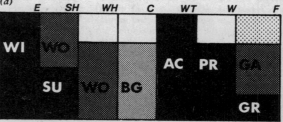

E	SH	WH	C	WT	W	F
WI / WO						
SU	WO	BG		AC	PR	GA
						GR

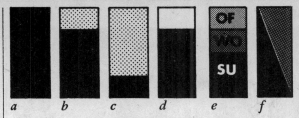

a   b   c   d   e   f

(*a*) for example, indicates complete autonomy in that subsystem, (*b*) a basic autonomy with mains backup, (*c*) 'symbolic autonomy'. Where there is no shading it indicates either that that subsystem is absent altogether, or does not match 'normal' mains standards, or customary levels of consumption, as in (*d*). (*e*) is an example of mixed sources, in this case, heating provided largely by solar energy, but backed up by wood and perhaps paraffin, (*f*) represents a case where an autonomous system needs some kind of external input for full functioning, for example grid electricity for a heat-pump, or external manure for a methane digestor. The use of the notation can be illustrated by considering three rather extreme cases.

(a) Almost perfect autonomy — the equivalent of the flow-chart in Fig 2; see also Fig A5
(b) A typical suburban mains-serviced house with central heating — equivalent to the flow-chart in Fig 3.
(c) An isolated country cottage with no services connections. In its own way, this is highly 'autonomous', and might be said to represent 'plain' as opposed to the 'fancy' autonomy of (a).

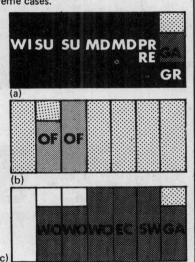

Most of the examples given in section IV can be regarded as intermediates between these three.

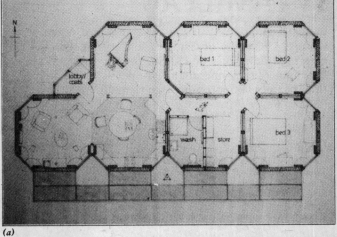

(a)

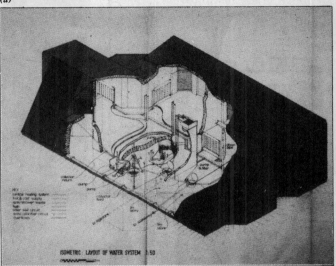

(b)

A2 *Autonomous house design by Simon Longland, Department of Architecture, University of Edinburgh. The prefabricated elements are assembled in octagonal modules. The design is aimed at mass-production. Occupancy '3-bedroom'.*

(a) Floor plan (b) South elevation (c) Cutaway showing water system (d) Pattern of autonomy

(c)

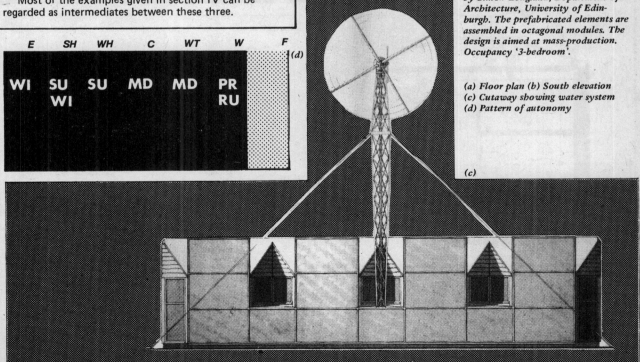

(d)

AUTONOMY

CAMBRIDGE DESIGNS

All these have some connection with the Autonomous Housing Study at the Department of Architecture, University of Cambridge. They all share certain assumptions, and although they are varied in appearance, they operate in very similar ways and their patterns of autonomy are virtually identical.

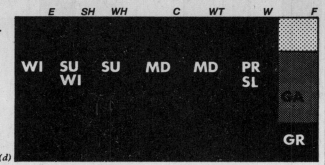

(d)

A3 *Design by Alexander Pike. Half the volume is given over to a tall greenhouse space which can be shut off to reduce heating load if necessary, but imparts a sense of spaciousness and could provide a certain amount of food. Occupancy 4.*
(a) Ground floor plan (b) Section (c) South side of model (d) Bar chart

(a)

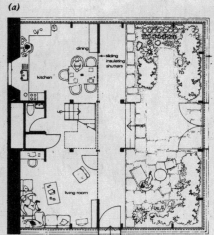

(c)

(b)

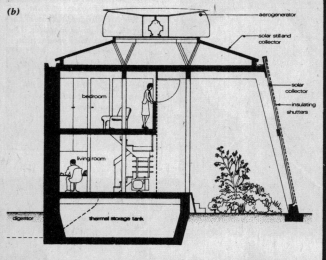

A4 *Design by James Thring and Gerry Smith. A relative of Pike's design, but smaller (occupancy 3). In this case the 'cheap space' is below rather than beside the living space, and allows a useful double function of the solar collectors, lowered during the day to admit light to the upper half, but raised during the night as insulating shutters. It can also be used for livestock, garaging and service elements, although most of these elements are contained in the central core.*
(a) Section (b) First floor plan (c) Pattern of autonomy

(a)

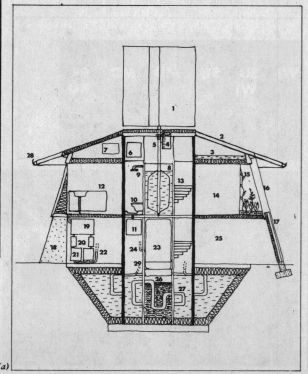

A5 *Design by Brenda Vale, awarded the British Institute Fund prize in Architecture. A long, wedge-shaped form with solar collector as roof, and light admitted via greenhouse on south side. First floor is smaller and can be shut off in the winter to conserve heat. Garden layouts are specified in the design, and examples can be seen in Vision No 3. Occupancy 4. Materials cost £10,000. See also Figs 5, 13, 15, 17, and compare Figs E2 and E3 in part VI, also by Brenda Vale and her husband Robert.*
(a) General view of the exterior
(b) Ground floor plan (c) Section
(d) Pattern of autonomy

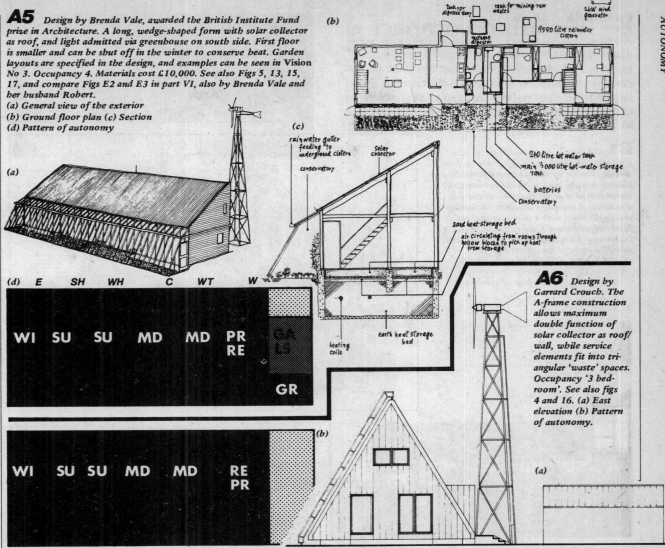

(b)

tank for digested slurry
tank for mixing raw wastes
2 kW wind generator
methane digestor
9550 litre rainwater cistern

(c)
rainwater gutter feeding to underground cistern
conservatory
solar collector
240 litre hot water tank
main 3 000 litre hot-water storage tank
batteries
conservatory
sand heat storage bed
air circulating from rooms through hollow blocks to pick up heat from storage
(a)
heating coils
earth heat storage bed

(d)

E	SH	WH	C	WT	W		
WI	SU	SU	MD	MD	PR RE	GA LS	
						GR	

WI	SU	SU	MD	MD	RE PR	

A6 *Design by Garrard Crouch. The A-frame construction allows maximum double function of solar collector as roof/wall, while service elements fit into triangular 'waste' spaces. Occupancy '3 bedroom'. See also figs 4 and 16. (a) East elevation (b) Pattern of autonomy.*

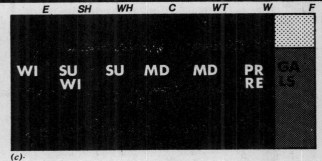

(a)

(b)

(c)

E	SH	WH	C	WT	W	F
WI WI	SU	SU	MD	MD	PR RE	GA LS

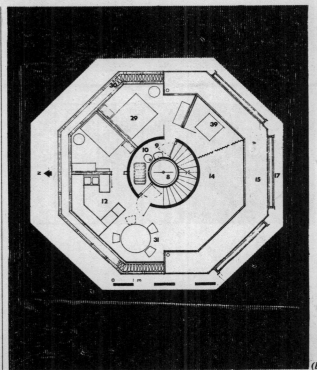

(b)

1 Vertical-axis rotor
2 Glass cover for still
3 Water in solar still
4 Electrical generator
5 Clutch
6 Batteries
7 Drinking water store
8 Callender water-heater and rotor brake
9 Shower
10 WC
11 Grey water treatment tank
12 Kitchen unit
13 Stairs
14 Living area
15 Greenhouse
16 Window
17 Movable solar collector and insulated shutter
18 Subsoil wall
19 Rain water tank
20 Slow sand filter
21 Earth water filter
22 To drinking water store
23 Methane gas store
24 Gas outlet
25 Livestock/garage space
26 Methane digestor
27 Heat exchanger
28 Rain collection gutter
29 Connection to solar collectors
30 Insulation
31 Dining area
32 Internal monitoring unit

B Modular/compact

These designs reduce space standards and have a tendency to feel poky inside, but costs are lower than in category A. The subsystem elements tend to be physically separated, giving greater freedom of overall layout. Autonomy is not so comprehensive as in category A.

(a)

B1   *Autonomous dome built by Jaap 't Hooft at the Small Earth experimental farm, Boxtel, The Netherlands. A very compact geodesic frame insulated with cork-cement. Window area is very low (2%) but the windows are carefully situated. The interior is a single room with a sunken lobby and separate bathroom. Solar collector, wind-generator and methane digestor are all removed from the main structure. Occupancy 1 or 2. Cost £3-4,000. See also Figs 14 and 22.*
(a) Layout of elements (b) The exterior
(c) The interior (d) Pattern of autonomy.

1   The house
2   Methane digestor
3   Solar collector
4   Wind generator
5   Vent
6   Non-opening windows
7   Opening window
8   Sunken doorway
9   Rain gutter
10 Methane digestor feed hatch
11 Stirrer handle

(c)

DE BOL VAN BINNEN

(d) ▼

(b)

E	SH	WH	C	WT	W	F
WI	SU	MD	MD	MD	RU PR	GA

B2   *'Integrated Living System' built by Robert Reines in New Mexico. A steel dome insulated with polyurethane foam, and heat-loss reduced by airlock and lowered ventilation rate. Lighting by 'portholes' and fanlight. Wind generator and solar collector separate from main structure. The system is oriented towards energy autonomy in an ideal climate. Cost equivalent to mobile home and potentially mass-producible. Occupancy 2.*
(a) General view of dome, collectors and generator (b) Pattern of autonomy

(a)

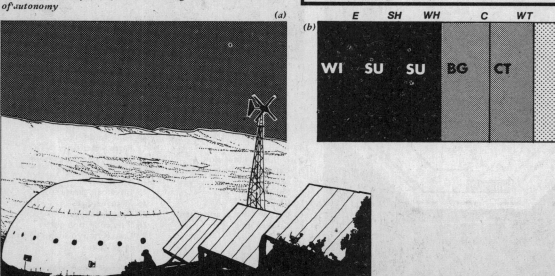

(b)

E	SH	WH	C	WT	W	F
WI	SU	SU	BG	CT		

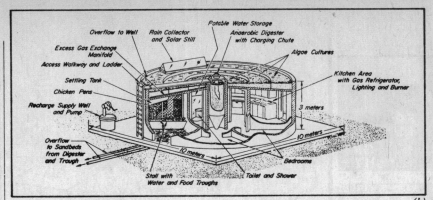

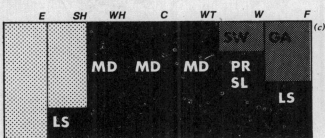

(b)

(a)

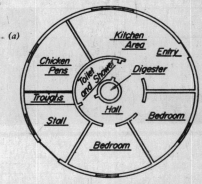

B3 *Design by C.G. Golueke and W.J. Oswald. This proposes a food/water/waste system for four people. The occupants and animals are housed in a single structure, and the waste products are used to grow algae and generate methane for cooking, refrigeration and water-heating. Food is fully supplied from the animals and a presumed adjacent site for vegetables. There is no special provision for electricity or space-heating. (a) Floor plan (b) Cut-away showing interior (c) Pattern of autonomy.*

C Low–cost

These designs are relatively cheap, generally made of lightweight materials, and showing partial and selective patterns of autonomy. Occupants are expected to live very carefully.

C1 *Street Farm House, designed by Graham Caine and built by the Street Farmers at Eltham, London. Timber frame insulated with wood wool. Basically a shed with a green-house, incorporating hydroponic beds and fishpond fertilised with effluent from methane digestor. Occupancy 2½. Cost £1000. See also Figs 10 and 24, and interview with Street Farmers in the book.*
(a) General view of the house (b) Cutaway diagram of the system (c) Pattern of autonomy — intended (d) Pattern of autonomy — realised

(a)

A Living part
B Greenhouse part
a Solar collector panels
   (radiators)
b Hot water tank
c Methane digestor
d Toilet seat
e Methane storage

f Kitchen
g Water collector
   and filtration
h Fish pond
i Sod roof
j Polythene screening (originally inflated)
k Openable panels
l Hydroponic beds
m Nutrient feed pipe
n Nutrient overflow

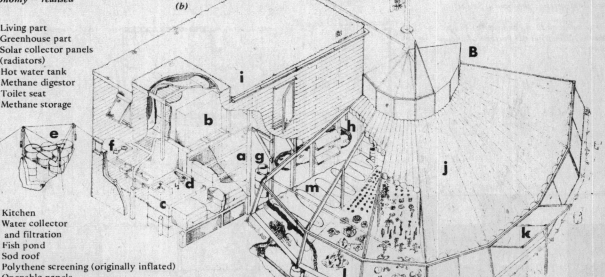

(b)

Street Farm - continued

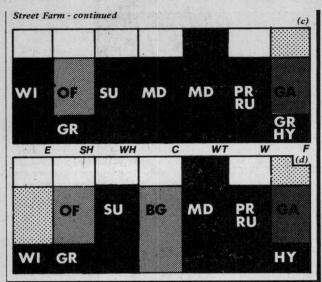

(c)

WI	OF	SU	MD	MD	PR RU	GA
	GR					GR HY

E   SH   WH   C   WT   W   F

(d)

	OF	SU	BG	MD	PR RU	GA
WI	GR					HY

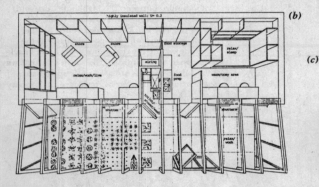

(b)

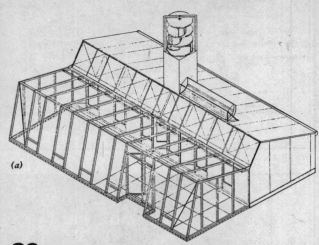

(a)

C2

'Integrated Solar Dwelling' designed by John Shore. Timber frame structure with greenhouse section, insulated with cardboard and cupboards, with a small 'retreat space' for very cold weather. Solar heat is collected passively in the greenhouse and south walls panels. The tower holds wind-generator and water-tank. Occupancy 2. See also Figs 12 and 14.
(a) Exterior (b) Plan (c) Pattern of Autonomy

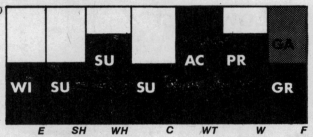

(c)

		SU		AC	PR	GA
WI	SU		SU			GR

E   SH   WH   C   WT   W   F

C3

'Ecol' built by the Minimum-Cost Housing Group at McGill University, Montreal. This is a simple two-part structure of wood and cast sulphur-cement components, intended for use in tropical areas. There is no need for space-heating. The water supply and waste-treatment unit is separate from the rest of the structure. Cooking is solar and done outside the house. See also Fig 11.
(a) General view of the unit (b) Floor plan (c) Elevation (d) Pattern of autonomy

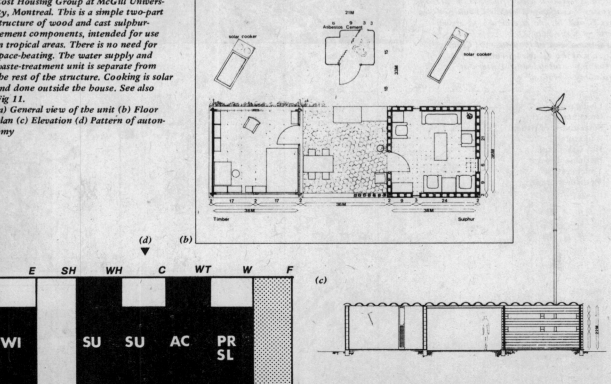

(b)

(c)

(d)
▼

E   SH   WH   C   WT   W   F

		SU	SU	AC	PR SL	
WI						

D Conversions

These are adaptations of existing structures. Two examples are given, both by Ian Hogan of Low Impact Design, one urban and one rural.

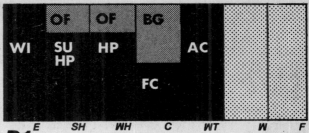

WI	OF	OF	BG		
	SU HP	HP	AC		
		FC			
E	SH	WH	C	WT	W	F

(b)

D1 *Urban house design for Conservation Tools and Technology Ltd. The walls are insulated on the outside and cladded with matchboard. The windows are covered with a floating greenhouse for passive heat collection. A heatpump extracts heat from the roof space and stores heat in butyl bags under the ground floor. Electricity is provided by an Elektro generator rated at 5kW and mounted on a mast next to the house.*
(a) Front elevation (b) Pattern of autonomy

D2 *Hillside Cottage, the designer's home. Originally little more than a ruin, it has been restored with vernacular materials in an unusual way. Ian Hogan remarks:*

The house lies on the boundry between the highland (Cotswold) vernacular of stone walls and roof, and the lowland (Vale of Berkeley) vernacular of red clay bricks and tiled roofs. So the uphill side of the house is the one, and the downhill side is the other. Ha Ha. By the time we'd built that stone roof, I was knackered, and the tiles are easier, so we finished the south side that way. But throughout, vernacular materials are used with up-to-date building-science information — damp-proof, insulated. Autonomy is possible, if you trim yr coat . . .

The cottage sits on a two-acre wooded site, and uses wood for all heating purposes. The next stage is a greenhouse to be built on the south wall for passive solar heating and 'parakeets, vipers, lemurs, grapes, figs . . . .'
(a) South side (b) North side (c) Wind generator (d) Pattern of autonomy

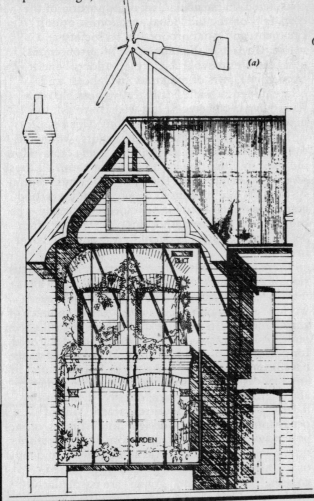

(a)

(a)

(a)

(b)   (c)

			WO	BG		
	WO					
WI		SU	WO	AC	PR	GA
GR						GR

(d)

V ECONOMICS OF AUTONOMY

Having described a number of built, planned or dreamed-of autonomous systems and the principles behind them, we have to try and make a more critical analysis of whether they are worth all the effort, or at least whether they *could be*. There are some pretty ideas, but one often gets the feeling that there must be a catch somewhere.

We have to weigh costs against benefits. A short discussion of the different aspects of cost is necessary before getting down to the substantive issues.

For a start, autonomists have different motives, so there is no universal yardstick for costs and benefits that applies equally well to them all. Purely economic motives are unusual, and autonomous units are usually justified on ecological or social grounds, or simply as a way of life. Of course, no unit can be built in complete disregard of financial constraints, but *money costs are not the only ones we need to consider.*

Secondly, the distribution of costs over time must be considered, especially where autonomous servicing is being compared with mains servicing. The initial *capital cost* — what the system cost to build — contrasted with the *running cost* — what it costs to keep it going. As we shall see, the overwhelming tendency is for the capital costs of autonomous systems to be high, and the running costs low; while the opposite is true of central servicing. Neither alone is a very good basis for comparison. From the point of view of running costs, autonomous systems can look miraculous ('Free Hot Water!' as the solar-panel ads say), but when capital costs are considered, they can seem absurd. The only fair basis of comparison is what is called the 'Whole Life Cost', which is the total capital and running costs of a system over its entire lifetime. The yearly average of this I shall call the *Average Annual Cost*. It has some disadvantages in that it involves making assumptions about inflation and interest rates, how long the system is likely to last, and so on, but it's the best we have.

Thirdly, the *social* distribution of costs must be considered. In particular, what proportion of the costs falls on the individual autonomist or unit occupant, and what proportion on society as a whole. Obviously the economics of autonomous units can seem favourable if the builders benefit from grants, gifts of materials and labour, and other hidden subsidies. It is always possible for a few to live in the cracks, but we have to ask the question 'What if everybody did it?' This requires ruthless exactitude about *all* the inputs: where did the skills of designers and builders come from? How did they find the time to do it? What about all those scrap parts? and so on. This cuts both ways: central systems too are subsidised from general taxes, and grants are available to householders for certain capital costs such as bathrooms. All this can often be difficult to assess in detail, but it must be borne in mind.

These distinctions will be important in the discussion of economics which follows. They allow a bit more precision, but underneath it is mostly guesswork. We know rather little about the economics of autonomous units because so few have actually been built, and even fewer properly costed or monitored for performance, although most of the sub-systems have been investigated in isolation. Furthermore, in any real case the costs will be affected by innumerable factors such as climate, density, distribution, pattern of autonomy, local resources, skills of occupants, efficiency of design, interest rates, monopoly powers of suppliers, and so on. It is therefore only possible to discuss general tendencies, and most of the numbers I give will be at best informed guesses. The 'generalised graphs' are particularly tendentious, but they do not need to be exact to make the points. The final joker in the pack is inflation, which could make nonsense of everything.

NON-MONETARY COSTS

Autonomous units are not generally built for short term economic reasons. They may be built as an experiment to try out potential economies, or as an investment, or as a hedge against troubled times to come. But the rationales given are more commonly ideological, in the broad sense, usually to do with environmental impact and resource depletion. The claim is that in these respects autonomous systems offer a substantial improvement over mains services. Is this a reasonable claim?

Consider environmental costs. The kinds of techniques typically used in autonomous units are often referred to as 'Low Impact Technology', and one can hardly dispute that, say, a wind-generator emits less sulphur dioxide, carbon dioxide and particulate matter than, say, an oil-fired power station. Neither does it incur the inevitable side-effects of oil delivery, nor require transmission lines. The analysis is often left at this, Q.E.D.

But the operation of a wind-generator does have an environmental impact. It is not likely to be pretty; it can make a lot of noise; and there is some danger from broken blades and collapsing towers. And we cannot fairly compare the impact of a 2kW wind generator with a power station producing perhaps a million times as much. Therefore we must consider the cumulative effect of a million such 2kW machines or, if larger ones are constructed, tens of thousands — with transmission lines. This is merely to trade one set of environmental impacts for another, and who is to say which is preferable?

But even now, we have only considered the running environmental costs. A fair comparison must include the environmental costs of making the wind generators in the first place, as against those of building an equivalent central power station. This would involve comparing the environmental impacts of mining, refining and working the steel, copper, aluminium and lead; the impacts of producing the energy necessary for all this; and the transport. Given the economies of scale, far more material *must* be necessary to create a million 2kW machines than a single 2GW (2 million kilowatt) power station. Assuming that the environmental impact per unit of material is about the same in both cases, we can conclude fairly firmly that the *capital* environmental cost of small wind generators is higher, pro rata, than that of central power stations. Whether this extra 'investment' is 'paid off' by improved environmental impact during the life of the small machines depends on one's assessment of the relative running environmental costs. It is at best an open question.

A similar argument can be applied to other autonomous sub-systems, with the possible exception of garden produce. It is true that their running environmental costs are probably lower than those of wind generators (think for example of solar collectors, greenhouses, methane digestors, water towers) but

BOX 2. 'ENERGY COST' OF BRAD SOLAR ROOF.

For a diagram of the structure of the roof, see Fig E1 c; for a diagram of the circuit, see Fig 7 in Robert Vale's article 'Sunshine Superpower'.

1: ENERGY COST

Component	Energy of Manufacture (kilowatt-hours per kilogram)	Weight used (kg)	Total (kWh)
Aluminium (plate and glazing bars)	85	176	15000
Glass-reinforced plastic (covers, tank)	29	204	6000
Copper (header pipe)	23	8	1700
Other (electrical components, gutters, transport etc)		(say)	2000
		Total	25000

2: ENERGY RECEIPTS (annual)

	kWh
Daily incident energy per sq metre, summer average	3
Useful heat, at 30% efficiency	1
Total for 60 sq metres (area of roof)	60
Total over 8 summer months (250 days)	15000
Less energy for 180W pump operating 5h/day, over 250 days (say 500W thermal)	1000
Net energy yield per year	14000

These calculations do not allow for the entropic differences between energy of manufacture (high grade) and the relatively low-temperature heat collected. But 'pessimistic' figures have been chosen consistently. For example, published estimates for the manufacturing energy of aluminium range from 16 to 85 kWh(t), and the latter has been chosen for these calculations.

The 'payback' period seems to be between two and three years.

they can hardly involve less sheer material than their mains equivalents and therefore almost certainly incur greater capital environmental costs. It is often argued that autonomous units would use less, and therefore mains-matching capacities of autonomous systems are not necessary: there would be fewer windmills, etc. But the same argument applies to central servicing: if households would use less, power stations could be shut down, tanker transits reduced, and flooded valleys restored, to exactly the same degree.

This general conclusion about materials inevitably raises the other 'ecological' issue: resource costs. Can autonomous units help to conserve scarce resources, given imminent shortages and the eventual exhaustion of a number of important industrial materials? Virtually by definition, the running costs of an autonomous unit are low. Some designers have attempted to use as far as possible abundant local materials in construction. Nevertheless many parts of any moderately 'fancy' autonomous unit must incorporate metals, that in many cases are scarce and non-renewable, and, further, require non-renewable sources of energy for extraction and processing — assuming that the ambient energy

resources, apart from hydropower, have not the muscle for such big industrial jobs.

Take again the case of wind-generators. If every household had one, the demand for copper and lead would increase enormously. Alternatives to mechanical generation of electricity or lead-acid battery storage tend to be even less efficient and also require non-renewable materials (platinum, arsenic, gallium, nickel, cadmium, etc). While there is a lot of scope for scrap-technology here,

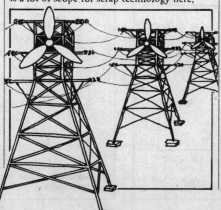

fundamentally it seems that any kind of electricity-generating system involves non-renewable resources, and decentralised systems only seem to reduce the efficiency with which they are used. This is a conclusion which autonomists of every hue will be called upon to answer.

If this seems harsh, there is some comfort in turning to other sub-systems. Although they share the capital-resource inefficiencies of small-scale electricity, their construction usually involves more abundant materials such as aluminium, steel, glass, plastics, cement, sand, etc. The problem with all these is not that they are going to run out, but that they need a great deal of energy to make, energy of a kind which is itself non-renewable. So the next question to ask is, do typical autonomous systems repay their energy costs?

Thankfully, this is a bit more encouraging. Take the case of the BRAD solar roof (Fig E1). It is made of aluminium, glass-reinforced plastic, plastic plumbing and tanks, and a small amount of copper that could in principle be replaced by another material. The total energy cost can be generously estimated at 25,000 kWh (see Box 2), whereas the expected annual receipts are well over 10,000 kWh. It should therefore recover its energy outlay in three years. It is expected to last at least thirty. A similar brisk recovery seems to apply to most alternative energy systems. As far as energy is concerned, they are good investments. Under this is another surprising conclusion: that 'low-energy building' (ie low capital energy cost), although possible, is generally such a low proportion of the total whole-life energy cost that it is not really worth bothering about unless it reduces running energy costs. The question of balancing scarce energy costs against scarce material costs remains to be answered, but if autonomous units can be built which save energy through use of abundant resources, they are clearly making a useful contribution.

A final category of non-monetary cost that must be considered is 'alienation cost'. This is a tricky one, but let's say it is the sum total of human misery involved in creating and running an autonomous unit. Generally speaking, the running alienation costs (except in as-yet hypothetical pluto-units operated by a corps of maintenance workers) fall on to the occupants themselves in the form of vigilance, effort, social tensions, discomfort and so on, as discussed under Making Do. The capital alienation costs are those required for building — which would be about the same as any small-scale construction job, and in making the materials: the unpleasant and ill-rewarded work involved in mining, manufacture of parts, cement, plastics, glass, wood, steel, aluminium, etc; which has to be set against those needed to provide coal, oil, electricity, food, water and sewerage for mains services. It would be difficult to compare these without a lot of assumptions and a lot of research, but we must be aware of the difference between building autonomous units in utopia where it's fair do's all round, and in this society where those who typically design and inhabit the things are not those who produce the wherewithal to make them. (Fig 31)

The general conclusions, then, are that autonomous systems probably change the nature of, rather than reduce, the overall environmental impact; that in some cases they increase the use of non-renewable resources; but can substantially reduce the use of non-renewable sources of energy. Whether they reduce social alienation in the long run is hard to say, but I would judge the autonomists probably have a case.

AUTONOMY

MONETARY COSTS

A discussion of non-monetary costs is necessary because the mere price of goods and services does not reflect all the aspects on which we want to place value. Prices are also distorted by inflated profit-taking, monopolies, cartels, subsidies, and so on. But prices do reflect many things we want to take account of: material costs, labour costs, capital costs, scarcities and current social values. And since in practice they deeply condition every choice that has to be made in the design of autonomous units, money costs assume a central place (as usual) in this analysis.

A few numbers will illustrate the typical cost comparisons between autonomous and central servicing. A 'typical 3-bedroom detached house' cost about £3,000 for materials alone in 1973. The Bill of Quantities for Brenda Vale's house (Fig A5), which is about the same size, came to £10,000. Mains servicing in electricity, gas, water and waste treatment for the typical house in 1973 cost about £80 a year (national average — it would be lot more now). Comparable supplies would be much cheaper in the autonomous house if the capital were provided free, but the average annual cost including interest on capital and maintenance costs would be at least twice as much and probably more. And this is not even quite as good as mains servicing. There are limits to the demands that can be made, and a certain level of daily or periodic maintenance is required. To mimic mains performance absolutely, for example to be able to run all electrical loads at once, flush noxious chemicals down the toilet, use sprinklers on the lawn, etc, raises the capital cost of autonomy (and hence its average annual cost) from high to astronomical. The point is, how near to mains standards of performance do we want to get?

The curious relationship between cost and standards of autonomy is reflected in the following remark of Ian Hogan's

> Spend a £1000 or so on AT gadgets, and any house can become about 60% self-sufficient in energy. Spend more, say £3000, on heat-pumps and windmills, and you may achieve 80% autonomy. The last 20% will be hardest and costliest to achieve.

What he is saying is that these are the kind of costs needed to achieve 'normal' standards of consumption at 'normal' standards of performance. It costs less if you have lower than normal consumption, put up with lower standards of performance, or mix mains and autonomous supplies. More of this anon. What is important is the general form of the curve, which crops up over and over again, and is illustrated in Fig 26. I shall call this **Hogan's Law**.

Fig 26 is a heroic generalisation of Hogan's remark, assuming the pattern applies to other services as well as energy, lumping all services together, and converting to average annual costs. What is implied is that, for a given level of consumption and standard of performance, the replacement of existing mains services with autonomous ones tends to get more and more expensive as 'total autonomy' is approached. On the graph, point 1 would represent a few autonomous systems grafted on to existing mains services, for example as fuel or food savers; 2 would represent autonomous systems making a substantial contribution to total demand, but with mains back-up; 3 would represent almost complete autonomy, but with 'emergency' stored supplies; 4 would be a hypothetical complete state of autonomy with exactly mains standards.

But what if there is no mains supply to begin with, and you are starting from scratch? This gives a different interpretation to the same curve, one that is more useful for our purposes. Here the different cases are all independent of the mains, and hence equally 'autonomous' in formal terms, but they give different levels of consumption and perform-

ance. 1 now represents the minimum survival level: simple systems that yield very little and behave erratically; 2 represents an austere but not gruelling standard, with systems of modest performance; 3 represents 'as near as dammit' approximation to mains standards less than which most people, Building Societies and Local Authorities would find unacceptable; 4 as before represents a hypothetical perfect mimicry of mains standards. 3 is an important case because it sits at what I shall call 'the threshold of bourgeois amenity'.

A number of interesting features of autonomous servicing are reflected in this curve. One, which I shall discuss in more detail later, is the hiatus between the spartan autonomy of the *nouveaux pauvres* and the autonomy of 'bourgeois amenity'. The average annual costs represented by cases 2 and 3 divide the graph's area in three parts. Zone A is cheap — perhaps under £200 a year. Zone B is intermediate — perhaps up to £500 a year. Zone C is expensive — over £500 (all these are for dwellings of 3-4 people). In zone C we find designs restricted by the threshold of bourgeois amenity. Zone A is inhabited by designs restricted by finance. Zone B is a kind of no-man's land where few venture, but which is probably where the future lies.

It seems to me that the curve will always have the same general shape, although the actual values will change in different circumstances. In Fig 27, curve A might represent costs in (for example) a sunny climate with mild winters, regular winds and well-distributed rainfall; curve B costs in a correspondingly unfavourable climate. Many families of such curves could be generated by taking into account all the factors which influence costs.

In contrast to these curves, mains service costs — at least to the consumer — are pretty well linear with consumption (the performance being virtually fixed), but again will vary under different circumstances, giving different slopes. Curve C in Fig 27 could represent true mains costs in ideal circumstances of settlement density, cheap fuels and labour, etc; curve D costs for sparse population where raw materials and labour costs are very high.

Fig 27 indicates how, under 'normal circumstances' (C and B) autonomy of any kind is hopelessly uneconomic. But under conditions favourable to autonomy and unfavourable to mains servicing, cost advantage passes first to the cheap-and-simple systems, then through the intermediate range, and finally to the dear-and-fancy ones. It is now necessary to explain just why the costs of mains and autonomous service systems are so divergent, and where they might go in the future.

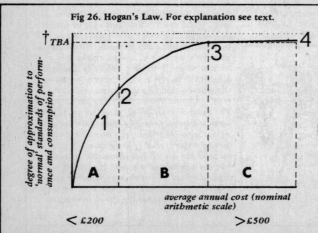

Fig 26. Hogan's Law. For explanation see text.

†TBA

degree of approximation to 'normal standards of performance and consumption

A   B   C

average annual cost (nominal arithmetic scale)

< £200   > £500

† TBA (threshold of bourgeois amenity)

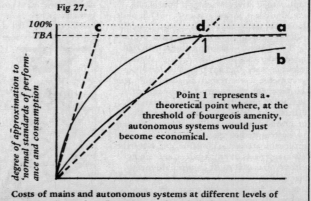

Fig 27.

100%
TBA

degree of approximation to 'normal standards of performance and consumption

Point 1 represents a theoretical point where, at the threshold of bourgeois amenity, autonomous systems would just become economical.

Costs of mains and autonomous systems at different levels of consumption and performance, under relatively favourable and unfavourable circumstances.

WHY ARE CENTRAL SERVICES SO CHEAP?

The costs of central servicing must include: plant (equipment); fuels and other running resources; distribution; labour, overheads, maintenance, etc. Normally these costs can be met economically owing to economies of scale, since many subscribers are served by a single plant, and in the case of densely-settled city-dwellers, by a single distribution system. Capital for new plant can be met out of turn-over or cheap loans. The running resources have been in steady supply, so there is no need for storage systems either centrally or in dwellings, nor for alternative systems in case of failure. Running resources have also been *cheap*: it is worth remembering that while they last, coal, oil and natural gas are as free as sunshine; the cost, as with solar energy, is in tapping and harnessing them.

The fact that except for appliances there is virtually no capital equipment in the houses — just holes in the walls and floors — means low costs for the subscriber, because no interest need be paid on loans for capital. Individual costs are further reduced by the availability of grants for what capital costs remain — bathrooms, for example. Even rates may not reflect the true costs, owing to grants from central government to local authorities.

WHY ARE AUTONOMOUS UNITS SO EXPENSIVE?

Autonomous units avoid certain costs characteristic of central servicing: fuels, distribution, overheads. Plant cost accounts for most of the total cost of autonomous systems, but these tend to be far higher pro rata than mains plant costs, for a number of reasons. Firstly, technical economies of scale are absent. Secondly the capital investment involves borrowing money, and interest rates are unfavourable for small enterprises. Interest payments can easily double the average annual cost. Thirdly, plant of extra capacity and complexity is needed to provide a guaranteed supply. More needs to be said about this last point. It applies particularly strongly to those designs constrained to conjure the silk purse of bourgeois amenity out of the sow's ear of mean and moody ambient resources.

To provide high standards of consumption and performance, autonomous units first need to spend more on 'Leak Plugging' (insulation, heat exchangers, water-saving devices, etc); for example the insulation materials alone in Brenda Vale's house (Fig A5) cost about £700). Then, it is usually necessary to design all the sub-systems, not for average conditions, but for the worst forseeable conditions. This means that for most of the time the systems are much 'too good' and represent capital lying idle. Fig 13 for example shows that in a typical year, a large storage tank for autonomous water supply is never less than 2/3 full. They are *overdesigned*. Where there is always *some* ambient supply (eg diffuse sky radiation, or low-grade heat) it is possible to increase the capacity of the collector elements. But it is more usual — and, where there are periods of absolutely no supply (eg wind and rain), necessary — to overdesign the store elements. Designers have to decide (usually from meteorological records) just how unusual the conditions are at which they will give up providing bigger and better stores and collectors 'just in case'. The water tank in Simon Longland's house, for example (Fig A2), is so large that on average the occupants would be one litre short of their daily water ration once every 72 years. This strikes me as taking it rather far — after all, even the mains break down sometimes.

Finally, autonomous systems may have to install more than one system to provide a given service. This second system is known as a *back-up* or auxiliary system, and it may be based on any of the four kinds of sources: ambient, local, stored or mains. Naturally this involves a certain duplication of capital costs, but the different cases have to be distinguished.

A second *autonomous* system for the same service is most feasible when two sources of supply are reciprocal, or at least independent, for example, when precipitation is low a solar still is likely to work well (see also Fig 21). This tends to be the most expensive solution, and remains vulnerable to quirks of the ambient conditions. The other solutions are cheaper yet involve a progressive retreat from pure autonomy. The commonest proposed local back-up is wood, and this looks cheap, but is not widely available. Its true cost should include land and labour, and there is a definite limit to the sustainable yield off a given area of woodland.

Yet another step away from 'pure' autonomy is the use of stored resources, giving the kind of intermittent dependency favoured by well-heeled 'siege autonomists': bottled gas, other solid and liquid fuels, dried and canned foods, stationary generator, water-purification tablets, etc. The cheapest back-up is usually the mains themselves, in accordance with the first interpetation of Hogan's Law. Mains and stored-resource back-ups allow autonomous systems to be simpler and smaller in capacity, operating only under optimum conditions and therefore the overall system is relatively cheap.

This is an important conclusion, with certain implications about the real purposes of autonomy. Trying to guarantee high standards of performance in highly autonomous systems is very expensive. Trying to reduce costs at a high level of autonomy leads to lower standards of performance. Trying to reduce costs at a high level of performance leads to lower levels of autonomy. Something has got to give.

MAINS V. AUTONOMY: NARROWING THE DIFFERENTIAL

Under what circumstances are mains services more costly, and autonomous services cheaper? In terms of Fig 27; what might move curve C to curve D, and Curve B to curve A? Some of these circumstances (eg location) have to be *found* or *chosen*. Others (such as fuel costs) are social or economic trends that have to be *anticipated*. Yet others (eg new designs or life-styles) must be *experienced* or *created*.

In remote areas transmission and distribution costs of mains services are already so high that autonomous systems may already be cheaper, even in capital costs. An isolated dwelling 1km from central plant would cost about £6,000 to provide with mains electricity, gas, water and sewerage. The advantage of living in such a situation is that land is much cheaper, but this in itself favours autonomous units which make intensive use of their land for food and wood production. The relationship between location and the economics of servicing is succinctly summarised in Fig 28, borrowed from Simon Longland. Running costs of central services will certainly increase as a result of higher fuel costs, labour and overheads, and probably social measures such as stricter pollution standards. Not much more can be said about these, because of the uncertainties involved: it is merely a question of waiting. The scope for action lies mainly in the other limb of the pincer: reducing the costs of autonomous systems, and I shall deal with this at greater length.

CHEAPER AUTONOMOUS SYSTEMS

First I'll consider those 'social trends' which, although largely beyond our control, may reduce the costs of autonomous units: technological improvements; mass production; and general recognition of the social costs of conventional servicing.

Technological breakthroughs are something we can always dream about — although, considering where all the research money is, they are far more likely to apply to centralised systems and end up reducing *their* costs. But research into alternative systems is increasing. In the wind field alone, recent innovations include the Canadian National Research Council catenary rotor; 'Windworks' octahedral tower (see 'Natural, Endless, Free' by Derek Taylor, Figs 9b, 35); and mass-producible teflon bearings for Savonius rotors. Other improvements and reduced unit costs are eagerly awaited in: selective absorbers for solar panels; photoelectric panels; simple and safe electrolytic hydrogen generation

Fig 28. Notional selection of plant at various distances from central supplies. (From Longland).

SERVICE	LOCATION			
	'Sub-Urban'	'Semi-rural'	'Rural'	'Remote'
Hot water	partially by solar collector	100% solar		full solar collector & storage +hydro or wind power to 100% nominal design load.
Space heating	central service but well insulated shell reduces energy demand.	full solar collector & storage to about 60% of nominal design load.		
Water supply	central service	central	from well or surface water course or by roof collection & storage.	
Electricity supply	central service	central	central - hydro - wind	hydro - wind
Gas/sewage	central service	digestor	digestor	digestor
	overshadowing problems reduce solar heating potential but 60% load factor may be possible on some sites	solar heat collection maximised to reduce load to central system. but complexity of on site electricity generation not yet justified. central services except gas & sewage still within economic threshold distance.	some sites - otherwise remote - may be close to 11kV grid transmission lines (i.e within 1 km) in this case 'economics' favours connection as before.	full autonomy. Plant alternatives listed in descending 'order of preference'

AUTONOMY

and storage; long-life batteries; fuel cells; insulation materials. And soya beans that really work in high latitudes.

Mass-production of components for autonomous systems could affect costs quite a lot, although most of the materials are already standard (batteries, dynamos, corrugated aluminium, glass-fibre, panel radiators, insulation, pumps, tanks, pipework, etc). It would need to be determined exactly when and where mass-production of total systems with formal labour would be more economical than self-assembly from basic materials and parts on a more informal, co-operative basis, more exactly tailored to the needs of the users. Some designs are specifically intended for mass-production (eg Figs A2 and B2) as complete units. It will certainly be interesting to see how Reines's system (Fig B2) fares on the market.

A final social trend that may affect the relative economics of mains and autonomous servicing is the recognition of the *social* costs of central servicing, for example certain kinds of environmental damage, resource depletion, balance of payments, political dependencies arising from resource needs and so on. This recognition might be reflected in extra charges for mains services (or reduction of various subsidies) or financial assistance for alternatives. Financial assistance might be to manufacturers, or to householders, possibly in the form of low-interest loans that could allow rational whole-life costing without an exaggerated burden of interest payments.

Quite a different approach to reducing the costs of autonomous units lies in exploring the category of Clever Ideas and taking more care to find exactly the best patterns of autonomy for particular circumstances. For example, designers should consider carefully for each sub-system whether Leak-Plugging, overdesign or back-up systems are going to be the cheapest, and in what combinations. In the case of back-up systems, designers must find the optimum balance between the autonomous system and the back-up. This can in favourable circumstances be cheaper than either system alone, as indicated once again by Hogan's Law (Fig 29).

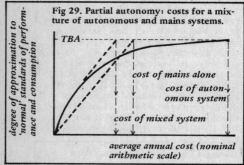

Fig 29. Partial autonomy: costs for a mixture of autonomous and mains systems.

degree of approximation to 'normal' standards of performance and consumption

TBA

cost of mains alone
cost of autonomous system
cost of mixed system

average annual cost (nominal arithmetic scale)

Economy may lie therefore in *partial* autonomy for certain sub-systems, and even more in *selective* autonomy: attempting it only for those services where it is most economic. This is pretty obvious really. BRAD's shows some examples (Fig E1). The solar roof is limited to summer hot-water heating, and for this needs no store and can be very cheap. Winter water heating is provided by wood and mains electricity. No attempt was made to achieve autonomy in electricity as a mains supply was already installed, the site is very sheltered, and reliable performance is essential for driving the heat-pump and solar collector pump. In a similar way most of the units described in this article have a mixed pattern of autonomous servicing and external supplies. This is what practicality dictates at the moment, and I see no reason why this should change.

Finally we reach a category of cost reductions which in my opinion are the nub of the whole matter: the social rather than technical adaptations and innovations. Hogan's Law indicates that the initial basic measure of autonomy is relatively cheap, and if its deficiencies can be tolerated, adapted to, softened, or compensated for in inexpensive ways, the lower end of the curve could hold all the best bargains. I shall consider two broad topics. One is the more-or-less systematic sacrifice of consumption/performance/reliability/comfort/convenience. This necessarily violates the canons of bourgeois amenity, and splits autonomous designs into two broad classes which I shall try and define more closely. The other topic is that of economies of scale, which raises the whole question of autonomy versus collectivity, and what the hell we are trying to do anyway.

SACRIFICES OF AMENITY

The spirit of this has already been invoked under Making Do. The art is in judicious sacrifice of nominal amenity factors in such a way as to reduce costs without a concomitant loss of perceived or subjective amenity. Work and effort are substituted for material or capital stock; consumption is reduced to levels that can easily be provided by the simpler autonomous systems; and discomforts and inconveniences which arise from the unreliable performance of the cheap systems are cheerfully (well then, stoically) borne. These sacrifices define another class of costs, namely *amenity costs*, which to a large extent can be exchanged for money costs.

As with other kinds of costs, there are both capital and running amenity costs. Capital amenity costs are incurred in constructing the unit, and if shouldered by the autonomists themselves may save perhaps a third of the capital money cost which would otherwise have gone to labour costs and contractor's profit. But of course, most self-builders hardly regard it as 'work' at all. It's kind of fulfilling, and gives the builders a commitment to and understanding of the unit which makes a lot of difference to the eventual running costs, amenity and otherwise. This is just the kind of thing we are looking for — nominal amenity costs with a silver lining.

Running amenity costs are those borne while living in the unit. Some of these go on all the time, others crop up occasionally. What might be called 'chronic' amenity costs include consumption limits on electricity, water, gas, heat and meat. Most of these entail arrangements disagreeable to conventional taste, for example no baths, only showers; no electric kettles for tea, or casual brew-ups; raw foods, one hot meal a day, Chinese-style cooking; bone soup, mince once a week or bacon from the unit pig; chilly bedrooms; small windows; stuffy air, etc. Lack of space in those units underdesigned relative to the service systems (Fig B1) is another continuous amenity cost, as is the extensive maintenance work needed to avoid the cost of fancy automated systems that adjust and regulate themselves.

'Occasional' running amenity costs may or may not be planned for. They are incurred when sub-systems do not work at their optimum level, and might involve simple procedures like lighting candles or putting on extra clothes when the electric or heat systems run low; or a systematic reduction of performance cutting out the inessentials first. John Shore's 'cosy retreat' (Fig C2) is a case in point, where ultimately the whole house is shut off to save heat. With wind-generated electricity, it is usual to automatically forbid heavy loads once the system is running off batteries. In Simon Longland's design, for example

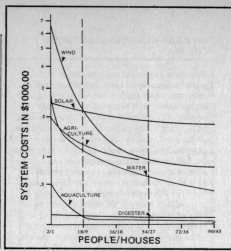

SYSTEM COSTS IN $1000.00

WIND

SOLAR

AGRI-CULTURE

WATER

AQUACULTURE

DIGESTER

PEOPLE/HOUSES

2/1   18/9   36/18   54/27   72/36   90/45

(Fig A2), calculations over a four-year period indicated that the worst windless condition would require 18kWh storage capacity, costing £650 in batteries alone, to ensure 'normal demand'. Cutting loads to essentials in windless periods reduces the storage requirement to 7kWh.

All these expedients concern life at the lower end of the Hogan's Law curve, where those for whom autonomy justifies itself find it rational to exchange amenity costs for money costs. Unfortunately this kind of life is quite unacceptable to the majority of people. At the same time, to provide the kind of life which *is* acceptable, by autonomous means, excludes the majority on financial grounds. This dichotomy produces two design syndromes.

Designs constrained by fixed, high amenity standards are restricted to technical rather social means of achieving autonomy. This tends to produce units which are costly, reliable, comfortable, convenient, permanent, constructed professionally from standard industrial materials, highly autonomous on completion, and relatively free of maintenance tasks.

Designs constrained by lack of money, but with no formal public responsibilities, can assume variable and low amenity standards. Units designed under these conditions tend to be cheap to build; often lightweight and perhaps temporary; unreliable and occasionally uncomfortable by ordinary or even extraordinary standards; self-built with partial or selective autonomy and pared-down back-ups, developing in time towards more complete autonomy and higher standards; making maximum use of local, on-site, scavenged or recycled materials; or existing structures; and requiring extensive effort in maintenance.

Recognisable examples of these two syndromes will probably always exist, but the likelihood is that they will move closer together. If the more pessimistic scenarios of world economic trends are within a mile of the eventual truth, cheaper systems must be

Fig 30. Economies of scale for renewable sources of energy, estimated by Richard Merrill from various sources. Assumptions as follows: wind/water (electricity) 2kW/2 people, 10mph average windspeed or equivalent head and flow of water, 20 year life; solar solar heat: 2 people/1000 sq. ft. house, 60% space heating, below 40° latitude, 20 year life; digestor (gas) 15 cubic feet/person/day, organic feedstock freely available, cooking only, 5 year life; aquaculture (food) 70 grams animal protein/day/person, 10 year life; agriculture (food): ½ acre of land, sufficient tools, water, seeds etc, vegetarian diet, intensive garden farming. (From Merrill).

favoured, and changes in habit, style and consumption may be forced on people anyway. When (if) this has gone on for a bit, the cheap systems which make a virtue out of frugality might come to seem less bizarre. At the same time, the more elaborate systems may be favoured if government and local authorities take an interest and offer grants or cheap loans, possibly under middle-class pressure and the influence of a new cost calculus based on whole Life Costs and weighted for resource scarcities and environmental impacts. With such official blessing, a whole range of mutually beneficial trends could gather momentum: courses in installation and maintenance of autonomous systems at Technical Colleges and nightschools; more research a favourable attitude to experimental structures on the part of Building Societies and so on. There could be strong forces towards basic utilitarian designs, and, perhaps, mild social experiments.

This favours the convergence of the two streams. Such a convergence is exemplified by the Brunel House (Fig E2), described by Robert Vale as follows:

> The Brunel House is the missing link between the eco-Concordes and the string and polythene bag brigade, designed to last a long time with low maintenance, to give a lower material standard of living than a centrally heated modern house with all-electric kitchen etc, but not as low as life in a tent; to be built by occupier or small local builder, using easily-available materials.

If the economic climate remains poor, there will be far greater scope for social adaptations than for autonomous reconstructions of conventional patterns of life. Of these adaptations, the most important is probably the revival of social and economic life at the local community level. That is discussed next.

Fig 31. No comment.
From Survivre et Vivre.

LOCAL ECONOMIES OF SCALE

Technicalities, difficulties and advantages of collective forms of autonomy have been met already under 'Sharing' and 'Size'. The principal conclusions were that, although inevitably amenity costs are incurred by sharing in the provision of services, there may be substantial savings in money costs that make the exchange rational; and that, above a certain size, clusters of buildings are favoured over large single buildings. Socially, the simplest form of such a cluster of buildings is a group of nuclear-family-size dwellings, sharing common services. Perhaps this is as good a place as any to start social experimentation into autonomous systems. Richard Merrill of the New Alchemy Institute has analysed economies of scale for this situation, and shown that different sub-systems respond differently to larger scales (Fig 30). This is an important contribution and worth describing in some detail.

Larger, shared wind generators make a great deal of sense, because power output increases with the square of the blade length and this is a relatively cheap parameter to increase. Sharing could permit siting the mill in the most favourable place, and this would also be safer. High voltage supply would be much more feasible, and there would be considerable savings in regulation equipment. With solar systems, economies of scale are less marked, since large collectors are no more efficient than small, and a central collector could not perform any double function as roof, wall or shutter. It would perhaps make sense to share long-term heat-storage among buildings close together, although the savings in heat-loss from the storage tank would have to balance against extra heat-losses in collection and redistribution pipes.

According to Merrill (Fig 30) methane digestors show virtually no economies of scale. This may be true in California, but in cooler climates the thermal advantages of larger systems must often outweigh the extra costs of distributing the gas — especially as digestors must be sited away from dwellings anyway. Larger digestors are also better buffered against changes of acidity, etc, arising from variations in the feed materials, which tend to upset the bacteria. Aerobic composters, too, probably work better on a larger scale. Other waste-treatment systems such as septic tanks are certainly much more economical on a larger scale.

Economies of scale in water supply must depend very much on the source, and the proximity of the buildings. Water from pump, well or stream will obviously need to be shared, and if it needs purifying, equally obviously this is best done on a collective level. Possibly 'purity B' water could be distributed in pipes, and drinking water collected by hand. If the supply depends only on precipitation, it may be found economical to arrange roof drainage to flow into a communal reservoir. From here it could be purified to various levels and wind pumped to header tanks in individual dwellings. Ideally this would avoid the need for having to recycle purity C water, but if this were necessary, again certain conditions would favour collecting dirty water and treating it in a larger communal plant.

Intensive food production, too, could benefit from a certain increase of scale, through specialisation, wider range of skills, better load factors on capital equipment (tractors, tillers, milking machines, etc), bulk purchases, smaller fluctuations of stock, and all those things you can do if there is a 'critical mass' but can't if there isn't. According to Merrill, costs for small-scale agriculture start to level off at about 60 people, while in the case of aquaculture they drop markedly to about 20 before levelling off (Fig 30).

If all these economic benefits accrue from sharing autonomous systems, where do we stop? Why not go right on back to central servicing? This is a question that autonomists would do well to ask themselves more often. The answer depends on the reasons for which autonomy is undertaken. There are those who think they are helping conserve resources or improve the environment; those who are investing now for economies later; those who just want to be 'independent'; those who wish to survive the Great Crash; those who want to reorganise work-patterns, and so on. Not all forms of autonomy serve all of these ends, and many of these groups are mistaken in thinking that they do, in general or in particular cases. Their aims would often be better served by honest-to-God mains supply. Others are not mistaken; but the rest of us ought perhaps to ask whether their aims are compatible with ours, and whether they ought to be getting away with it (Fig 31). The fact remains that the optimum balances between autonomy and collectivity differ for all these groups, and for individual sub-systems in ways characteristic for each group. I cannot possibly discuss all these in detail but I shall give a couple of examples.

From the ecological point of view, the virtues of autonomy in certain sub-systems are doubtful. Water for example is a renewable resource provided in great quantity at high levels of purity by the Water Boards at under a fiver a head per year. Domestic consumption is only 1/3 of the total, and the public interest is probably better served being a bit less wasteful and reducing industrial demands, than by fancy recycling systems for bath water. For a more militant view on autonomous water supply, see 'Each Piece of Land to Each Piece of Sky', by George Woolston. Likewise, as argued before, small-scale wind-electric systems are not really justifiable on environmental grounds, and scarce resources would probably be better conserved by larger wind generators like the 1.25MW Grandpa's Knob machine than zillions of copper and lead-hungry backyard numbers.

For 'siege autonomists' looking to survive troubled times ahead, cost is no object, neither are resources, neither is environmental quality. All that matters is that they do not depend on mains supply. Often this goes with a mistaken notion of total independence, and is a logical extension of 'privatisation', going now beyond personal transport, personal laundry, personal garden, to personal power plant, water works, sewage farm. In straitened times, economies of scale may lead to more gruesome developments. It is possible to imagine fortified laagers of the wealthy, with huge stocks of stored resources (food, fuel, spares) and squads of technicians to maintain sophisticated autonomous systems. It is an unsavoury prospect.

Such reasoning as these examples represent cannot and should not be used to justify autonomy. It seems to me that more solid and honourable justifications from the resource point of view are only to be found in the countryside, where network costs from central plant are high, ambient resources are abundant and are not feasibly collected, concentrated and redistributed again. The communal level would reduce *plant* costs over the private level, and reduce *network* costs over the larger public level. This would help save the concentrated resources whose existence makes feasible the functioning of central plants which are absolutely necessary in the cities. Here the primary justification of the intermediate scale — the communal level of servicing — is not technological but social.

Collective-scale semi-autonomous units achieve economies over the private level through co-operation, specialisation, and in communal use patterns as well as communal production patterns. As against the public level, savings are achieved through the emergence of 'residual factors', the production of useful goods and services with little apparent cost, with hardly anyone noticing it because they are part of the social life of the community, or games, 'bees', festivals, neighbourly gestures. That these can become a major part of economic life is a basic article of faith with many radical economists. Their operation could be seen in, say Barcelona of the late 30's, or in contemporary China. But there is no doubt that the infraction of the conventionally clean separation of public production and private consumption would strike most people in capitalist cultures as a loss of amenity.

Keeping the distinction is regarded as one of the marks of a high standard of living. Once again, therefore, the social unorthodoxy of communal arrangements prevents 'responsible' designers or planners from considering them. Perhaps this is just as well? Meanwhile, the initial expense and difficulty of finding and obtaining the use of groups of buildings and/or land is a severe restriction on 'nouveau pauvre' builders, although they can at least envisage the possibilities (Fig E4, E5, 33, 34, Vision Nos 1, 3 and 4).

All this is not to argue against the validity and necessity of the private and public spheres, only against their exclusive dominance. One cannot be dogmatic about the balance because circumstances vary so much. City and country demand radically different patterns. But the nettle must be grasped somewhere, and here is a rule of thumb.

Richard Merrill remarks that, according to his investigations, a group of 20 family-sized units captures most of the economies of scale for autonomous systems. This agrees fairly well with the social criteria that separate co-operation among friends from transactions among buyers and sellers, and define a 'village' or 'tribal' (?) scale as a useful intermediate level.

Once more, this is not instead of, but as well as, the private and public levels. It is a question of finding appropriate balances.

VI COLLECTIVE AUTONOMY

This part takes up the story where part IV left off. It describes some proposals (alas, only one yet realised) for collective autonomous units. Other collective proposals are discussed in part VII (see Figs 33 and 34) and in Visions No 3 and 4. The interpretation of the bar charts is given in part IV.

E1
BRAD (Biotechnic Research and Development), Eithin-y-Gaer, central Wales. This is strictly a 'conversion', one which dwarfs the original structure, although the shape and orientation were strongly influenced by the small stone cottage which forms the north wall. The main frame is timber with polystyrene insulation, and a 60m^2 open-type collector for summer hot water (see Box 2 for energy calculations). Food and wood-fuel are provided from a 40-acre site. Occupancy 12. The structure was built by the occupants with a little help from their friends, and cost about £10,000.

(a) North aspect during construction, showing shell of original building; (b) South west aspect, showing frame and solar roof under construction; (c) Detail of solar roof (see also Fig 7 in 'Sunshine Superpower', by Robert Vale, for diagram of circuit and for drawing of completed house); (d) Pattern of autonomy.

E2
Brunel House, designed by Robert and Brenda Vale. This is a slightly larger version of Fig A5, occupancy 6, under construction on the campus of Brunel University near London. Fig A5(a) gives an impression of the general appearance, but the roof is steeper in this version, and the systems are simpler and cheaper. Robert Vale describes it as 'the missing link between the eco-concordes and the string-and-polythene-bag brigade'. Autonomy is approached in two stages. (a) Section; (b) Pattern of autonomy — phase 1; (c) Pattern of autonomy — phase 2.

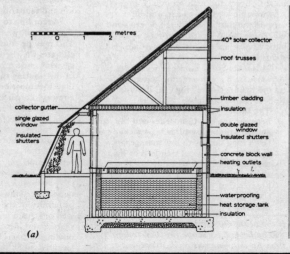

E3
Eithin 2. This is another, much larger variant of the Vales' basic wedge-shaped design (Fig A5). It is a communal house for 16 people, intended for the BRAD site in Wales. The same long, flat structure with greenhouse is retained, with an extra floor for bedrooms cantilevered out over the concrete or monolithic earth walls of the ground floor, which is used for communal facilities and services. The standard of autonomy and performance is high, but owing to economies of scale and shared facilities, the capital cost per head would probably be less than for an ordinary family house. (a) Ground floor plan; (b) First floor plan; (c) South elevation; (d) Section; (e) Pattern of autonomy.

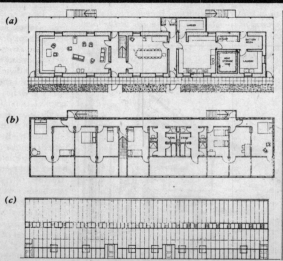

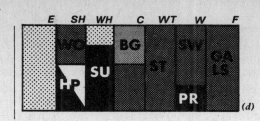

(d)

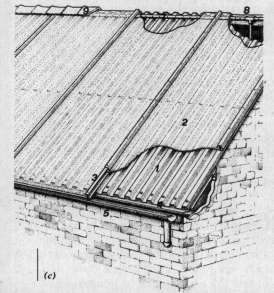

(c)

1 Anodized cor-
rugated alum-
inium
2 Glass-reinforc-
ed plastic
covers
3 Standard alum-
inum glazing
bars
4 Hot water
gutter (pvc)
5 Rain gutter
(pvc)
6 Polystyrene
insulation
7 Perforated cop-
per header pipe
8 Cold feed pipe
9 Ridge tiles

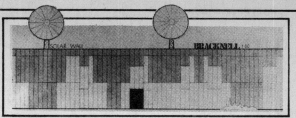

(a)

E4

*Brack-
nell Housing
Estate. Mick
Bedford's fanci-
ful but possible
idea for suburban
housing. Rows
of low-rise houses
might be ideal for
solar heating,
wind-gengrators
could be used to
share grid loads
and garden space
for co-operative
vegetable product-
ion. This might be
a suburban
compromise
between Vision 3
and Vision 4. (a)
South elevation;
(b) Layout; (c) Pat-
tern of autonomy.*

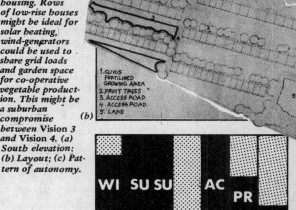

(b)

(c)

E SH WH C WT W F

(b)

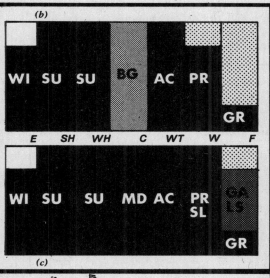

(c)

E5

*Radial House. Another basic idea,
proposed by Herbert Girardet. The rooms
have different functions and heating standards.
The central room (around the stove or furnace)
is completely surrounded by other rooms,
therefore well-insulated, and suitable for communal use in the winter. Exterior cladding can
be removed in the summer, and part of the
outer girdle of the house used as a greenhouse.
The house is intended to be set in a circular plot
of land for garden crops, in a community of
similar plots with shared service facilities. See
Fig 33 for the layout. (a) Floor plan; (b)
Section (c) The model (d) Pattern of autonomy.*

(a)

1 GREENHOUSE
2 LIVING SPACE
3 ENTRANCE
4 STUDY
5 WORKSHOP
6 BATHROOM/WC
7 KITCHEN

8 WORKROOM
9 STORE
10 FIREPLACE
11 ROOF SUPPORT
12 OUTER SUPPORTS
13 SLEEPING AREA
14 ROOF WINDOWS
15 ROOF

(b)

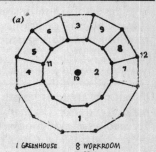

(d)

(c)

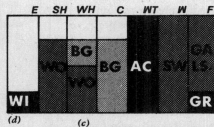

(d)

SOLAR ROOFS

CONSERVATORY

(e)

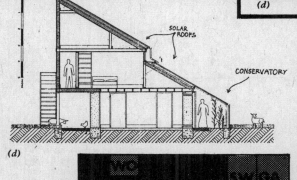

VII PRACTICAL FANTASIES

It is clear that most of the autonomous unit designs described in this article are technically feasible. Many have already been built and, after their own fashion, function successfully. But they are nearly all special cases, built with unusual supplies of cash, material subsidy or dedication. And the household unit is in many respects too small, so rather uneconomic, even in the long term. We need to explore ways in which autonomous units could be better integrated into the existing patterns of servicing so as to make a positive contribution to problems such as resource depletion, food supply, housing, unemployment and inflation; help people live in a free but neighbourly way; and ease the transition to a no-growth economy.

It's hard to keep a straight face after writing such a sentence, but I shall outline two general proposals for the servicing of semi-autonomous communities, one for the country, and one for the city. Both involve a group of dwellings with many shared facilities. I assume that local authorities are willing to co-operate and would make planning conditions reasonable, perhaps even give grants. I also assume co-operating groups of occupants in the form of a housing association or some such organisation with some kind of legal status, whose members are willing to adopt new work-patterns and living arrangements.

THE COUNTRY

I shall not argue at length over the case for increasing rural population. In many ways, life would be more agreeable for everybody if the population were better distributed. Cities could be less oversized and overcrowded; and the countryside would be less lonely and boring. With more people on the land, intensive cultivation could raise food yields per acre, at the same time reducing the need for resource-hungry machinery and chemicals. Since the use of ambient resources is easier in the countryside, the more people they serve, the less the load on over-stretched central services.

The main function of a semi-autonomous rural community should be agricultural, yielding a food surplus while requiring as little input from outside as possible. A range of technical possibilities is indicated in Fig 32, based on three existing units. Layouts would depend on local circumstances. Two possible kinds of layouts are suggested by Fig 33 and **Vision** No 3 but these are rather more ideal than anything likely in practice. Although the emphasis would have to be on new building, there would presumably be extensive rehabilitation of old structures. The more diversity the better. Size is a completely open matter, but 'village' gives the general idea. As an autonomous unit, the village would run its own services, and be site-specific, tuned in to the local resources as closely as possible.

Probably solar heating would best be done at the private level, perhaps with shared storage between close clusters of buildings. Other services could be shared. Electricity might well be provided by a pair of large wind-generators (eg 50kW) with no storage, but backed up either by mains or by a liquid-fuelled generator whose waste heat would be used to provide communal hot water, say for laundry or bathing, or for topping up heat-storage tanks. In a basically agricultural community conditions would be ideal for producing methane gas, with plenty of animal and vegetable waste. This would be done in large central digestors (as with the wind-generators a pair would be preferable to allow for breakdowns and maintenance) and the gas piped to individual dwellings. Great care would still be needed in using gas, and back-ups of bottled gas might be necessary. Human sewage would be a small proportion of the total and would probably not be worth piping to the central point. It could be treated in smaller digestors, composters or earth closets. Grey water could be stored for use on crops, or disposed of via land drains.

Water supplies would depend on local conditions. In most rural areas streams or springs would be adequate, and a communal reservoir could be constructed to buffer peak demands. Well-water could be pumped up by windmills. Purification could be done centrally and the water piped to households. Drinking water could be provided centrally and collected by hand, or by filter-candles in individual dwellings. Food would almost all be produced locally. Herbert Giradet's plan (Fig 33) strikes me

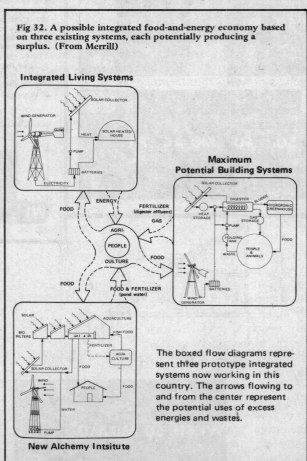

Fig 32. A possible integrated food-and-energy economy based on three existing systems, each potentially producing a surplus. (From Merrill)

Integrated Living Systems

WIND GENERATOR

SOLAR COLLECTOR

HEAT

SOLAR HEATED HOUSE

PUMP

BATTERIES

ELECTRICITY

Maximum Potential Building Systems

SOLAR COLLECTOR

DIGESTER SLUDGE

HEAT STORAGE

GAS STORAGE

HYDROPONIC GREENHOUSE

PUMP

HOLDING TANK

FOOD

PEOPLE & ANIMALS

WASTE

WIND GENERATOR

BATTERIES

ENERGY

FOOD

FERTILIZER (digester effluent)

GAS

AGRI-

PEOPLE

CULTURE

FOOD

FOOD

FOOD & FERTILIZER (pond water)

SOLAR

AQUACULTURE

BIO-FILTERS

FISH FOOD

FERTILIZER

AGRI-CULTURE

SOLAR COLLECTOR

FOOD

WIND

PEOPLE

FOOD

WATER

PUMP

New Alchemy Intsitute

The boxed flow diagrams represent three prototype integrated systems now working in this country. The arrows flowing to and from the center represent the potential uses of excess energies and wastes.

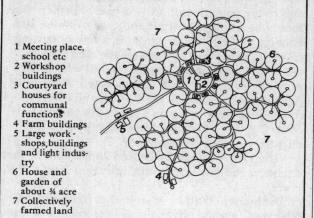

Fig 33. A possible layout for new rural communities. The method of circular plots gives a rational but varied mixture of private and community land. Many variations are possible on this basic pattern. Contrast Vision No 3 for a layout with rectangualar plots. (After Girardet).

1 Meeting place, school etc
2 Workshop buildings
3 Courtyard houses for communal functions
4 Farm buildings
5 Large work-shops, buildings and light industry
6 House and garden of about ¾ acre
7 Collectively farmed land

as a good one for intensive horticulture and agriculture. The plots round each building are for use at the discretion of the occupants, but there are 'interstices' where trees, flowers and other 'free' crops are grown. Beyond the private plots is collectively worked land with heavy crops (cereals, winter feed) and animals. Elsewhere there would be glasshouses and facilities for the less orthodox food technologies if necessary (hydroponics, aquaculture). Part of the land could be used for sustainable timber-growing, partly for wood as a material, and partly as a winter back-up fuel.

Socially, the arrangements would obviously be up to the inhabitants. Little need be said about a collective meeting place, food store, medical centre, bowling green, school if the community is large enough, and any other facilities that might be required. The mixture of work inside and outside the community would have to be decided. Perhaps all work would be done 'inside' and external supplies paid for by the food surplus. There could be a certain amount of light industry, particularly that using agricultural products like hides and wool. Food could be processed (dried, etc) as well as sold or exchanged direct. Alternatively, inside and outside work could be done in rotation, or depending on skills and preferences. Much of the on-site work would be in maintaining the service systems. The legal form of landholding might be Land Trust, with no private ownership, an arrangement with promising precedents in the USA.

Other precedents are less encouraging. Anyone who writes about such 'ideal' villages must feel the weight of previous examples of rural utopian communities (see Jos Kingston's article 'It's Been Said Before — And Where Did That Get Us?'). These have usually ended in collapse after a few years. It is possible to argue (and I would) that developments in technology since the nineteenth century make the establishment and running of such communities much more practical today. Even so, many of the 'community technologies' of today were anticipated, notably by the Owenite William Thompson as early

as 1830. What I have outlined is a mixture of the kind of community envisaged by Thompson, the kibbutz in its pristine form (as envisaged by, say, Buber), and the Chinese Production Brigade, laced with alternative technology. As yet, this form of rural life has never been widely successful in the industrial world, but its economic and social rationality seem plain enough. I could go on theorising endlessly about why it has not worked in the past, but the point is always to try again each generation, (yes, even *before* the Revolution).

One final remark needs to be made. The occupants of such a unit must remember that self-sufficiency is not enough. They can only exist by virtue of investment provided in large measure by the sweat of the wider society, and *must return a useful surplus*.

THE CITY

The urban counterpart of the rural utopian dream has concentrated on regenerating the sense of community; of commitment to a neighbourhood, making it unique, cared-for, and a good place to be in. This must involve sharing because the sense of community is the antithesis of 'little boxes' and the private, private life of passive consumers. A vision of 'how it could be' was suggested a few years ago by *The Berkeley Tribe* in a dashing proposal called 'Blueprint for a Communal Environment' (Fig 34). Streets would be closed off and made into gardens

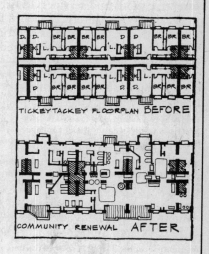

Fig 34. 'Blueprint for a Communal Environment' put forward by the *Berkeley Tribe*. (a) Floor plan showing possible pattern of communalised space by removal of partitions. (b) The possible appearance of a neighbourhood after 'communalisation'. Most buildings remain as dwellings, but some houses are made over to public use. Compare *Vision No 4*.

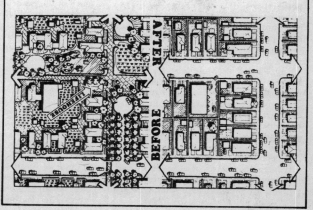

and play grounds; party walls broken down and the house-spaces shared; trees would be planted and bridges and walkways constructed to connect buildings; social services of all kinds would be organised locally; one house would become the community 'Life-House'.

There is something of a 'sixties period flavour about some of this, but let us not debate that socially it is on the right lines. What we have to ask is how the social aspects of such a scheme can be blended with a certain amount of productive (economic) activity, and with reorganised utility services in such a way as to be practical, economical, and beneficial both to the inhabitants and to society as a whole.

Autonomous units of the kind discussed in this article tend to be impractical in large cities. It is almost certainly better to concentrate on making better use of existing services, possibly supplemented by autonomous systems but chiefly by Clever Ideas and Making Do. It is necessary to find a rational mixture of mains, communal and household scale services.

By way of assumptions, let us suppose that prices of everything continue to rise faster than wages. Costs of fuel and other non-renewable resources rise even faster. Unemployment is at record levels. Balance of payments difficulties are acute. Labour and supply problems constantly threaten mains services. Under these circumstances there would be greatly increased demand for social security payments, unemployment benefits, and subsidies on essential goods and services. In other words, government and local authorities would find themselves faced with greater demands at a time when their means to meet them was stretched to the limit. The pressure could be eased by encouraging co-operative self-employment, and self-provision of services, including food.

Local authorities, statutorily obliged to provide housing, will prefer the rehabilitation of old buildings to the construction of new ones. Further, they should be willing to permit and even subsidise self-building and self-maintenance, as a way of cutting costs. Imagine, then, a block of terraced houses, emptied and awaiting demolition, but with service runs still intact — merely disconnected. A Housing Association approaches the council and offers to rehabilitate the terrace on a long-term basis. The council agrees and offers financial support. How might the terrace be organised?

Vision No 4 shows the general appearance of such a terrace, and one way it might develop after a few years.

The houses could be organised as follows: two groups of four are physically collectivised, and one group of two. The remaining two become the 'Centre House' whose facilities are shared by all occupants of the terrace. Up to 50 people would live in the terrace including kids, in the three collectivised dwelling units, one housing perhaps ten and the other two twenty each. Bedrooms are private and vary in size according to need. The rest of the space is collective, some parts more regulated than others. Each unit has a kitchen and common room. Other rooms are used either for purposes of the unit itself, or of the whole terrace: playrooms, pottery, weaving, darkroom, library, games, music, storage, etc. Activities with heavy uses of energy or materials are concentrated in the Centre House: bakery, laundry, sauna, workshop, perhaps also meeting space, food store, office, etc.

◆ **Electricity:** In most cases wind generators are not feasible in cities, and have other drawbacks, as discussed before. Since mains electricity is available, it is better to use it, but sparingly. In the living units, loads should be restricted to lighting and small appliances — perhaps 5 amps. The lighting should be fluorescent, or with low-wattage focused bulbs. In the Centre House higher load ratings would be needed, for tools, etc. Metering would be at the unit level, with costs shared for the Centre House.

◆ **Space Heating:** Heat loss would be cut by extensive external insulation, covered with weatherboarding, as in Fig D1, and double glazing. Extra insulation may be applied in communal rooms. For heat sources, various possibilities exist. Solar energy, except in rather unusual circumstances, is out of the question. A large boiler in the Centre House could provide central heating, but this tends to be too indiscriminate and therefore wasteful, keeping too many spaces warm that are not needed. Probably small gas fires are the best solution, larger ones in communal rooms. Gas is good because (i) if economically used, supplies of natural gas (for Britain) are considerable; (ii) oil gasification is possible, but more particularly, direct underground gasification of coal is likely to become feasible and economic by the end of the century and coal deposits in Britain (and the U S) are very large (the hazards of subsidence must not, however, be forgotten); (iii) future wind-power developments may involve hydrogen generation, and possibly a 'hydrogen economy' (which would operate through the present gas systems) rather than an 'electricity economy' relying heavily on nuclear power.

◆ **Water Heating:** This would be for washing and washing up. Demands would be cut by using spray-mist showers. The craving for sensual bathing would be met by daily collective saunas in the Centre House (gas-fired, with cold showers). The sauna could also be used by others outside the terrace. Hot water would be provided by gas geysers, and in the summer much of the load could be taken by roof-mounted solar collectors optimised for the job. Laundry would be done collectively in the Centre House.

◆ **Cooking:** This would not account for much of the gas demand, and would anyway be reduced by collective cooking. Baking is a much heavier load and would be done in the Centre House. Although methane *could* be generated for cooking, it would only allow the meanest of meals and would look quite ridiculous beside the therms tumbling in their hundreds through the gas main for space-heating. In the summer, some cooking could be done on concentrating solar collectors, but this would be just for fun.

◆ **Waste Treatment:** The aim here should be to conserve water and nitrogen which would otherwise be rendered unusable by contamination with industrial effluent (toxic metals etc) in the sewers. Although the houses would be connected to the sewers, autonomous treatment would be preferable for sewage and 'grey' water, leaving the sewers to handle all other liquid wastes (ie not much). Sewage could be treated either aerobically or anaerobically. Aerobic treatment could be carried out in composter units such as those shown in Fig 10 — say two for each living unit. The advantage of these is that they need no water and preserve the existing connections between the wc and the sewer, leaving a handy access to the sewer for toxic wastes unsuitable for the garden. The disadvantage is that they might need extra power for heating during the winter to keep the composting processes going. Alternatively, anaerobic treatment in digestors is best done collectively, and would involve rerouting the soil-pipes across the garden. Gas output would be used exclusively to maintain optimum fermentation temperatures. The advantage of this system is that no extra power would be necessary, the disadvantage that water is needed for transport — wasting water which might anyway be too much for the digestor to handle, and need separating. A 'vacuum' system might solve this problem, but again needs extra energy. The output of composters or digestors would of course provide fertiliser for the garden.

◆ **Water Supply:** Water-use in the terrace would be heavier than average owing to the needs of the garden. As far as possible rainwater and grey water should be used for the garden, and mains supply for drinking, cooking and washing, since purification is costly on a small scale, and city rainwater has a high lead content. Demand would be reduced by communal laundry, shared kitchens, and showers in place of baths. Grey water could be used for flushing toilets if that were necessary, either by hand-pumping back into cisterns from holding tanks (Figs 11, 14), or by using hand basins over cisterns as in 'Ecol' Water from roofs and greenhouses could be collected and stored in tanks at ground level, overflowing to a larger reservoir/swimming pool/fishpond for garden use. By such means demand for mains water could probably be reduced 70-80%.

◆ *Food:* Land is scarce but labour and capital in this situation is high, so the most intensive methods are favoured, particularly glasshouse cultivation. Glasshouses as extensions of the houses would have the many advantages already referred to, and could even perform better than comparable rural setups because cities are warmer — although high pollution could effect crops in some areas. Hydroponics would be ideal, and could be fed largely off the digestor effluent (Fig 18). Chickens and/or ducks could provide eggs and if there were a large garden it might be feasible to keep goats. Intensive aquaculture on the New Alchemy model (see interview with John Todd, and 'After the Goldfish' by John Wood) would also be a good source of primary protein economical of land. The animals might need a certain amount of supplementary feed, but they should be able to provide all the primary protein for the community. Bulk carbohydrate could be provided by potatoes. Bread costs could be reduced by buying grain direct and grinding it in the community. For this purpose a low-gear slow-speed wind machine, made out of scrap parts and operating whenever the wind was right, might be a pleasing return to a traditional pattern. Bread would be baked collectively at the Centre House. Vegetables could be grown in the usual way, with communal cultivation and proper rotations (see **Vision No 1**). Exotics could be grown under glass in summer. Loft-spaces could be used for germination or mushroom-growing, or, if glazed, as extra greenhouses, perhaps with hydroponics. Such a community could hardly hope to be self-sufficient in food, but it could cut its bills by a very great amount, and at some times of the year would have a surplus for sale.

◆ *Facilities:* Bakery, workshop, sauna and laundry could be in the Centre House. Shared uses would require co-ordination. Other rooms in the Centre House could be used as offices, foodstores, etc. The workshop would be tooled for all routine repairs on the service systems (eg **Vision No 2**). The living units would each contain facilities for communal use, apart from their own kitchen, common room and bedrooms — for example, weaving and clothes-making, darkroom, pottery, lib library, music, meditation, kids TV, games etc.

◆ *Work:* The necessity to work outside would be greatly reduced because the community would be generating most of its own essentials. The work that *ought* to be done outside would be producing the external materials and facilities which the community used, ie working for the local authority in power stations, sewage and water works, roads, libraries, parks, etc: being doctors, technicians, toolmakers; working in shops, foundries, mines, hospitals, schools — rather than banks, advertising agencies, boutiques, military installations and universities.

Such a collective unit could be integrated into a wider community with a wider range of facilities and more scope for external employment. Some of the possibilities are illustrated by the **Visions** throughout this book — workshop and garage; media centre; school. There could also be a building co-op or a small self-managed factory.

VIII CONCLUSIONS

Such a scheme as this communal terrace, in the middle of a town, dependent on mains supplies for its basic services, thoroughly embedded in the wider economy, and with not a windmill in sight, is a far cry from the brave new self-sufficiency of Fig 1.* Yet the terrace still expresses the spirit of autonomous action, and is a logical outcome of the conclusions drawn during this enquiry into technical autonomy. Perhaps it is now time to summarise some of those conclusions.

The notion of autonomy exists at a number of levels — existential, political, economic, technical for example. It can apply to individuals or groups of virtually any size. It is not an empty moral or political expression which is by definition a good thing, but has its sick and healthy manifestations. In this study I have focussed on the most practical form — material and technical autonomy. There are firm limits to the scope of autonomy in most basic needs, but in food and the utility services, a fairly efficient functional autonomy, even at the household level, can be achieved in the countryside, once the initial equipment is provided. By almost any criteria, optimal solutions for town and country are very different. It's harder in the town, but then, maybe priorities are different there.

'Autonomous houses' are unlikely to gain widespread acceptance as homes because if they are up to conventional service standards they cost a fortune, and if they are cheap enough to buy they fall sufficiently short of conventional standards that the rigors of operating them are culturally unacceptable. But if these rigors can be borne, adapted to, made good or whatever, cost-effectiveness is much greater at the low-cost, low-performance end of the cost/performance curve. In certain cases, mixed mains and autonomous systems may give high performance at costs even lower than mains. The general trends of mains as against autonomous system costs is generally in the latter's favour, but for small dwellings at comparable levels of performance autonomous systems typically cost 2—5 times as much to run, taking into account interest on capital.

Even though the economics is currently unfavourable, many autonomists press on in the belief that they are acting in the public interest. This is often mistaken. In many cases the overall non-monetary costs (in say, resources, unnecessary work, environmental impact) exceed those of conventional systems pro rata. Of course, they can be regarded as experiments and in this respect may have more than paid their dues. But autonomous systems cannot be indiscriminately applied on a mass scale.

Social variables must come to the fore. It seems that the most promising ways forward in technical autonomy, which make a tangible contribution to public as well as private problems and explore new social possibilities, are through group projects doing all their own dirty work, reducing overall demand by shared facilities, exchanging subjective amenity costs for money costs, and using a mix of technologies carefully assessed in terms of wider social criteria. Should they wish to extend the range of their autonomy to other basic requirements such as goods and social services, they would need to work in a wider community. This would mark the beginning of a new phase (see Visions 5 and 6).

* The two drawings sum up very nicely the change between the Alternative Technology priorities of 1972 and the Radical Technology priorities of 1975. They were both drawn by the same person, with advice from friends, including me. I wonder what 1978 will bring?

It is a seeming paradox that each extension of the scope of economic and material autonomy, if it is to remain honest and non-exploiting, requires commensurate measures of collective participation. If healthy autonomy can only grow through co-operation, I can think of no better moral on which to end.

Fig 35. Peasant's painting of a pig farm in China. Surrounded by crops, bicycles and honest muck, a nice example of collective autonomy.

VISION 4/AUTONOMOU

This scheme is described in detail on pp 166 and 167. It's not so much an autonomous as a communalised terrace, in which shared facilities reduce demand for central services. Space inside the houses is reorganised, with groups of them being run together as a single unit. One pair of houses is used for heavy-consumption communal facilities such as the workshop (see Vision No 2) bakery, sauna and laundrette, as shown here, and coffee shop. Gas, electricity and water is supplied from the mains, but the community is set up to use these very economically. It treats its own sewage and uses it as garden, greenhouse and hydroponic fertiliser. More details of possible garden layouts can be seen in Vision No 1. Neighbourhoods of such communities would run larger facilities such as community workshops (Vision No 5) arts centres (Vision No 6) and such institutions.

A Library
B Loft hydroponics tanks and mushroom boxes
C Shower room with composting toilets
D Bakery
E Sauna
F Laundry

1 External insulation with wooden cladding
2 Rooftop solar water heaters
3 Extension greenhouses
4 Rainwater tank with overflow to pond
5 Kitchen
6 Chicken house
7 Centre House with communal facilities
8 Holding tank for soapy water
9 Reservoir/pond/swimming pool
10 Anaerobic digestor.

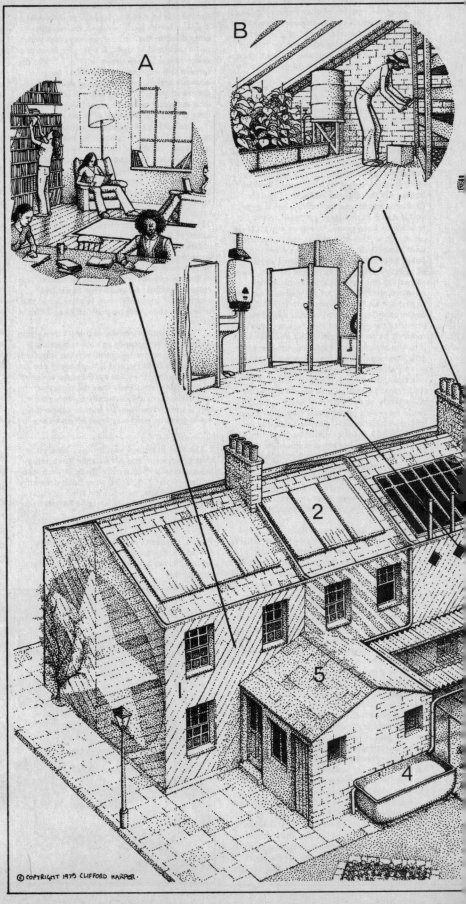

S TERRACE

INTERVIEW
STREET FARMERS

Godfrey Boyle

Imagine it. You're walking along amid the bustle of London, traffic flowing noisily past, tall office blocks on either side. You turn a corner and, suddenly, you come across a group of hairy freaks with a tractor, cheerily ploughing up the street in broad daylight.

Some distance away, a vast army of sheep is placidly advancing towards you, nibbling bits off parked cars as they pass by, while uncomprehending City folk scurry off into side roads, clutching their briefcases. Cows ruminate languidly beside the tube stations. Across the square (Trafalgar Square, to be precise) Nelson's Column lies supine, its base backed away by a gleeful rustic in rubber boots. Nearby, gangs of whooping 'unbuilding squads' are attacking the office blocks with pickaxes. Beside them, women plant corn on the pavement. Imagine . . . that's the vital thing. For, as the Street Farmers phrase it, echoing the revolutionaries of the Situationist International who took the streets of Paris by storm in the glorious May of 1968, "The revolution is impotent without a vision, as the dreamer is impotent without a revolution." The vision from which the Street Farmers derive their name — the vision of a band of revolutionaries humanizing the urban landscape by ploughing the streets — was first articulated in a series of fantastic collages and cartoons in Street Farmer I in 1972.

The Street Farmers are not keen to be squeezed into the straightjacket of definition, but if I describe them as a London-based group of anarchists practising, and preaching, a unique brand of guerilla architecture, I don't think they would disagree too much.

Guerilla architecture? Here's an example. In 1972 the town of Bracknell invited architects to enter for a competition to design a housing estate of some 90 dwellings. Graham Caine, who with Bruce Haggart founded (if that is the right word) the Street Farmers, decided to submit an entry.

Graham suggested a group of self-built houses constructed of Japanese Giant Bamboos, which grow to a height of 20 metres in only three months under the right conditions. The bamboos would be planted on the site in the appropriate pattern, then bent into the desired shape by ropes as they grew, forming a framework for the dwelling. The framework would then be covered in a double skin of plastic, and filled with expanded polystyrene for insulation. In the middle of the "housing estate" would be hydroponic gardens and a fish farm, fed on the digested sewage waste of the members of the 'People's Housing Association' who would live there. "Totally preposterous," you can just hear the judges say. But why is it totally preposterous: that's the point.

The Street Farmers really hit the headlines in a big way in August 1972, when the London Observer splashed across its front page a story called "Living on the Sun in South London", which described the 'ecological house' which Graham and Bruce were then building. The eco-house, subsequently christened 'Street Farm House', was officially Graham's fifth-year project at the Architectural Association school.

The local council gave temporary permission for it to be erected in a corner of the playing fields of the Thames Polytechnic at Eltham on the understanding that it was an 'experiment'. Street Farm House has now been lived in by Graham and his lady Fran (and, lately, daughter Rosie) for more than two years, and the council are now pressing for the house to be demolished. ("How much longer will your experiments last, Mr Caine?" they ask.)

Although in any sane society the Authorities would slap a preservation order on such an historic architectural landmark, the Street Farmers are philosophical about the possibility of its demolition. Graham, Fran and Rosie in any case spend an increasing amount of time nowadays at 'The Vicarage', a splendid old church with adjoining house in another part of South London where Bruce and Kate Haggart and some friends are living communally in a style vividly reminiscent of Alice's Restaurant. Peter Harper and I taped a discussion with them there in the autumn of 1974. Where, we wondered, were the Street Farmers at, nowadays?

Bruce There's no way of defining what the Street Farmers are about these days. At one time, we were students of architecture doing a project, and we had a whole load of polemic and theory about the State, capitalism, freedom, collectives and anti-capitalist society. Our main motivations were never ecological, really, though Graham was working on a house called the Ecological house . . . that was unconscious. A house organised the way the Street Farm House is seemed appropriate to the sort of anti-capitalist society we were talking about. For a long time after we built the house there was this feeling that it was an experiment, but that's gone.

The house is now essential to the way we live — it's a house for Graham and Fran and Rosie to live in, and there would be a real problem finding another place to live; it's become a necessity. The fantasy has become a reality. I don't know if that means we haven't got any more fantasies or whether we just live in our dreams.

Peter What about living in Street Farm House after a couple of years . . . Does it get fucking cold during the winter?

Graham We're applying for a grant from the council to get a hot water system! No . . . I would say that my comfort levels have changed.

Peter You mean you've got used to the erratic environment?

Graham I think I *like* it.

Peter What's the main source of space heat?

Graham Just the energy from the greenhouse. And there's very good insulation.

Peter Do you have any backup systems?

Graham We've got a paraffin heater. Last year we used only three gallons of paraffin.

Peter What about hot water in the winter? Do you find there is none for several days at a time? What about the washing up?

Graham We've got plenty of dishes!

Peter What about the crops?

Graham Well, with the size of place we've got, we couldn't be self-sufficient in food. We're growing a lot, though.

Peter The cultivation was originally supposed to be semi-hydroponic . . . do you keep that up?

Graham It's semi-hydroponic in as much as we've got some totally hydroponic and some in soil. We found that the hydroponic stuff was no better than soil, and the soil no better than the hydroponics. That might just be because we don't really know how to organize it. But we've learned . . . I used to have this naive attitude to gardening . . . I thought, whatever you put down comes up. And it's just not like that!

Peter Have you fed the hydroponic stuff off the shit?

Graham Yes. We've grown stuff straight off what's normally called 'pollution'. To us, pollution is a greenhouse full of tomatoes and cucumbers and it's pretty healthy pollution. All you do is shit in at one end and in the morning, out comes something that looks like — tea, I suppose.

Godfrey Without the leaves . . .

Bruce Doesn't come in bags, either . . .

Godfrey Presumably the tea-like stuff's been in there for a long time, anaerobically digesting . . . But what about the E Coli and all those other nasty things that public health inspectors don't like?

Graham The thing is, the process takes so long that pathogenic bacteria die of old age. And in addition to the anaerobic environment there's an aerobic environment and the bacteria that survive through the anaerobic environment normally can't survive through the aerobic environment. In any case it goes

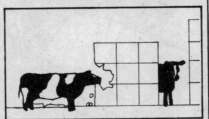

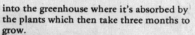

Street farmhouse: (*Top left*) **Installing the Savonius.** (*Top right*) **The greenhouse.** (*Bottom right*) **The solar collectors.** (*Bottom left*) **The solar water heater at the vicarage.**

into the greenhouse where it's absorbed by the plants which then take three months to grow.

Peter Have you come across a successful digester design that actually produces more methane than it takes to keep it warm?

Graham Well, you're just talking about the methane aspect. But the main point about shit treatment is to change shit back to food.

Peter But that can be done aerobically with compost heaps and all that; maybe aerobic decomposition is the best?

Graham No. I think that the anaerobic digestion system is better than the compost system just purely from the aesthetic viewpoint. Having some raw shit straight outside your window in a confined space like this can cause problems. But if the system's anaerobic and it's treated before it comes out you just put it on the plants without any objections.

Peter Well, they seem to manage the aerobic system in China all right. What would you say is the proportion of food you buy to food you grow?

Graham We buy dairy produce, and cat's meat — because we haven't got a vegetarian cat. Of the vegetables, I would say that we grow about 70 per cent over the year; during summer the supply is total. We also have to buy bread. We use the greenhouse to grow the sort of stuff that makes your staple diet really tasty. It's also used, of course, as a heat source and as a rain collector and as a nice space to live in.

Peter What about the pond?

Graham We couldn't fish farm with the pond because the water level goes up and down. We had a fantastic drought this year.

Peter You're not on mains water?

Graham No. We had to take some water out of the pond to water the plants, and we lost a few of the fish. Of course, the possibilities of what you *could* do are fantastic. But it's a house not a laboratory, though we enjoy tinkering around with a few things.

Peter What about building eco-houses? How do you look on other people who build them, not always for the same reasons as you — like the really fancy Cambridge design that costs £20,000?

Bruce Some people can build a canoe to go up and down river on and some people can afford to buy a yacht!

Graham How do you define an eco-house? Presumably the reason you refer to the Cambridge design as an eco-house is because of the technology?

Peter The Cambridge house is an eco-house only in the sense that it mimics nature. Everything goes round and round. I could call it an autonomous house but of course it's not autonomous to build.

Bruce I don't really regard these houses as eco-houses. There's no logic in the technology that allows them to be done up as a consumer product. The reality is that twice a week you've got to get elbow-deep in shit . . .

Peter But what would you say to people who argue that that position is *elitist* because, the way society is now, most people just could not do that — and because it must be restricted to the few people with technical aptitudes and skills who can do their own self-maintaining, even build their own houses?

I suppose that we, collectively, have a very deep faith that it's the birthright of human beings that they should have this self-determination in all the things they do. That worries me, because I don't know how to answer some very cynical people who say that: (a) people don't want to do it; and (b) they couldn't do it anyway.

Now if they couldn't do it anyway, well, that's an appalling thing for me to contemplate . . . But if they don't *want* to do it, then, I mean, whose side are we on? If they *really* don't want to do it, is it because they've been, as it were, corrupted and they just *think* they can't do it? They have an illusion of impotence? It might be that. But might be that they just *don't* want to, they really do want to do something else. So we remain a sort of fringe minority, articulating our own tastes and values.

Graham I wouldn't say that our position is elitist; or if it *is* elitist, I wouldn't say that it's exclusive. Whereas a house that costs £20,000 to build *is* exclusive.

Godfrey This theory that all of us seem to have at the back of our minds — that inherent in every human being is the desire to be creative and be self-sufficient — I think it's like an act of faith. It's not corroborated with any particular evidence — it's like the belief that all men are equal: there's not much evidence for that. It's just something that we have to accept as a basic premise until proven otherwise. Of course it's just as hard to *disprove* the hypothesis that people are born *with* an innate ability to take control of their lives, as it is to suppose that people are born *without* that innate ability. But don't you think that behind all this there's a notion

somewhere of the 'whole man' or 'whole woman' — of a person who spends some of his time growing vegetables, some of his time playing guitars, building houses when the need arises and writing books or drawing cartoon strips? That, to me, is the ultimately seductive idea, and I don't think it's necessarily elitist to have that point of view.

Peter Well, as you say, it's not proven. But other people can cite the evidence that if you go round the Ford factory they're just not interested in this kind of thing, by and large. And they can ask you, "Are you helping, are you any use to them?"

Godfrey But if you take that further — say, if you went to some people on a remote Pacific island who'd never heard of transistor radios or other baubles of civilisation and said, "Do you want a transistor radio?" they'd say, "What's a transistor radio?"

What I'm getting at is that these people, never having experienced the sort of things that we're talking about, would have no words with which to express approval or disapproval of them. Therefore to say that the people in the Ford factory don't want autonomous houses or alternative technology or whatever is a bit meaningless.

Bruce "Alternative technology": it's an abstract concept. It's a point of reference, but it's one I'm less and less happy about. I can't get to grips with that lingo any more.

Peter It's funny that other people *have*, you know. I mean, it's appalled me, what's happened to 'AT'. But Alternative Technology *has* become a movement in the sense that people use the term to refer to each other — but actually they're all doing completely different things . . .

Bruce It's obvious *why* it's become a movement . . . I mean it's the media . . .

Godfrey Yes, but I think a more subtle reason may be because people in this era have faith in gadgets as a solution to problems. If the present gadgets won't solve the problems then alternative gadgets may solve them . . .

Peter So is the essence, for you, building it yourselves?

Bruce Well, there's a reason for that essence — you're part of it, it's an extension of you and you're an extension of it, and you know it and you love it and you hate it, and you can do things to it: you can modify it, change it, and it can modify you, change you. You can't phone up a plumber . . .

For the same reason, the loveliest houses are squatted houses, where it's a free house, a liberated house. People can carve up the inside, take the floors out, punch holes where they want . . . because it's out of capitalism. A squat is about the only example of something that's out of capitalism. Albeit it's only temporary, and it may be convenient for capitalism, it's still something where there's no market repression.

Godfrey An essential aspect of what you're saying seems also to be that the act of creating shelter for yourself should be, at the same time, an act of affirming your independence of the State and the System?

Bruce But there's more to it than that. There's got to be thoughts about what can survive in the future, realistically — not so much ecologically as politically. There's something happening that's making it harder for people to live with any kind of self-determination. And if there's going to be something that *can* survive — though it's not going to be one thing, it's going to be umpteen things — then one of them might well be a kind of Street Farm-type scenario. In twenty years time, what are we going to be doing? Who knows, but we're going to be doing something the way *we* want to do it. Not the way we've *got* to do it.

MATERIALS

A certain amount of knowledge of the physical and chemical properties, and of the behavioural characteristics of materials, is essential if you intend to design and build your own AT hardware. *Why do things break? Why are some materials stronger than others? Why do materials have any strength at all?* Before you read this section you should know the answers to these questions, which may be found in *The New Science of Strong Materials or Why You Don't Fall Through the Floor* by J.E. Gordon (Pelican, 1968). But to give you *some* idea of the answers, here are a couple of quotations from the book:

> "If I weigh 200 pounds and stand on the floor, then the soles of my feet push downwards on the floor with a push or thrust of 200 pounds; that is the business of feet. At the same time the floor must push upwards on my feet with a thrust of 200 pounds; that is the business of floors. If the floor is rotten and cannot furnish a thrust of 200 pounds then I shall fall through the floor. If, however, by some miracle, the floor produced a larger thrust than my feet have called upon it to produce, say 201 pounds, then the result would be still more surprising because, of course I should be airborne. The force need not be a stationary weight.'
> 'The wind, blowing where it listeth, pushes on my chimney pots, but the chimney pots, bless them, push back at the wind just as hard, and that is why they don't fall off."

When you climb a tree the deflections of the boughs are clearly visible, but when you walk across a stone bridge the deflections are imperceptible. There is always some deflection—just enough to build up forces which counter the external applied load. This is basic to all structures. If the load is greater than the structure can take, it will become deformed, and break.

There is no *general* relationship between the tensile and compressive strengths (see glossary of terms) of various materials. Cast iron, cement, plaster and masonry are all strong in compression, but have hardly any tensile strength; like a pile of bricks, they are full of cracks.

Chains and ropes are strong in tension, but fold up in compression. They can best be regarded as *structures* rather than materials. Wood is three or four times stronger in tension than in compression, because its cell walls fold up in compression (yet wood is mainly thought of as a material rather than a structure). Compressive failure of this kind is a more complicated process than tensile failure, since there are several ways in which a material can 'run away' from a compressive load. If the material is in the form of a short, squat column, and is soft, like mild steel or copper, it will simply 'squish' out sideways—like Plasticine. If the material is brittle, like stone or glass, it will explode sideways in a very dangerous manner, into dust and splinters.

Most metals and timber, rubber, fibreglass, bones, teeth, cloth and rope, are *tough*—that is, you can bash them but they don't break easily. Most minerals, glass, pottery, resin, bakelite, cement, and biscuits are *brittle*—ie they crack easily. Cellulose, the main constituent of wood, cane, bamboo, and all vegetable fibres, is very tough. Yet chemically it is a sugar, and all crystalline sugars are very brittle.

At the end of this section, I will explain the terms *stress, strain, stiffness,* and *strength,* and basic methods of calculating values for them. But technically I shall say no more, as *The New Science of Strong Materials* explains admirably the theory and

Rob & Al Hitchings

practice of materials and structures for anyone who wants more information.

Ecologically, however, there are many conflicting arguments about the way we use, or do not use, various materials. Aluminium, for example, is easily cut and machined, light, strong, will not oxidize or rot (in a pollution-free atmosphere), and potentially can be used in very long-lasting products. However the spoil heaps beside the associated mines, and the massive hydro-electric schemes needed to provide cheap energy for its processing, both cover vast acreages of good farm land. In view of the pollution and eco-disruption thus caused, we certainly should not be designing aluminium into throw-away products.

Copper has a similar history of production. As for its consumption, we in the Western world already have more than our fair share. If the known world copper reserves were divided by the world's population Americans would have only one third of what they currently use. But where does all the copper go? The amount in cars and luxury items is minute; in houses some is used in copper water cylinders, water pipes, and wiring. But most copper

is in massive motors in industry, sewage works and power stations. Think of the tons of the stuff in those (thicker than car battery leads) over-head wires of the national grid. (Maybe they put the high voltage in them to stop people nicking the copper!).

The political implications of high technology materials should also be considered. Are we obtaining them at the expense of the living conditions and standards of those in other parts of the world? Or of the working and health conditions of those who process them? Is the system for obtaining them only possible with large, all-powerful corporations? And by using these materials are we becoming dependent on these corporations, who will ultimately control every facet of our lives?

An example of an ecologically OK material is *clay*. The continual silting up of river estuaries produces more clay than is currently consumed. Its availability is not dependent on large corporations or high technology; many potters dig clay locally. Ceramics are not only good for cups, bowls and plates, but for food, grain and drink storage, for furniture, and of course for houses. Bricks are made of clay and although a lot of energy goes into firing them, the process could be performed more ecologically with a solar kiln (used on those frequent hot summer days!), or by having a kiln centrally situated in a house and making full use of the waste heat from the kiln chimney for domestic heating.

If you are a purist, the only materials you can use with an ecologically-free conscience are those that are available *naturally*, preferably in your immediate surroundings. Most places have rocks, stones, earth, clay or sand, and some wood. Particular areas have chalk, slate, lime, peat, granite, etc. Then there's coal and metal ores. Most deposits are owned by someone, but even if they weren't someone would soon start ➡

mining and processing them for a living. So we may as well accept that such materials as iron, copper, tin, and lead exist and—so long as we recycle them—always will.

Generally speaking then, wood, clay, glass and the more common metals are all right for us eco freaks, but synthetics and plastics (which obviously *depend* on high technologyλ are out. (Except perhaps in these early days, when cost and time force us to use these nice, easy-to-put-up plastic drains, and that bit of plastic sheet to cover the roof while it's off for re-building—oh yes and a few inches of polystyrene insulation just to save energy now . . . But we'll investigate organic insulation later.

Finally a word about my pet hate: *fibreglass.* I speak not in ignorance. I have used fibreglass very successfully in making moulds and bucket-type seats. Although it is a marvelously versatile material, it is un-recyclable. After a number of years it loses its strength, becomes brittle and chips and cracks, and crazing sets in—so you really have no alternative but to throw it away. In scrap yards I have seen fibreglass body panels, roofs and car fronts, which, due to this process of deterioration, are no good to anyone. (It's the sun's ultra-violet rays and continued temperature changes which break fibreglass up). It is instructive to set out the pros and cons of fibreglass in tabular form:

Pros	Cons
Light.	Un-recyclable
Strong (when new).	Non degradable.
Can make moulds for repeat items.	Loses strength when old.
Can be sawn, drilled, tapped.	Very messy to use, however much care you take.
Can be translucent or opaque.	Uses up resources of oil and chemicals.
Can be used to repair itself and other items (but different co-efficients of expansion often cause failure after a while).	Depends on high technology for its manufacture.
	Can cause dermatitis if the resin gets on your skin (so you must wear *throw away* plastic gloves whilst laying it up!)

In a moment, we'll be looking in more detail at the various characteristics of specific materials and the methods and tools needed to work them. Let's begin, however by examining the basic material which makes this book possible.

It's odd that the technology of paper-making is so taken for granted in our society, the control and functioning of which depends almost entirely on paper-based information. Radicals tend to forget (except, perhaps, when paying print bills) that they depend utterly on today's high-capital, centralised, high technology paper industry for the basic vehicle on which the dissemination of all their thoughts and values depends.

If 'The Revolution' ever happens, its leaders are unlikely to announce the event by taking a full-page advertisement in The Times: *equally, one would have thought that the dissemination of revolutionary new and propoganda could be effected in a more independent manner than on the products of Reed, Bowater and the other International paper giants.*

But can 'the movement' ever expect to be able to produce its own paper, on a scale greater than that achieved by the few small, hand-made paper manufacturers who still sell their beautiful but prohibitively expensive sheets today, but smaller than that of the mammoth paper mills that gobble up enormous acreages of trees and vast amounts of energy each year, and spew out millions of tons of largely-useless packaging and advertising?

Derek Burns looks at what we might be able to do . . . .

Stress is simply *load per unit area.* If I weigh 200 lbs and stand on a brick 3" x 4" (=12 sq ins or 12 in^2), the *compressive stress* in the brick is:

$\frac{200}{12} = 16^2/_3$ pounds per square inch, ie $16^2/_3$ lb/in^2

The calculation is the same for *tensile stress.* In short:

stress (S) = $\frac{\text{load (P)}}{\text{area (A)}}$

Strain is the *amount of stretch per unit length* of the material under load. If a rod 100 inches long stretches one inch under load, then it is subject to a strain of $\frac{1}{100}$ or 1.0 per cent. In other words:

strain (e) = $\frac{\text{stretch (1)}}{\text{original length (L)}}$

Stiffness is the *flexibility* (or springyness) *of a material* up to the point where it becomes permanently deformed. Stiffness (measured by *Young's Modulus* (E) is found by dividing stress by strain, ie:

Stiffness (E) = $\frac{\text{stress (S)}}{\text{strain (e)}}$

Across the whole range of solids E varies by about 200,000 to 1. In substances we normally think of as rigid E varies by about 1,000 to 1, so E is a very useful yardstick for comparing materials.

Strength is the *force needed to break a material.* Most frequently it is thought of as *tensile* ("pulling") strength. Strength is the stress on the material just before it fractures. So ạ strong steel could have a tensile strength of 450,000 lbs/in^2 (that's 200 tons on each square inch!), while brick or cement might have a strength of only 600 or 800 lbs/in^2 (in tension, that is: in compression they could withstand a much higher stress).

PAPER: ROLLING YOUR OWN

DEREK STEWART

Paper is one of the simple but essential things of life and, like sugar, its future supply is likely to be erratic and expensive. The implications of such a situation are vast: the simplest and cheapest channel of communication is the written or printed word—on paper. This is especially relevant for Left and Movement groups, to whom channels of communication are important for mutual support, propaganda and information.

The most obvious response is to look at possibilities of making one's own, either from new materials or by re-cycling old. In attempting this one comes up against a curious fact of history; paper leapt from the phase of being a hand-craft to almost total automation with hardly a pause in between. Hence any remarks about alternative modes of manufacture waver uneasily between the old 'crafty' methods and the intimidating demands of modern technology. What is needed is a great deal of research, experiment and discussion into this middle ground, and an attempt to graft technology onto craft methods to produce a variety of systems to suit individual requirements.

Such requirements would differ according to (for example) basic attitudes to technology, the level of sophistication that can be handled, and the output and quality of paper desired. One can rough out three basic approaches—the very simple 'craft' approach; an attempt to graft on such technology as a general handyman might be able to handle; and, finally, the construction of a small-scale, high output plant. This differentiation will be used from now on, though the last will receive only cursory mention because of its complexity. And all these remarks are aimed only to start people thinking; they are in no way a set of instructions or recipes.

First one needs to know what paper is. It is simply a mat of fibre. Any fibre will do so long as it absorbs water and 'felts', ie the fibres hook onto one another naturally. Reeds, grasses, leaves, bamboo, flax, jute, maize stalks and—especially—cotton rags have all been used successfully, but for the last hundred years pride of place has been taken by the tree. All these things are basically cellulose fibres glued together by complicated substances called 'lignins'.

How is paper made? In simplest terms there are four stages. First, the original material is 'cooked' in some way to extract the pure fibre. Then the fibre is bleached and washed to make it white.

Next the fibre is 'beaten' to fibrillate it and allow it to mat easily. Finally the fibre is made into a thin gruel with water, spread on to a supporting mesh and drained by suction, pressure, heat or plain gravity. In the last stage various things can be added like 'filler' to make it heavier, 'size' to make it print clearly and colour to hide off-whiteness.

Presumably the primary aim of an alternative process would be to provide paper for writing or printing purposes. This means that considerations like strength or water-resistance can be forgotten. What is sought is a reasonably white paper that can withstand moderate handling and that has a good 'take' surface. In essence this means using fairly long-fibred material, some bleaching, some sizing and considerable pressing.

The question of whether to use primary materials or re-cycle existing paper is one for individual choice. Re-cycled paper is inevitably weaker than the original product so that use of the obvious material—newsprint—is beset by difficulties. It needs to be mixed with other larger-fibred paper to provide adequate 'felting' because newsprint is made by a different process. Instead of being 'cooked' fibre, newsprint is made by simply grinding the logs of wood and using the resulting 'splinters' directly for paper. The individual fibres are very much shorter and less fibrillated, and hence break up more easily. The other problem with newsprint is removing the heavy ink content, and as it was only lightly bleached in the first place a rather dirty coloured sheet is produced the second time around, despite second bleaching. The choice of the exact mix of materials for re-cycling can be left to experiment, but an obvious starting point is the addition of rag to the newsprint.

Having some idea how paper is made, decided what sort you want to make and settled what your starting material is going to be, how do you begin? The simplest approach, the 'craft' approach, would best start with re-cycled paper. This can be 'mushed' in a *large* kitchen mixer or a small baker's dough machine. Rags should be first cut up into small pieces and boiled vigorously for a couple of hours in a mild bleaching solution, and then added to water already swirling in the mixer. Paper sheets, torn to a suitable size, could then be added, though ensuring that the mixture never thickens beyond the consistency of a very thin porridge, ie about 5% fibre by weight. The mush should be beaten in the mixer for a considerable time—an hour or so— to improve felting, and then tipped into a *large* tub into which a 'mould' can be dipped.

A mould could be made of any fine wire or plastic mesh stretched across some stoutly joined 2" x 1"s made 1"–2" larger all round than the sheet size required. A3 is a good size to start with, moving larger as expertise develops. For the mesh the material used for screen printing should serve reasonably well, though the very fine weaves should be avoided.

The frame is quickly dipped into the mix and lifted out; the 'porridge' is swirled around to get an even layer and excess poured off. Only experience with a frame and the mix consistency can tell you

Fig 3. Fibres, greatly enlarged, before (left) and after beating.

what is 'excess'. The aim is to finish up with neither a tissue paper nor a heavy board.

The frame is then put aside to drain for up to half an hour. After draining, with the 'mat' still containing over 70% water, the mould is reversed on to a piece of thick felt-like material, and a pile of alternate semi-dry sheets and 'felts' (to help absorb moisture) built up. This is known as 'couching'. The pile is then pressed to squeeze out more water on a simple mechanical press. Then the sheets are separated again and left to dry by some convenient method that keeps them flat. Laying on a canvas frame and raising it out of the way by pulleys is one way; pegging them on a line is another and simpler method, if slight marking is not objected to.

For improved writing surfaces sheets may be dipped in a bath of either gelatin or animal glue before the final drying. Bathing in starch increases the firmness of the paper and gives some surface improvement, particularly if subsequently each sheet is lightly ironed. For colouring, kitchen colourings, like cochineal, can be used—sparingly!

Thus, for this simple method, the equipment needed is a beater-mixer; moulds; tub; screw press; press 'felts'; a drying system; and a plentiful supply of water. But such a method is no way to produce quantities of paper, nor to accommodate variations in the materials used. For this, some simple equipment, specially made, is necessary, such as a simple refiner and a roll-press. The first is, essentially, a means of grating the fibres between a heavy ridged roller rotating in a tub with a ridged bottom. Using such an item after the primary mixer can reduce the beating time to five to ten minutes yet produce much superior fibrillation. The mangle-type roll press improves surface finish enormously, especially if a means of heating the rollers can be devised.

Moving on to the third level of paper-making one enters two complicated areas which it is difficult to discuss briefly and can best be studied in, and adapted from, the basic texts on paper-making. These areas are the 'cooking' and bleaching of fibres. And beyond them are the rather remote possibilities of continuous paper production.

Cooking involves boiling the basic materials with strong caustic soda, about a 10% solution, for several hours. This will work well for all materials, but for wood two variants have been developed—the

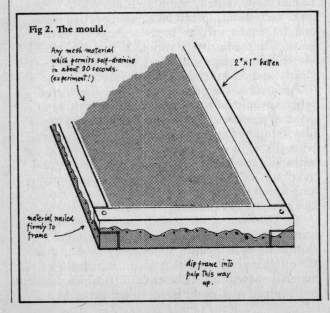

Fig 2. The mould.

Any mesh material which permits self-draining in about 90 seconds. (experiment!)

2"x1" batten

material nailed firmly to frame

dip frame into pulp this way up.

Fig 4. Dipping and couching.

acid method and the alkaline method. The first uses calcium bisulphite mainly as the solvent and produces particularly pure, long fibres. The second uses sodium sulphide as the cooking liquor and produces exceptionally strong fibres known as 'kraft' fibre.

Bleaching involves treating the pulp with sodium hypochlorite (common bleach), followed by washing. This can be done in the mixer stage by adding bleach solution to the water mix, or it can be done by the much cheaper, but more tricky, method of bubbling chlorine through a closed vessel. Either way it needs careful 'washing', ie replacement of the bleaching liquor by plain water, as well as carefully planned handling procedures, before it is attempted.

If one is going to this level of sophistication, the use of 'wet-end' additives could probably be handled as well. These additives are basically rozin and china clay. Rozin does the same job as the gelatin—it gives a good finish for printing or writing purposes. The clay is a filler, giving a more solid and whiter sheet.

Continuous paper production involves designing some form of endless wire or plastic mesh rotating over rollers, followed by steam-heated rollers for drying. Vacuum drying boxes under the wire and differential speed drying rollers—so that one roller 'skidding' over the sheet provides it with a 'polish'—are extras. The chances of realising such alternative production of continuous sheet seem remote, yet it is possible that plain economics might drive us to it. A few figures may make the point. A competent vat-man can produce about 250 A2 sheets an hour after a sizeable investment in frames, etc; a *small* slow paper machine will produce 25,000 A2 sheets an hour, and a fast one 2,500,000. To buy, hand-made paper costs about 18p per A2 sheet, machine-made paper about 0.75p.

But there seems no intrinsic reason why even this level of alternate technology should be beyond our ingenuity. So the message is—try things out, start with the simplest methods and graft on the technology slowly. And keep the juices of invention flowing steadily.

Fig 5. Early paper machine — to set your handyman ideas going.

Derek Burns

MATERIALS

WORKING THE PLANK

The "Back to Nature" movement of recent years has turned many people on to wood as *the* ecological all-purpose material. But the trouble with wood is that it is scarce and that new wood costs more than mass-produced plastic equivalents. Sources: Apart from the wood sources mentioned in the *recycling* section, you can also pick up driftwood, and wood from local derelict land. Building contractors sometimes return at 'knocking off' time with a lorry load of scrap wood to take to the tip next day—they'll be glad if you relieve them of it.

Once you've got some wood, to make the best use of it the first thing to do is to grade it. Separate out the wood that is good for interior use, and exterior use, the pieces with rotten ends, and others with woodworm and other infestations for use as fire wood. Then pull all the nails out of the good wood and stack it—vertically—with the big bits at the back, progressing to approximately 3ft bits at the front. Any bits shorter than 3ft can be stacked in a box or bin. Make sure to cut off any rotten bits; watch out for nails—look carefully all around *before* sawing.

If you buy new wood, get it from a timber yard, (not Do-It-Yourself shops). Have a look at their 'off-cuts' (by the saw mill) and ask for them at a reduced price. Ask for trade discount, say you work for yourself, and are doing a job for someone else. You might even go to the trouble of getting a small rubber stamp made (eg JOE BLOGGS—Gardener/Handyman followed by your address. No VAT number is required as your turnover does not exceed £5,000). You can then make up official-looking 'orders' by stamping your name at the top of orders in a standard order book, obtainable from any stationer.

BASIC TOOLS

If you intend shaping large beams—perhaps from driftwood or tree trunks—you'll need an axe, a log saw, an adze, a drawknife and a pair of boots with steel toe caps. You'll also need a wet stone and an oil stone to keep the adze and drawknife razor sharp. Also useful are a set of steel wedges and a lump hammer, for splitting. But a basic tool kit for lighter work should include: a handsaw (approximately 24" blade with seven teeth per inch), a claw hammer, rule, pincers, a small bradawl, a malet, three chisels, an oil stone, two screwdrivers, a spokeshave, a combination square, a hand drill and drill bits up to ¼", a brace with bits from ¼" to 1", a smoothing plane, and carpenters' pencils. Further additions could include a ripsaw, jack plane, tenon saw, pad saw, marking gauge, pair of compasses, pliers, chalk and line, and a spirit level. For even more ambitious work, add a coping saw, more chisels, gouges, another screwdriver, pin hammer, coarse files (flat and round), saw sharpening files, saw set, G cramps (two large and two small) and combination plane.

Which tools you get first, after the basics, will depend on the jobs you tackle first. Generally speaking, older tools were made of better quality steel, and stay sharp longer. Wooden planes are *much* better to handle than metal ones and are just as easy (if not easier) to adjust once you've got the knack. (Incidentally, put a little furniture wax polish on the sole plate and you'll be amazed how much easier planing becomes). Apart from second-hand shops, watch out for old carpenters' tools in 'Articles For Sale' columns in newspapers and magazines. When looking for specific second-hand tools, know the brand name, and the current price new. But look carefully for worn, broken or missing parts.

MACHINE TOOLS

The most useful power, or treadle, tools for general work are a *circular saw, planer,* and perhaps a *lathe,* all of which can be built from scrap (plus a few new) parts, or purchased second-hand. A circular saw with a 9" or 10" blade, powered by a half-horsepower motor or by a treadle and flywheel, is the next step from handsaws. Electric drill circular saw attachments are not worth bothering with—in fact most drill attachments will rapidly wear your drill out. (But Bosch jig-saws and similar attachments are purpose-built and last for ages). Compressed air tools can also be obtained—drills, jig-saws, orbital sanders, nail guns, and the like—and in conjunction with a compressed air energy storage system (powered by your windmill or watermill?) are very safe and versatile. They cost a lot but last much longer than their electric equivalents.

STORING TOOLS

If you're only going to use them in one workshop, then arrange them on the walls, each tool having its own place, clearly visible, and marked by its outline or silhouette. On the other hand, if you know you will be moving from place to place, it is well worth fitting them into a tool chest. Again, each tool should have its own slot or clip, and should be easily accessible without having to take other tools out first.

TOOL CARE

Don't leave tools out in the open, or edge tools on the ground (particularly on stone or concrete), whilst working. This also applies to saws.

Never use any tool (or allow it to be used) for any other purpose than that for which it is primarily intended. Screwdrivers, and even chisels, for example, should never be used to prise up nails or scrape paint and rust. Despite all my ideals of mutual trust and

TOOLS FOR REMOVING NAILS

Claw hammer

Tack lifter

Pincers

Crowbar, jemmy or wrecking bar

The 'Victor' nail puller —will even remove headless nails level with surface of wood!

A homemade nail puller

Plan

sharing, my experience has taught me that the only way to prevent misappropriation of your tools is to keep them under lock and key! If you're trying to use them communally, then allocate the workshop key to an elected person, and have a book to 'sign out' tools from the workshop—it's worth it in the end.

Saws and edge tools must be kept sharp. When they are not, work becomes difficult and the result is often far from satisfactory. Before I explain how to sharpen such tools, it is important that the actual cutting action is understood.

Wood fibres, as can be seen from the grain, run in more-or-less parallel lines. They can be cut in only two ways: splitting or paring (as when sharpening a pencil with a knife); or by severing (as when cutting a head off with a guillotine). A sharp chisel can be used for either purpose.

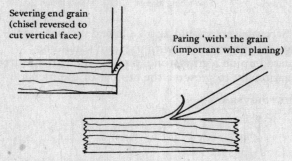

Severing end grain (chisel reversed to cut vertical face)

Paring 'with' the grain (important when planing)

A saw with teeth sharpened for cross cutting is not very efficient for ripping (cutting with the grain). It is, therefore, much better to have two hand saws: one as in the basic tool kit; plus a rip saw with approximately 26" blade and four teeth to the inch.

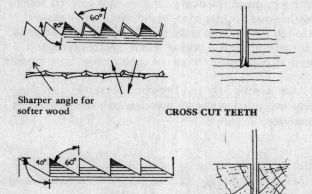

Sharper angle for softer wood

CROSS CUT TEETH

RIPSAW TEETH

Both types of saw have a 'set' (alternate teeth bent slightly to each side), so they cut a slot wider than the blade, to avoid sticking. To sharpen a saw, first check with a steel rule or straight edge to see that all teeth are level.

CHECKING LEVEL OF TEETH

Steel rule or straight edge

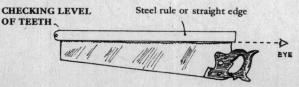

EYE

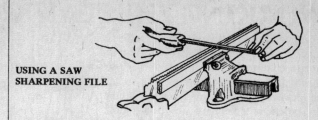

USING A SAW SHARPENING FILE

If not, file them with a fine flat file along the blade, or grind them off using a guiding piece of metal or wood, clamped to the blade approximately one inch from the teeth, and resting against the grinder's tool rest. When a small flat has appeared on each tooth, stop. Clamp the saw between two pieces of wood (say 2in by 1in) using a vice and two G cramps. You need a triangular (three square) fine file, (a double ended one with a handle is obtainable for this purpose). Position the file at the correct angles for your saw (see diagram). Hold the handle in your right hand, and the file tip under your left thumb and as you push it forwards apply a certain amount of pressure. The file will cut much better on the teeth bent away from you, so concentrate on these first, and then turn the saw around. Check that you are making each tooth the same size (counting the file strokes may help). When no light is reflected by each tooth point, then it must be sharp. Remove any side burrs thrown over by the file with the edge of your oil stone, rubbed lightly along the blade, taking care not to blunt the tip of the points. Finally, to set each tooth, tap alternate teeth with a flat-ended punch, resting the blade on a hardwood block. Or use saw-setting pliers. (You can make a saw set from a strip of 1 inch by $\frac{1}{8}$ inch mild steel).

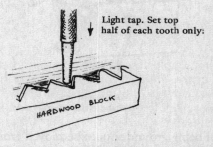

Light tap. Set top half of each tooth only.

HARDWOOD BLOCK

The slot should be only half the depth of the tooth. In order to bend each tooth by the same amount another piece of metal bolted to the first can be adjusted to give the set you want (and prevent you from snapping teeth off).

HOMEMADE SAW SET

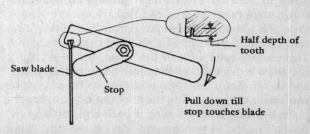

Half depth of tooth

Saw blade

Stop

Pull down till stop touches blade

Circular saws are basically the same, but you can get a combination blade which rips and cross cuts.

CIRCULAR SAW TEETH

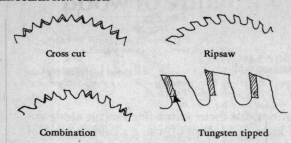

Cross cut   Ripsaw

Combination   Tungsten tipped

Some hand saws, however, have hardened teeth which must be ground off completely and new teeth cut. Some circular saws have tungsten teeth which can only be sharpened on a green grit grinding wheel.

Chisels and plane irons should be sharpened at two angles: 25 degrees and 30 degrees, the first on a wet stone, 12 to 18 inches in diameter, and 2½ to 3 inches wide. The stone should rotate towards the operator, and grinding should be done with the tool held near the top, almost horizontal, otherwise water from the stone will run down the hands and arms—which is disagreeable, especially in winter. The water ensures that the temper of the steel is not lost, and should be drained from the trough after use, as the stone will deteriorate if left submerged. Alternatively, mount the stone in such a way that it can be lifted clear of the water when not in use.

GRINDSTONE AND TROUGH

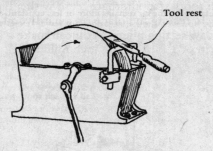

Tool rest

Con rod to treadle
(hand crank on other side)

The tool being ground should be moved from side to side to ensure even wear of the wet stone. The process is much easier if a tool rest is fitted, as shown in the diagram. Check the squareness of the cutting edge. The final edge is obtained on an oil stone. First clamp the oil stone horizontally in the bench vice, and squirt some thin oil onto it. Hold the plane iron or chisel as shown, and rock it up and down to 'feel' the angle you've ground on the wet stone, then raise the free end slightly so that only the tip is touching the stone. Proceed by sliding the tool up and down the oil stone in a figure of eight. This ensures even wear of the stone, and cuts the metal away far quicker than just going straight up and down. Keep the angle constant, as far as possible, and finish off by placing the tool flat on the stone (as in drawing 8) and sliding it back and forth a few times. Finally, to remove any burr on the tips, rub it up and down on a leather strop, or on the palm of your hand.

FOR CHISELS AND PLANE IRONS

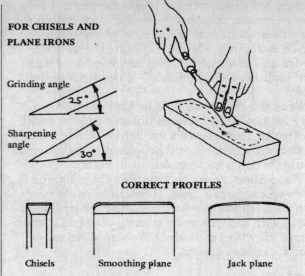

Grinding angle   25°

Sharpening angle   30°

CORRECT PROFILES

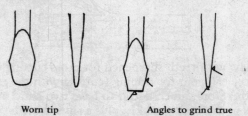

Chisels   Smoothing plane   Jack plane

Screwdrivers should also be 'trued up' occasionally. Tips get rounded with use, and should be squared up on a grindstone, dipping the end in water occasionally to preserve the temper of the metal.

SCREWDRIVERS

Worn tip   Angles to grind true

Having sharpened your tools, the most useful thing to make is a heavy, and/or well secured bench, with woodworking vice, bench stop, and a central trough for tools to rest in whilst working. The next thing to make is a sawing 'horse', with a wide top and 'v' cut end—or a pair of such trestles with smaller tops.

For sawing logs and firewood, a trestle with six legs extended as shown is well worth the time spent making.

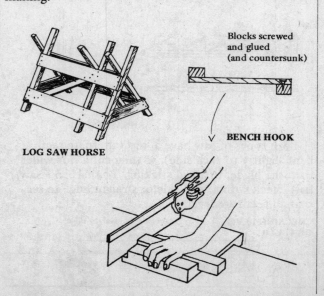

Blocks screwed and glued (and countersunk)

LOG SAW HORSE

BENCH HOOK

Make yourself a bench hook for light sawing jobs, and four hardwood wedges. These can be used in many cunning ways instead of sash cramps. For example, to clamp a box up, strings are tied round the planks (A) and sticks inserted (B). These are twisted up and rested on the box, and the blocks are screwed to the boards so that the wedges can be inserted at C. These are tapped home, and the contrivance checked for squareness. The wedges can be used similarly for table tops and window frames.

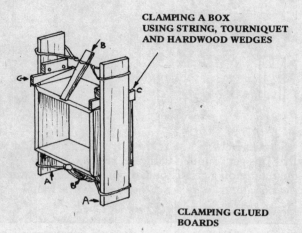

**CLAMPING A BOX
USING STRING, TOURNIQUET
AND HARDWOOD WEDGES**

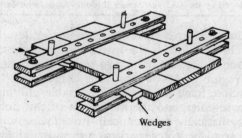

**CLAMPING GLUED
BOARDS**

Wedges

Another useful cramping device is a car jack. I recently cramped a window frame up as shown in the drawing below, using a car jack between the walls.

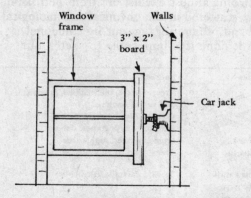

Window frame

Walls

3" x 2" board

Car jack

NB Only tighten until glue has oozed out from joints. Don't overdo it!

Wood is a warm, versatile material, and renewable to boot, but we can't use too much at once. So it needs care and imagination. Treat it like a friend.

Rob and Al Hitchings

The nature of wood

Structure of wood

Wood, like all plant material, is made up of cells, or fibres, which when magnified have an appearance similar to but less regular than honeycomb.

The walls of the honeycomb correspond to the walls of the fibres, and the cavities in the honeycomb correspond to the hollow or open spaces of the fibres.

Softwoods and hardwoods

All lumber is divided as a matter of convenience into two great groups, softwoods and hardwoods. The softwoods in general are the coniferous or cone-bearing trees, such as the various pines, spruces, hemlocks, firs, and cedar. The hardwoods are the non-conebearing trees, such as the maple, oak and poplar.

Moisture content

While the tree is living, both the cells and cell walls are more or less filled with water. As soon as the tree is cut, the water within the cells, *free water*, begins to evaporate. When practically all of the free water has evaporated, the wood is said to be at the fibre-saturation point, i.e. what water remains is mainly in the cell or fibre walls.

Except in a few species, there is no change in size during this preliminary drying process, and therefore no shrinkage during the evaporation of the free water. Shrinkage begins only when water begins to leave the cell walls themselves. What causes shrinkage and other changes in wood is not fully understood; but it is thought that as water leaves the cell walls they contract, becoming harder and denser, thereby causing a general reduction in size of the piece of wood. If the specimen is placed in an oven which is maintained at 212° F., the water will evaporate and the specimen will continue to lose weight for a time. Finally a point is reached at which the weight remains substantially constant, meaning that all of the water in the cells and cell walls has been driven off. The piece is then said to be "kiln dried".

If it is now taken out of the oven and allowed to remain in the open air, it will gradually take on weight, due to the absorption of moisture from the air. As when placed in the oven, a point is reached at which the weight of the wood in contact with the air remains more or less constant. Careful tests, however, show that it does not remain exactly constant, for it will take on and give off water as moisture in the atmosphere increases or decreases. Thus, a piece of wood will contain more water during the humid, moist summer months than in the colder, drier winter months. When in this condition it is in *equilibrium with the air* and is said to be *air-dry*.

A piece of lumber cut from a green tree and left in the atmosphere in such a way that the air may circulate freely about it will gradually arrive at this air-dry condition. This *air-seasoning* process takes from one to three months.

Shrinkage

As a log shrinks, the parts season differently. These characteristics are important to know for use of the wood as lumber. The shrinkage from end to end is negligible, but in cross section it shrinks approximately half as much at right angles to the annual rings as it does parallel to them. This is important in framing and flooring: a stud will not shrink much in length, but will shrink somewhat in the 2" and 4" way. Likewise, a green joint will change in depth as it seasons. In flooring, edge or vertical grain flooring, if green, will shrink about half as much as green flat-grained flooring.

Density

The tree undergoes a considerable impetus early every spring and grows very rapidly for a short time. Large amounts of water are carried through the cells to the rapidly growing branches and leaves at the top of the tree. The result is that the cells next to the bark, which are formed during the period of rapid growth, have thin walls and large passages.

Later on, during the summer, the rate of growth slows up and the demand for water is less. The cells which are formed during the summer have much thicker walls and much smaller pores. Thus it is that each year's growth is of two types, the spring wood as it is called being characterized by softness and openness of grain and the summer wood by hardness and closeness, or density, of grain. The spring wood and summer wood growth for one year is called an *annual ring*.

There is one ring for each year of growth. This development of spring wood and summer wood is a marked characteristic of practically all woods and is clearly evident in such trees as the yellow pines and firs, and less so in the white pines, maple, and the like.

Reprinted, with revisions, from *Light Frame House Construction*, printed 1956 by HEW.

MATERIALS

SKEPTIKAL CHYMIST

At present the major sources of many highly useful and valuable organic compounds, ranging from plastics to medicines, are non-renewable hydrocarbons—oil and coal. This article looks at the possibility of obtaining these chemicals on a small scale from *renewable* sources—such as wood and seaweed.

On examination of the present and past processes for the production of chemicals from renewable natural resources, the following significant points emerge:

◆ *Many of the resources are renewed in a fairly short life-span (1-10 years).*
◆ *They are often labour, as opposed to capital intensive.*
◆ *Many processes use only 'waste' by-products of normal production.*
◆ *Many of the processes are based on pre-industrial techniques; and are thus readily adaptable to the criteria of Alternative Technology.*

Products to which these criteria apply include: *Plant Products:* wood, sugar, starch, natural dyes, insecticides, oils, fats, waxes, cosmetics, cork, drugs, pectins and peat. *Marine Products:* seaweed and drugs. *Animal Products:* drugs, enzymes, gelatin, glue, dairy products (rennet etc).

Space (and personal ignorance) will not permit me to discuss all of these processes. I have therefore chosen three. The first is as yet theoretical, but should become of increasing importance, namely the extraction of *organic chemicals from carbohydrates.* And two others of proven use: *wood* and *seaweed.*

ORGANIC CHEMICALS FROM CARBOHYDRATES

Organic chemicals are very important to humanity today. They supply the starting materials for: plastics, perfumes, drugs, colouring dyes, petrol and other solvents, fats and waxes, and a host of other everyday substances. At the moment the major sources for most of these organic 'building blocks' are petroleum and to a lesser extent coal—both non-renewable.

Up to twenty years ago a significant quantity of chemicals such as ethanol (the alcohol in booze), propanol, acetone and butanol were produced from carbohydrates such as starches, sugars and molasses, but the wide availability of cheap petroleum in the middle 1950's rapidly killed off this more ecologically sound process.

The greatest natural source of energy is the Sun. Plants trap and store the Sun's energy in the form of carbon compounds. These compound carbohydrates are formed from carbon dioxide, water, and trace elements, in a reaction sustained by light and catalysed by chlorophyll, the total reaction being called *photosynthesis.* These carbohydrates occur in a variety of forms (See table below).

Although, in theory, any of the above sources may be utilised, the most promising candidate

A modern still for the distillation of turpentine from Oleoresin developed by the US Naval Stores Station, Olustie, Florida.

would appear to be cellulose, and to a lesser extent starch. Cellulose is the world's major industrial carbohydrate, annual world production being in the region of 100 billion tons (American). Cellulose itself is a rather intractable polymer of glucose units, and the hydrolysis of this polymer (enzymatically or chemically) to glucose would appear to be a necessary step in most schemes making use of it.

The reactions of glucose, of interest to anyone hoping to use it as a starting material for synthesising the organic building blocks which currently come almost exclusively from petroleum, are widely scattered in the chemical and biological literature and require digging out by someone! Until this is done it is impossible to sketch out

Carbohydrates	Sources
Cellulose	Trees, shrubs, plant stalks, grasses, and so on, bacteria
Starch	Cereals, roots, tubers, pith
Glucose	Starch, honey, grapes, dates
Sugar (Sucrose)	Cane and beet, maple tree
Gums, pectins and mucillages	Trees, fruit of all kinds, seeds
Hemicelluloses and pentosans	Trees, Leafstalk, corn-cobs
Alginates, agars and carrageenans	Sea weeds
Copra and nuts	Coco-nuts, trees
Honey	Bees
Microbial polysaccharides	Bacteria and moulds
Specialist sugars	Fermentation industries, polysaccharides
Biologically active carbohydrates	Animal tissues and fluids, micro-organisms, synthetic compounds

From 'Industrial Uses of Carbohydrates', Maurice Stacey *Chemistry and Industry* pp. 222-226 (1973).

realistic schemes of relatively straightforward syntheses suitable for those who do not have the resources (money and technicians), or desire, to slave away at some complex route. Reactions, such as the aromatisation of glucose to catechol (1, 2-Dihydroxybenzene) are well known and may provide some starting points, (ironically, catechol is one of the few organics readily available from natural resources).

But the most direct way of producing some chemicals may be by reviving some of the earlier fermentation techniques. Ch. Weizmann, the first President of Israel, did pioneering work in this area, and a recent (1974) report from the US National Academy of Sciences suggests that the Americans may also be taking it seriously.

WOOD

Until the middle and late 19th century, when the distillation of coal assumed prominence, the distillation of wood supplied many of the common organic chemicals (especially solvents). As Fig 1 indicates, wood could supply a very wide range of organic chemicals.

Rather than go into further detail on all these processes some of which are fairly complex, I shall select one which illustrates the potential of wood chemistry and which, due to its long tradition, may be of immediate use, namely: wood distillation.

For many thousands of years wood has been used as a fuel and as a source of charcoal for the reduction of ores for their metal content. However, it was not until the beginning of the era of modern chemistry that the real usefulness of all the by-products came to be recognised. By the end of the 17th century it was known that wood burnt in closed vessels produced vapour from which could be condensed a tar and a watery liquid, termed pyroligneous acid. In 1658 Glauber identified the main product of this distillation as acetic acid (vinegar), and Boyle, in his *Sceptical Chemist* (1661), noted the presence of an inflammable volatile liquid, 'wood spirit', later named methyl alcohol, signifying the wine of wood. However, it was not until the Frenchman Lebon, in 1799, took out a patent for, "a new method of employing fuel more efficiently, for heating or lighting, and of collecting the various products" (soon all Paris was to admire his gas-lamp in the Hotel Seignelay), that things really got going.

The basic details of the process are given in Fig 2.

Fig 3 shows the section of a battery of retorts (A) of the Mathieu type. The wood is charged automatically from the running buckets, (c), suspended at g. At the end of the operation the charcoal is discharged into the vessel, (P), which is provided with a cover to prevent the hot charcoal from igniting in the air. The vapours from the distillation pass into the tube, (H); which conducts them into a coil cooled by the water in T and then into the barrel, (J), where the tar and the pyroligneous acid separate; the gas, which does not condense, but is still partly combustible, is washed and passes through the pipe, (k), to be burnt under the furnace-hearth, (D); there is no danger of explosion, since, if there is any air in the retorts, it cannot communicate with the hearth, the barrel, (J), serving as a water-seal.

The products obtainable from a typical dry distillation operation are as shown in Fig 4. See overleaf.

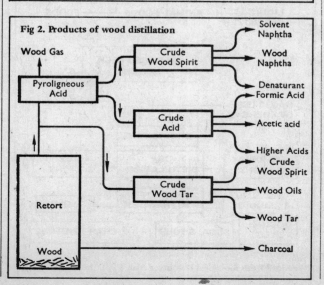

Fig 1.

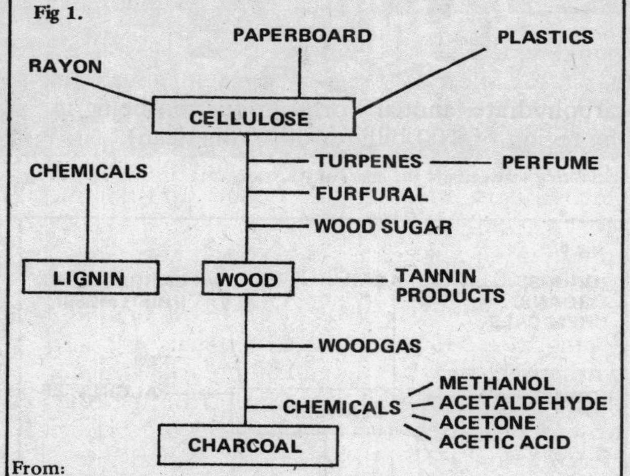

From:
'Chemicals from Biological Resources' Alan J.P. Dalton *ITDG* (1973)

Fig 2. Products of wood distillation

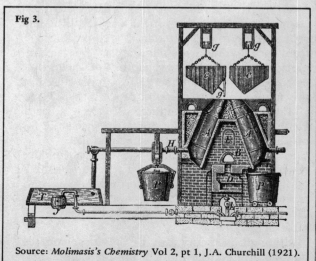

Fig 3.

Source: *Molimasis's Chemistry* Vol 2, pt 1, J.A. Churchill (1921).

MATERIALS

Fig 4.
Products obtained by dry-distillation of 1 ton of hardwood scrap (ca. 70% maple, 25% birch, 5% ash, elm and oak)

Charcoal	600 lb
Gases:	5,000 cu ft
Carbon dioxide (38%)	
Carbon monoxide (23%)	
Methane (17%)	
Nitrogen (16%)	
Methanol	3 gall
Ethyl acetate	15 gall
Ethyl formate	1.3 gall
Acetone	0.7 gall
Creosote oil	3.3 gall
Sol. tar	22 gall
Pitch	66 lb

Source: Alan J.P. Dalton, 'Chemicals from Biological Resources' *ITDG*, (1973).

SEAWEED

From the 17th century until the development of the Le Blanc process, in 1781, seaweeds formed the major source of alkali (sodium and potassium carbonates) in Europe, their ash being known in Scotland and Ireland as 'kelp'. From then until the 1930's there was a lull in the industry, but from then on increasing use was found for one of the major products: Alginic acid. Figs 5-8 give some idea of the products available from seaweed; the earlier manufacture of soda and iodine; the three major products of the industry; the organic chemicals (sugars and steroids) that have been produced by simple laboratory procedures; and the occurrence of seaweeds throughout the world.

Harvesting seaweed off the coast of Australia

The giant kelp *Macrocystis pyrifera*

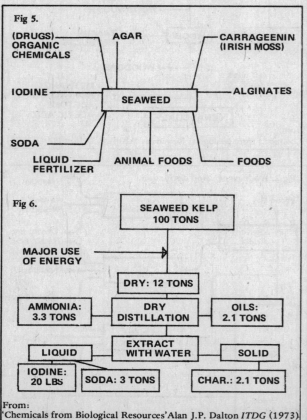

Fig 5.

(DRUGS) ORGANIC CHEMICALS — AGAR — CARRAGEENIN (IRISH MOSS)

IODINE — **SEAWEED** — ALGINATES

SODA —

LIQUID FERTILIZER — ANIMAL FOODS — FOODS

Fig 6.

SEAWEED KELP 100 TONS

MAJOR USE OF ENERGY →

DRY: 12 TONS

AMMONIA: 3.3 TONS — DRY DISTILLATION — OILS: 2.1 TONS

EXTRACT WITH WATER

LIQUID — — SOLID

IODINE: 20 LBS — SODA: 3 TONS — CHAR.: 2.1 TONS

From: 'Chemicals from Biological Resources' Alan J.P. Dalton *ITDG* (1973)

A. POSTELS/F. RUPRECHT

DR. F. MOLYNEUX

CIBA-GEIGY REVIEW

Fig 7.

Chemicals potentially available per annum from 1,000 tons of fresh 'L.Cloustini' (whole plant)

Chemical	*Calculated tonnage present in weed*		
	May	October	Average
Alginic acid	28	31	30
Mannitol	10	33	18
Laminarin	Nil	40	14
Fucoidin	6	9	7.5

Source: *Organic Chemistry Today* F.W. Gibb, Penguin (1964).

Fig 8.	**Product**	**Uses**
	Agar	Microbiology
		Foodstuffs
		Pharmaceuticals
	Alginates	Pharmaceuticals
		Foods
		Rubber
		Textiles
		Paper
Source:	Carrageenin	Largely foodstuffs
Alan J.P. Dalton,		Ceramics
'Chemicals from		Alcoholic drinks
Biological Resources'		Electroplating
ITDG, (1973).		Leather finishing

It would appear that much Scottish and Irish seaweed is still gathered by hand—which cannot be much fun on a rainswept and windy beach at the height of winter. The processes for the extraction of these chemicals have been developed by the now defunct Scottish Seaweed Research Institute, during the 1950's, and may well have been improved on by now. The original methods were simple and admirably suited for communities located near large amounts of seaweed; for most practical purposes the North West coast of Scotland and the West coast of Ireland.

Incidentally, it is possible to cultivate seaweed (the red seaweed, *Porphyra tenera,* has been cultivated for food in Japan for years), but the problem of interference to shipping and fishing, coupled with the major changes in the environment which would occur as a result, led to the dropping of such proposals from the British industry, under pressure from the Ministry. Anyone familiar with the apparently uncontrollable growth of red seaweed now going on along Britain's south coast, will understand the need for caution. In short, the problems may well be social and ecological rather than technical.

Alan Dalton

Part of an alginate producing plant in Scotland

MATERIALS

ANY OLD IRON

THE ECOLOGICAL ARGUMENTS

The environment, that is all living things, the air, water, and soil, forms a 'whole system' usually referred to as the ecosphere.

The Earth developed randomly from deserts into forests and vegetation capable of remaining relatively stable in the face of internal or external changes—capable, for example, of ensuring an optimum balance of oxygen and carbon dioxide in the air, of regulating run off to rivers, of periodically shedding the leaves which build up humus, so ensuring soil fertility. Solar radiation, during photosynthesis, organises nutrients in the soil into complex plant tissue. Herbivores digest and reorganise this into still more complex animal tissue, and having processed it, return the valuable nutrients to the soil.

During these self-regulating processes, waste or random parts are generated. If this consequent randomness is less than the degree of organisation gained, then the system's overall stability will have been increased.

The environment can only absorb waste by recycling it, so it ensures that the waste from one process serves as the materials for the next. Whereas the ecosphere is an open system as regards energy (direct solar), it is a closed one as regards materials—hence *all* materials *must* be recycled.

Until relatively recently, the environment was a very stable whole system. Now it is endangered because the subsystems are not capable of the increased rate of operation demanded of them by man's ever faster 'progress'.

When more *waste* is supplied than the system can use it becomes 'overloaded'; the self-regulating mechanisms cease to function, and the waste simply accumulates. The slightest amount of synthetic products, when introduced to the ecosphere, constitutes pollution. Some pollutants accumulate in living organisms, causing cancers and mutations.

If man wishes to survive, he must:
(1) Ensure the proper functioning of the self-regulating mechanisms, respect the essential structure of the ecosphere, and deviate only within acceptable limits.
(2) Reduce and flatten out exponential growth of consumption of energy and non-renewable resources.
(3) Re-cycle the materials we have, and the wastes we produce.

WASTE

The term 'waste' covers not only those household and industrial materials which we want to be rid of, but also waste by extravagant use of materials and energy. Of the latter type the greatest is 'production' waste. When design is tied to sales rather than product function, and when marketing strategy is based on frequent style changes, the results are: tendency to use inferior materials, short cuts in sound product development, neglect of quality and inspection. This built in obsolescence comes as a disguised price increase to the consumer in the form of shorter product life.

When you buy a car you are also buying the tens of thousands of gallons of water used in the processing of the steel. An aluminium window frame, for instance, can be traced via rolling mills back to the smelters (perhaps in Ghana where vast hydro-electric schemes produce cheap energy), then to a mine (perhaps in Jamaica) where bauxite is extracted, using more energy and creating vast mine tailings.

Inferior short-life goods often compound their waste by performing absurd (and perhaps, in a starving world, obscene) functions which do not need fulfilment.

Repair and re-use are treacheries against the consumer ethic: so when our products fall apart we throw them away. Having concentrated materials from dispersed sources we re-disperse them by burying or burning—reducing them to oxides in a jumble of other materials. This is hardly rational behaviour.

Yet industry is more interested in mining afresh than in using what it has, claiming that recycling materials cost more. When this is true it is invariably for the wrong reasons.

Recycled materials are unnecessarily expensive because most wastes are intended not to be recycled. And the price of new materials reflects neither their true social cost (eg smelter pollution, indirect energy costs, loss of windlands) nor the irreversible depreciation of a fixed capital asset.

PRESENT METHODS OF WASTE RECLAMATION AND RECYCLER'S GUIDE

These vary from composting kitchen wastes to large plants for shredding up car bodies. The two largest channels being Local Authorities and commercial reclamation.

◇ *Local Authorities* have to collect and 'dispose of' domestic refuse, 90% of which gets tipped and buried, but with increasing land shortages many are turning to total incineration. Almost all the Authorities who already do this do not even use the heat evolved (equivalent to half that of coal).

Domestic refuse is expected to double in volume and increase by 70% in weight over the next decade. Consisting of paper, kitchen waste, tins, bottles and foil trays, it should be looked upon as a valuable source of raw materials rather than as a nuisance to be disposed of.

Separate your own waste at source. Compost your vegetable wastes. Wash tins for re-use, or remove the base and flatten them. Paper and card should be flattened and bundled. Wash and save milk tops and silver paper. Some ideas for uses are given below:

◆ *Paper* Some local authorities already collect paper separately and sell it to board manufacturers, but even they do not separate the paper mixed in with the refuse. And we *import* wood pulp at an annual cost of approx £100 million. At £11 a ton for waste paper we are dumping an equivalent of £64 million a year.

TONY DURHAM

If you collect paper locally as a fund raiser remember that a special trip to deliver a pile of newspapers could cost more in petrol than the scrap value of the paper.

◆ *Vegetable and putrescible matter* During the last war many local authorities provided neighbourhood bins for collecting such matter, for use as pig food or compost. (Jersey still does). In Holland, domestic waste is composted on a large scale at a few strategic sites.

Every family which owns a garden could compost their waste, so reducing the pressure on the refuse collection service and improving the fertility of their gardens. Others could put it in bags for communal composting.

◆ *Metals* Over a million tons of iron are discarded every year, yet ferrous metals can be recovered easily by magnetic separation. Non ferrous metals are mostly hand sorted, but some larger industries are developing automated methods. The worst problem is that products made of a mixture of metals are very hard to separate.

Dismantle your own junk, save useful parts, and separate metals for scrap.

◇ *Commercial reclamation* The scrap trade operates at two main levels:

(1) The small yards, who depend largely on 'tatters' (rag and bone men), sort scrap by hand, and sell it to larger yards who supply bulk buyers of scrap, such as steel works.

(2) The larger yards, who will buy direct from tatters and individuals, rely mainly on 'contracts' with firms and corporations as their main source of materials. They use cranes, lorries, shears for chopping, and bailers for compacting scrap. Hand sorters are still employed, efficiency depending on ability to recognise various metals in a dismantled mixture. Oxy-acetylene or oxy-propane cutters are used to cut up larger steel objects, but cutting car bodies this way is uneconomical so large firms are developing mass-reduction methods, (eg Proler Cohen at Willesden). Steel extracted from such plants is often contaminated with non-ferrous fragments. These form blemishes in the rolled plate produced.

Attempts to overcome this have been made—for example, freezing in liquid nitrogen and smashing, which produces small fragments for magnetic separation. For non-ferrous metals, colour 'sortex' machines and fluidised beds have been developed.

◆ *Non metals* Some commercial reclaimers also deal in rags, woollens, paper and card, and some specialise in these. A few deal in plastics and chemical effluent, but the technical problems are great, and usually only a second grade material is produced.

WASTE AS A RAW MATERIAL

Most commercial reclaimers see their 'scrap' only as a material to be re-processed into 'raw' material. There are exceptions; clean rags are cut up for 'wipers', woollens and clothes are sorted and some sold to second hand clothes shops.

Some metal yards put aside girders and pipes, old lamps, benches, pub tables and antiques generally for re-sale at greater than scrap value.

There is still a good amount of 'good' scrap, such as lengths of tubing, rod, shelving, and ex-stock (but new) machine and vehicle parts, (including bearings, nuts and bolts), which cost the earth new and can be got for a few pence.

◆ *Wood* Often not thought of as worth bothering with, it's useful to know where your nearest second hand timber yard is. Most towns have one, and prices are about half that of new wood or less, with the advantage of being well seasoned. You can also get large pieces, and woods such as pitch pine and oak which are almost unobtainable elsewhere.

◆ *Rubber* Reclaimed motor tyres are used in producing new ones, in road surfacing, and basic rubber products. But used (cured) rubber can never be un-cured, so just fills out the new, producing a poorer quality rubber as a result.

◆ *Glass* Some glass is separated by local authorities, and small quantities used in road surfacing. Most glass can be re-melted, but manufacturers again prefer *clean* raw materials on economic grounds.

◆ *Slag* From blast furnaces, processed, can be used for road building and construction purposes.

◆ *Lubricating oil* Motor vehicle and industrial plant produce hundreds of thousands of gallons of waste oil a year. Some garages save it for collection and refining for re-sale as a cheap oil. Engine oil filters have been developed which greatly increase the life of the oil, but are unlikely to be generally available, as it would not be in the interests of the oil companies!

Keep an oil-soaked rag by your tools, particularly wood chisels and drills and wipe them after use: this prevents rust and dulling sharp edges. Use old oil on your housing stone, hinges, catches, nuts and bolts, shears etc.

Build a drip-feed oil burner—can be very efficient. Oil drips onto a very hot plate, vapourises, and flash ignites.

Keep a large tin of old oil on your work bench to quench hot metal in—it gives a blue finish which also helps prevent rust.

◆ *Sewage* The one waste few people think of using, can, by anaerobic digestion, be degraded into a first class fertiliser, giving off methane in the process. Milan's sewage is treated this way and enough electricity is generated from the gas for the entire city. In this country a few sewage works do the same (Bournemouth, Worthing and others), but some even treat the gas as a waste product and burn it off!! —What does your local sewage works do?(See energy section on methane for more information.)

TOTAL USE

It is worth looking at China's example where, in an attempt to be self reliant, each area scrupulously re-uses all its resources.

Animal and human excrement is used for manure, waste wood fibre and water from paper making are turned into resin and sulphuric acid for making synthetics. Alcohol is extracted from other liquid waste. The Fushun No.3 petroleum plant pumps waste gas into bottles for use in domestic cooking. Factories are encouraged to make their own machine tools, often from scrap metals. They may not be the most efficient tools, but they have a very low social cost.

The western recycling industry would be improved if it spread out into small, local, low technology 'recycling yards', stocking unwanted but still usable materials and selling the remainder to larger re-processing industries. This *would* mean that materials would cost more.

However, if articles were designed to last longer, industry encouraged to re-use its own waste, and people shown the potential of articles which they would otherwise throw away, the scrap trade generally would decline.

GEORGE BOWDEN

the highest or to the yard which has the sort of scrap you want. Ask the price again when you get there, and have your scrap 'weighed in'. Don't argue with him over a few pence! Then tell him what you are looking for and ask if you can have a look around—buy something before you go and you'll be welcome back next time.

Rag and bone men will gladly sell direct off their carts.

◆ *Demolition sites* These are good for wood, junk, shop fittings—private contractors are best. Take some grotty wood they want rid of and they may let you have some good stuff free. When asking the foreman try and sense the reaction—a tip may be expected. Corporation sites are a pain—you'll spend hours following official channels to get permission and when you return they'll have burnt it! Try, but the best bet is quiet removal in the evenings. Don't take metals or valuable objects then if you get copped you may get away with it. Some corporations store wood, poles, lamp standards, baths and sinks, water tanks etc from demolished buildings and will sell them.

◆ *Corporation tips* are a haven of useful objects— again, try the foreman—Sundays and evenings are quiet.

◆ *Electricity boards* and the Post Office have old telegraph poles—get the right man, chat him up a bit, and you're away.

◆ *Industrial estates* often have small tips on vacant plots and at the end of dead end roads. Ask permission of nearest firm, and go during working hours, or you'll get 'done'. Many firms have junk outside which often they are glad to get rid of—see the manager.

◆ *Shops* —most have dustbins. Camping, sailing, Army and Navy, DIY shops—all produce useful wastes. Ask when they're going to clear out old stocks and be there. Watch out for shops under-going alteration. The same goes for warehouses, and garages; the signs are workmen's vans and skips—ask politely and you'll get. Grocers' old vegetables are ideal for feeding goats . . .

◆ *Manufacturers* throw out offcuts eg furniture manufacturers, sail and tent manufacturers—canvas etc.

◆ *Garages* throw out old exhausts, tyres and inner tubes.

◆ *General* Develop a keen eye for useful unwanted items you see in back gardens and yards. A few friendly words and they could be yours.

SCAVENGING

At the moment we are fortunate that, with the right approach, and a bit of searching, materials for most jobs can be got for little more than scrap value.

The first place to look through is at home, making best use of things you already have. Old bottles can be washed out with soap and hot water, obstinate dirt dislodged by the addition of sand, or a concentrated solution of caustic soda. Tin cans washed out make good containers for painting jobs, storing nails, screws, nuts and bolts, etc. Save jars for jam making. Dead branches from trees are as good as seasoned timber, but rotten wood is valueless and should be burnt as soon as possible to avoid spreading. Woodworm should be treated immediately (at least before May, when they fly to new breeding grounds). If only a few holes show the wood will not be weakened too much and can be re-used.

◆ *Scrap yards* Just to 'get in', they must think you'll provide good custom, but let them know you're not a sucker either.

First, if possible, collect some scrap (say ½cwt cast iron—old fire fronts or car engine blocks, or 5lb copper tube, etc). *Then* phone around a few yards asking the buying price, per lb or cwt. Go for

UTILISING SCRAP

Vehicle scrap

Ball bearing races from wheel hubs and gear boxes—mount in hardwood blocks, grease well and keep dirt and water out.
Fanbelts for drive systems. Uses—workshop equipment, windmills, water wheels, potters wheels, treadles, etc.

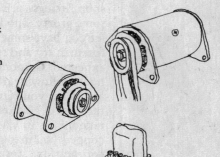

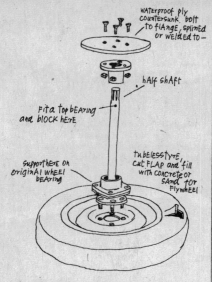

WATERPROOF PLY COUNTERSUNK BOLT TO FLANGE, SPLINED OR WELDED TO—

half shaft

Fit a top bearing and block here

support here on original wheel bearing

TUBELESS TYRE, cut FLAP and fill with CONCRETE or SAND for flywheel

Rear half shafts (from the back axle)—columns for potters wheels, and lay shafts for treadles.
Steering columns provide useful lengths of tubing as do
Prop shafts —which are useful in windmill turret construction.
Head lights —can be used in house and workshop 12v lighting.
Doors and roofs —cut out useful sheet. Van rear doors have useful hinges for gates etc.

Alternators and generators plus control box for charging batteries—wind or water driven.
Dynamos, and windscreen wiper motors can be used as 12v dc motors—for pumps, fans, light machinery.
Starter motors have high torque, could drive a wheel chair or trolley—but will soon flatten your battery. Fit a fan and drill cooling holes for long running.

The engine —mount on heavy base and convert to gas. Can drive generator, circular saw, lathe etc. —or use the whole car!

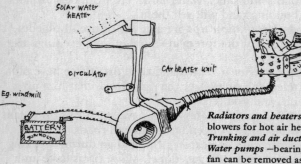

SOLAR WATER HEATER

CIRCULATOR

CAR HEATER UNIT

Eg. windmill

BATTERY

SAW bench

Radiators and heaters can be used with blowers for hot air heating systems.
Trunking and air ducting —use as same.
Water pumps —bearing, shaft, pulley and fan can be removed as a useful unit (no good for pumping to any great height, though).

Tyres make good playthings, and shoe soles. Use a wide large diameter one, the more flexible the better; avoid tyres with steel webbing. Cut them with a hack saw and tin snips.
Scooter wheels can be adapted for barrows and trolleys eg carrying oxy-acetylene bottles.

wooden jockey pulley using bicycle hub

SCOOTER WHEELS

bicycle tyre TETREADS

Lorry —air brake tanks for compressed air storage etc. Inner tubes are useful for large thick rubber sheet—diaphrams, bellows, flap valves etc.
Bicycle —dyno-hub wheels are useful for wind generators, wheel hubs, bottom brackets and steering bearings for pulleys, polishing spindles etc.

Tyres cut up for shoe soles. Two strips are needed. (See also *workshop* below.)
Motorcycles —bearings used as above. Wheel hubs and alternators, for windmills.

bench grinder using bicycle wheel hub. Could fit on TREADLE SEWING MACHINE.

The workshop

Many things for the workshop can be made from old junk. Here are just a few.
Storing materials Bins for wood and metal can be made from oil drums (5 gallon).

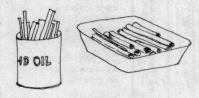

Trays for small offcuts of tube, etc, made from roasting tins—which can be found in dumped cookers.
Old bread tins are good for nails.

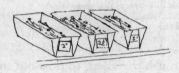

Large matchboxes can be made into small chests of drawers for small screws etc. Yoghurt pots are reasonably good for similar purposes.
Typewriter tins are good for washers, tobacco tins for nuts. Metals should be stored horixontally on a wall for easiest access. Anything under 1 ft is put in small trays.

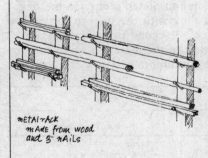

metal rack made from wood and 3" nails

A few minutes sorting may save hours of hunting.

Containers

1 gal oil tins —cut up for quick exhaust pipe repair.

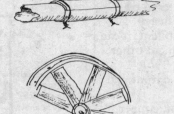

—bicycle wheel windmill blades.

Part cut for scoops

and oil drip trays

55 gal drums —water barrel; coal/grain storage; forge; Savonius rotor; water wheel.
Plastic bottles —cut off bottom half, use top as funnel, bottom for liquids or small objects.

Miscellaneous

Old Pianos —lead from the notes, hinges, piano wire from strings (good for making your own springs), and good quality wood. Some have cast iron frames and brass pedals—weigh in as scrap.
Filing trays and ex supermarket baskets— garden sieves and veggy racks.
TV's radios, tape recorders etc. provide a host of useful components for the electronics fiend. Some may be repairable —bad jointing being a frequent cause of circuit breakdown.

SWAPPING AND TRADING

As a final thought on re-cycling and if you've got the room—collect anything, buy bargains etc as they occur, don't just look for something when you need it. You may be able to swap at a later date with someone else for something they have got that you need.

(the heading for this one had to be put at the bottom because the layout guy f-

Tool rack from cycle tyres

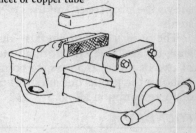

old bicycle tyre   cut

Soft jaws for the vice from that old ally, sheet or copper tube

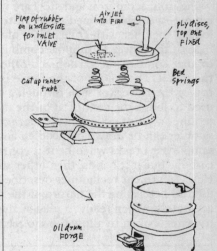

Hammer handles that are broken can be replaced, keep the old one for wedges and making smaller handles.

Bellows for forge from plywood and car inner tubes

FLAP OF RUBBER on UNDERSIDE for inLET VALVE   AiR jet into FIRE   PLY discs, top one FIXED
cut up inner tube   BED springs

oil drum FORGE

Electric motors. Found in scrap yards, are often still serviceable—for bench grinders, compressors, etc.—but for less dependence on CEGB get into *Treadles.* For these, fly-wheels are needed—old flat belt pulleys and mangle wheels are OK, and car wheels with tyres filled with concrete serve well for heavier work and for potters wheels.

Old files ground down make useful cutting tools, and ideal scrapers for removing rust, paint etc. If not too blunt they can be re-sharpened by cleaning in strong soda, then immersing in 1 part nitric acid and 4 parts water, until metal is etched away—wash well and dry.

FILE SCRAPER

Tools

DE RE METALLICA

Alan Stewart

The Industrial Revolution was made possible by the abundant supply of iron ores and coal necessary to manufacture iron and steel. Modern technology still depends on the supply of cheap steel. Without it, Western society would collapse. Because of its availability and strength, steel is the bulk material of machinery, railways, bridges and similar heavy engineering products. Through heat treatment, it can be hardened to make cutting tools which cut other metals, organic materials and steel itself. Table 1 shows the properties and uses of the basic irons and steels.

The other common metals—aluminium, copper, lead, tin and zinc—are normally used in combinations of two or more, as *alloys,* to complement steel. Table 2 shows the properties and uses of these metals and of some common alloys.

FOUNDRY

The foundry is the place where metals are melted down, refined or alloyed, and cast into moulds. Intricate shapes can be produced by *casting,* without cutting away or otherwise wasting metal. The foundry is also the place where metal is recycled.

Pig iron, scrap iron and steel are melted in a *cupola*—a fire-brick lined tower, into which metal is loaded together with coke. Air is blown in at the base of the tower to support combustion and to oxidize some of the carbon and other impurities in the metal. The colour of the flame issuing from the top of the tower (or seen through a spy-hole) can be used to judge the condition of the melt but this requires a lot of experience. Alternatively small samples can be drawn off, cooled and tested. If a sample bar breaks when bent it contains a lot of carbon. But if it bends, then other simple tests, using Heat Treatment techniques described below, can be used to determine the nature of the sample more accurately. When ready, a plug at the base of the tower is broken to allow the molten metal, which

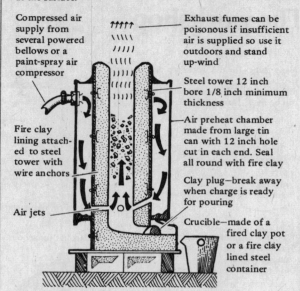

Fig 1 Miniature Cupola: 5 inch bore x 3 feet tall.
Used for melting iron and steel scrap. The scrap metal together with coke and chale is ladled into the tower. The chale forms a slag which floats on the liquid metal and prevents oxidisation at the surface.

Compressed air supply from several powered bellows or a paint-spray air compressor

Exhaust fumes can be poisonous if insufficient air is supplied so use it outdoors and stand up-wind

Fire clay lining attached to steel tower with wire anchors

Air jets

Steel tower 12 inch bore 1/8 inch minimum thickness

Air preheat chamber made from large tin can with 12 inch hole cut in each end. Seal all round with fire clay

Clay plug—break away when charge is ready for pouring

Crucible—made of a fired clay pot or a fire clay lined steel container

Note: *Be very wary of old oildrums as raw materials for furnaces. Never try to weld, braze or solder them either. No matter how well cleaned they are, enough oil is always left in crevices to cause an explosion.*

has drained down through the ashes, to flow out and into a crucible. A small, simple cupola can be made with the internal diameter of the tower ranging upwards from four inches. (Fig 1).

The crucible furnace (Fig 2) is a means of melting or alloying metals. It has the advantage that contamination from the fuel cannot occur and that exact quantities of base metal and alloying elements can be loaded into the clay crucible before firing. A typical charge might consist of sawn-up bike handle-bars and other chromium-plated scrap. On melting, the chromium will alloy with the steel to form a low-carbon stainless steel. A second firing is necessary, involving the addition to the melt of a small amount of aluminium. The aluminium acts as a catalyst and

Table 1. Iron and Steel

Iron and Steel		Properties	Uses	Working Processes
Pig Iron 3.1 to 3.7% Carbon 1.5 to 2.8% Silicon	Blast furnace	Hard, Brittle	Raw Material only	
Cast Iron 3.2 to 3.5% Carbon 0.9 to 2.8% Silicon	Cupola	Hard, Brittle Black Rust Self-Lubricating Easy to Machine	Machinery bases and gears. Brackets	Casting Cutting
High Carbon Steel 0.7 to 1.3% Carbon	Cupola and Open Hearth Furnace	Strong and Tough Elastic Red Rust Hardness Induced by Heat Treatment	Cutting Tools	Casting, Forging, Coldworking, Welding, Cutting
Mild Steel 0.12 to 0.25% Carbon	Cupola and Open Hearth Furnace	Soft and Tough and Elastic Red Rust	General Fabrication	As above
Stainless Steel 0.1 to 1.3% Carbon 10% Nickel and 18% chrome	Crucible and Electric Arc and Electric Induction Furnace	Hard and Very Tough and Elastic Corrosin Resistant can be non-magnetic Work Hardens	Corrosion Resistant	As above

Fig 2. Crucible furnace, used to melt and alloy steel and other metals. Metal is loaded into crucible. Coke is packed round the crucible and lit. When the fire has died down, 1 to 2 hours later, the metal will have melted. A small piece of aluminium is now added to the crucible, the fire is rebuilt and relit. This is in order to boil off gases from the molten metal. When the fire has died down again, the crucible is lifted out with special tongs and the metal can be poured directly into moulds. The advantage of this method is that the purity of the metals in the crucible is retained and that an alloy can be made from exact quantities of different metals which have been individually weighed out before loading into the crucible.

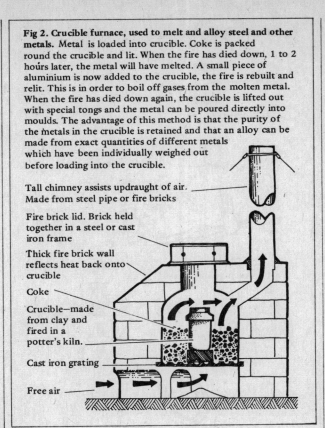

Tall chimney assists updraught of air. Made from steel pipe or fire bricks

Fire brick lid. Brick held together in a steel or cast iron frame

Thick fire brick wall reflects heat back onto crucible

Coke

Crucible—made from clay and fired in a potter's kiln.

Cast iron grating

Free air

will boil off gas from the melt, which would otherwise produce very porous castings.

MOULDS

Sand moulds are relatively inexpensive and are widely used for the production of iron and steel and other metal castings. They can be constructed using a wooden pattern embedded in moulding sand. *Cores* are used to form shapes or voids that cannot be made strong enough from packed moulding sand. Alternatively, they can be made from moulding sand first formed in a wooden mould and then baked until hard in an oven (Fig 3).

There are many other casting techniques. One of the most interesting is *investment casting,* often

Fig 3. Sand mouldings—made in two halves, sand is packed round the wooden pattern. The sand must be packed hard enough so that it does not drop out of the moulding box but not so hard as to prevent gas escaping from the molten metal.

Moulding box.
top box
bottom box

wooden pattern

bottom box
packed sand
baseboard

top box
inverted bottom box

pouring gate pattern
rising pattern

mould ready for baking; pattern is removed before pouring

Table 2. Other Common Metals and Alloys

	Properties	Uses	Working Process
Aluminium	Light grey colour Light weight Soft, Alloys are brittle	general Fabrication where light weight is important	Cast, Machine cannot be soldered Weld in inert atmosphere only
Copper	Soft and ductile efficient electrical and heat conductance	Electric Cables Soldering iron bits Boiler tubes	Cast, Machine, Solder, braze, weld, Forge and Coldwork
Lead	Very heavy weight Soft and ductile Low melting point	Solder (Alloyed with tin) Wiped joints plumbing weights	Cast, Coldwork
Tin	Corrosion Resistant Brittle, Weak. Low melting point	Tin plate (on steel sheet) Solder	
Zinc	Corrosion Resistant Brittle, Weak	Zinc coating steel (galvanising) Perforated sheet	Hot dip Cold rolled
Bronze	Copper Tin Alloy harder than copper	Statues and sculptures Bearings (alloyed with antimony)	Cast, machined Coldworked
Brass	Copper Zinc alloy, harder than Bronze Brittle	Electrical terminals and other components	Cast machine Coldwork

MATERIALS

known as the 'lost wax' process. This method was well established by the fifth century BC in the Western Chou Dynasty to produce seamless castings of intricate shape and surface detail. The pattern is constructed from wax and is an exact replica of the required casting. The wax pattern is coated with a thin wall of clay to form the mould. The clay mould is then baked in order both to burn out the wax pattern and also to harden the clay. The hollow clay mould can then be filled with molten metal. When the metal has cooled the clay mould is smashed to free the casting.

FORGING

The art of the blacksmith is as old as the art of refining metal from ores. The essential equipment required—hearth, bellows, hammer, tongs and anvil—is simple and inexpensive and, once a forge is set up, any other tools required, such as flatters, punches or hot chisels, can be forged from crude lumps of steel. Modern technology only uses forgings in cases where the very high strength achieved by forging is essential and "justifies" the high tooling costs involved in mass production of forged items, such as car engine con rods and spanners.

This high strength arises because forged material has a fibrous nature which reaches its ultimate in the Samurai sword. The sword blade is beaten out from a small cube of steel and then rolled up and beaten back into a cube. This is repeated until the final blade is of an extremely fibrous nature. The forging is carried out with the metal almost white hot, so that the resulting layers weld themselves together. Horseshoes are forged rather than cut out of flat sheet, not only to save metal but also to benefit from fibrous strength. The piece of flat rectangular metal used to make the horseshoe (Fig 4) is inherently fibrous, due to the process of its original manufacture, *cold rolling*. These fibres are preserved during the forging of the shoe. Similarly the tapered parts of chisels and screwdrivers are stronger if forged rather than filed.

It is possible to weld metal at the forge. The pieces to be welded must first be dipped in a *flux*, then heated until almost white hot and finally hammered together. The weld will not hold unless a flux is used. The flux melts at a high temperature and seals the metal surfaces from the air, so preventing the surfaces from oxidizing. A suitable flux for welding mild steel is calcined borax.

HEAT TREATMENT

If a piece of high carbon steel is heated until red hot and then quenched in water, it will become extremely hard but brittle. Strength, necessary for the cutting edge of a tool, for example, can be achieved by *tempering*, ie by heating the hardened steel to a temperature of between 230°C and 300°C. The higher the tempering temperature the stronger the steel will become, but at the expense of hardness. A very simple and ancient method of judging the required tempering temperature is by the use of "oxide colours". If a polished piece of steel is heated slowly, coloured oxides will form on the polished surface. The oxide colour changes from straw to

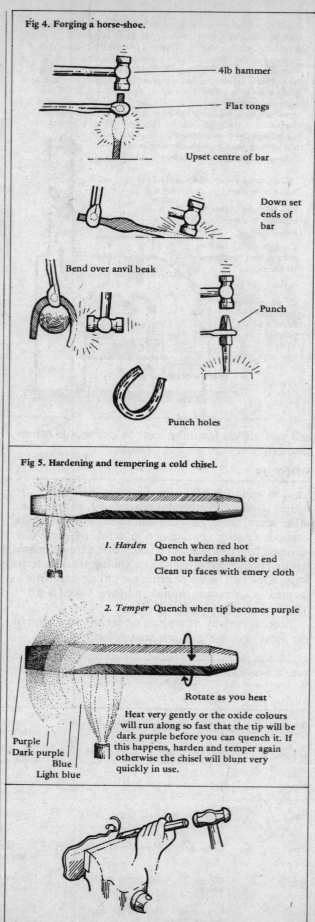

Fig 4. Forging a horse-shoe.

4lb hammer

Flat tongs

Upset centre of bar

Down set ends of bar

Bend over anvil beak

Punch

Punch holes

Fig 5. Hardening and tempering a cold chisel.

1. *Harden* Quench when red hot
Do not harden shank or end
Clean up faces with emery cloth

2. *Temper* Quench when tip becomes purple

Rotate as you heat

Purple
Dark purple
Blue
Light blue

Heat very gently or the oxide colours will run along so fast that the tip will be dark purple before you can quench it. If this happens, harden and temper again otherwise the chisel will blunt very quickly in use.

Fig 6.

brown then to purple and finally to blue as the temperature increases from 230°C to 300°C. Table 3 lists various cutting tools together with appropriate oxide colours for tempering their cutting edges. Fig 5 shows the hardening and tempering of a cold chisel. It is important that only the tip of the chisel should be hard and that the shank and the end which is hit with a hammer should be soft, otherwise the shank will crack or the end will splinter when hit.

Mild steel cannot be hardened and tempered because it does not contain enough carbon. It can, however, be *case hardened.* If a piece of mild steel is heated until red hot and then thrust into a pile of carbon dust, some of the carbon will be absorbed by the surfaces of the mild steel. By repeating this several times, enough carbon will be absorbed so that the steel can be hardened and tempered in the normal way, but the resulting hardness and tough-ness will only be skin deep. However this is useful for giving such things as screw-drivers and pen-knives hard, wear-resistant surfaces. The skin can be as thick as 1/16th inch, but to achieve this thickness the steel has to be 'soaked' in carbon, ie packed in a box together with carbon-rich granules and kept at red

heat in an oven for three to four hours. Hoof-clippings are a traditional carbon-rich material used in this process (showing the influence of the black-smith) but charcoal will do just as well.

When copper or aluminium are cold worked—ie bent, beaten or stretched—they gradually become hard and brittle, and if the cold working is to be continued, the metal has to be softened by annealing (heating the metal, usually by gas flame, and then quenching it). If aluminium is quenched in brine, and copper in killed-spirits (dilute sulphuric acid), the oxides which form on the surface of the metal during heating will be purged to leave a dull clean surface.

FITTING AND MACHINING

◆ *Bench Tools* A sturdy bench made from timber (or angle iron and timber) and an engineers vice, are vital when using most hand tools. (Fig 6). The vice, rigidly attached to the bench, has many uses. Among them are: rigidly gripping a work piece while it receives heavy blows from a cold chisel and hammer; firmly holding work for scribing lines in it ('marking out'); holding cold or red-hot bars in order to bend them to a right angle; squeezing metal together; and pressing dowel pins into tight holes.

If something is to be made from a sheet of tin plate, copper or aluminium, the flattened out plan is first marked out on the sheet using a pencil, straight-edge, compasses and a rule. When marking out work on iron or steel, pencil lines would be difficult to see and would be easily erased so lines are scratched using a scriber and dividers. Also, a 'centre-pop' is used to make small 'pop' marks at regular intervals along all marked out lines, so that, when metal has

Table 3. Tempering Chart using oxide colours which form on steel as it is heated

Tool	Tempering colour	Temperature °C
Lathe tools	Pale straw	230
Large drills	Dark straw	240
Taps and tin snips	Brown	250
Wood axe and chisel	Brownish purple	260
Cold chisels	Purple	270
Springs	Dark purple	280
General	Blue	300

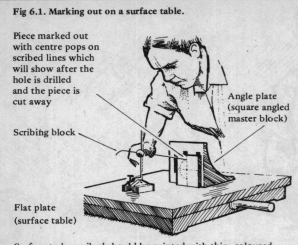

Fig 6.1. Marking out on a surface table.

Piece marked out with centre pops on scribed lines which will show after the hole is drilled and the piece is cut away

Angle plate (square angled master block)

Scribing block

Flat plate (surface table)

Surface to be scribed should be painted with thin, coloured lacquer or chalked so that scribed lines show up. Aluminium and other soft metals should not be scribed because it will cut in too deep and weaken the metal. Better to use a pencil.

been cut away down to a line, the pop marks will show even though the line has disappeared. The scriber can be held in a scribing block (Fig 6.1) and used on a surface table for scribing accurate parallel lines.

A piece of metal can be cut roughly to shape with a cold chisel, or sawn with a hack-saw, and then finished to the required size and shape with files—using first the large, rough variety, and ending with small fine-toothed files. When extremely flat surfaces are required, the final flatness can be achieved by using a scraper to take off 'high spots' of the order

of 0.0003 inches. It takes a lot of practice to produce flat surfaces even to within plus or minus 0.002 inches, and the bigger the surface the harder it is. If a smooth polished surface, rather than a flat one, is desired, then a piece of emery cloth wrapped around a file can be used. A little oil on the surface to be polished helps the cutting action of the emery cloth.

The simplest way to test the flatness of a surface is to place the straight edge of a scale on it and hold it up to the light. The low spots on the surface show light while the rule, resting on the high spots, causes the high spots to be dark.

◆ *Power Tools* The main workshop power tools are the *lathe*, the *shaper*, the *drilling machine*, the *milling machine* and the *universal grinding machine*. (Fig 7). The *drilling machine* (see **Vision 5**) is a must for any workshop; it will be used more than any other machine. Secondhand machines are inexpensive and are usually a good buy since they don't wear out easily and are cheap to mend.

The next machine, in terms of usefulness, is the *lathe* (see **Vision 5**), used to produce flat surfaces by *facing*, or to make splined bores and key-ways (by keeping the work still and moving the tool along the bed), or to produce circular rods and bores. When buying second-hand lathes watch out for wear of the bed slides near the head since this fault is difficult to rectify and will produce tapered work. Wear of the lead-screw can be easily rectified by removing it and reassembling it the other way round since the tail-stock end will not be worn.

The *shaper* is used to produce flat surfaces. It is really a powered cold chisel but is much more versatile. Second-hand shapers are a good buy and wear in old machines will not reduce their performance.

The drilling machine, the shaper and the lathe are the only power tools really needed in a general work-shop. They are inexpensive to buy and cheap to run and maintain. The necessary cutting tools are also cheap and, apart from drills, can be home-made on the forge. The *milling machine*, which can also produce flat surfaces, wears out very quickly and

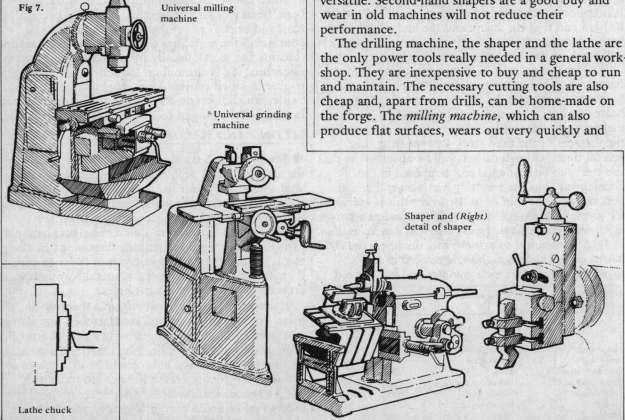

Fig 7.

Universal milling machine

Universal grinding machine

Shaper and (*Right*) detail of shaper

Lathe chuck

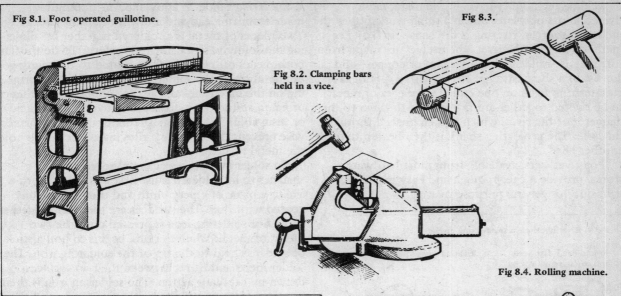

Fig 8.1. Foot operated guillotine.

Fig 8.2. Clamping bars held in a vice.

Fig 8.3.

Fig 8.4. Rolling machine.

second-hand ones cost a lot to repair. (The necessary tools are also expensive). *Universal grinding machines* are used to produce extremely smooth, flat or curved surfaces to very accurate dimensions, but are a bit of a luxury for a general purpose workshop.

SHEET METAL WORK

After marking out a job on sheet metal the sheet can be cut roughly to size with a hack-saw or a cold chisel and then cleaned up with files. However, a foot-operated guillotine (Fig 8.1) can do this much more easily. Your hands are free to position the sheet accurately and, as the foot pedal is depressed, the machine first clamps the sheet firmly and then shears the metal cleanly.

To make boxes or brackets with sharp corners the sheet can be bent using clamping bars (Fig 8.2). Position the sheet between the bars clamped in a vice, and the sheet is bent over using a soft (or *hide*) hammer so as not to damage the surface. Alternatively, a foot operated bending machine can be used. This works in the same way as the guillotine but bends instead of cuts.

Cylindrical and conical shapes can be made by beating the sheet, again with a soft hammer, over a circular rod held in a vice (Fig 8.3). The rolling machine (Fig 8.4) makes short work of this job.

Sheet metal can be made very strong and stiff by pressing or beating it to a spherical or bowl shaped surface (Fig 8.5). The car body is a good example, being entirely built of pressed steel sheet with every surface curved, usually in more than one plane. You will find that the more a sheet is beaten the harder it will become to bend it and that it might even crack. This effect is called *work hardening* but it can be reversed by annealing, described in the section on heat treatment.

To make a bowl from a flat sheet, the sheet should first be annealed. The centre of the sheet is then rested on the spherical head of a ball-headed stake and a light planishing hammer used to distend the centre of the sheet by beating in concentric circles working outwards from the centre. When the sheet gets stiff, anneal it again and continue beating, turning the work as you go. You will probably need to anneal the bowl several times before it is finished.

PERMANENT FIXINGS

◆ *Riveting* In the Victorian era most metal objects—from kettle and saucepan handles to the great steel ships of Brunel — were held together by rivets. Modern X-ray inspection of welded joints and development

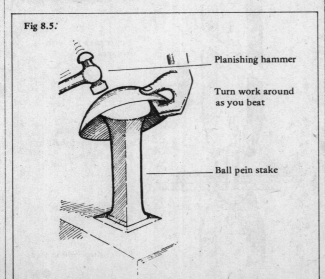

Fig 8.5.

Planishing hammer

Turn work around as you beat

Ball pein stake

of welding techniques have, in the main, made riveted joints obsolete, but in a small workshop with modest resources, riveting is the cheapest fixing method (Fig 9). The rivets themselves are made from soft metals—mild steel, aluminium or copper—and consist of a short, straight shank with a spherical or countersunk head on one end. Two pieces of metal to be riveted together are first drilled through to the diameter of the rivet, which is then pushed through the hole. The projecting shank is then beaten to form another head.

'Pop-rivet' sets, available from most hardware stores, provide a cheap, quick and easy means for light duty or general purpose riveting.

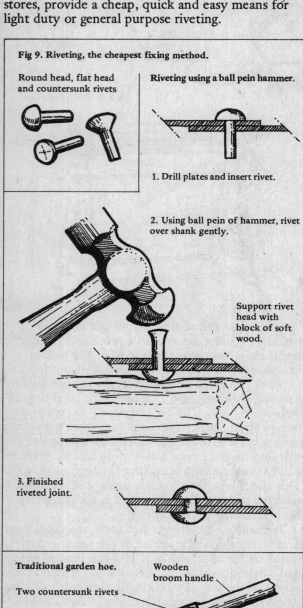

Fig 9. Riveting, the cheapest fixing method.

Round head, flat head and countersunk rivets

Riveting using a ball pein hammer.

1. Drill plates and insert rivet.

2. Using ball pein of hammer, rivet over shank gently.

Support rivet head with block of soft wood.

3. Finished riveted joint.

Traditional garden hoe.

Wooden broom handle

Two countersunk rivets

Two round or caphead rivets

Ferrel-sawn off piece of pipe pinned to handle with small round nail.

Swan-neck stem ¼" dia. mild steel rod forged to shape with flattened ends.

Blade — 1/8 " sheet mild steel.

◆ *Soldering* Solder is a low-melting point alloy, made from tin, lead and a tiny amount of antimony. Two pieces of metal are soldered together by alloying the solder with each metal surface. To do this both pieces of metal must be heated to the melting temperature of the solder. To prevent oxides forming on the metal surfaces as they are heated, a flux of *killed spirits* (zinc dissolved in hydrochloric acid) or resin (Fluxite) is used. The oxides would otherwise prevent the necessary alloying of the solder to the metal surfaces.

To solder two pieces of metal together, the surfaces to be soldered must first be cleaned with a file or a piece of emery cloth and then completely coated with flux. The surfaces are then held together and a hot soldering iron is pressed onto the two pieces of metal. When the flux begins to boil a stick of solder is held to the tip of the soldering iron. The solder melts and flows between the two surfaces, drawn by capillary action. The soldering iron is then removed and the solder quickly cools and solidifies. If the flux used was killed spirits then the joint should be thoroughly washed to prevent the remaining flux corroding the metal. Resin flux is not corrosive and requires no subsequent washing. The soldering iron can be electrically heated or heated in a gas flame. Alternatively, a small gas torch can be used instead of a soldering iron.

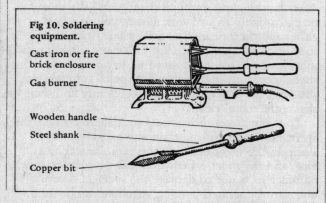

Fig 10. Soldering equipment.

Cast iron or fire brick enclosure

Gas burner

Wooden handle

Steel shank

Copper bit

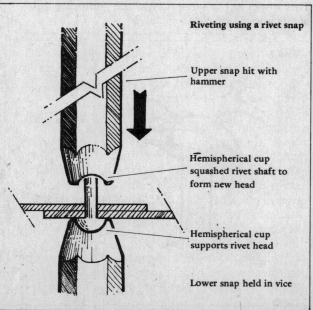

Riveting using a rivet snap

Upper snap hit with hammer

Hemispherical cup squashed rivet shaft to form new head

Hemispherical cup supports rivet head

Lower snap held in vice

◆ *Brazing* The principle of brazing is exactly the same as soldering with the stick of solder replaced by a brazing rod, made of copper/zinc alloy, which has a much higher melting point than solder and produces a much stronger joint. To reach this high melting temperature a gas torch with an air supply provided by a foot-operated bellows can be used. The flux used is Borax. This can be obtained as a solid stick and a paste is made, as required, by rubbing the stick on a glass surface with a drop of water.

◆ *Welding* This is similar to Brazing but steel alloy welding-rods are used. To reach the high welding-temperature necessary to melt steel welding-rods, an oxy-acetylene torch is used. The oxygen and acetylene gas is supplied from a compressed oxygen cylinder and a compressed acetylene-cylinder. These cylinders must be kept several feet away from where the welding is taking place since an explosion would be fatal. Another danger with acetylene is that it is very unstable and will explode if it comes into contact with oil. Never wipe the outlet connections from an acetylene-cylinder with an oily rag. The welding-torch is supplied with different sized gas-nozzles which are used to produce a suitably sized flame for the job in hand. A really large nozzle can be used to produce a flame that will burn through steel sheet. This can be used for cutting sheets to a required shape or size or for salvaging pieces of metal from large scrap. The welding rod is coated with the flux and so no additional application of flux is required. A welding mask, which has a very dark visor, must be used, since the light radiation from the welding will eventually cause blindness.

Electric arc-welding is a lot safer than gas welding, but it is not so portable since it needs a 3-phase electrical supply.

REFERENCES

Workshop Technology Pt I. by N.A.J. Chapman. Chapman's Workshop Technology is a bit quaint but is the best introduction to workshop practice that you can get. For specialized information, eg foundry practice, technical libraries in Technical Colleges all over the country are crammed with such information.

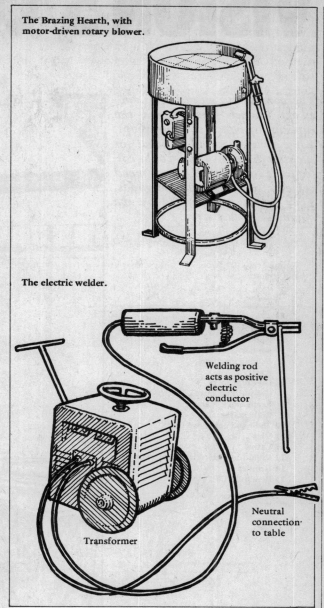

The Brazing Hearth, with motor-driven rotary blower.

The electric welder.

Welding rod acts as positive electric conductor

Neutral connection to table

Transformer

EXPERIENCE AND SAFETY

The potential danger element in a workshop is much greater than most people realize. Workshops can be a nightmare. Young people in particular seem to have an urge to insert their fingers into holes—no doubt a sexually based desire—but if the hole is in a machine tool the finger can get chewed up. Long hair can easily catch on the rotating shaft of a drilling machine. Once caught, the shaft will wind up the hair and scalp the victim and new hair may not grow over the scalped area. Necklaces and neckties can catch on rotating work in a lathe. A jacket or boiler suit sleeve can be caught by the rotating chuck of a lathe or the rotating tool of a milling machine: these machines have the power to throw a person right over the machine. Another common accident is dropping heavy weights on feet. Most people in factory workshops wear shoes with steel toe caps.

Safety consciousness—the thing that stops you hurting yourself—can only be gained by experience in a workshop. To prevent yourself getting seriously hurt while you gain the necessary experience, you should limit yourself to areas of low potential danger, such as hand tools and bench work, soldering and brazing. When you find that you have stopped cutting your hands in one way or another (this may take six months to a year), you should be safe enough to use powered machines or welding machines, or to handle metal and use the forge.

Evening classes in workshops at technical colleges are good places to learn some of the skills of metal work and to learn safety consciousness.

VISION 5/COMMUNITY

The community workshop is aimed at heavier jobs beyond the capacity of household workshops. Large garages would be ideal for such workshops. They would collect and sort useful scrap, mend vehicles, and make useful goods. They would be operated by the community they serve.

1 Exhaust fan
2 Hood
3 Bender
4 Drilling machine
5 Anvil
6 Oil-drum forge
7 Gas-welding gear
8 Earth block making
9 Collected scrap
10 2nd-hand collective truck
11 Vice
12 Lathe
13 Liquid-fuel electricity generator
14 Grinder
15 Bench drill

WORKSHOP

INTERVIEW
Robert Jungk

Robert Jungk's work in the peace movement of the fifties and sixties led him to become one of the pioneers of futures research in Europe. Unlike some other 'futurologists' he stresses that the people must decide their own future, and that his job is only to make them more aware of the alternatives. He won the Nobel Peace Prize in 1961, and is currently professor at the technical University of West Berlin.

Robert Jungk thinks that we don't necessarily all have to go back to the land for our lives and work to become more creative and meaningful. His technology for the future is based on electronics and cybernetics, not hand-looms and treadle-lathes; but it is, by many if not all of the usual criteria, a 'soft' technology and perhaps also a 'radical' technology. He began by talking about his vision of the 'human revolution'.

I see the human revolution as the possibility of every human being to make a mark, to make his individual mark on his times and on his work.

◆ *Don't you think that some people could in fact be very happy not making a mark, not ever having an original idea, but just leading a quiet life?*
Sure, there are people who are happy to live a dull life because they have been conditioned that way. But if you look closer, you will soon see that what is alive and original in them has been swept under the carpet—suppressed. For instance, take those young women working on assembly lines: I have seen quite a number of them, and spoken to them. They really don't want anybody to change their work or put them to creative work, and I asked them why. One of them told me, "I have a film running inside. I don't notice my work. I do it mechanically. I sit here at the conveyor and I am far away. My *real* life is what I *dream* about." And I said, well, do you ever get to that life, or does it stay a dream? And she said, "Sure, it just stays only a dream" and I asked her, wouldn't you like to have some of these dreams fulfilled or live them in reality? She said, "Yes, sure. But how could I? The only way for me is to dream." This kind of dissociation of life and dream is what is so terrible about modern work styles. Simple people, in the past, living in a village or somewhere, had a certain possibility of putting their dreams and their reality together. But in industrial society this possibility has gone. So we have to reform industrial society, even if it takes a lot of pain. You'll find people will first suffer because they are not used to it. It demands an effort

from them. Sure, at first some of them will refuse, but later, more and more won't refuse. I meet lots of young workers, and I see that really the most important thing for them is to get their own ideas out, to unearth their buried creative abilities, to do something on their own initiative and not always be told what to do. To turn from passive man to active man.

◆ *Do you think that industrial society can actually physically survive, I mean, faced with this resource crisis, this global crisis?*
Yes, I think it can, if it revises its goals and its methods. I myself am a professor at a Technical University, so I am discussing that all the time with the students, who are the future engineers. These students are very interested in a technology which is socially responsible, which is more in tune with human aspirations and human style, or human rhythm even. Recently, for instance, we have had a very interesting discussion: is it possible to construct machines which actually respond to the human rhythm rather than the human being responding to the rhythm of the machine?

◆ *What sort of machine would it be?*
Well, you can do it with electronic sensors. The machine picks up signals caused by your movements and actually follows *your* style of work. If you work slower then it turns slower, because it has artificial 'senses' which feel, or see that you work in this or that rhythm. So it becomes more and more adjusted to your rhythm, to your speed. You could have such a system in many new devices. I think that the possibilities of electronics and cybernetics in technology have not yet been fully explored . . . we are only at the beginning of that. For the first time technology can have 'eyes' and 'ears' and 'touch'.

◆ *Does a machine of the kind you're talking about actually exist anywhere?*
Yes, I've seen such machines being experimented with at the Massachusetts Institute of Technology at the Centre for Artificial Intelligence. I have seen a very interesting thing called the Architecture Machine, made by Nicholas Negroponte who is also

at MIT where you can actually design your own house and this is then automatically translated into exact terms and into exact plans. Most of this work goes on at MIT though there are some people in Manchesters in Holland and in the Technical University in Berlin working on similar lines. But it's all very much at the beginning, and I'll tell you why it's at the beginning: because our whole idea of machines now is that they should work efficiently and cheaply, so that they will produce more *profits*. As Professor Thring, in England, keeps telling me, the technology of today is a *cheap* technology—cheap in the way that it makes people cheap, and cheap in itself.

◆ *What social change has got to take place to divert us from continuing to just make more cheap technology, into this kind of intelligent and beneficial technology?*

Well one change is that more and more of the routine work, the old kind of work, is taken over by automation. There was a very interesting article by Peter Laurie recently in *New Scientist,* in which he showed that actually it will be more and more difficult to replace jobs, because more and more jobs are taken over by automation. Now what are these displaced people going to do? They will have to work on new kinds of labour-intensive machines which won't produce fast. In order to give them work we will be forced to have machines which are less productive but more human.

◆ *You seem to think that people should work. Isn't there a case to be made for freeing people from work?*

Indeed. I feel that everyone should work; but maybe *work* is the wrong word. Every person, every human wants to *create,* rather than work. The Japanese distinction between *arubaito* which is repetitive, routine, painful work, which you take on only because you have to earn money, and creative work like painting, like singing, like trying to learn a language, like fashioning a gown, building a table, or a house according to your own designs. I feel this kind of creative employment of the faculties is what should go on. I don't believe in the *lazy* man. Man should have more time for meditation and recreation and for play, but this itself demands some effort, is a kind of work. If you go into meditation, you want to attain certain levels; if you play, you want to win, or you want to perfect your game. Whatever we do we always want to get results of some kind. The results we have wanted in the past have been merely material goods and money. Now we are going more for other results, and other rewards.

◆ *What do you think about the small groups of people in certain countries, particularly in the United States, but also in Europe, who have abandoned the technological way of life and are trying to live much closer to nature. Do you think this is a significant trend?*

I think it's a very significant trend, only they shouldn't turn it into an ideology, because they couldn't live if there wasn't some kind of technology carrying them and all of us through. So it's a little like the people who retire into a garden and say, "Well, I want to go gardening, and I don't care about the world." But the world is going on, and I don't think that tending your garden is a solution to its problems. Sure, it may work as an individual solution, which I understand, but it's not a real solution that goes to the roots. Despite the criticism, however, I do feel that more and more people should be able to retire from society. And society may well be able to carry them on its back. Why not?

◆ *I'm not really talking about the people who renounce work, though, I'm talking about people who do work, but they perhaps chop down trees and build their own houses in the wild, that sort of thing.*

But yes, why not? I think there should be latitude to do that. But it shouldn't be seen as a kind of panacea. It would be wrong to make an ideology of it. Many new approaches fail, because every new thing aims at totality, is turned into a '100 per cent thing', though it could very well exist if five per cent or ten per cent take it on. I believe in a pluralist world where you may have people who are chopping wood at the same time as other people are working with, say, interesting new electronic gadgetry which will be closer to human beings and human rhythms than before. You may also have people who want to do scientific research and other people who want to meditate. You will have people who can paint and dance and other people who will be more interested in doing calculations. The important thing is that the *creative* factor in man should be given more—and here I *would* generalize—should be given more attention.

◆ *What do you think is the chance that what you've described as your desirable future will actually come to exist?*

The chance depends on the number of people who are willing to create such conditions. I see among young people movements which amount to a kind of 'conversion' comparable to the profound change from antiquity to the Christian era. These movements seem to have subsided to some extent at the moment, but they will probably come up again. There will be another generation after seven years; usually every seven years there comes another 'schub' as we say in German, another 'shock'; I think that there will be more and more people turning to new values and new lifestyles, but it certainly won't be *all* people. We will have certain parts of the world where there will be few experiments of this kind, and we may have other sections of the world where a more human lifestyle will be created, and I hope that these can set the example for the others. I am very much in favour of social experiments, for setting up islands of other 'worlds to come' in the midst of the old world.

◆ *Where will these islands be?*

They exist already in the USA, in Scandinavia, in England, in France. I think they will be everywhere where people have the courage to change their souls and the direction of their development.

Tony Durham

They tell us we are somewhere in the middle of the transition from a money economy to an information economy. No doubt the precise moment of transition will depend on whether the value of money falls faster than the value of information, or vice versa.

Make no mistake, most of the information around these days is rubbish. Some excitement was expressed recently when computers overtook people as the chief users of the US telephone network. I don't know what the people talk about, but I know the computers talk mainly about global business and military power games which would not be necessary in a differently organized world. Thus at the very least half of the information passing through the US telephone system is rubbish—either harmless or dangerous.

The global village is no such thing. It is a global castle, in which the barons may chat over their wine, while the serfs outside may overhear a few fragments of merriment.

Our planet does indeed boast some fine communications systems: there are only a few holes left to be darned in the net of radio, TV and telephone which covers the continents. The engineers praise the vast capacity of their systems. They talk of bits and bauds and erlangs. But their voices merge with those of the advertisers boasting of peak-hour audiences and market penetration.

The fallacy that *more* information, *more* communication *must* be good spreads even into the counterculture. Underground film-makers machine-gun their audiences with random images and subliminal cuts. Alternative newspapers boost their data density by printing each paragraph on multiple undercoats of coloured image.

The "information economy" stresses *quantity* rather than quality. It values complex data above simple truths. Computers now thrash through mega-

bits of information in order to direct-mail us an advertising circular.

Words were not wasted in the days when people could only engrave them on stone.

This overload of our senses by man-made information sources blinds us to the subtler flux of data from the natural world—from the land, the weather, and other living things around us, people included.

Although those living in advanced capitalist countries are exposed to such a lot of information, at the same time they never seem to have the particular piece of information they need at a particular moment. Unaware of invisible design faults, they buy inferior goods. As the bailiffs arrive, they find they don't know the law on squatting. The well-off young couple throws out a fridge; they don't know that the old lady next door needs one. The railway enquiries phone number doesn't answer, so people travel wastefully by car instead.

The mass of information is so irrelevant to the individual's real life that she or he begins to build a fantasy life around the information provided by the mass media. In the Great Depression, the cinemas were fuller than ever. Nowadays, the audience has been swollen by the poor of Asia, Africa and Latin America, feeding on the same old American movies and the martini-and-Cadillac lifestyle.

Each generation of the West's rulers perfects its own techniques of cultural subjugation on its own people, and exports them. This is not to say that cultural imperialism is necessarily the work of evil men: today's media men are as heroic and naive as the missionaries of the nineteenth century, they just have more powerful instruments.

There is a real risk that the twentieth century will

GEORGE BOWDEN

TONY DURHAM

leave our planet not only as an ecological desert but as a cultural desert. Having mined out the music of its own oppressed people, America looks abroad for new raw material, from India, Africa, the Caribbean.

Transport was once seen as the bringer of riches; now it is understood to be a waste of scarce resources. Similarly, communication may appear to be the key to cultural riches; but it may prove to have been the main destroyer of cultures.

Economic and ecological self-sufficiency are respectively the prerequisites of both national liberation and of global survival. Cultural self-sufficiency must be established as part of the same revolutionary process. If a community is to be free of outside domination it must generate its *own* crafts, stories, music, architecture and rituals. This is not an argument for cultural apartheid. But it clearly presupposes radical changes in a global communications system whose greatest achievement to date has been to let ten million Japanese watch Princess Anne's wedding. One day, the serfs must storm the global castle.

The wastage in communications is cultural and political, not ecological. Electronic communication

uses energy, but so little that this is never likely to be a serious limitation. Paper shortage is a genuine problem, but it may be overcome by recycling, by substitution of an electronic for a paper media where appropriate, and by the elimination of unnecessary uses of paper, such as over-packaging.

This book is aimed in the direction of self-sufficiency and community autonomy. But arguably local communities never will be, nor should be, self-sufficient in information. Communities which have deliberately cut themselves off, like Japan before the Meiji restoration, have generally been afraid of outside influences. Cultural imperialism will only disappear finally, however, when communities are strong enough to take or leave the outside influences. They will, for example, be able to select those technological developments from the rest of the world which genuinely serve the community's own needs. And even in a utopian future where large authoritarian organizations have disappeared, some tasks might require global co-operation. The state of the earth, the ocean and the atmosphere affects everyone. There would almost certainly be a demand for rapid worldwide exchange of meteorological data. No farmer would choose to do without a weather forecast. Some kind of permanent "Earthwatch" programme, monitoring pollution and the general health of the biosphere, might also be needed. That, too, presupposes efficient worldwide communications.

But it is quite conceivable, and I would say desirable, that there should no longer be such a thing as a world-famous singer, actor or novelist, and definitely no such thing as a world-famous statesman or politician. Exactly this situation existed, of course, until a few centuries ago.

The physical structure of communication systems

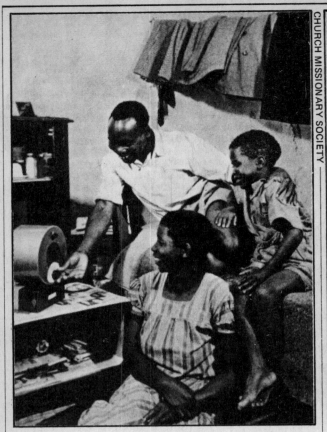

CHURCH MISSIONARY SOCIETY

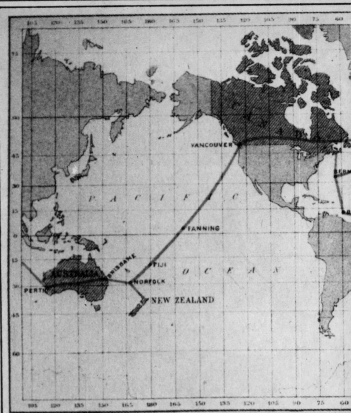

duplicates the structure of political power. A map of the world's submarine cables is quite a good record of the history of colonialism. If centres of political power are eventually to disappear, then probably the great knots in the world's communication systems, like those at London and New York, will have to be teased out. As far as possible, A's communication with B should not be under the control of a third party C. In practice some centralization may be inevitable, since it is well-nigh impossible to engineer direct point-to-point communications between *every* pair of communities in the world. However, it should be possible to decentralize to the point where there is a great variety of alternative routes between any two points. In fact this is beginning to happen already, under the influence of the multi-national corporations, which are centres of power not tied down to a single physical location.

So much for the far future, which will inevitably be different from anything we try now to imagine. The immediate task of reducing the volume of communication is not necessarily simple. We can, however, begin to use *their* clever inventions to help *us.* The phone companies laid the cables and built the exchanges. All the phone-phreaks had to do was to find a way to use the system without paying for it. With IBM typewriters and photo-litho printing equipment, the underground press, as if by magic, was re-born. Similarly, the Sony portable video recorder, in contrast to its use in industry and education, became a trendy gadget for community organizers.

It is a maxim of guerilla warfare that you get your arms from the enemy. This has two snags. The first

is that you are not truly independent. This problem is discussed in other chapters in this section, notably in the chapter on video. Snag number two is that the equipment you get may not really be what you need—worrying thought if you believe that the medium is the message, since it follows that by using *their* medium you end up spreading *their* message. This of course is an absurd overstatement, but one shadow does hang over many "alternative" communication activities. The book, the newspaper, and the broadcast are each in their own ways authoritarian. Each can, to some extent, respond to public needs; but no individual reader, viewer or listener can have very much control. And instant reply or criticism is impossible. Anyone who has worked on an "alternative" newspaper or magazine must have experienced dismay the first time a ruthless editorial decision "had" to be taken. The next shock is when readers whom you thought you understood start writing in with violent criticisms.

Radio and TV stations have tried to modify their authoritarian image with so-called "public access" programmes. But the BBC's "Open Door" is not quite as open as it seems. The limited number of programmes in each series has meant that some groups have had to make do with a very short appearance, and some groups don't get on to the screen at all. Of programmes of this type, Boston's "Catch 44" is perhaps more honestly named.

Phone-ins are another variety of "public access" broadcasting. A phone-in gives the lonely person someone to talk to. And it gives the angry person a chance to let off steam without taking direct action. But only at rare moments do phone-ins break the

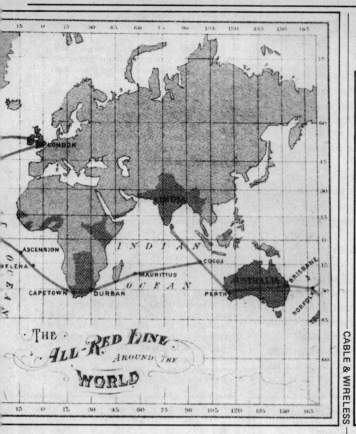

(Far left) '. . . Today's media men are as heroic and naive as the missionaries of the 19th century, they just have more powerful instruments.' *(Centre)* 'A map of the world's submarine cables is quite a good record of the history of colonialism.'

THE VC BIKE VERSUS

THE USAF PHANTOM

THE BIKE IS WINNING IN VIETNAM
IT CAN WIN IN LONDON

CABLE & WIRELESS

patronizing attitudes of the broadcasters; normally they do not undermine, but *underline* the authoritarian nature of the medium.

The public is slowly discovering how to resist and even exploit the arrogant attitudes of the media. People are realizing that TV crews don't have the automatic right to invade their privacy, interview them, record and edit them. Ordinary people are discovering what the PR men of big business knew all along: that the media respond in predictable ways. A rat in a Skinner box turned to its friend and said: "I've really got this psychologist well trained. Every time I press the button he gives me a food pellet." Likewise, the media will come running, cheque book in hand, if you offer them what is in their terms a "good story". The *TV Handbook,* published recently by a group called Scan, is a good summary of the techniques available to us rats. Among other things, it contains instructions for removing the film from an Arriflex camera, and gives plans showing where to find control rooms and administration offices of some British TV stations.

So we move towards a situation where (in an optimistic view) the squatter being evicted, for instance, has a good chance of being noticed either by established or alternative media. But still, it's quite probable that he doesn't know the details of the law, or doesn't know who owns the house, at the vital moment. What he or she needs is not just access to communication media, but access to information.

At the moment people read the papers and watch telly, and gradually collect a random selection of

information in their heads. Most of it will never be useful to them. The information has to be kept in the head because their is no other readily accessible storage. Working people cannot spend hours retrieving information from libraries.

But electronic communications can change this. Cities in the US, and some in Europe, now have hotlines, switchboards and information centres for women, gays, people up against the law and others for whom the authorities provide no help. Often not only information but also concrete assistance is available from other involved in the same struggle or from radical professionals.

The technological requirements are minimal: a room with a telephone. The strength of a centre of this kind is in *people,* not technology. Rapid access to information can be achieved without computers, whatever the banks and the airlines would like you to think. There may, of course, be very exciting things to be done with community access computer services such as Resource One in Berkeley, California. But let us not use computers simply as electric substitutes for a card index.

There is a paradox in the argument: our long-term view of communications can be summed up in the word "decentralization"—though perhaps Peter Van Dresser's term "recentralization" is more appropriate. However, our best immediate tactic is to set up centres of our own: little centres, friendly centres, responsive centres, but at the same time, *powerful* centres.

Eric Lowbury

HOLD THE FRONT PAGE

Jonathan Zeitlyn

You can make your own paper, of a sort, and you can print from hand-made wood blocks, if you have the energy, the devotion and the time. Most people haven't. So, however suspicious you may be of advanced technology, you are almost bound to tangle with it when it comes to printing. Fortunately, many of the recent innovations in printing technology have been such as to give ordinary people more control over the process.

In this chapter we shall concentrate on one printing process: offset litho (short for 'offset lithography'). If you're going to use a commercial printer you'll get on fairly well if you just think of offset litho as a kind of mass-production photo-copying. If your original is good, so should be the printed copies. But if you are printing by an offset process, you must produce 'camera-ready artwork' to be photographed. This means you must have the copy typeset; you will then paste this up for the printer. Knowledge of the skills of typesetting, headlining, paste-up and layout is fairly widespread these days. The best way to learn is by watching someone else do it and then doing it yourself. The version we give you here is from Alternative London *(Nicholas Saunders and Wildwood House, London, 1974) which gives the essentials in two highly concentrated pages. A good talk with your printer can also help to avoid time-wasting mistakes.*

WORDS

Can be written by hand in ink, with a ball-point or a felt-nib pen. Or a dark pencil. Or with a manual typewriter Or with an electric typewriter Or use **Letraset** transfer lettering Or — the usual way — TYPESET.

TYPESETTING

The easiest machine to use is a glorified 'golfball' typewriter called an IBM composer. This book is done on one. *You change the 'golfball' for each face and size of type.* The smallest it can take is 6 point and the largest size is 12 point. The spacing between lines is called 'leading' (pronounced 'ledding').

It has a device that makes it possible to justify — even out the right-hand margin like this — but to do this you have to type every line twice: first for the machine to measure how much space is left and second for it to space out the words to even it up. You have to be dead accurate to get it right.

You can hire composers for about £100 a month. It's sometimes possible to use one belonging to a college or small newspaper. These machines are very liable to go wrong — especially on justified copy.

Paper for typesetting. You can use any good white paper, but the easiest to handle comes from Addressograph, Aldwych House, WC2 (836 8474).

Getting it done for you. You should be able to find a local individual with his own IBM composer who will charge £2—£3 per thousand words or £3.50—£6 if you want justified.

Buying your own machine. There's an older, slower but more robust machine called the Addressograph Varityper. Although over £2,000 new, you can get a second-hand one with 6 typefaces from £450.

Headings. 'Letraset' transfer lettering comes in a very wide range from 6 to 288 pt (about 3 inches high).

Tip: If you want your heading to fill a certain space, first trace it out with the letters touching, then divide the space left over equally between the letters.

PHOTOS OR SHADED DRAWINGS ('Half-tones')

You can't print grey with black ink — only black. So anything in between black and white — 'half-tones' — has to be changed into black and white dots: this is called 'screening'. You'll probably need to use a photographic studio or your printer to get this done. The result is called a 'screened bromide', and they cost £1 or so each.

You can do shading in a form of Letraset called 'Letratone' which is made up of dots like a screened photo.

PEN & INK ('Line drawings')

These print fine without any treatment — so long as the lines are clear and black with no greys.

REDUCTIONS

If you need any part changed in size to fit, this can be done by photography using bromide paper. These photos are called 'bromides'.

LAYOUT

When you've got all your typesetting, drawings and screened photos ready the next step is to assemble your page complete with headings and page numbers.

What you need
1. Sheets of white paper larger than your page size to paste onto, and masking tape to hold it onto the drawing board or table.
2. A light blue pencil. This is very useful for marking the copy as light blue doesn't come out when photographed.

3. A ruler and set-square (or, if possible, a drawing board and T-square) to line up the pieces.
4. 'Cow Gum' and spreader ('spatula'). It's easy to spread; you can slide the pieces to their exact position and remove them. And it cleans off easily.
5. 'Process White' (a white paint) or 'Liquid Paper' — or even white sellotape to cover up mistakes, smudges, edges of paper etc.
6. A 'scalpel' — a very sharp knife to cut up the pieces of paper. Scissors will do.

What you do
1. Fix the white paper to the board or table with masking tape and use the square to mark out the edges of the finished page in light blue, allowing plenty of space at the sides for notes etc. Also mark out the printed area — allowing at least ¼'' clearance from the edge lines.

Tip: If you've got lots of pages to paste up, extend these lines onto your drawing boards, it saves measuring each time.

2. Lay out the pieces of type, screened bromides, line drawings and headings as you want them. Be careful not to cut too near the actual type, as if the cut edge gets dirty it will show up — and it can't be removed without also removing the type. This is also the stage to put in page numbers and ruled lines. These are best done with a Rapidograph pen or (an expensive luxury), 'Letraline'.

The whole sheet is A0 : 841mm × 1189mm. A1 : 594 × 841; A2 : 420 × 594; A3 : 297 × 420 ; A4 : 210 × 297; A5 : 148 × 210; A6 : 148 × 105; A7 : 74 × 105.

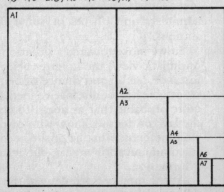

Note: 'Solid' black areas take more ink and tend to dry out a band around the printing roller, leaving whatever's in line with the 'solid' paler than the rest. So try to balance solids — or avoid them.

3. Put each face down onto a clean sheet of scrap paper and spread the Cow Gum thinly right over it, then put each roughly in place. Finally, use the square to adjust and straighten the whole page. Keep this operation as clean as possible. *Tip:* To remove a piece of paper after the Cow Gum has set, squirt it with cigarette-lighter fuel and let it soak through — this softens the Cow Gum.

4. Clean up. Use a lump of congealed Cow Gum as a rubber and to pick up loose bits of Cow Gum off the page. Obliterate any other marks with 'process white' or white sellotape.

5. Corrections. You can remove pieces of your paste-up with lighter fuel as (3) above, or small errors can be cut out with a scalpel. A neat trick is to place your correction (or clean paper) precisely under the mistake and cut right through both — the correction can then be sellotaped in the hole from behind to fit perfectly.

Size. Don't worry if you find it won't all quite fit in. So long as the page is in proportion the printer can enlarge or reduce as he makes the plate — this costs nothing extra, but remember to tell him.

Proportion. The trick is to draw a diagonal. The way to instruct the printer: "reduce the 9½" dimension to 8¾" " or whatever.

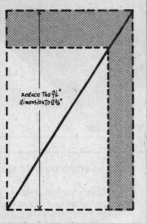

reduce the 9½" dimension to 8¾"

(Left above) The IBM 'Selectric' composer. *(Left)* Some transfer-lettering type styles. *(Below left)* The 'A' series of paper sizes. *(Below)* The first step to justified type; the code to the right tells the machine what space to leave between words.

It has a device that makes it possible to	o8
justify — even out the right-hand margin like	b7
this — but to do this you have to type every	b10
line twice: first for the machine to measure	o6
how much space is left and second for it to	o5
space out the words to even it up. You have	o1
to be dead accurate to get it right.	

BRITISH STANDARD PAPER SIZES:

Foolscap	13½ × 17	Demy	17½ × 22½
Crown	15 × 20	Medium	18 × 23
Post	15¼ × 19	Royal	20 × 25
Large post	16½ × 21	Imperial	22 × 30
			(inches)

The next step is to do the actual printing yourself. We are going to concentrate on offset for two reasons. First, it illustrates and involves all the technological advances which made the 'alternative press' possible. Second, it's still the process that people are most scared of: not many people have actually tried operating a press themselves. There are of course other printing processes that may meet your particular needs better. (Silkscreen printing was the chosen propaganda weapon of the Paris students in May 1968.) Or for a few hundred copies of a leaflet your best choice might be a stencil duplicator with hand-made or 'electronic' stencil. (Electronic stencils allow you to duplicate pictures. Many duplicating firms will make them for you.) But there's not much point in describing these long-established techniques: your public library should be full of books on silkscreen printing; best buy (at 3p) is the 8-page Silkscreen *leaflet published by* Peace News; *US readers could consult p. 359 of the* Last Whole Earth Catalog. *As for duplicators (both spirit and stencil), wherever one of these machines exists there seems to be at least one person who knows how to use it.*

One book which does consider just about all the available forms of small-scale printing, from a point of view other than that of an office manager, is called Print: how you can do it yourself. *A London group called REDesign produced it in 1974. The original limited edition of 500 included at least one page actually printed by each of the methods described. (A revised edition of the book has now been published by Interaction, Malden Road, London, NW3, Price 75p.) We are grateful to REDesign for the following extracts.*

YES, YOU CAN DO IT YOURSELF

Everyone knows that technological development has turned printing into a multi-million-pound industry. Printing books, leaflets and newspapers can only be done by enormous organisations. Large firms alone can afford the expensive and complicated machinery, with the skills of trained printers, the expertise of designers, craftsmen and editors.

This book is written to show that none of these statements need be true. And that you, the reader, can be your own printer. What has happened is that the same technology that provides the giant four colour machines has also been used to provide small printing for the office. The past twenty years have seen the quality of small offset printing improve to a point beyond any other copying method. The actual process of printing has been simplified. Electro-static cameras for example make plates for offset machines almost instantly. The high street has its 'Instant Printers' if the boss wants copies of his memo.

Some of the implications of this development are now becoming clear. Recently small offset presses have been getting into the hands of other people than the office printers. They've been bought by schools, by community and political groups. Community presses have started to teach people who want something printed how to do it themselves. And really the technology implies exactly this use. Small offset lithography hasn't yet reached its full potential, but is nearly at the point where good quality printing can be done by anyone.

The concrete result of this is an ability to produce our own newspapers, posters or books. In writing them, laying them out and printing them we gain collective control over something (even if it is only paper). Using minimal techniques, such as those described here, we can produce good results, by ourselves on a small scale and in an unalienated way. It is ours. The reader and the producer are neighbours. We can start using the language meaningful to us and our friends, neighbours and mates. We can learn from each other and start the collective task of re-inventing our own culture.

But arranging our ideas as words, articles, chapters etc., is important. With headlines and boxes, bubbles and illustrations our ideas can be developed and organised into something that communicates. Print, even using the simplest method, can reproduce a graphic language of words and pictures that really comes from and is used by the people who read it.

The techniques are very flexible. We can do anything we like with enough time, imagination and care. So understand the limitations but don't respect them.

For too long people have written for us. We have read other people's views of *our* lives; seen other people's ideas on how *we* should live. Those other people — journalists, designers, professionals — don't live like us, the majority of working people. The professionals' 'media' are anyhow made for the advertisers and politicians. Their content becomes almost incidental and the advertisers and the politicians have even less common interests with us than the journalists and designers.

We have to understand clearly what is around us and start developing our own media, our own language and our own organisation.

Everyone can print their own newspapers, leaflets, books, etc. and do it collectively. But most print is organised for one person to dictate what the rest (the workers) produce. But such hierarchical and divisive organisation isn't necessary any longer. Almost anyone can do all of it themselves; all together as one group.

The possibility exists for the Silent Majority to break the silence. But in the process of gaining a voice, that majority (us) will overthrow more than an out-of-date print industry.

OFFSET LITHO

Offset litho works because grease and water do not mix. A plate, a sheet of metal, plastic or paper, carries an image of a greasy, water-repellent nature, applied by hand or by one of several photo-mechanical techniques. The non-image areas of the plate's surface remain attractive to water and therefore repellent to greasy ink. Greasy ink and a watery solution (fount solution) are applied simultaneously to the plate. The ink adheres to the image, but not to the damp areas. When the plate is brought in direct contact with a rubber pad, called the blanket, mounted on a second roller, a reversed image transfers to the blanket. A sheet of paper passes between the blanket and an impression roller to receive a right-way-round print of the image.

Each plate prints one colour so more colour means more plates. (All the rollers must be cleaned before printing a new colour). One of the essential aspects of good quality printing is the proper making of plates, having already the best possible preparation of the artwork. The quality of the print depends firstly on the type of plate used and secondly the development and plate-making process and thirdly care on the press. Care on the press means regulating the pressure from the plate to the blanket cylinder so that early wear on the plate won't occur. Excess ink roller pressure will also reduce the life of the plates by starving the plates of ink.

Many different companies make offset plates and each claims certain advantages for its own type. Generally companies that make their own printing presses also market a range of products that accompany the machine — inks, plates, cleaning fluids, fount solutions and other chemicals (vertical integration). So be careful that if you buy another company's plates, they fit your machine's plate clamps. Standardisation is limited by the manufacturer's profit motive, so check everything before committing yourself.

The Rotaprint 30/90 prints to a maximum size of 13½" x 20"

◆ *Pre-sensitized plates & chemical transfer*

Pre-sensitized are the most widely used. The image is transferred onto these plates by making a negative on a process camera. The plate is then exposed through the negative, so that only the image area is lit. A process camera uses line film and makes negatives the size of the finished copy. You can reduce or enlarge by moving the lens or the artwork. By photographing a photo through a dot screen a half-tone negative can be made. It can then be cut and taped into the line negative of the rest of the page. Dots, shadows and unwanted bits can be painted out with an opaque paint on the negative. Using the finished, painted negative on top of the light-sensitive plate, only the image area on the plate is exposed to ultra-violet light. The plate is treated with gum-arabic solution, developed and treated again. The unexposed areas are made ink-resistant and the plate is ready to print.

In this process screened photo negatives can be stuck into the full negative. But in the Chemical Transfer method (see below) you have to have the photo screened, printed and stuck to the artwork just like already-screened photos taken from other newspapers. This can be done by contact printing from a screened negative (made on a process camera). But if you have the original negative you can simply print onto a 'Letratone' screen (85 lines to the inch) with photographic paper underneath, and the photo will be screened ready for the artwork.

◆ *Making the plate*

There are a number of other methods of making plates but the simplest is direct hand made paper plates. *Paper plates* are a paper or paper-plastic plate with a grease sensitive surface. By drawing or typing with a greasy pencil, ink or typewriter ribbon a mark is made on the plate which will pick up ink and print that image. Once the plate has been drawn or typed on, the rest of the plate is desensitised by lightly wiping with 'fix'. You can then print from it. Paper plates do not produce particularly good quality work. But they are easy to make and for ordinary people who have the time but not the money or machinery to make better plates they can be very useful (unlike in the office where time is money and profit rules out creativity). A little experience is necessary to produce copies with the right intensity. Paper plates have quite a short life — about 1,000 copies, but can cost as little as 5p each. Once used they are not easily stored and tend not to produce a good second run.

Plates can be made using the *photo-copying* methods now developed and being improved all the time. The electrostatic photo-copier is the most widely used. A xerox machine can copy onto a paper plate, though the quality is not particularly good. Electrostatic methods have been developed into a camera, which is very expensive, and used in instant print shops. It turns out good plastic plates almost instantly but can't do half-tone photos well.

THE ELECTROSTATIC METHOD

1. Image is projected on the positively charged printing surface. Light erases the charge from the unwanted areas.
2. Negatively charged dry pigment is spread over the printing surface.
3. A new charge transfers the image to paper.
4. Paper is peeled away.
5. Heat fixed the image on the sheet.

Easier for the small user is the *Chemical Transfer* method. In this system light is reflected off the artwork, transferring the image onto an intermediate light-sensitive yellow sheet which is used to process the metal plate. The artwork has to be black and as flat as possible. Once the plate is made you can remove the shadows and mistakes with a rubber and cover it with fix before it is printed. To have photos printed with this method it's necessary to pre-screen and stick the screened photos onto the artwork. Obviously reductions or enlargements aren't possible either so this too has to be done beforehand. A process camera that produces prints (like an enlarger) used with a chemical transfer system can make really good and interesting work.

Generally chemical transfer plates are not as good in quality as pre-sensitised plates.

HOW A BASIC SMALL LITHO PRESS WORKS

The ink is placed in its trough and the rollers inked up. The fount solution (water) is mixed and poured into its trough. The plate is then fastened onto the plate roller, and washed clear of gum with water. You turn on the motor (*a*), turn up the water (*b*), ink the plate (*c*). To even out the ink, depending on the image, adjust the screws on the ink trough. To increase the ink going through the machine you push (*e*) up. The paper is stacked, squared and loose with air between each sheet.

It is raised to 2 level so that it will feed into the machine (*f*). The inked plate transfers its image onto the blanket (*g*). A few test sheets are printed and the position (*i*) and the ink are adjusted. And you are ready to print. The speed can be adjusted (*k*) and away you go. Print on.

The blanket rollers are washed when all the printing is finished or the colour is changed. A spirit called blanket wash is used for this.

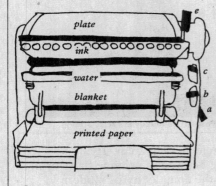

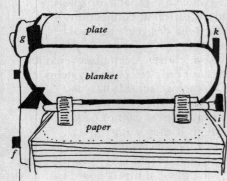

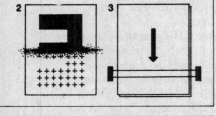

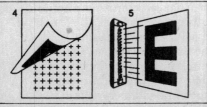

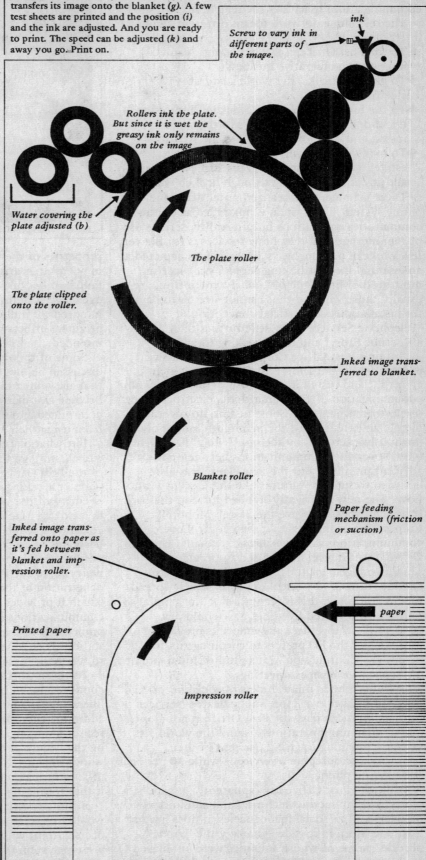

Screw to vary ink in different parts of the image.

ink

Rollers ink the plate. But since it is wet the greasy ink only remains on the image

Water covering the plate adjusted (b)

The plate clipped onto the roller.

The plate roller

Inked image transferred to blanket.

Blanket roller

Paper feeding mechanism (friction or suction)

Inked image transferred onto paper as it's fed between blanket and impression roller.

Printed paper

paper

Impression roller

UNFAIR EXCHANGE

This section is about one very important part of the communications machine: the telephone.

The telephone network means different things to different people:

◆ To the Post Office, a fast expanding, capital-intensive and lucrative business
◆ To phone-phreaks, the world's largest electronic game
◆ To the businessman, a luxurious loud-speaking telephone with instant access to the share index, and direct dialling across the Atlantic
◆ To many of us, a single kiosk in a housing estate, with the worst lines, the highest charges, and street noise blaring through broken windows.

There is immense unrealized potential in the phone system. The system is portrayed as uniting communities and nations but, in reality, serious use of the international telephone services is for the very few who can pay the heavy charges. It is depicted as an essential tool for linking people, yet those in most need of links, the old, lonely and infirm, are usually those whose means cannot stretch to paying for installations: the official conception of 'Telephone Services' goes little further than 'Dial a Bedtime Story' and the 'Speaking Clock'.

Britain's Post Office Corporation has massive powers, under the 1968 Post Office Act which created it and vested in it exclusive control over all communications, "electromagnetic, electrochemical, or electromechanical". Some of this, however, was merely an extension of the mammoth monopoly previously exercized by the old General Post Office (GPO) over any communications between non-adjacent premises. But the new clause was also designed to supress ventures like the nascent Radio Love. The new Act neatly stabbed Love in the back. It went further, and gave the State's Monopoly Corporation as much totalitarian control over communications as it considers expedient. The Post Office, for instance, has refused to provide a simple arrangement for the Open University to conduct tutorials by telephone with widely spread groups. Although this is technically quite simple (anyone who rented five lines, say, could just connect them together) and indeed is provided unwittingly, the PO prefers to encourage its extensive 'Confravision' inter-studio closed circuit TV service for business meetings.

In its continued unawareness of social needs, and desire to market ever more sophisticated 'services' to those who can pay, the Post Office is not alone. Many other administrations around the world are similarly planning to give 2 per cent of their countries a picturephone service — while 30 per cent still have no phone.

While the Post Office can, apparently, escape scorn for its numerous technical and administrative blunders and its social inadequacies, it does have at least one thorn in its side — namely the 'phone phreaks', some of whose activities were publicized in a now famous court case in London in 1973 (1). Phone phreaks discover and exploit unseen

Fig 1. 'Bomb-proof' Post Office microwave relay station.

properties of the telephone system. Their opportunities arise because of genuine flaws or faults, or because the complexity of modern exchange systems — which are capable of forming hundreds of millions of different connections — produces effects which the designers had not intended.

Some of the flaws which have been discovered are discussed below. It is not only telephone systems that are vulnerable to such attacks. It has also become axiomatic to those who run computers that determined and unwanted users cannot be kept from using their systems if they want to.

But what place have such individual acts in an overall strategy for changing technology? In the eyes of the Post Office, the principal threat posed by phone phreaking is not to finance, but to the 'security of the system'. The phreaks demonstrate that no machine is invulnerable. They, the consumers at the lowest level of the system, have been able to force changes in the system itself. Such power is anathema to the planners. Equally worrying to the Post Office has been the phreaks' penetration of the military and industrial networks which it provides — for the importance of communications in maintaining social control is immense, and the Post Office's network of radio stations is designed around the need of the military to retain ultimate control.

To those who see shoplifting as the liberation of goods produced by exploitation, techniques for liberating telephone calls will be a welcome addition. The lesson of the phreaks and of the technical underground is perhaps best epitomized by the widely-publicized story of the blind boy who, using just a tin whistle, can control the action of an orbiting communications satellite. The lesson is that technology will never be invulnerable.

But the future of the telephone system, as *we* would like to see it, stands apart from the details of its current vulnerability. The organization of the present system (described in detail below) is a direct result of interplay between two factors — the engineering of the links, and the centralization of the control points. Although the rationale behind the current system was largely one of minimizing cost, the balance which must be struck by proponents of an alternative system is representative of organizational problems as a whole. We must face the conflict between the greater economic and cultural wealth enjoyed by the large combines — the cities — and the relative freedom of a small commune. In a highly decentralized society, links may be long and tenuous, and 'efficiency' correspondingly lower. But greater efficiency, with centralization, results only at the expense of having an authoritarian paradigm of society. For the links of communication and transport are also the links of control. The nature of society is determined by the manner in which control is exerted. The provision of a communications system must involve *some* centralization — just as a community must meet together to discuss matters. But effective freedom may well depend on communication being poor. Then unified control, which *must* not work, *cannot* work.

We need to run and license small communications systems. These would all be served for long-distance and international purposes by a special organization, perhaps run by the federation of local groups. Each community group could mould its system to its own particular area, providing special facilities — group conversation lines, message services, perhaps even an open line for those who are bored or unhappy to talk to other people. A tie-up to the local community radio station would be useful. Advice by telephone on, say, legal and medical matters could be supplied by the local telephone service.

There is a prototype of a local service of this kind already in existence, in Hull, Yorkshire, where the local council runs the telephone service independently of the Post Office. Sadly, even there, little attempt has been made to provide a better service to the community, for instance by subsidizing lines for the needy. The Hull system's only major departure from the Post Office norm has been in its provision of free local calls, the cost of which is included in the rental fee.

DEMYSTIFYING THE SYSTEM

What lies behind your phone is two wires, leading all the way to your local telephone exchange, over poles and through green pavement-mounted junction boxes. The electrical signals coming into the phone are connected to the earpiece, which is like a little loudspeaker. A direct electrical current from the line goes into a microphone, which is composed of carbon granules which change their resistance with the vibes of your voice. A dial sends electrical impulses down the line, at the rate of ten a second.

In the exchange, a 'selector' moves electrical connections across rows and columns of contacts, in response to the pulses sent down the line by your dial. This is the method of the 'Strowger' system, invented more than half a century ago and still used extensively in the UK. Other systems do the same job less visibly, less mechanically. If you have a

phone (or say you have) you can get a tour of a local exchange to see it happening.

The network is hierarchically organized. Its separate sub-networks thus have only restricted access to each other (see Fig 2). The simplest functional unit, the single telephone, is grouped round the simplest central unit, the *local exchange.* Local exchanges can centralize a wide range of communities, from a dozen crofts in the West Highlands to several tens of thousands in a crowded London suburb. Almost all are now automatic. The traditional vista of sad-eyed ladies before immense switchboards, inserting and withdrawing plugs on leads with hidden weights and springs, has virtually disappeared. Huge banks of electrical relays now do the job, and do not organize to ask for better working conditions.

The wires also run between exchanges, linking up to form the *local network,* over which one can dial

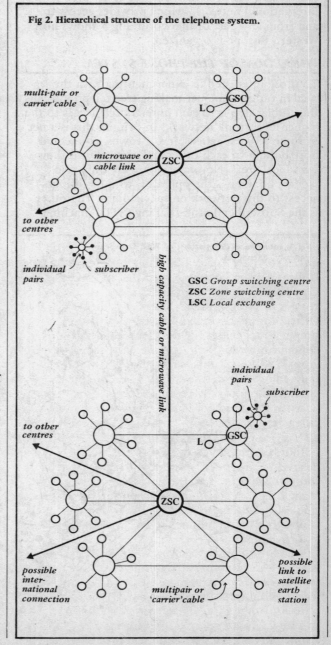

Fig 2. Hierarchical structure of the telephone system.

multi-pair or carrier cable

microwave or cable link

to other centres

individual pairs

subscriber

GSC *Group switching centre*
ZSC *Zone switching centre*
LSC *Local exchange*

high capacity cable or microwave link

individual pairs

subscriber

to other centres

possible international connection

multipair or 'carrier' cable

possible link to satellite earth station

directly, and the *trunk network* to which direct access is not normally possible. The special exchanges which handle trunk calls, called *trunk exchanges,* normally serve a large number of local exchanges, because of the economic advantages of centralizing the long-distance switching. Normally, a long-distance call will be routed over local lines to the nearest trunk exchange, then on the trunk line to a distant trunk centre where it 'comes down' again to the local exchange that serves the called subscriber.

The highest level shown is that of the international trunk network. This is the most sophisticated and expensive part of the system, and the most rapidly expanding. The enormous cost of international switching, and the advantages of centralizing the intercontinental and international lines, leads to centralization of the facilities into a single 'gateway' exchange in each country. Every nation also has its own unique code on the international network, which provides access to and from any part of the world. **Fig 3** shows how Western Europe is organized.

PHREEDOM OF THE PHONE SYSTEM

To those interested in experimenting with the system rather than just making free telephone calls, the crucial step is to gain unrestricted access to the higher level trunk network. In Britain, this is a net of some 330 exchanges, in big towns, connected horizontally to each other and vertically to their own local areas. Normally, there are only two ladders up. One is the operator, who has direct access to this network on special lines. The other is the Subscriber Trunk Dialling (STD) machine,

which accepts instructions dialled into it by the user in the form of a standardized code indicating the destination exchange, plus the number wanted. It then contacts the trunk network, to which it is directly connected, and 'translates' the information into the specific codes used by the trunk network equipment. These are special codes, never published, since the public is denied direct access.

By gaining direct access to the trunk network, it is possible to dial round the entire country, weaving back and forth at will. A corresponding technique gives access to the lines on the highest level, the international network. Once there, the right equipment can work the same tricks, on a global expedition.

Phreaks therefore need a way on to the trunk network, without restruction. Two principal ways are used in the UK and abroad. The first involves the use of *bleepers* ("Blue Boxes" in the US), which are tone generators that imitate the control signals normally sent down the telephone line from the STD machine to the distant exchange. With the bleeper, old signals can be countermanded and new ones sent, so complete control over the system can be obtained. The other way in is to find a stray line that accomplishes the step-up directly. These convenient 'trunk accesses' are not, of course, put there to help the phone phreak. They arise, rather, from the action of a telephone engineer who wishes to liberate the system a little for his own use, or from careless construction.

But true phone phreaks, it must be emphasized, are *not* usually interested in devising techniques for avoiding payment for calls. It is so easy to defraud the Post Office by plain deception that those whose primary interest is in saving money — crooked businessmen, separated lovers and similar individuals — have no need to build Blue Boxes or to discover obscure technical loopholes. No, the real phreak is more like the keen railway enthusiast, fascinated by the minute intricacies of a machine much larger and more powerful than himself which can transport him briefly to far-off lands at the mere utterance of a string of electronic pulses.

Somewhere beyond the extremes of technical legerdemain on the one hand, and petty fraud on the other, is a simple gadget called the Black Box *(2)* whose implications are at once anarchic and altruistic. A Black Box attached to your phone does not allow you to make calls free of charge, nor does it allow you to play around on international trunk circuits. What it does do, however, is allow *other people* to call *you* without payment. It does this by disabling the charging meter connected to the phone of the person calling you. Although in Britain such calls are automatically cut off after two minutes, the Black Box probably poses the greatest threat there is to "the security of the system".

Ian Morton

REFERENCES
(1) See 'Are Telephones Addictive', *New Scientist*, December 13th, 1973. See also 'How the Secret Telephone War Came to Britain', *Sunday Times*, October 15th, 1972.
(2) See *Ramparts* magazine, June 1972.

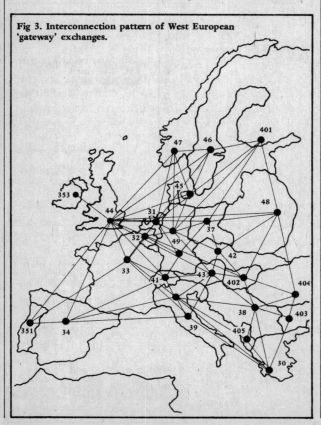

Fig 3. Interconnection pattern of West European 'gateway' exchanges.

R.T. CRAFT
Community radio

The nearest approach to community radio in Britain is, surprisingly, the BBC local radio service. Though there are not nearly enough stations and though those that exist are restrained by the paternalistic doctrine of "We know best what you want," BBC local radio has nevertheless made at least some attempts to put listeners in control of programmes. In the United States, too, there are a few listener-sponsored stations capable of keeping their listeners happy enough to go on supporting them.

But these are exceptions. And they will remain exceptions as long as the airwaves are administered in the way they are now. Community radio should have nothing to do with big business, no matter how carefully restrained the businessmen may be by watchdogs such as the Independent Broadcasting Authority and the Advertising Standards Authority in the UK, and the Federal Communications Commission in the US. Nor can a structure like the British Broadcasting Corporation, on a (loose and well-concealed) State leash, do anything but ultimately hinder the development of community radio.

One of the basic requirements of a dictatorship or autocracy is a monopoly of the means of communication. Such a monopoly may not appear to exist in Britain, but physical control of the means of communication is to an astonishing extent in the hands of one organisation — the Post Office. It is the Post Office that pursues any independent broadcaster who doesn't bother about the Wireless Telegraphy Act 1949, the Marine (etc) Offences Act 1967, or the Post Office Act 1969. But such broadcasters, including the commercial 'pirates', may have achieved something more important than merely irritating the Post Office. Among their listeners and supporters they have created a body of opinion which may, in the long run, help to get the monopolistic communications system changed.

Public pressure for freer broadcasting would be much stronger if people understood the possibilities of genuine community radio. This article shows that it is already possible, though difficult, to provide a community radio service. We are not suggesting that anyone break the law; we merely report how it is already being broken and thereby discredited.

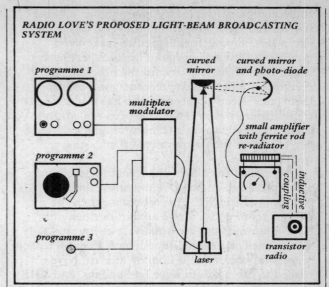

RADIO LOVE'S PROPOSED LIGHT-BEAM BROADCASTING SYSTEM

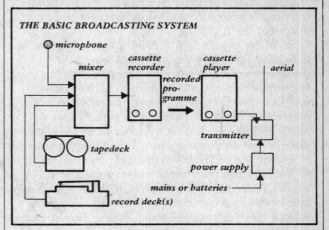

THE BASIC BROADCASTING SYSTEM

Most unlicensed broadcasters use medium wave. AM transmitters for this waveband are easily built using cheap parts or components 'liberated' from old equipment — the price of a transmitter can be well under a fiver. A good VHF/FM transmitter, on the other hand, can cost up to £100. Cheap VHF/FM transmitters can be built, but there is little point in choosing VHF unless the aim is to provide a really high quality service.

On the other hand, FM has a smaller audience, so any programme aimed at a maximum audience, such as a news and alternative information service, will be broadcast on the medium waveband.

A transmitter needs to be backed up by some

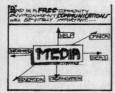

audio equipment: at least a microphone, a music source, and something to mix the two together. Given this, anyone is equipped to make live broadcasts. But underground broadcasters have found it much safer to record the programmes, even on a simple cassette recorder, and broadcast them later. Nearly everyone who has made regular transmissions has at some time been raided. But often all they lost was a transmitter and a cassette player, rather than a complete broadcasting installation.

Experience has taught them that the weekends, and especially Sundays, are the safest times for general broadcasting. This is because then the officers required for a raid are not normally on duty. Transmissions are usually at night, especially when aimed at a specialist audience. For this reason, 'pirate' broadcasters, in London at least, have tended to use medium wave on Sundays, and VHF at night. It's a compromise between the best times for the audience and the worst times for the postmen.

Security, together with technical considerations, has called for clever siting of transmitters. On medium wave a friend's house may be OK, but eventually you run out of friends. Mobile power supplies — surplus rotary transformers or DC/DC inverters — mean the gear can be run off car batteries in a wood or on a common. But medium wave aerials are long and not always easy to conceal.

Unlike MW, VHF travels roughly in *'line of sight'* so VHF transmitters have to be somewhere high like a local hilltop or tower block roof. VHF signals can also be beamed into the locality from a distance, using a more directional aerial. People choosing sites for VHF transmitters have used everything from an ordinary contour map of the area to maps of reception conditions kindly provided by the local (legal) VHF station. The horizontal dipole used to transmit VHF is inconspicuous since it is no different from a VHF receiving aerial.

LION M. KEEZER

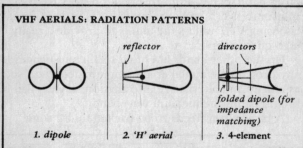

VHF AERIALS: RADIATION PATTERNS

reflector   *directors*

folded dipole (for impedance matching)

1. dipole   2. 'H' aerial   3. 4-element

Basic rules of the game seem to be to have a well organized lookout system, and to use a different location for every broadcast. It is only considered safe to break the second rule if the station's service area is very localised and its operators are certain the authorities haven't heard them — though it is very hard to be certain, of course.

Lookouts are placed at strategic sites giving both a good view of possible entrances and escape routes, and a means of rapid communication to the transmitter personnel. The latter might be by walkie-talkie, but this means that in the event of a

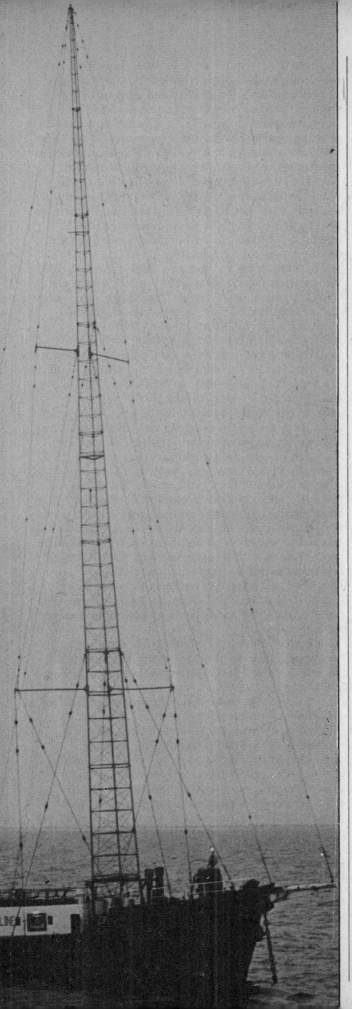

raid the lookouts cannot walk away as 'innocent bystanders' unless they throw away expensive gear. And one can be prosecuted just for using the walkie-talkie without a license. What's more, someone might eavesdrop on the walkie-talkie conversations.

Experienced lookouts know the methods of their local officials — and the actual officials themselves. Some 'pirates' keep photos of their local Post Office men. Such is the comradeship between pirates that this kind of information is exchanged quite freely; but usually they do not tell too many people about the station or its operations since infiltrators are not unknown.

If it comes to a raid: it can take the Post Office only 25 minutes to catch a station from scratch, assuming good weather and a medium wave broadcast. This is because they can use as little as a simple transistor radio, a map and compass, and a private car, to track down MW broadcasts. For a VHF broadcast at night, it may take as long as an hour or two, because they require a special van. (This usually seems to be a green or yellow Austin A40 van with side-windows and a pump-up mast sticking through the roof, surmounted by a 4-element VHF aerial.) They then have to find the exact area, which can be quite hard in the dark. However, after a station has been going for a few weekends they know when to expect it, and lie in wait on top of local hills until the transmission comes on. So pirates can't feel much safer using VHF than they do when using MW.

The pirates who have survived are those who have followed the unwritten rules, which must go something like this:

1. Use a frequency band appropriate to the purpose.
2. Build a transmitter of as high technical quality as is possible. Bad transmitters cause interference, which annoys people and increases your risk of being nicked.
3. Broadcast at 'safe' times, ie nights and weekends, unless circumstances justify the risk.
4. Choose a transmitting site on considerations of service and safety. Sacrifice safety only when absolutely necessary or when all sites have become unsafe.
5. Don't use the same site twice unless there is no other choice.
6. Know your enemy.
7. Don't broadcast for longer than necessary.
8. Do be nice to your local Post Office men, because they'll take it as a personal insult if you aren't. This could make the difference between a small investigation and a full-scale raid with police assistance.

One real station which follows almost all of these suggestions has on average three raids per year, only 40% of which result in court cases. As they broadcast every week, this represents a failure rate of just over 2%. The risks may be sufficient to put most people off illegal broadcasting. But from the point of view of the law, this is not a very high success rate. Such a law can hardly be regarded as enforceable.

Richard Elen

Ham radio and TV

Here in the United States we're exploring some alternative uses of amateur radio. The basic idea is to put amateur hardware and frequencies into the hands of people actively trying to get their own lives and their world into somewhat better shape.

Unlike radio broadcasting, which is basically a one-way medium where those in control decide what will be aired, and where there are few opportunities for listener involvement and feedback, ham radio is a two-way medium permitting a real-time dialogue at a distance.

One of our first activities, launched in September 1973, we call the New Directions Roundtable. On Sunday afternoons we gather at 1900 GMT on a frequency of 14253 KHz. Participants check in from many sections of the US and Canada. Sometimes we just share what is on our minds. Other weeks we have relatively structured sessions where one of the group makes a 'presentation' on some topic, followed by a question/answer/rap session. Often there is a 'guest of the day' who participates directly from one of the stations, or by telephone 'patched' into some station's transmitter and receiver. We have done book reviews (*Limits to Growth* and *I'm OK — You're OK*), had sessions on the energy crisis, the work/job/employment scene, organic gardening, agribiz, computer networking, the women's movement and media.

On a typical Sunday we will have a dozen to fifteen stations involved. This group size is small enough to allow participation by everyone.

Cop Macdonald at home in Minnesota with his radio and SSTV equipment. The unit with the round screen is an oscilloscope he converted into a slow-scan TV monitor. (Slow-scan pictures are normally viewed with subdued room lighting to maximize contrast.)

There is a group of 'regulars' who participate in most sessions, and some additional stations which just happen upon the activity and drop in. The core group is made up mostly of people oriented to alternatives and change. The transients, however, often represent the reactionary majority of the ham population, and we've had a few out-and-out fascists advocating 'retroactive birth control' and World War III as solutions to the world's problems. The only real difficulties we have encountered so far are the same ones that affect all amateur radio activities: the erratic nature of the ionosphere as a radio mirror, and interference from other stations sharing the same band of frequencies.

The Roundtable stations use single-sideband voice transmission, which is standard practice on the HF (high frequency or shortwave) amateur bands these days. Reception of these signals requires either a receiver designed for ham use, or a shortwave receiver with a BFO (beat frequency oscillator). Since most home-type shortwave receivers do not have this feature, broadcasting to the general public is a technical impossibility, even if we wanted to (which we don't). Our philosophy has been to operate strictly by the rules. In the USA, these rules allow us to do almost anything we'd like to do. The law in this case protects our activities, and we are happy to co-operate. I might mention that the US is unusually liberal about the content of amateur communications. They can't involve 'pecuniary interest', 'secret codes', 'profanity' nor 'music' — but these restrictions present no real problems. We are not otherwise restricted as to content, and are allowed to let others communicate over our stations and to transmit 'third party' messages for others. But many countries having nationally owned telephone and telegraph systems (including most Commonwealth nations) are wary of people finding a way around the state's communication monopoly via ham radio.

In Britain, I know, the Post Office does not permit any relaying of messages for 'third parties'. There is no 'third party' agreement between Britain and the United States. This means that the international regulations which prohibit third party communications prevail between us, and limit international communications between amateur stations in the US and Britain to 'messages of a technical nature relating to tests, and to remarks of a personal character for which by reason of their unimportance, recourse to the public telecommunications service is not justified'. The story I've heard is that the US would be happy to enter into a 'third-party agreement' with any country, and that lack of an agreement means that the other country is not willing. The US currently has agreements with 25 countries, mostly in Latin America.

Another of our activities is the Alternative Sources of Energy Net. Several members of the group live in rural areas, and the primary focus so far has been on wind generators.

Our goals are somewhat diffuse, but include keeping each other abreast of what is going on, trying to minimize re-invention in our own projects, and acting as a resource group to help communes and individuals with their energy projects.

It's almost a cliche that many British visitors to the US have a hard time grasping the size of the place. It is, of course, 3,000 miles between coasts, and 1,500 miles North to South. The sheer size of the US makes it difficult for a small change-oriented minority to get together. There are Berkeley; and Cambridge, Massachusetts; and Madison, Wisconsin; and freaky neighbourhoods in every large city. But the rest of us are dotted about on the other 3 million square miles. The US population is only 4 times as large as Britain's, but the area is 32 times as large. Because of this, decentralisation and going back to the land are still real possibilities here, but communication is more difficult. Our long-term aim is to help large numbers of change-oriented people to find the ham radio tool. The first step was finding those of us who already have ham licences. (Out of 280,000 hams in the US there had to be a few!) The biggest helps have been my Slow-Scan TV column in *CQ*, a ham magazine; and a series of articles on New Directions Radio in *The Mother Earth News*. I haven't counted lately, but the number of us hams who have made contact in some fashion must be over a hundred by now.

PLANS AND POSSIBILITIES

There are a number of possibilities which we are exploring, and what happens in these areas will depend a lot upon available time and energy within the group. First, we'd like to have on-the-air get-togethers with people of similar outlook in other countries. Problems in doing this include the sunspot cycle which is heading for a minimum in 1975-76 (resulting in poor long-distance radio conditions), and the fact that we don't have the most elaborate ham stations. I'd be delighted to hear from any of you reached by this book. Let's see what we can work out.

Of particular interest to me are Third World tie-ins. Having spent a few months in Central and South America I came to feel that we have a lot of worthwhile sharing to do in AT and other areas. Among the possibilities are learning exchange activities where we get learners and sharers together, a technical information reference service, and possibly a medical hotline. And more of us could get a better idea of what simple, basic living is like in other parts of the world — its advantages and its problems.

Just as soon as a few more communities sprout ham stations, we hope to get some Roundtables going, directed specifically to the needs of communes and back-to-the-landers. There is already a precedent for 'swapping' things over the air (a net devoted to radio equipment swapping), and it would certainly be nice to foster the growth of a non-money economy. There are lots of other things to share, from AT to veterinary problems.

Another area of interest is providing a fast-response communication network for the social change movement. The straight hams already run

networks for forwarding short written messages. These facilities could be used to some extent by social change people. Additional possibilities include the use of radio-teletype. Surplus machines are available in the US for $50 to $100. (Similar Government-surplus machines are also available in the UK. Look up the adverts in *Wireless World* or *Radio Communication*, the magazine of the Radio Society of Great Britain.)

The radio equipment required is even simpler than for voice, and the range is greater, for a given power level. One station in a city could feed many local machines via telephone or short distance VHF radio. The fantasies that this conjures up include daily newsletters transmitted and printed all over the country. Another is a tie-in with community access computer systems like the one now operating in Berkeley. (For info on this system write to Resource One, 1545 Dwight Way, Berkeley, Ca 94703, USA.)

SLOW-SCAN TV

There is a ham radio technology that I've been excited about and involved with since 1957. It's called slow-scan TV, and is a technique for transmitting images over a single voice channel. In essence it combines TV pickup and display techniques with radio facsimile modulation and demodulation techniques to allow transmission of a 120 by 120 line TV picture in an 8-second period.

Conventional TV requires a very large bandwidth because each picture contains roughly a quarter of a million picture elements, and because (in Europe)

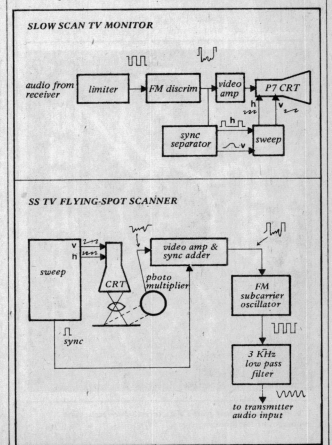

SLOW SCAN TV MONITOR

SS TV FLYING-SPOT SCANNER

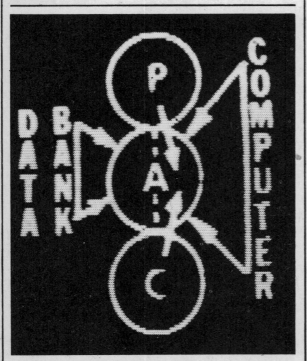

120 line amateur slow scan TV pictures. (One-frame time exposures of the monitor screen.)

25 complete pictures are transmitted every second to maintain the illusion of motion. If we change the groundrules so that motion is not required, and the detail in each frame is reduced, a great reduction in bandwidth is possible. The picture bandwidth in the amateur system is less than 3 KHz.

In conventional TV the eye and brain provide the frame-to-frame storage necessary to avoid flicker. With SSTV some external means must be used to store the received image as it arrives during the 8-second transmission period. The least expensive device in 1957, and still today, was the long-persistence phosphor cathode-ray tube developed for radar use in World War II. In the US we call the phosphor 'type P7'. It is characterised by a short persistence blue fluorescence, and a yellow phosphorescent afterglow which lasts for a number of seconds. The display is subjectively much like radar. A bright horizontal line moves, in 8 seconds, from top to bottom of the screen, leaving an image in the afterglow behind it.

The standards are shown in table 1. The slight differences in standards dictated by the frequency of the local power system make no difference in practice. Slow-scan monitors will lock-in on signals from both areas. The sweep synchronisation is provided by bursts of 1200Hz subcarrier. This same subcarrier is frequency shifted by the video signal to transmit various shades of grey. 1500Hz is Black, 2300Hz is White, and the frequencies in between represent intermediate shades of grey.

Hams in the UK have been involved with SSTV since its earliest days. John Plowman (G3AST) was at the receiving end of the first transatlantic tests in 1959, and members of the British Amateur Television Club (BATC) have been quite actively involved in the design of equipment and the use of slow-scan on audio tape. Unfortunately, the regulatory bodies in both countries were very slow to approve this mode of transmission in the ham bands. The Federal Communications Commission finally said OK in 1968, and the Ministry of Posts and Telecommunications came around even more recently. There are now about 2,000 hams in over 60 countries equipped for SSTV.

Since commercially available slow-scan gear is not cheap ($325 for a camera and $295 for a monitor here in the US) present users tend to be well-off establishment types, and I have not had very much success in turning them on to our New Directions activities. New Directions enthusiasts generally don't have much cash. Building your own is a way of trading time for money, and if you can latch onto an oscilloscope with P7 CRT it won't take much extra hardware to turn it into an SSTV monitor and flying-spot scanner. If you would like to explore equipment building possibilities, I suggest that you contact the BATC. Hams in general, and BATC members in particular, are a friendly bunch, eager to help a newcomer get technically involved.

Since the SSTV signal does occupy most of a voice channel, the general practice is to alternate voice and picture during a transmission. By equipping an audio tape recorder with a continuous

AT radio

In the society which many of us would like to see in the future, a society based on relatively small communities each of which is a group of semi-specialized craft collectives, radio would be an ideal medium for disseminating information. Unfortunately, the forms of radio communication used these days depend on very sophisticated technology: though silicon, the key material, is abundant, the production processes involve large amounts of energy and offend a number of the criteria of what we have come to term 'Alternative Technology'. Many other electronics products would also be useful in an 'alternative society' — for instance computers like that being used by the Resource One community group in Berkeley, California — but again the problem is how to produce them in an acceptable manner.

Here are some suggestions:

1. A 'high technology centre' could be set up to produce components for a large area.

2. The centre would be situated on a river or near another suitable energy source.

3. It would produce relatively large quantities of standard active components, of which the most important would be a standard Integrated Circuit package (like the present "741" series) that would operate satisfactorily in all low power audio and switching/control applications, and a standard transistor type for use in high-power switching, audio or RF equipment. The centre could also produce standard passive components, unless these were produced locally, which is quite feasible.

4. These parts would hardly ever need replacement, because: (a) they would be used and fitted by people who understood their correct mode of operation (ie the local 'electronics collective') and would seldom fail from misuse; (b) they would be made for quality and not profit as at present; and (c) all parts would be thoroughly tested before being sent out (up to 50 per cent of all Integrated Circuits supplied by a well-known US manufacturer are 'dead on arrival').

5. Members of the electronics in the area served by the centre would work in the centre for, say, one week every two years. They would take with them all faulty components for recycling, and would return with a stock of new bits.

6. Equipment at the centre itself would be designed to eliminate, or at least minimize, undesirable environmental effects and to make maximum use of all materials.

7. The centre could also house an intercontinental communications centre if necessary.

But even if this approach is deemed unacceptable, a large number of electronics components *could* be made on a small, local scale. Active components — vacuum tubes, not transistors — could be made from recycled glass and metal. Making vacuum tubes would entail a basic level of vacuum technology, but would require nothing like the ultra-hard vacuum conditions of transistor manufacture.

Either way, radio could then be used as it ought to be used: as the free information and entertainment medium of a free society.

Richard Elen

---

tape loop slightly longer than one frame, it is possible to 'snatch' a single frame as it arrives and store it for continuous viewing after the transmitting station switches back to voice. In the US (and perhaps the UK also) it is legal to transmit voice and picture simultaneously if one mode is transmitted in the upper sideband and the other in the lower. Unfortunately, this requires an addition to the transmitting and receiving gear and only a handful of slow-scan hams currently have this capability.

I'm hoping that as various groups pick up the ham radio alternative, the cost-sharing among members will reduce the economic barrier to using slow-scan TV. It is useful to be able to transmit visual material in many situations; and seeing the person you're talking with is a definite psychological plus. I see SSTV, ham radio, facsimile, teletype, and maybe even small computers as a communications bag-of-tricks that can help us in our attempts to change the world today. If high technology production capability survives the coming changes, then these could be among Illich's 'convivial tools' for helping individuals gain dominion over their own lives in a new society. On the grim side: if industrial society falls apart, these communication tools might at least allow some survivors in enclaves dotted around the world to keep in touch with each other.

Cop Macdonald

Table 1 Amateur slow-scan TV standards

| | Local Power Frequency | | Ministry of Posts & Telecommunications Rules |
	60 Hz	50 Hz	
Lines per picture	120	120	128 ± 8
Aspect ratio	1 : 1	1 : 1	1 : 1
Horizontal frequency	15 Hz (60 Hz/4)	16 2/3 Hz (50 Hz/3)	16 2/3 ± 1 Hz
Vertical time	8 seconds	7.2 seconds	6.79 to 8.68 seconds
Sync pulse duration:			
Horizontal	5 milliseconds	5 milliseconds	5 milliseconds (nominal)
Vertical	30 milliseconds	30 milliseconds	30 milliseconds (nominal)
FM subcarrier frequency:			
Sync	1200 Hz	1200 Hz	1200 Hz (nominal)
Black	1500 Hz	1500 Hz	1500 Hz (nominal)
White	2300 Hz	2300 Hz	2300 Hz (nominal)
Direction of scan:			
Horizontal		Left to right	
Vertical		Top to bottom	

TWO-WAY MIRROR

The old woman watches herself on the television monitor. Slowly she sits up straight. Approvingly, she looks at the change. Her mouth becomes firmer. She is transformed.

It is the same with a community. "A group may see itself in the 'mirror-machine' and begin to change as a result." That's how John Hopkins of the Centre for Advanced TV Studies in London puts it.

The 'mirror-machine' is a video-camera and tape recorder which uses half-inch video tape. It weighs 25 pounds. The tape records an amazing amount of information on that thin ribbon.

The camera has a zoom lens and a built-in microphone (which most people do not use). We call it a 'mirror' but usually it is an 'ear' listening intently to people. Because of this, sound is very important and an external microphone is used.

It can be operated by one person. Two people can share the equipment; one using the camera attached to a long extension cable; the other carrying the recorder and microphone, monitoring the sound through earphones.

Basic half-inch equipment costs £1,000, although a quarter-inch system sells at just over half the price. But two video-tape recorders and monitors are needed if the video material is to be edited.

The most obvious technical defect of half-inch video is electronic noise or 'roll over' before each shot. It can be overcome in various expensive ways.

Any new system is confused with previous methods. Half-inch is mobile and relatively cheap but people worry because it is not as sharp or stable as broadcasts made with £250,000 cameras and two-inch video-tape.

Sixteen millimetre cine cameras and 35 mm still cameras were also considered toys when introduced. But their convenience easily overcame their technical disadvantages and changed the film industry and photography.

The technique of using video in the community reflects political tactics. Both Communists and special military operations rely on a cadre of 'agitators' and 'tech sergeants'. Community television is no different. They call the agitator an 'animator', but his task is the same.

Many ideas about half-inch have been developed by the Canadian National Film Board which spends £500,000 a year on its Challenge for Change programme. The Board realised its films had become remote from the people for whom they were intended.

They abandoned elaborate film crews that spent weeks re-arranging people's lives to 'record' them, and substituted two-person crews consisting of a video operator and animator.

The animator or agitator unearths issues and the video operator teaches local people to use the equipment. Instead of being burnt by the media, people tell their own stories. Elsewhere, video has been used to 'trigger' community action.

Challenge for Change has shown that video can be a useful community organising tool. "But the

MICHAEL SHAMBERG

media work involved takes a great deal of time," one of their producers warns, "and there are advantages to having a person, volunteer or paid, working full time with the videotape." This full-time worker would be guided by the citizens' group, as normally the latter cannot afford much time themselves on the media arm of their activities.

" . . . a media resource centre . . . can be of real use to citizens' groups—on these conditions: (a) that the resource people are simply not media crazy, and trying to get into television, (b) . . . understand the citizen groups and their problems (c) . . . sense that people need to be taught the medium and left to do it themselves . . ."

Other safeguards are needed. John Hopkins suggests people interviewed should be shown their tapes as soon as possible; erase anything they don't like; and know how the tape will be used to help them.

The animator should be neutral; act only when invited; help, but not direct, the selection and debate of issues, Hopkins adds. The Challenge for Change worker, as he says, becomes a "spark plug for *process* rather than a creator of *product*, and could use his previous liability as an outsider to mediate difficulties and bring conflicting parties together."

Community television looks for consensus. It

MICHAEL SHAMBERG

MICHAEL SHAMBERG

uncovers 'issues', records opinions supporting either side, and then tries to resolve them by getting people together to watch the tapes and talk. It hopes for 'media-tion'.

Video is prolific. Little community voice is left after cutting thirty hours of tape to thirty minutes. Standards rapidly become 'production' ones. Is this man interesting? Can this accent be understood? Does this woman help the argument? The editor has to choose.

Half-inch video benefits from the shadow of the BBC and network television. 'Television' remains a magic word. It takes moral courage not to talk to television.

Part of the 'magic' of portable television rests in the power handed down from the corporations. Community television must avoid abusing this power.

Broadcast television has established a convention of aggressive questioning. The danger is that community video can quickly become as bland.

The 'good life' has become a television commercial. Community must not become a television dialogue.

Community TV offers the technological fix— using the technology of an oppressive society. Like an Arab firing a Sam 7 missile, the video freak depends on high technology. If that is switched off, he is out of business. As long as his 'freaking out' is profitable and amusing he can continue. But when it becomes revolutionary he is soon back to the pot of whitewash and a wall.

Half-inch video has another similarity to the Sam 7 missile. Both are 'black boxes' which cannot be touched by the user. Even if you have the knowledge—and many have—you cannot service half inch without specialised and expensive equipment.

Victor Papanek has pointed out that a Japanese TV set selling for $119.95 retail costs $18 to make. He claims an 'inexpensive educational TV set' for use in Africa can be made for 'considerably less than $9'.

The companies will protest that they need the money for research. In fact, video freaks in America have sparked most of the modifications.

Servicing is slow, expensive and unreliable.

Half-inch video is a technological break through that cannot be distributed because the channels of communication are owned by the State and controlled by corporate and commercial bodies.

As for cable TV, Andrew Kopkind in the *New York Review of Books* recently put down the cable-cast utopians. "The spread of cable TV," he noted, "suggested to some that all aspects of the established broadcast media could be reformed by an upstart technology. Instead the opposite seems to be happening: cable is becoming simply an adjunct of the existing power grid."

The record industry shows what can happen. Technically it has long been possible for anyone to record anything they want onto cassette tapes. Instead a revolutionary rhetoric is used to sell long playing products of an established industry. 'Rock-'n'- radical' radio in America is not the 'people's'

voice but that of the market-place.

Community TV has many allies when people are trying to get cable concessions. How many remain after the concessions are granted and it becomes cheaper to run cut-price American films and tired comedy programmes?

A communications system, which promised the people a voice, is being taken over without protest by local authorities. Many British boroughs already have their own video units attached to housing or public relations offices.

The Home Office has paid for an investigation into 'Video in Community Developments' carried out by one of London's most respected video freaks. The Arts Council and its local associations, and the British Film Institute pay for equipment for many independent video groups. Some of this is being used for 'artistic' purposes, but much of it is used for community animation or agitation.

Somebody is mistaken. Either the authorities do not realise the revolutionary nature of controlling communications or the users are making closed-loops to which no-one listens.

Half-inch video combines two possibilities—remote eye and a recording capacity. In our increasingly paranoid society these are being used more and more frequently for 'security' and 'surveillance'.

Fitted with image intensifiers, television cameras can see in the virtual dark. Monitors trigger an alarm when movement appears on the screen. Time lapse records two frames or less a minute for 24 hours and plays the whole day back in 40 minutes.

Prisoners are watched in their cells by television cameras. A television company does tests for the Home Office to see if a 60 watt bulb provides enough light for their cameras.

Police and soldiers record demonstrations and riots to play back for identification. Just one example: during the Prince of Wales' Investiture ceremony a City of London Land Rover equipped with a television camera drove slowly along the waiting crowds looking for Welsh 'extremists'. Big Brother is watching you *now*.

Tom Picton

THERE'S NO TRANSPORT LIKE NO TRANSPORT

Inside your jet, wallpaper music lulls you before take-off, and the air hostess glides smilingly from seat to seat. The decor is restful; the trip that follows is quick, smooth and safe.

Inside your car, stereo hi-fi tapes enhance the scenery and help you while away the time spent in jams. The soft seats caress you as the automatic shift takes you from nought to 70 in seconds—a speed you can hold indefinitely once the motorway carpet is laid out before you.

In long-distance trains or ocean-going liners, the accent is the same—on speed and comfort for the traveller in a hurry. Freight also gets VIP treatment: whether goods go by road, rail, sea or air, the massive thrust of technology has been channelled to ensure they arrive intact and on time.

The business of moving people and goods from one part of the world to another has become a major preoccupation. In Britain and the USA, up to a fifth of the national output goes into it; in the USA it absorbs nearly 40% of net energy input; the world's four biggest multi-national companies are all involved in it—as are at least a fifth of the top hundred British and European companies.

Faced with such an array of might, it is easy for us to believe that the present transport system is inevitable, despite obvious imperfections. The dubious economics of our highly specialized, centralized, technological society, with its cumulative concentration of power in the hands of the already powerful, actually depends on the continued diversion of resources from essentials into the luxuries of excessive personal mobility and freight movement. It could be otherwise. How has such economic perversion come about?

Before the Industrial Revolution, goods were made by local craftsmen from local materials, primarily for local use. There was little movement of either people or goods. As factories grew in size, and products became more complex, so raw materials were sought from farther afield, and finished products travelled to more distant markets.

While coal was the chief energy source personal mobility was still limited; since oil took over and the internal combustion engine arrived, however, frequent long-distance travel has become accepted as the norm in most industrialized countries. In the process, cities succumbed to suburban sprawl, and commuting became a part of every day life; government and industry discovered that, despite the phone, they could not survive unless executives and salesmen travelled constantly; workers—both blue and white-collar—were forced to move to where the work was; the escapism that is mass tourism grew within a decade to become one of the world's biggest industries.

Meanwhile, the movement of freight was growing exponentially, shifting from rail to road as hauliers took advantage of a concrete track generously donated by the state. Today that track shudders under the pounding of juggernauts carrying virtually identical loads in all directions: a truck driver takes his vehicle from Dorset to Glasgow laden with one manufacturer's jam, only to bring back a load of another manufacturer's jam; on the new motorway, a heavy lorry stacked with cabbages hurtles regularly from Covent Garden, London to Wales—though cabbages grow splendidly there . . . and may even have travelled to London on the same road!

Just conceivably this Alice in Wonderland way of running things could be justified if it satisfied a few elementary criteria. If, for example, conventional transport modes were non-polluting, used renewable energy sources, and were miserly in their use of other resources—including land—they could perhaps be condoned . . . especially if their benefits were available to *all* rather than a privileged minority . . . and if they could be shown to be non-violent.

Demonstrably they are not. Take energy for a start: in the USA 90% of inter-city travel is by car, yet in energy terms the car is at the bottom of the league: while a fast train about half full requires a mere 980 British Thermal Units (BTU) per passenger mile, a car half full needs 4,100 per passenger mile—or quarter full 8,100. And a 707 jet 62% full demands 6,200 BTUs—for every passenger.

Or pollution: in the USA transport is officially estimated to cause half the country's tonnage of air pollution; and in Britain nearly a third of the

population endures unacceptable levels of aircraft noise.

Or violence: in Britain a serious road accident happens every six minutes; since the last war the country has suffered more than seven million road casualties, well over 300,000 of them deaths.

The Road Lobby would have us believe that the benefits of conventional transport are available to all, and the planners of New Towns have fallen for it. But facts do not bear this out. As car ownership has grown, public transport services have declined steadily and car ownership is far from universal. Even in the affluent, 'fully motorized' USA, 20% of families do not own a car, and in some places—such as Washington, the capital, — the percentage rises to 50. In Britain less than half the households have a car, and only 20% of the population has *exclusive* use of one: those that suffer are wives and children, the elderly, the disabled and of course the poor.

The deeper one probes, the more apparent it becomes that a just society is impossible without an alternative transport system. We need a fresh approach: alternative ways to travel which are non-polluting, low in energy intake, non-violent, simpler and available to all. Moreover, we need a fresh look at the *amount* of travel: in a time of energy shortage and ecological awareness, mobility can no longer be merely a reactive response to an ill-organized, wasteful economic system; in the near future, society will have to re-organize itself so that fewer of its scarce resources are squandered on perpetual motion, and take steps to reduce the insidiously harmful social effects of excessive mobility.

The car, as we know it, will have to go. In place of a private transport system based on millions of sexy polluters, we shall see a relatively small number of low-speed, unglamorous runabouts, mostly owned by the populace; and, in towns and cities, available for hire strictly for essential purposes where public transport is unavailable. They will be safe, with at least as much emphasis on protecting pedestrians as occupants—in marked contrast to current priorities. Like all manufactured products, both cars and buses will be built to last, and when their day is done, they will be capable of easy dismantling for 100% recycling. Sturdy and unglamorous, they will answer the needs of the Third World as much as the so-called 'developed' world: for rough roads and heavy loads the Western car, bus or lorry is unsuitable; it is also over-priced, in common with the typical farm tractor. What the majority need is economy and reliability; and if the thing does break down, it should be able to be repaired by its owner or a friend—with readily available simple parts.

Unless the problem of economically storing methane under pressure can be solved, urban vehicles will probably be electrically powered, although steam propulsion is a possible contender.

The electric vehicle, recharging its batteries with energy supplied by conventional power stations, is about 20% efficient—at least four times more efficient than its internal combustion counterpart. However, the greatest energy loss occurs not in the vehicle, but at the power station. There, less than a third of the raw fuel energy is converted into available electricity: most of the energy is lost as heat, the rest chiefly in transmission lines. Of the remaining 30% of energy, the electric vehicle uses about 65%, losses occurring in motor control, battery storage and mechanical transmission. If the electric bus and car were used only for short runs, mainly in urban districts, their efficiency compared with the internal combustion engine would rise, for they use no power when 'idling', and perform best at the low speeds appropriate to urban conditions.

However, the most important factor is the efficiency of power stations—upon this, the electric vehicle stands or falls. Clearly, power stations should utilize the heat that they now let run to waste, but this is not all: the whole centralized system of electricity generation needs re-appraisal. Socially and technologically, there is much to be said for a system with thousands of small, friendly, neighbourhood generators in place of the inefficient centralized giants.

If the railway network were revived, along with other forms of public transport, there could be a power station at each station, supplying the transport and other needs of the district. As the accent on high-speed, long-distance travel is replaced by low-speed, short-distance travel to meet the needs of a decentralized, non specialized society, locally powered trains become an attractive proposition.

Coal-powered 6-cylinder Buick frequently seen in Great Britain during the 1914-18 war. A gas capacity of 100 cubic feet was equivalent to half a gallon of petrol.

A train of 'Tom Puddings'—35 ton compartment coal boats.

Canals too deserve attention. Britain has 1,500 miles of navigable rivers and canals, and with a relatively small expenditure they could carry millions of tons of 'dry' goods and even oil with remarkable efficiency in energy terms, and with minimal environmental impact. The existing network could be dramatically enlarged by opening up disused waterways, with the bonus value of places of recreation and beauty.

There will be little flying. Aircraft are the most costly means of transport in energy terms; aircraft noise is a major health hazard, and the thousands of acres of fertile land now rendered sterile by airports could be released for food production and recreation. For a society where speed and glamour rank low on the value scale, airships hold possibilities, chiefly because of their low energy usage: some calculations put the direct operating costs of an airship at less than a third of those of an aircraft. But this is not all: they are relatively quiet and since they need little space for take-off and landing, their environmental impact is reduced. And, if the huge area of the airship's upper skin could be used as a solar collecter, and the resultant energy made to propel the craft, the proposition would become still more attractive.

As oil supplies dwindle, any alternative form of propulsion takes on a new significance. At sea we can expect a revival of interest in sailing craft, some of traditional design, others incorporating new technologies. Tradition need not be ignored: vessels such as the East Coast barge, which could sail unassisted and fully laden to a quay with 150 tons of cargo, drawing a mere six to eight feet of water, could have a place in an energy-starved society. In 1900, 2,000 such vessels were registered: today the only seagoing survivors are tourist-attracting luxury conversions. Variations on the original theme of sail have already

been explored, and in future we can expect to see more research. Some schemes have used aerospace experience with 'sails' made of light alloys; another has employed windmill-like blades to drive an underwater propeller. In the twenties, a German engineer, Anton Flettner, exploited the 'magnus effect' of an airfoil by spinning large vertical cylinders mounted on the decks of his ships, and in 1926 his converted schooner, the *Baden Baden,* crossed the Atlantic. His system needed auxiliary power to spin the cylinders, however, and this disadvantage was overcome by the Finnish inventor, Savonius, who used his now famous rotor, not only to spin the Flettner cylinders but also drive a propeller.

Certainly, the future will see a revival in that old-fashioned, but neglected alternative form of propulsion—muscle power. Already farmers are showing renewed interest in horses: no tractor has yet reproduced itself or manufactured first-class fertilizer, and, as oil prices rocket, horse power reverts to its original meaning. But horses are not the only

A cylinder rotating in an airstream experiences a sideways force. This curious effect was exploited by Flettner in creating a wind-driven vessel that can tack much closer to the wind than an ordinary sailing ship.

draught animals: throughout the world, the cow family not only pulls the plough, it keeps the farmer's family in milk.

For personal mobility, walking, roller skating and cycling will be the norm. Although walking remains the principal way of getting about in the Third World, in so-called 'developed' countries this century it has steadily gone into a decline. One paradoxical

Low gear tricycle designed by Victor Papanek re-assembled for carriage of heavy loads.

result is a swelling of their GNPs as the medical-chemical industry tries unsuccessfully to cope with the ensuing deterioration in health. Provided these countries can secure an adequate diet in the forthcoming world food shortage, more use of muscle power will help solve at least two of their problems—ill health and immobility.

Cycling has already regained popularity: Americans bought eight million in one year. Philip Brachi, author of *The Bike Book* has studied this quiet, non-violent way of getting about and has concluded that the bicycle is the most efficient means of transport known to man. He has calculated that a mere 250 kilowatt hours—equal to the energy in seven gallons of petrol—go into mining and manufacturing the materials for the modern 28lb bike—a sixtieth of the energy input needed to make the average European 2,000lb car. And he quotes doctors as saying that a person cycling five hours daily adds about 1,500 calories to his diet, which means that, with 40,000 food calories equal in energy to a gallon of petrol, a cyclist does a cool 1,500 miles to the gallon!

The alternative technologies for the transport of the future are widely varied, but they have a number of things in common. They seek to reduce the use of scarce resources, to be non-polluting, low-speed, simpler to build and run, and available to all. Because these are the criteria, the list omits such esoterica as high-speed trains, monorails and moving pavements. Yet the criteria are stringent, and even the examples of alternative transport quoted are unlikely to fulfil all of them completely. Short of a dramatic technological breakthrough, the job of moving people and goods from one place to another cannot be accomplished entirely by using renewable sources of energy and materials. Some leakage is inevitable. For a lasting society therefore, the accent must be far more on *reducing* the amount of travel

than on looking for the technological 'fix'.

The crucial changes must be *social* rather than technological. We shall have to live closer to our work and shop locally, buying locally grown food and locally made goods consisting far more of local materials. We shall have to develop communities—of streets, of districts, of villages and communes; for a start we could try making friends with the people next door—for we shall see less and less of those who live far afield. We shall take holidays at home rather than abroad: finding it harder to escape physically, we shall either seek escape via drugs or use the resources saved by reduced travel to improve the local environment so that the urge to escape becomes less pressing.

Industry can expect to be taxed according to energy units used. Since goods imported from far afield will bear the tax incurred through energy used in transporting them, local materials will be more attractive. Similarly, since finished products sent to distant markets will bear the tax incurred by transport, manufacturers will cater chiefly for local markets. In consequence, the volume of freight hurtling in all directions will drop sharply. Since railways are far more efficient in energy usage terms than road transport, the remaining freight traffic will be transferred to them. Long-distance travel will be drastically reduced, and will be almost entirely by public transport. Motorways will present an unusual spectacle: empty save for express buses, a few local lorries, an occasional car on an essential mission. Cycling on them, far from being prohibited, will almost certainly be encouraged—they could be allotted the slow lane. With the fall of monopoly capitalism and an acceptance that economic growth is no longer sustainable, there will be little need for the present battalions of travelling salesmen and executives. The company car, which has recently accounted for about half the annual expenditure on new cars, will be a thing of the past. In fact, much work will be able to be done at home, and commuter traffic—already cut by decentralization—will shrink still further.

In short, the key to alternative transport lies in the alternative *to* transport. As values change, mobility will be recognized as having been essentially an ingredient of the throwaway society, a temporary middle-class cult, which had some connection with an immature need for constant stimulation. And another connection will become apparent: that when people are able to buy mobility on the cheap, the difference between one place and another disappears: variety throughout the world is lost, and a Hiltonesque sameness descends over everywhere. Conversely, as travel and transport are made to bear their true social and energy costs, they shrink into their correct proportions. Each place then develops in its own way according to the differences inherent in its people, its geography, climate and other life forms. And it is well known to ecologists that in diversity a species has more capacity to survive when it encounters adverse conditions.

Patrick Rivers

VISION 6/COMMUNITY

Churches, nowadays mostly disused or under-used, would make perfect locations for community arts and media centres. Their tall spires could carry radio and TV transmitting antennae. Their interiors could be used for mass meetings, concerts, theatrical productions, jumble sales, exhibitions — even religious services.

The solid foundations of their crypts would provide ideal supports for heavy printing machinery. Radio, TV and recording studios could also be located in the sound-deadened crypt environment. The main Nave area, when not being used for major events, could be sub-divided by means of flexible partitions into areas serving specific purposes — smaller meetings, advice centres, health clinics, yoga classes and so on. Aisles, vestibules and other peripheral rooms could be used as administrative and control rooms—perhaps also housing the local telephone exchange and Post Office.

1. Telephone Switchboard for phone-in listener feedback
2. Tape cartridge player
3. Control console: mikes, switching, monitoring etc.
4. Turntable
5. Tape deck
6. Nave of church being used as auditorium.
7. Transmitting antennae mounted on spire
8. Vision switching
9. 'Wipe' unit
10. Vision mixer
11. Monitor
12. Videotape recorder
13. TV camera
14. A2 size offset litho press
15. Vertical A3 size letterpress machine
16. Process camera
17. Guillotine

STEPHEN JAMES/PHOTON WEST/LNS

OTHER PERSPECTIVES

RSPECTIVES

Most of the articles in this book have been written within the framework of fairly conventional categor-isations of Technology — Food, Energy, Shelter, Tools, Materials, Communications and so on — even though they have dealt with their subject matter in an un-conventional way.

But in this section, we widen our perspective to embrace the social and political context in which a radical technology might be applied. We also look at the possibility of metaphysical changes in our out-look which might enable us to synthesise the Western, externally-oriented conception of techno-logy with the 'inner technologies' of the East.

The first two articles consider the possibility of a completely different conception of Nature and of our relationship to it, a conception whose main

quality would be to change what it feels like to act in the world. One implication of this way of think-ing would be to pay as much attention to ways of changing our needs as to ways of meeting them. Such an approach might not seem like technology at all.

Alan Watts illustrates the difference between the two modes of thought (1):

A king of ancient India, oppressed by the rough-ness of the earth upon soft human feet, proposed that his whole territory should be carpeted with skins. However, one of his wise men pointed out that the same result could be achieved far more simply by taking a single skin and cutting off small pieces to bind beneath the feet. These were the first sandals.

To a Hindu, the point of this story is not its obvious illustration of technical ingenuity. It is a parable of two different attitudes to the world,

Nerve Gas Arsenal, Hermiston, Oregon.
(Inset: Men-an-tol stone, Cornwall)

JANET BORD

attitudes which correspond approximately to those of the progressive and traditional types of culture. Only in this case the more technically skilful solution represents the traditional culture, in which it is felt that it is easier for man to adapt himself to Nature than to adapt Nature to himself. This is why science and technology, as we know them, did not arise in Asia.

Joss Kingston's article on the Owenite communities of the 19th Century provides a historical perspective on present attempts at radical reorganisation of social life and of the means of production. It makes sobering reading, but we have to recognise the mistakes of the past for what they are and learn how to avoid repeating them.

The rest of the Section concerns itself with Technology in non-Western social and political contexts. Jimoh Omo-Fadakah discusses the general problems involved in applying advanced industrial technology to the Third World, and looks at the alternative approaches that are possible. Satish Kumar's article on Ghandi examines the Ghandian philosophy of production, a philosophy no longer regarded as eccentric and backward-looking but one which (aside from the hyprocrisy of the 'Gandhi cult') is increasingly being acknowledged as not only feasible but essential to a sane future for India.

Josefina Mena's piece on Chilean Peasants Communal Commands and Popular Power contrasts sharply in mood and style, but likewise concerns the need for a grass roots movement to relocate the means of production in the hands of the people. For the peasants in Chile and elsewhere, Land Reform is the *sine qua non* of any alternative approach to technology.

Finally, the article on China by Tony Durham, who went there to see for himself and took the photographs, illustrates an experiment on the re-direction of technology that is probably the most successful and significant ever carried out. While we are thinking about it, the Chinese are doing it.

We have more to learn from the Chinese than from any other source save our own imagination.

1. Watts, Alan W. *Nature, Man and Woman* Pantheon Books, NY, 1958

OTHER PERSPECTIVES

THE MOON IN THE MIND

Lyn Gambles

There is pollution at the point of production,
No litter in a forest,
And no sunshine
On the assembly line.
Production and pollution in the home too
Where the only muscles you let me develop
Are in my uterus
And forced labour makes us
Producers of producers.

I am the mercury[1] in the belly of a deepsea
*   fish*
Where once I was the world.

©Lyn Gambles, 1974

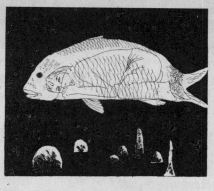

D. HOCKNEY

1 Spellbound in the fish—a symbol of the living contents of the unconscious—Mercury is the god of magicians, representing the epitome of all dualities, the winged and the wingless, fire and water, spirit and matter. Also a trickster the alchemists sought to tame, a god of healing. "They call him the Spirit of the Lord which fills the whole world and in the beginning swam upon the waters. They call him also the Spirit of Truth which is hidden from the world," according to a 17th century alchemical source. He is also designated as anima, hence a feminine being. Carl Jung summarises the rich alchemical symbolism of Mercury in *The Spirit Mercurius* in vol 13 of his collected works published by Routledge and Kegan Paul in 1968 as "*1. Mercurius consists of all conceivable opposites. He is thus quite obviously a duality, but is named a unity in spite of the fact that his innumerable inner contradictions can dramatically fly apart into an equal number of disparate and apparently independent figures. 2. He is both material and spiritual. 3. He is the process by which the lower and material is transformed into the higher and spiritual, and vice versa. 4. He is the devil, a redeeming psychopomp, an evasive trickster, and God's reflection in physical nature. 5. He is also the reflection of a mystical experience of the artifex that coincides with the* opus alchymicum. *6. As such, he represents on the one hand the self and on the other the individuation process, and, because of the limitless number of his names, also the collective unconscious.*"

Sulphur as sun and Mercurius as moon bridging the river of 'eternal water'. (Barchusen, *Elementa Chemique*, 1718)

Astrologically Mercury represents rational, logical thinking, communication with others, the most human qualities of adaptability and intelligence, a capacity for choices. In the Tarot Mercury is associated with the Magician or Juggler, a clever man who uses his mind to conquer the elements. In its negative aspects a trickster, a liar and a thief.

2 In the mid-50's the people of Minamata Bay in Japan suffered the worst case of mercury poisoning ever recorded. Mercury in contact with organic wastes produces methyl mercury which attacks the central nervous system and causes defective sight, failure of muscular coordination, and sometimes death. The disease was first spotted in the local cats which frequented the fish quay. Incapable of walking properly, they fell into the sea and drowned.

3 Fenugreek: bitter aromatic seeds in pods, 20-30 ins tall with yellowy-white flowers. Research currently being undertaken by Dr. Ronald Hardman in the pharmaceutical department, University of Bath. See *Pharmaceutical Journal*, 1974, 213, 274—6; 'Steroid plants as a source of contraceptives', *Excerpta Medica* (in press).

It's quicksilver cold down here in the belly of this fish. Watch out that I don't rise up and Minamata[2] the lot of you. The feminist case has been well-aired up there on land. The four minimum demands still stand rockfast, uncompromising and unfulfilled, at the head of the Women's Movement. Equal pay, equal education, free contraception and abortion, and 24-hour nurseries. In 1974 a fifth demand was added—the right of a person to determine their own sexuality. Feminism is alternative because it is revolutionary. It brooks no reformism, except as a tactic. Everyone in the AT movement pays lip-service to feminism, some even embrace it warmly. Liberated women are ATtractive. But the White Goddess is watching every man jack of you, so beware.

Like the moon the Women's Movement has two mature aspects—the full moon which you see, and the new moon which is invisible; or, like the bright side which shows her face, and the dark side which few have seen. The bright side of the moon is the women's struggle—on your streets and in your beds. She illuminates the five demands, and frowns on all the men making all the windmills while all the women weave all the rugs. She triggers the flight of women from communes up and down the country. Women need to stand on two feet in the world of action, it is too early to return so soon to the world of householding on smallholdings. She despairs at the total lack of alternative research into contraception and abortion. The yam is being hunted to extinction in South America. Don't laugh! It is the source of the pill. Hunted not farmed, while fenugreek[3], which provides the same contraceptive properties grows to seed, a weed in your own alternative gardens, cheap, decentralised and forgotten. Menstrual extraction, safe, simple, reliable: a people's tool of abortion, easy to decentralise, with precise but teachable skills needed for its operation, yet it remains the exclusive preserve of a few prestigious big-city hospitals. Do you take the population explosion and my right to my body seriously? Do you?

Its dark down here in this big fish. Dark, like the dark side of the moon, but the darkness makes it clear the world is forged of opposites: not males and females, men and women, but feminine and masculine. Two modes requiring a synthesis in one person, male or female, to integrate a personality. When one mode, any mode, disconnects from its opposite number and develops alone, then collapse is inevitable. Science and rationalism have already gone too far. Alternative technology is the intuitive response to this. The dark side of the moon knows at least half the world is not amenable to rational analysis and so rational solutions are not appropriate to that area of human experience. The dark side of the moon is poetic, free and fun and quite likely to place any one of those values above the pursuit of profit, or to stop work to play with a child, to watch a butterfly, to consider a dream seriously, to know nature like a lover.

White Goddess scares you good;
1 + 1 = androgyny;
Clever speedy wise magic Mercury the two-
timing bastard;
Eve and Adam together over an original
matter;
Bound to moon about every month;
Sometimes hard to believe;

INNER TECHNOLOGIES

The present technological paradigm is clearly in need of replacement. The principal *raison d'etre* of this book is the growing awareness that a new paradigm must be structured, one that is holistic, ecologically sound, non-exploitative and culturally sensitive. But it is unlikely that a truly holistic-ecological ethic can be built into technology if it is not already built into us as well. 'Built in', not just in the sense of being understood—nearly everyone understands that we are inseparable from the rest of the biosystem—but as a fact of life, as an unavoidable premise of all our feelings, thoughts and activities. We need not only to know that we are an integral part of the total system, but also to *Know* it—to grok it, in the words of Robert Heinlein.

There is a fundamental, and very natural, duality in perception as a result of which we automatically relate to the world as a set of objects to be manipulated and controlled. This duality is not the whole truth, however real it may seem. It is a useful model which develops in early childhood as the individual begins to break away from the mother and interact with his/her own body and immediate environment. At a biological level the sense of separateness is very necessary for individual survival, but to have gained this awareness of individuality at the expense of the awareness of one's essential unity with the whole of nature is now proving a considerable handicap as far as species survival is concerned.

In order to maintain this sense of separation from the rest of the world we build up an identity derived from our interactions with the 'outside' world.

When the feedback from the surroundings is weak or threatened we have to assert ourselves and reaffirm our sense of identity. Since the world around is continually changing we need continually to act and experience in order to sustain ourselves psychologically. Without this feedback from our surroundings most of us would die psychologically (ie literally cease to be) as surely as we would die physically if deprived of food or oxygen.

This continual need to maintain a derived sense of identity is the mainstay of a consumer society. The man who trades in last year's Ford Granada for this year's model is not doing so out of any physical need but only out of psychological one. Most advertising psychology preys upon the individual's need to bolster his inadequate and artificial self-image. We smoke the 'right' cigarettes, use the 'right' brand of petrol, buy clothes from the 'right' store, etc., not because those products are materially superior but because they give us a stronger sense of identity.

We reaffirm our sense of separation from the world by taking from the 'out there' to feed the 'in here'. It is preserved at the expense of what is not-I, ie the environment, and in this respect other people and even one's own body must be included as part of the environment. Consequently any 'I versus It' awareness automatically gives birth to an exploitative element in our thinking.

Now this is not to belittle or ignore the political factors involved, only to suggest that the use of technology for short-term financial goals or for the preservation of a sense of social supremacy, for

FRIEDLANDER

'THE JUGGLER' JOHN A. GLOVER

example, may, in many cases, also be traced back to an individual need to maintain a sense of personal identity. The situation can only be fully resolved if both sides of the situation are dealt with together.

A METAPARADIGM SHIFT

History proceeds not from intellectual ideas but from social and personal realities. It is no good knowing intellectually that we are inseparable from the rest of the world if reality is still *perceived* on an 'I versus It' basis. Rather than structure a truly holistic paradigm we will only succeed in remodelling the structures existing within the old paradigm and the exploitative elements of consciousness will continue to condition our thoughts and actions. This applies as much after the revolution as before it.

What I am advocating is far more than a paradigm shift in politics and technology. We need not only to change the models which dominate economics, social policies and the use of technology but also to change the model which dominates the whole of our thinking and action.

In a sense the paradigm on which all our thinking is based is one's image of one's self. But since it underlies all human activities, including the establishment of ordinary paradigms, I prefer to call this a *metaparadigm.* I shall define it as the dominant psychological model on the basis of which we construct our perception of reality.

All the time that one appreciates oneself as separate from the rest of the world thinking and action will contain an 'I versus It' element. What is needed is a shift in metaparadigm away from the present model towards a more holistic I-Thou model in which the self is spontaneously appreciated as an aspect of the whole—as a part of the total system rather than apart from it. When this shift occurs our immediate awareness of reality will be correspondingly restructured. We will then *Know* that all aspects of the environment are as much as part of us as the body is and it would become as difficult to create an overall imbalance in the total system as it is to chop off our own fingers.

When the self is appreciated as separate from the rest of creation there is a continual battle between the apparent good of the individual and the good of the whole, but when the self is appreciated in terms of the whole there is no longer any conflict. Action for self interest automatically becomes action for the good of the total system. The latter state represents a high-synergy system and in biological terms is equivalent to a healthy organism. But if a cell loses the genetic information, which defines its relationship to the whole organism, it ceases to function as part of a system and upsets the delicate organic balance on which it is ultimately so dependant. We say it has turned malignant. On a global level the situation is very similar. Mankind appears to have become a malignant growth ruthlessly eating its way across the planet's surface. And for remarkably similar reasons. We have lost the information which ties us back to the whole—our awareness of our essential oneness with the rest of

The sema, or whirling dance of the Dervishes. 'Sema is to fight with one's self, to further, to struggle desperately like a half-slaughtered bird, bloodstained and covered with dust and dirt. It is to be aware of Jacob's grief and know its remedy; to know the vibration of meeting Joseph and the smell of his shirt . . . Sema is to attain that place where even an angel cannot go'

nature.

It is not enough that a few enlightened individuals should come to see (or rather, to grok, to *really* see) what our environmental policies should be. Such a metaparadigm shift must be virtually universal if it is to be effective. We know (with a small 'k') that we shall have to reduce our oil consumption, for example. But without strict rationing or exorbitant price increases few people will spontaneously cut their petrol consumption while they still derive a strong sense of identity from driving a car—and from driving faster, thirstier cars at that. The necessary changes have not only to be accepted by most of the people, but positively desired. Otherwise, if the demands of the people are not in accord with the decrees of the pundits, it will become difficult to implement the changes without either some form of 'friendly fascism' or benevolent dictatorship.

A holistic, and thereby ecological, ethic needs to be structured within us all. But not, let me repeat, merely on the level of a rational/intellectual understanding but at the centre of our consciousness. We need to possess it organically, at the very heart of our being, rather than just cerebrally as part of our reasoning.

RESTRUCTURING MENTAL ACTIVITY

How then does one go about producing such an inner change? If a mere intellectual understanding is not sufficient, and if the fallacious 'I versus It' metaparadigm is structured into our awareness shortly after birth, what chance is there of ever developing an alternative model?

Any paradigm retains its status through its continued ability to solve problems in its given field. It is only when new facts are encountered which cannot be fitted in to the existing model that a paradigm shift occurs. It is the same with the mental metaparadigm. Nearly all the phenomena encountered in everyday experience can be satisfactorily accounted for on the hypothesis that 'I' in here am separate from the world out there. Most of our cultural traditions strongly support this assumption and we rarely have cause to doubt its validity.

It is only when new experiences that cannot be fitted in to the old model are encountered that the old model cracks.

There is one obvious experience that rocks the 'I versus It' metaparadigm and that is the direct personal experience of oneness with the whole of Nature. It is precisely this experience that mystical and religious traditions have been on about for so long. They all aim to give one a direct experience of the essential unity of creation. But in most cases only a few of the most diligent aspirants ever gained such an experience. Today, however, we are witnessing a resurgence of interest in spiritual techniques of one kind or another. In the past dogma and ritual have dominated the 'established' religions but now much more emphasis is being laid on the practices themselves, the actual psychological techniques of changing consciousness and experiencing that transcendental unity. Consequently there is now a far greater likelihood of a large number of people partaking of the kind of experiences that will produce a natural shift to the new metaparadigm.

Recent research into how these techniques work suggests that they restructure the way in which the brain functions. The cortex of the brain is divided into two halves. The left half is usually responsible for verbal, analytic thought and is specialised to functioning in a serial mode, dividing up data and analysing it bit by bit. In contrast, the right side functions in a more synthetic mode and specialises in parallel processing, items being considered simultaneously rather than sequentially. Our cultural preference has been for left-hemisphere, analytic thinking: it is now being suggested that the more holistic mode of thinking characteristic of the right side of the brain is equally important in life. Analysing and dissecting a situation is very necessary but on its own it is not enough and needs to be balanced by the complementary thinking-processes of the right hemisphere. It has been found that during 'meditation' there is a progressive synchronisation of the EEG patterns recorded from the two halves of the brain suggesting that some such balancing may well be occurring.

The third benefit of such an inner development is the clarity of thinking which is said to follow. We need to see clearly where we are, where we have to get to, and how best to get there. To do this we obviously have to use our heads effectively. It now appears that even the well-worn suggestion that most of us use only 10% of our full mental potential is probably an over-estimate, and that compared to what is really possible in terms of clarity of thought and breadth of vision most of us are living in a pretty dozy state—a tragic waste of one of our most valuable and plentiful resources. Although you would hardly leave it to a group of semi-anaesthetised and lobotomised people to decide on the future of this planet, this effectively is what we are doing when we try to get the world together without simultaneously getting ourselves together. Clearly a more expanded consciousness will be capable of delving deeper into the intricacies of a situation, appreciating it in a wider context, and seeing its implications further into the future.

SUPPLY OR DEMAND?

The predominant approach to alternative technologies has been focussed on the redirection and redevelopment of technology itself—a change in the *supply* of technology. Here I have tried to take a general look at how changes in individual consciousness might tackle the other side of the problem—the *demands* that we make of technology.

The two approaches are not in opposition: they are complementary. If AT is to fulfil its goals and not be swallowed up by the system which it is

reacting against, it is of paramount importance that as well as political and social changes there should be fundamental changes in the way in which we, as individuals, appreciate and approach the world around us.

Immediately I hear the cry that "social being determines consciousness." True! But that is only half the story, and to take this one-sided perspective to be the whole truth is hardly in the best traditions of dialectical thought. Our images of man and his potentialities, and the way in which we set about actualising these images, are themselves determined by the way we are: →inner→outer→inner   . . . tick-tock-tick-tock . . . It's a chicken and egg story. You do not break the cycle by getting rid of the chicken, because the egg will still hatch; nor by cracking the egg, because the chicken can easily lay another. Both aspects of the problem have to be dealt with simultaneously.

It is then possible that a synthesis of the inner technologies of the East with the outer technologies of the West could give birth to a truly holistic and radical technology for the world—a possibility which was foreseen two and a half thousand years ago in the *Tao-Te Ching*:

When the Tao is present in the Universe
The horses haul manure
When the Tao is absent from the Universe
War horses are bred outside the city.

# of pyramids & razorblades

The centre of the Great Pyramid at Cheops possesses strange and inexplicable properties which would seem to account better for the mummification of the bodies than all that embalming. These properties are not, however, a unique function of its particular shape—a fact which you can easily test by building yourself a scale model.

The proportions of the Great Pyramid are mathematically very interesting. The area of each of the four sides is equal to the square of the pyramid's height. This may not sound particularly fascinating but if you solve the algebraic equation which this relation defines you come up with the Golden Mean which so intrigued Greek philosophers two thousand years later.

If you let the base of the pyramid be two units long then the height of each of the triangular sides is exactly the Golden Mean (1.618 . . . units) and the height of the pyramid itself turns out to be the square root of this (1.273 . . . units). If you are really building another monster and need more accurate proportions, the Golden Mean is $(\sqrt{5}+1)/2$. Having constructed your pyramid you should align it along local magnetic North-South.

Blunt razor blades placed exactly one third the way up the centre of the pyramid and with their edges parallel to the magnetic field will be sharp again in a week. No-one has yet satisfactorily explained how it works, but work it does as thousands of people have verified—a Czechoslovakian even patented the idea (after it had been checked out by the patent office) and made a small fortune out of it. If you don't believe it, try it: if you do believe it still try it—there's a truly amazing difference between idly (or gullibly) believing it and that *Knowing* which comes when you take the blade out and it is unquestioningly sharper than the similar blades you left outside.

You must build it accurately, however, if it is going to work. A friend rang me up to say that it didn't work for him, but when I later went round and saw his model the proportions were out by nearly 10%. So build it accurately, neatly, from stout card (if you're using card) and align it carefully. Also you will get better results from the older blue-steel type of blade rather than the newer super platingum varieties.

Other things you might like to investigate are the mummifying properties—meat will dehydrate in a month and not decay so long as it is kept at the centre point (the record is four and a half thousand years) —plants fed on water and kept in the pyramid are said to grow four times as fast, and typewriter ribbons apparently come out rejuvenated.

People sitting inside pyramids are reported to show increased alpha waves, and I've also heard of a cat who turned into a strict vegetarian after living in a pyramid for six weeks.

Pete Russell

IT'S BEEN SAID BEFORE—AND WHERE DID THAT GET US?

1. This has all been said before, with increasing self-confidence over the past few years. For what are now the standard counter-culture criticisms of Marxism, see M. Bookchin, *Post-Scarcity Anarchism* (Wildwood House, London 1974); T.Roszak, *The Making of a Counter Culture* (Faber, London, 1971 ed.). And for a more sensible approach to fascism, of which the orgone theory isn't an indispensable part, see Wilhelm Reich, *The Mass Psychology of Fascism* (1946; Condor, London, 1972).

2. For a splendid example of Marxist hagiography see *Reminiscences of Marx and Engels* (Foreign Language Publishing House, Moscow, n.d.) especially Introduction, p.11:

> 'In these reminiscences we see Marx and Engels not only as thinkers of genius and outstanding revolutionaries; we see them as human beings, personifications of the most beautiful and noble human qualities: crystal-clear moral purity, modesty, simplicity and truthfulness, unbending moral endurance and unconquerable optimism, the roots of which lay in their profound understanding of the objective laws of historical development and their unshakeable faith in the inevitable dawn of a new era in the history of humanity, the era of communism.'

3. See in particular Pauline Robinson, *The Environmental Crisis: A Communist View* (Socialist Library No.5, C.P., London, n.d.). For a broader approach see A.Schmidt, *The Concept of Nature in Marx* (1962; NLB London 1971), especially Chapter 4.

Apart from references to sewage going to the wrong places if people live in large urban agglomerations rather than spread out over the country (see *The Poverty of Philosophy*, and *Capital*, I, 19) the main source for Marxist environmentalism is Engels: *The Dialectics of Nature*, especially the essay entitled 'The Part played by Labour in the Transition from Ape to Man'. But Engels gets into a bit of a muddle over the tension between seeing man as master of nature and man as part of nature, and the essay breaks off without the contradiction being resolved.

4. For the way this leads to a complete trampling on the peasant and any idea of attachment to the soil, see in particular Engels: *The Condition of the Working Class in England*; and *The Housing Question*. Note also Lenin's conception of the 'martyrdom' of the peasantry—sanctifying them in compensation for sacrificing them. (See the pieces by Lenin in *Reminiscences of Marx and Engels*.) Hence any recognition of the potential for socialism in peasant co-operation is firmly denied.

I want to talk about a radical context for a radical approach to science. At the risk of making generalizations to which there are numerous (but too few) individual exceptions, I'm trying to say the following as briefly as possible:

We find ourselves in a position where many people who feel themselves to be genuinely committed *radicals*—that is, actively conscious of the necessity of *fundamental* social change, of locating and tackling problems at the *roots*—are faced with a very real problem of self-definition, of political identification. A basic commitment to egalitarian principles isn't sufficient to make acceptable the definition of oneself as a Marxist. The likes of me go along to meetings of 'established' Marxist groups (International Marxist Group, Communist Party of Great Britain (Marxist-Leninist), International Socialists—the first mentioned being perhaps the worst offender)—and perceive in their activities, to varying degrees, a bureaucratic formality which is stultifying, repressive—a *parallel* counterpart to the politics of the 'Establishment'. The basic ideas of an authoritarian hierarchy, the elitist role of leaders, remain virtually unchallenged; there's a *correct* line, a *correct* dogma, to be learnt, phrased with a mechanical air, in the *correct* slogans. And for women, there's been the particularly obvious issue of the hard work needed to break down the male chauvinist piggery on the part of Marxist men—behaviour which can't be excused simply by the fact of living under capitalism, since much of it is in economic terms unnecessary and immediately remediable. And you can watch Marxist academics constructing socialist intellectual frameworks while they live and act as competitive, grasping, arrogant, individualists; or watch the IMG at an anti-National Front demo, chanting, fists clenched: "The National Front is a fascist front. *Smash* the National Front." The feeling, for me anyway, is that *their* revolution isn't *the* revolution. For all the common ground, the apparently common goals, there are whole areas of revolutionary concern which are neglected, and further than that, negated, by the strategic priorities of the 'straight' left.[1]

One way out of this is to suggest that it's only *institutionalized* Marxism that's at fault, and if we go back to Marx (and Engels and Lenin) we'll be put on the right tracks again. But criticisms can be levelled at such tendencies towards sanctification of texts and individuals,[2] and at the interpretative academic nit-picking which this can lead to. Nor does this approach help us to confront the problem caused by the *internalisation* of precisely those values which uphold a growth-centred, consumption-centred, 'unliberated', ecologically irresponsible social organization. For the exclusion of a radical self-questioning from Marxist revolutionary priorities, and the complacency and blindness which this involves, a large portion of the blame has to be laid fairly and squarely on the shoulders of Marx himself.

And of fundamental importance to the theme I'm concentrating on here—a radical context for a radical approach to science—Marx, Engels and Lenin don't help us sufficiently to incorporate into a socialist framework what now appear as necessary criticisms of the role of science and technology. Of course it's possible to pick over the texts and find references which demonstrate, for example, a consciousness of the possible consequences of the unrestrained exploitation of nature:[3] approaching nature solely from the viewpoint of economic utility, it made sense to give at least a little consideration to this. But against the occasional reference to such problems we have to set an overwhelming faith in technology, in man's capacity to control nature; and most significantly, we have to consider the assertion that the *only* path to socialism is that of jumping on the bandwagon of the process of large-scale industrialization.[4] A very real objection to this is that

MERLIN PRESS

LONDON going out of Town — or — The March of Bricks & Mortar.

such a path leads to *statism,* and not to socialism.[5] And we can ask, too, whether we have *time* to wait for history to take its course. 'Come the revolution', will the world still be worth living in, assuming even that it's still possible to live in it? For those of us who find some of our greatest happiness in fresh air, open space, room to breathe freely—a happiness at least as rational and worthy of respectful consideration as a happiness centred in abundance of material goods—this becomes an issue of real importance.[6]

But, on the other hand, if you're committed to the ideal of a society which holds as fundamental the equal right of each and every person to realize his or her full potential, it becomes impossible to stomach the patchy, piecemeal, unrealistic nature of much of the activity directed against industrial, technological society: the jumping from one concern to another—CND to environmental doom to alternative technologies; communes in the country; growing marrows and making beads; making no connections between one area of concern and another; ignoring many of the most significant overall criticisms which need to be made of our society. Friends of the Earth and Conservation Society in particular, take note: the reality of *class* in this society is a *fundamental* reality. The middle-class eco-freak who refuses to recognise the extent to which he or she has been determined by class, by the privileges, the sense of superior self-confidence which being middle-class bestows, can never do more than scratch at the surface of the problems which face us.

And to those who stubbornly refuse to recognise the need for a broadly speaking political dimension, we can say yes, ideals of harmony with nature, attacks on industrial civilization, *are* politically unattached, separable from particular political positions; but they're *also* ideologically manipulable—and dangerously so.

Striking examples of the way in which ideas of 'harmony with nature' can be manipulated in order to bolster up a reactionary status quo can be found by glancing through nineteenth-century popular works on natural history. J.T. Burgess's *Old English Wild Flowers,* published in 1868, will serve to demonstrate this point. Burgess sees the flowers of the field as 'the most natural emblems of the life and immortality of man'. 'The humblest amongst them plays its part not only in the economy of the universe, but in some degree ministers

Cruikshank's vision of Suburban Development.

5. S.Stojanovic: *Between Ideals and Reality,* (Oxford University Press, New York, 1973).

6. To Marx (or at least the older Marx) such considerations appeared 'childish': See Schmidt, op.cit., pp.131–2.

7. J.T. Burgess: *Old English Wild Flowers* (London, 1868) p.29. See almost any nineteenth-century flower book for the same sort of thing; and also books like Mrs Gatty: *Parables from Nature* (London, n.d.). Great stuff, this, especially the parable called 'Kicking' where the old horse Taffy tells two colts about all the nice things that will happen if they learn to 'obey their masters, and love them a bit too'.

8. Hans Suren, *Man and Sunlight* (Slough [!], 1927. Highly recommended for the title of the most repulsive book ever—and with 127 illustrations too. The Dean of St Paul's

predicted that it would 'do good', so the foreword tells us. For Hitler's use of idealization of the natural, see for example Ernst Nolte, *Three Faces of Fascism* (London, 1965), pp.419–25; Wilhelm Reich, op cit. Ideological forces are just as much at work in academically influential studies of modern ecology. Howard Odum's *Environment, Power, and Society* (Wiley, New York, 1970) is a particularly obvious example, in which the author's views on 'power and society' are dressed up as energy-flow diagrams and made to seem logically necessary. See also Robert M. Young: 'Evolutionary Biology and Ideology: Then and Now', *Science Studies*, I, London 1971.

9. Bookchin, op.cit., p.244.

more or less to the comforts or necessities of life'. 'It will be seen that every flower and every plant has not only an individual existence, but each and every one has its appointed place in the universe, filling some mission . . .'[7]

And further than bolstering up the status quo, the idea of 'harmonization with nature' can be used to back up an extreme right position, as it was with fascism.

Victorious power to all who stand in stern conflict for our being, for our natural heritage, for humanity and sunlight! Truly, what we see and endure around us is no fit heritage for man. Like slaves, they totter under the heavy fetters of drudgery for their daily bread, far from sunlight, far from Nature in the dungeons of the town. Tied by the merciless conventions of a short sighted and pernicious morality, they pursue, groaning, their struggle for existence. It is for you to bring light and healing to those who hunger . . . Fight your way through the darkness of the age! Let sunshine and Nature be your actual experience, and you will realize with wonder that a marvellous power grows in your souls, raising you above the vicissitudes of the day.

Therefore—victorious power to you who will be warriors— fighters for the rights and joys of sunlight! You know that even the sun-lover is not spared earthly trouble, but in truth we followers of nature have power constantly to rise afresh, in patience and the insight of understanding. Such power of sun and soul do we receive from thence, where our home is—and the home of mankind is Nature. Only the pride and presumption of times wildly out of joint can make us forget, and even deny our true being. Yet we questing sun-lovers hasten to find our home again— to return to the bosom of Nature. We all, we who are seekers and lovers of nature, have a sacred duty imposed by our sun-faith—to be torchbearers and bringers of light!

That's from the 1927 translation of the sixty-seventh edition of *Man and Sunlight* by Hans Suren, Chief of the German Army School for Physical Exercise. The idea of 'harmonization with nature' is here made to support an emerging fascist ideology through the idea of the 'natural superiority' of the German race, through the idea that it's a 'law of nature' that the superior should rule over the inferior. In this respect, the idea of nature can be used in much the same way as the idea of God—its laws can be set forth as transcendentally and immutably ordained, and yet the only interpreters of these laws are men. Thus Hitler could use the idea of a natural order of society, a natural life in contact with the soil, to back up a rigid caste system.[8]

Recognizing the fundamental importance of a critical approach to the role of science and technology, and at the same time recognizing the fundamental importance of a commitment to genuinely equal rights and opportunities, we begin to ask how to set about bridging the gap between ideals and reality. One piece of advice we've had is this: 'It is vitally necessary that we return to the generalized terrain that pre-Marxian socialism established, and then go forward again.'[9]

Does this get us anywhere? I'm going to leave aside the ideas and activities of socialists in Europe and America before Marx, and concentrate on radicalism in early nineteenth century Britain, especially the socialism of the Owenites, whose strength and support as a popular movement ebbed and flowed and finally crumbled between the 1820s and 1840s. For anybody who's involved in today's making of an alternative culture (which excludes the large majority of academic historians studying the radical movements), the similarities between what went on then and what goes on now seem almost uncanny. So let's look back to their ideas on the role of science and technology, and the framework in which they placed them; by doing so we can both place our own concerns in a wider time perspective, and hope to learn something from the strengths and weaknesses of past movements.

Of what avail are the revelations of the telescope respecting the myriads of systems of suns and planets, which roll in the dim abyss of space? That if, laying down this instrument, we can take up the microscope, and magnify the minute organisms which people every portion of our own planet; that the nature of beast, bird and fish have been carefully studied and noted down; or that we can describe with accuracy the structure of every individual of the vegetable world, "from the cedar that grows on Lebanon, to the hyssop that springs on the wall"; what matters it that we have penetrated the caves of ocean, ascended the mountains, and wrung from the bosom of the rock strange tidings of the events and inhabitants of this earth before human eye looked on its varied surface, or human foot and voice awakened the echoes of its forests: what is the value of all these stupendous achievements, if, in the midst of them all, the being who masters them, is less amply supplied with the requisites for the preservation of existence, and the enjoyment of pleasurable sensations, than the meanest and minutest insect that sports its ephemeral life in a drop of water or an inch of moss? Vain, too, is our boasting respecting the mighty automation powers which science has brought to the aid of man, if these have only increased his toils and sufferings. If these modern giants with iron sinews, and into whose nostrils steam has breathed vitality, have only produced luxury and its consequent diseases and follies on one hand, and destitution with its sufferings, its recklessness, and debasement on the other. Alas! that such has been, and is now the result of our discoveries, is no hypothesis, and needs not to be prefaced with an "IF". Strange anomaly! Science and ignorance, wealth and poverty, are co-existent!

Perhaps the style's unfamiliar, but not the message. That was part of an address given by the Owenite George Fleming, and it was titled 'The Right Application of Science'.[10] It was delivered to an audience of Owenite socialists, mostly self-educated working men, at the opening of their Hall of Science in Huddersfield in 1839. The Huddersfield Hall of Science, and a few others like it dotted over the country, were products of a radical culture which had emerged in England by the 1830s—a culture that created, among other things, a co-operative movement aimed at establishing communities on the land through the profits of trading stores; a massive and militant illegal underground press; and Chartism. It was a culture which maintained its strength through local grass-roots organizations, providing its own educational institutions, its own entertainments, its own welfare measures, and raising social and political consciousness through debates, mutual instruction societies, and mass meetings. Owenite socialism was just one element in a widespread impulse to create some kind of alternative to 'artificial', 'irrational', capitalist industrialism.[11]

The Owenites were especially concerned about the role of science and technology in society. Science wasn't rejected, but acclaimed as the great improver of mankind. This verse by Allen Davenport—a radical shoemaker whose great dream was to get back to the land, and whose great virtue was that 'because not able to do much, he did not—as the many do—sit down and do nothing'—gives an idea of how Owenite radicals generally regarded science.

Hail, glorious Science! for thou can'st impart a charm to humanise the savage heart; If not for thee, this beauteous earth had been, a wilderness,—a den of savage men; Without a language, and without a mind—With bodies naked, lashed by every wind. Had not fair Science worked out Nature's plan, the brute had held dominion over man.[12]

10. G.A. Fleming: *The Right Application of Science* (J. Hobson, Leeds, 1839) p.11.

11. See E.P. Thompson: *The Making of the English Working Class* (Penguin, Harmondsworth, 1968); Pat Hollis, *The Pauper Press* (Oxford University Press, London, 1970). For a basic book on Owenism with a comprehensive bibliography see J.F.C. Harrison, *Robert Owen and the Owenites in Britain and America* (Routledge & Kegan Paul, London, 1969).

12. Allen Davenport: *The Origin of Man and the Progress of Society* (London, 1846).

(*Upper*) *Owenite handbill. Owen thought that a weapon powerful enough to destroy the world would act as the ultimate deterrent — once invented, people would see sense and war would end. It's unlikely that he imagined the level of destruction which people would come to take for granted; nor the level of devastation which a ruling class could afford to inflict without losing its vested interest in holding on to power. (Lower) Owenite hymn. The Owenites purposefully established direct parallels to confront the dominant social culture — they had their own religion (rational religion), their own churches (Halls of Science), social hymn books, their own (rational) wedding ceremonies etc.*

OTHER PERSPECTIVES

MANCHESTER UNIVERSITY PRESS

13. Sampson Arnold Mackey: *The Age of Mental Emancipation* (1836) and other works, in *Mackey's Astronomy & C* (collected pamphlets, Norwich, c.1830–9). Like many of the other nineteenth-century writings mentioned here, this is probably impossible to find outside the British Museum.

14. For further details see Eileen Yeo: *Robert Owen and Radical Culture*, in S.Pollard and J.Salt (Eds.) *Robert Owen, Prophet of the Poor* (Macmillan, London, 1971).

15. See J.F.C. Harrison; op.cit.; Robert Owen: *A New View of Society* (Penguin, Harmondsworth, 1969) for accessible introductions to Owen's thinking.

(Upper) Harmony Hall, Hampshire, before it was burned down in 1902. The architect was Joseph Hansom, of Hansom cab fame. There was a striking contrast between the lavishness of the building, and the poverty-stricken frugality of its working-class inhabitants. Owen and his wealthy friends fared better, which was a bone of contention. In its final year the working-class members began to challenge the paternalistic regime of Harmony Hall and moved towards establishing a workers' demoncracy. But by then the financial situation had deteriorated beyond salvation. (Centre) New Harmony, Indiana (1825-8). This Owenite community was fragmented by dissension and separatism from the start. See A. Bestor: Backwoods Utopias (Philadelphia 1950); G. B. Lockwood: The New Harmony Movement (1905; Dover, NY, 1971); J. H. Noyes: Strange Cults and Utopias of C19 America (1870; Dover, NY, 1966). (Lower) 'A dream of tranquillity' – illustration from John Minter Morgan: Hamden in the Nineteenth Century (1834). A constant theme of the C19 community-builders was the perfect synthesis of industry and pastoral bliss.

One aspect of this kind of enthusiasm was a great faith in the virtues of Baconian inductive philosophy. Science meant facts, order, consistency, ('whatever is doubtful or incapable of demonstration, it is not science')—and as such it was the natural enemy of superstitious religion, of the grip of priestly dogma on an oppressed population. But science wasn't seen as the exclusive province of the expert. A sacrosanct body of initiates into scientific rites would have appeared as dangerous and despicable as their clerical equivalents. Through places like the Halls of Science, the light of truth would be 'constantly sought; and, whenever found, freely shed abroad to all men'. Another impoverished shoe-maker, called Sampson Arnold Mackey, saved up for years in order to publish pamphlets in which, under such titles as 'The Age of Mental Emancipation', he attacked the theories of Christian so-called scientists, who were concerned, for example, to demonstrate that the world could have been created in the 12,000 years allowed for it by the Bible. Mackay's aim was *"to instruct those who are in search of knowledge. And as the country is infested with books calculated to prevent the induction of knowledge, by rendering it very abstruse, I shall clear away the obstructive rubbish, and leave the road open."* (He didn't have an easy time of it—on one occasion, when he heckled a speaker at the Norwich Philosophical Society, who was reading a typical Christian essay on the chronology of the world, he and a supporter were compared by the speaker to the two Jews who stoned Christ!)[13]

So science was the great demystifier. It was also good fun. This kind of report of Owenite branch activities isn't unique:

> On Friday last—the Good Friday of the Christian world—we had an excellent social tea party, about 280 persons were present . . . The philosophical experiments, under the management of Mr Thorne, were of a superior description. Amongst some of the experiments, were oxy-hydrogen and Bude lights, and the last new invention of Mr Gurney for lighthouses; decomposition of various chemical compounds, as sugar, potass, etc.; and with a good electrical machine we were enabled to electrify nearly all present at the same time. Besides other experiments, a model of a Montgolfier balloon ascended in the hall twice during the evening, and at the close was committed *ad nubes.* The nitrous oxide, or laughing gas, exerted its full powers on this occasion, delighting all by its singular effects. Between the leading experiments the lively dance was indulged in, thus at once blending the acme of mental and physical enjoyments.[14]

In *The Making of a Counter Culture* (p.264), Theodore Roszak argues that 'the reality which scientific knowledge examines cannot be translated into either art or ritual which the community can participate in experiencing. The research of experts can be popularized or vulgarized as a body of information—and inevitably distorted in the process. It cannot be democratized as a form of vital experience.' The popularity of Owenite festivals like the one described above goes against this, and I think demonstrates the kind of activities that are essential if science is ever to be genuinely for people.

This was one side of the general notion that the right application of science was its application to the happiness of everybody. The same belief led the Owenites in other directions too: first and foremost, scientific methods of enquiry were seen as providing the only means to a true understanding of the nature of man and of society. The aim of this was not just to *collect* a mass of sociological and psychological data, but to establish the principles upon which individuals and society could be *regenerated.* The basis for such principles were Owen's 'fundamental facts', which he regarded as the immutable laws of human nature, and the basic precept of which was that "The character of man is formed *for* and not *by* himself."[15]

"The character of man is formed *for* and not *by* himself"—this was *the* truth upon which the Owenites built their revolutionary science of human nature and society. The Owenites were confronting a social structure which depended for its moral justification on Christian notions of free will and original sin—themselves conflicting views of human nature, but views which, taken together, were most convenient for those who had a vested interest in the continued existence of a social order based on exploitation. Whether people were seen as 'sinful' because Adam and Eve had fallen from God's grace, or 'sinful' because they had freely chosen to be so, these Christian doctrines justified a pessimistic, reactionary view of human potential. "Human nature being what it is" (bad), the social structure being in no way held to blame for this, the field's open for the capitalist to cash in on it. It's a free choice on the part of the individual whether he (the theory would be still more transparently ridiculous if the vocabulary wasn't male-dominated) rises up to become a 'respectable' exploiter, or remains one of the 'feckless', 'thriftless' exploited.

Against this prevailing view of human nature, the Owenite stance emphasised heredity and, most especially, the effects of environment on character. Seeing human nature not as something independent of the social order, not as something for which the individual could be *blamed,* but in large part as the product of society, they recognised that human nature could be changed by changing the social order. Taking this as fundamental, the Owenites could have fallen into the crudest extremes of determinism, which would have forced them to believe that it was impossible to change those who had been born into the old immoral world—the educator must be educated. But on the whole the Owenites avoided crude extremes, realizing at least to some extent that an awareness of how one is determined can itself become a determining factor.

Like other utopians (and particularly like the Perfectionists, whose community at Oneida lasted for over thirty years, and, in a much modified form, still exists today), the Owenites believed that conscious self-improvement and communal living must go hand in hand if ideals were to be translated into reality. Phrenology, which was popular among the Owenites, wasn't so ridiculous as it's usually made out to be—the phrenological motto was 'man, know thyself', and the basic notion that this was the first step to self-improvement makes sense, even if analyzing the lumps and bumps on one's head might not be the best way of doing it. (Nor of course was their motto best expressed in a male-dominated vocabulary—for which apologies on behalf of the Owenites throughout. I'm sure they wouldn't do it now.) To the same end of self-improvement, some Owenites introduced the habit of systematic observation and reporting on the behaviour of their fellow socialists. At an Owenite community in Spa Fields, families who joined were instructed that 'each member should appoint from among the congregated members his own friendly monitor', who would give notice of his errors of conduct and temper. At Harmony Hall in Hampshire (1839-45), the longest-lasting of the short-lived Owenite communities, there was a similar emphasis on honest observation. Regular Saturday night group meetings were held, and it was reported that 'We are beginning to feel and acknowledge the purity of each other's motives, as we know and are known, and we can now bear to hear the truth spoken of us without generating that spirit of antagonism which once existed under such circumstances.'[16]

And, crucially, the Owenites realised that physical science could not be rightly used unless it was combined with a *science of society*. In Halls of Science, the sciences of morals and society were to assume 'that precedence in the list of human wants, and that claim on human attention which their intrinsic importance warrants, but which is rarely accorded them in other institutions, professedly scientific'.[17] (This was an attack on Mechanics' Institutes, and their refusal to move outside a 'safe' syllabus, a syllabus from which all subjects which could challenge the bases of a capitalist society were rigorously excluded. The Society for the Diffusion of Useful Knowledge, which was closely allied with the Mechanics' Institutes, was being challenged at the same time by

16. Robert McCutcheon: *Queenwood* (unpublished MA thesis, Sussex University, 1972). For the most readily available accounts of Owenite community activities like this, see R.G. Garnett: *Co-operation and the Owenite socialist communities in Britain 1825—45* (Manchester University Press, Manchester, 1972). Frank Podmore, *Robert Owen* (2 vols London, 1906) contains many details.

17. G.A. Fleming, op.cit., pp.11—12.

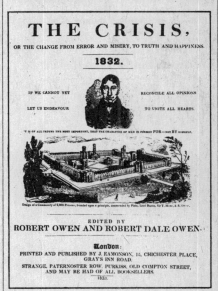

(*Upper*) *The National Equitable Labour Exchange, Gray's Inn Road, London. The magnificent premises initially rented for this venture were typical of Owen. The goal was, through direct exchange, to give workers the full fruits of their labour. Workers exchanged their products for labour notes (Centre), intended to give a fair valuation for raw materials and labour used. These were in turn exchanged for other goods. But within three years the project collapsed — people took advantage of the exchange to dump their unsaleable goods; 'labour value' couldn't be satisfactorily detached from current market values, which meant unequal returns for labour continued; and no satisfactory system for valuing goods was ever worked out.*
(*Lower*) *Title page of the Owenite* Crisis. (*1832-4*) *This newspaper, and the* New Moral World, (*1834-6*) *were the major organs of Owenite socialism.*

18. For a detailed and good account of what the Owenites meant by a 'science of society', by far the best thing to read is Eileen Yeo, *Social Science and Social Change: A social history of some aspects of social science and social investigation in Britain, 1830—90* (sadly an unpublished Ph.D., Sussex University, 1972—hopefully forthcoming as a book).

19. *The Man. A Rational Advocate* no.8, August 25th, 1833, p.58.

20. William Thompson: *Practical Directions for the speedy and economical establishment of communities, on the principles of mutual co-operation, united possessions and equality of exertions and of the means of enjoyments.* (London, 1830), p.5.

'Rational desires will soon under such arrangements, where the trouble of production is an efficient check to waste of consumption, supplant artificial desires or those of antipathy, valued for the mere contrast which they afford to the wretchedness or comparative destitution of others, or pursued by the idle and ignorant for the mere purpose of inducing temporary excitement as a refuge from habitual languor of mind or body or both.'

21. *Bronterre's National Reformer*, no.1 (January 7th 1837) p.1.

such radical organizations as The Society for Diffusing *Really* Useful Knowledge.) The Owenite science of society demonstrated that order and harmony could only exist within the framework of communitarian socialism—within capitalist society, competition, division and coexistence of irreconcilable interests made it absurd to hope that concord and unity, order and precision, could ever be achieved.[18]

And within capitalist society it seemed, too, that it was inevitable that machinery, with the widespread unemployment and devaluation of labour that it caused, should be the working man's curse. Within the framework of communitarian socialism, on the other hand, it could become man's blessing. Some Owenites, including Robert Owen himself, got carried away by fantasies about the kind of life that would be ushered in by the right application of technology within a communistic society: Owen's lavish plans for Harmony Hall included towers from which 'would be reflected at night, by powerful apparatus, the new koniophostic light, which would brilliantly illuminate its whole square.' But in general it was with technology as a means to increased leisure, as opposed to unnecessary luxury, that the Owenites were concerned. 'A rational being can only require a sufficiency of food, clothing, and lodging; to desire more than a sufficiency would be both unjust and unnatural', as one of them put it.[19] William Thompson, the best of the Owenite theorists, argued along these lines in his "Practical Directions for Establishing Communities", which was published in 1830—consumption for the mere purpose of ostentation would be out of the question in a community.[20]

In the Owenite communities, the emphasis was on simple mechanical devices to eliminate unnecessary drudgery. At the Irish community in Ralahine, County Clare, a potato-washing machine was invented, while at Harmony Hall food was carried from the kitchen to the dining room by a miniature railway.

The Owenite rejection of 'consumerism' was linked to a wide spread assertion that the right kind of life was 'more or less of a country life'. Partly this was a matter of a simple pleasure in nature; but it was also argued that a *rational* man would live in harmony with nature; if civilization continued to deviate from this path, if man persevered with his attempts to construct for himself an artificial society, the final result, many felt, would inevitably be disease, decay, and destruction. So behind Owenite attempts at community building, Chartist efforts to establish villages of peasant proprietors, and a host of lesser-known schemes, lay the ideal of a life based on the land, as the healthiest and best existence for man. As Bronterre O'Brien, one of the foremost English radicals of the mid-nineteenth century said: 'Of all human occupations, agriculture is not only the most essential to Man's existence, but also the most conducive to his health, his innocence, and his happiness . . . let us exchange as little as possible the healthful and harmonizing pursuits of the field for the withering and demoralizing occupations of the factory.'[21] For the Owenites, this didn't involve turning one's back on science and civilization, but creating a *synthesis*—"the fullness of triumph of Nature and Art". And yet at the same time they could still firmly believe, for example, that the best way of farming the land was simply by means of the spade. (Although on one occasion an Owenite did suggest that the spades should be mechanical self-acting ones!) Spade husbandry was regarded as the truly scientific method of cultivation: experiment had demonstrated to the satisfaction of the Owenites and many others that the land could produce perhaps four times as much food through labour-intensive farming with the spade than through large-scale farming with the plough. Estimates of the number of people who could be fed on the soil of Britain ranged from about seventy million to as high as 300 million; and it was generally held by the Owenites that no more than three hours work on the land a day would be sufficient to provide for all rational desires. William Thompson, who produced detailed instructions for crop rotation and farming methods in his 'Practical Directions', suggested in addition that it was highly wasteful to use the land for meat production, or for crops to be employed in the making of alcoholic drinks.[22]

Thompson was in fact generally concerned with the prevention of needless waste of resources—his communities would be heated by means of the waste heat produced by the condensed steam from steam engines, and the refuse and waste from the community would be 'always directed by suitable pipes or covered drains for the agricultural purpose of manuring the soil, directly, or by being pumped over composts'. And his cautious wisdom extended still further than this—although here he was exceptional. Most of the early socialists rejected completely the Malthusian arguments of the dangers of population growth (a rejection that is of course hardly surprising where poverty coexists with great wealth and extravagance)—for them it was a bridge that need not be crossed until it was come to.[23]

But William Thompson saw the problem in another light: 'The power of peopling the whole of the globe in a comparatively few years with the human race, we have at command. Let us pass over these few years and fairly meet the difficulties of overpopulation, instead of shrinking from the consideration of them until the dreaded day of evil comes'. He allowed that the problems *might* be solved by improvements in chemistry or mechanics, but not that they certainly would: 'With this admission, we are not an atom more justified in hazarding the risk of human happiness on mere possibilities which may or may not be realized; *because we will not in the mean time increase human happiness by incurring any such risk*'.[24]

It would be possible to continue demonstrating parallels between present-day activities and ideas and those of the Owenites and their contemporary radicals almost endlessly—and as a final 'curiosity value' example, I'll give a plug to one John Etzler, an American. Etzler's motto was: "The wise man examines before he judges. The fool judges before he examines." His major work was entitled "The Paradise within the reach of all men, without labour, by power of nature and machinery. An address to all enlightened men." What Etzler was setting out to show was 'that there are powers in nature sufficient to effect in one year more than hitherto all men on earth could do in many thousands of years; and that these powers may be applied to do all human labour.' And the powers which Etzler was principally concerned to harness were those of the wind, the tide, and the sun.[25]

Does the Owenite experience really have anything to teach us? I think the answer's yes: we can learn from both the strengths and weaknesses of Owenite socialism. Having shown that the Owenites were deeply involved in a radical questioning of the role of science and technology, we can look more broadly at Owenism and establish what it was about their way of thinking that led them to regard these issues as of crucial importance in the development of a socialist life-philosophy.

In the first place, it's useful to consider the contribution of the Owenites to the evolution of a socialist vocabulary. It was the Owenites who coined the word 'socialist', and who developed the term 'social science'.[26] What's important about this is the *purity* of the words as they used them, before they were subjected to later distortions. Thus the word 'socialist' didn't have the connotations of state control and party politics which it's burdened with today—the Owenite idea of socialism was closely connected with their ideal of community, and had strong personal, moral, as well as economic implications. Hence the popularity among Owenites of such slogans as "**SELF LOVE AND SOCIAL ARE THE SAME!**"; their dedication to living as far as possible a life in accordance with socialist ideals; and their emphasis on means which were in harmony with their ultimate goals. And similarly, it's worth emphasizing that when early nineteenth-century radicals called themselves radicals, they really meant it—they were applying the label to themselves consciously, constantly asserting the literal definition of the word, tackling problems at the *root*. And the problem of the debasement of key revolutionary words and concepts, the consequent problems of definition, can best be overcome by returning to such an

22. Thompson: op.cit., p.101.

'Every person that consumes a pound of animal food per day, or who uses a quantity of intoxicating liquor made from vegetables equal in value to two pounds of wheat during the same period, keeps out of life, or from an existence which might be rendered happier than his own, another human being, besides predisposing his own frame to various inflammatory diseases, lessening its capacity for various enjoyments, and shortening its duration.'

23. Henry MacCormac: *On the Best Means of Improving the Moral and Physical Condition of the Working Classes* (London, 1830).

'To be sure in the year eighteen thousand and thirty, when the earth is crammed with human beings, the ocean with junks, and men grope in diving-bells over the beds of the sea for submarine food, or chase the birds in their native elements, some new Malthus of the then Church of England, may usefully employ his time and talents in devising means to check the prolific tendency of mankind, but not till then.'

24. Thompson: op.cit., p.231.

25. J.A. Etzler: *The Paradise within the Reach of all Men . . .* (London, 1836; first published Pittsburgh, 1833). Etzler produced a follow-up to this, *The New World, or Mechanical System* (Philadelphia, 1844), with detailed plans of his machinery. He also wrote *Emigration to the tropical world, for the melioration of all classes of all people of all nations* (Ham Common Concordium, 1844, price 6d), in which he calculates that the tropics alone could feed 1280 thousand million people, and that all could be comfortable there in huts which can be built in a day.

26. See A. Bestor: 'The Evolution of the Socialist Vocabulary', *Journal of the History of Ideas*, IX (June 1948); and Eileen Yeo, op.cit.

27. Again, for a detailed and serious account of Owenite theory, all that can be done is to wait for Eileen Yeo's Ph.D. thesis to be published.

28. William Thompson: *Labour Rewarded* (London, 1827). This is a classic, at the same time short and easy to read, and somebody should reprint it fast.

29. Robert Owen: *The Revolution in the mind and practice of the Human Race; or, the coming change from irrationality to rationality.* (London, 1849).

30. For women's liberation, the best (but far from the only) Owenite writing was again by William Thompson: *Appeal of one half of the human race, women, against the pretensions of the other half, men, to retain them in political, and thence in civil and domestic slavery* (London, 1825). Thompson knew that a woman should have written this book, and he only did so himself because his friend Mrs Wheeler didn't get it together.

And for animals—again William Thompson realized the problem of defining the boundaries between 'superior' and 'inferior' forms of life. After all, women were habitually regarded as inferior. (A remarkable number of Owenites were also vegetarians, for both humane and utilitarian reasons.)

assertion of the literal meaning of these concepts.

And, connected with this, the Owenites made tremendous advances in developing and popularizing the necessary vocabulary for an analysis of society—although they rejected the notion of revolution through class *struggle,* this wasn't due to a lack of class *consciousness.* The Owenites fully recognised that machinery and a capitalist mode of social relations were the new and defining features of the age they lived in.[27] But transcending class was a still broader conception of human consciousness, and the potential for social regeneration which this offered. If only people would see how irrational they were and start thinking *rationally*—in other words, if fundamental to every consideration was the cause of justice, the greatest happiness of the greatest number—the Owenites believed that there would be no need for violent revolution. Thus William Thompson took this quotation as the motto on which to base his work, *Labour Rewarded:* 'As the labourers acquire knowledge, the foundations of the social edifice will be dug up from the deep beds into which they were laid in times past; they will be curiously handled and closely examined, and they will not be restored unless they were originally laid in justice, and unless justice commands their preservation.'[28] Thompson's method might be called 'qualitative cost-benefit analysis'—rather than trying to weigh up qualitative considerations quantitatively, in money terms, he weighed up quantitative considerations qualitatively. And in the same way, although not so effectively, Owen could use his faith in the doctrine of circumstances as a yardstick by which to evaluate attitudes. He repeatedly emphasized that the view of man as a creature of circumstances "is the root from which emanate all true and valuable ideas respecting humanity—the *one idea,* with which, to be true, all other ideas must be consistent."[29] And again, there was the belief that once the rationality of this position was recognized, a peaceful regeneration of society would automatically take place.

This overwhelming faith in the powers of reason has been classed as the 'illusion of the epoch'—but it did have its advantages. It was *because* the Owenites were attempting to weigh everything against the standards of humanitarian rationality that their concerns were so all-embracing. Not only did they question the values of a social system based on material greed; they were also, among other things, pioneers of enlightened education methods, advocates of women's rights, and even, in the case of William Thompson, of the rights of animal life.[30]

Owenite socialism was popular amongst that section of the working class which was self-educated—and self-education has, I think, got a lot to do with its appeal. Without the deadening effect of a state education system designed to suppress any tendency towards fundamental questioning, a substantial number of working people possessed a tremendous appetite for discovery, and an untrammelled, free-ranging way of looking at the world. Owenite socialism, and generally, the radicalism of the early nineteenth century, had about it a vitality, a contagious hopefulness, and a deep sense of the rightness of the cause. Radicals in general had an enthusiasm, a revolutionary commitment 'from the heart'. There was an evangelical spirit about it, and especially among the Owenites, with their social missionaries and their vast propaganda efforts.

These qualities are all worth recapturing—especially the lack of inhibition in standing up for what you believe in—and the Owenites did this without diminishing their capacity for enjoyment, without lapsing into grim, dour, puritanical forms of struggle. Their aim, after all, was happiness. But we have to come to terms with the fact that in the end the Owenites failed. They had hoped that such would be the attraction of their 'new moral world' that the old immoral world would wither away. But instead, the 'old immoral world' extended its sphere of operations—into bureaucratic democracy, into education, into social services, into leisure. The Owenite vision faded. Where did they go wrong?

Perhaps the most comforting explanations of failure lie in saying

that 'the time wasn't ripe'. Historical conditions didn't produce *enough* Owenites, and by the 1850s capitalism no longer seemed as insecure as it had a few years before; hence the Owenite attack lost some of its rationale. Perhaps we could go on to say that given the nature of the crisis which faces us now, there *won't* be the same kind of increase of faith in the security of unrestrained capitalist (or statist) industrialism as there was in the mid-nineteenth century. (Although it might prove foolish to depend on that.) Perhaps we could also suggest that socialists of the Owenite-William Morris tradition weren't in a position to confront the vices as well as the virtues which were to accompany the growth of state provision of education, social services etc., the numbing and delusive sense of the people's welfare being provided for. But if the appeal of socialism of the Owenite variety faded as capitalism developed a more acceptable face, it has to be admitted that these socialists can't have managed to communicate their ideas convincingly enough.

And here there's a sense in which the strengths of Owenism were also its weaknesses. Their enthusiasm reached millennial proportions, particularly over the establishment of Harmony Hall in 1839. This community was to be the beginning of the new moral world—the foundation stone of their palacial residence, laid in 1841, bore the initials 'C.M.'—Commencement of the Millennium. But discord reigned at Harmony Hall, particularly due to an excessive optimism over the ease with which the land could be made productive by urban dwellers unfamiliar with agricultural techniques, and partly due to tensions between Robert Owen's vision of community and that of working-class Owenites. It was Owen who determined that funds should be expended lavishly on the building of Harmony Hall, and Owen who insisted on a paternalistic form of government there, convinced as he was that only he and his closest (also middle-class) disciples had grasped the principles of socialism with sufficient fullness to establish what should be done. But at the same time it has to be said that Owen's followers were prepared to accept his leadership uncritically for far too long before they

(Upper) Life on St Kilda: 'outpost of nowhere'. Romantic travellers in the eighteenth century described this community as a utopia, untouched by the corrupting influence of civilisation. Life certainly couldn't have been much closer to nature. (Puffin porridge for breakfast etc.) Decisions were taken from day to day by the 'St Kilda Parliament'. This was a men only affair, although the women's roles were far from conventionally feminine. It was they for instance who did all the heavy carrying, in order for the men to maintain the physical agility essential for their bird-catching activities. See: Tom Steel: The Life and Death of St Kilda (National Trust for Scotland, 1965); D. Maclean: Island on the Edge of the World: Utopian St Kilda and it Passing (Tom Stacey, London 1972). (Lower) Pig for victory: wasteland farming in wartime London. It's interesting that in the nineteenth century, arguments were waged amongst the ruling class over the merits and demerits of workers having access to plots of land. Some felt that this would lead to a dangerous degree of independence (and indeed allotments have sometimes been a valuable fall-back during lengthy strikes); others saw them as a convenient alternative to providing adequate welfare provisions to meet times of crisis.

31. H. Michels: *Political Parties* (1915; Dover reprint, New York, 1957) p.148. Quoted in Maris Kirkham—see below.

32. M.J. Kirkham: *Industrial Producer Co-operation in Great Britain. Three case studies.* (Sheffield MA thesis, unpublished, 1973) synopsis. For the tension between deference and self-assertion on a mass individual level, see W. Reich: *The Mass Psychology of Fascism* yet once more. And his other writings, especially *What is Class Consciousness?*

began to assert themselves. There was always a tension in the minds of working-class Owenites, and most radicals of the period, between their desire for hero figures to put all their faith in and their confidence in their capacity to control their own lives.

Such contradictions have tremendous significance. Generally, in the history of attempts to establish communities and co-operatives, we're faced with the workings of 'Michels's iron law of oligarchy':

> The history of co-operation shows that all the societies have been faced with the following dilemma: either they succumb rapidly owing to discord and powerlessness resulting from the fact that too many individuals have the right to interfere in the administration; or else they end by submitting to the will of one or a few persons, and thus lose their truly co-operative character.[31]

But perhaps a constant awareness of this itself provides some way forward:

> Success in resisting these tendencies seems to have followed the extent to which members of the potential oligarchy were aware of the undemocratic potential of their own position and consciously sought to prevent it by conveying knowledge of the tendency, as well as of the running of the firm, to the rest of the workers.[32]

As far as the Owenites were concerned, when Harmony Hall collapsed in 1845, their hopes crumbled with it. A hard core continued to dedicate their lives to the furtherance of their social ideals, placing their energies in diverse channels; but no longer did they hope that the example of community could be the sole means by which the inhabitants of the 'old immoral world' would be attracted to building a new moral one. Possibly they gave up too easily, and certainly they were foolish to put all their eggs into one very unsatisfactory basket, as they did with Harmony Hall.

It's hard not to be disillusioned by the fortunes of the Owenites, especially when they're seen in connection with the failure of countless other attempts to translate similar ideals into reality. But still, if we're going to build a *genuinely* liberating socialism, work towards a society where all have the capacity to make full use of their potential, to make their own history, we can't simply dismiss the Owenite vision, or Owenite strategies, as utopian, irrelevant to the *real* struggle. A recognition that a revolutionary consciousness must embrace all areas of life inevitably involves a recognition that means must be as broadly based as ends. A revolution in the ownership of the means of production simply isn't enough. And because many people now find the limitations of 'conventional' socialist priorities unacceptable, it's not surprising that ideas of community, alternative culture, alternative values, should once more become of fundamental importance in revolutionary strategy.

Owenism provided the basis for an all-embracing life-philosophy, a socialism which has far more in common with the vision of the great anarchist philosophers than with that of the Marxists. It's a socialism which can offer much inspiration, and at least some grounds for optimism in the fact that the vision didn't appeal exclusively to middle-class intellectuals. From the practical failures of the Owenites, we can come to develop a greater awareness of the limitations and likely pitfalls of our own strategies. We all have to make a choice to channel our energies into whatever activity provides the most effective and fulfilling expression of our particular abilities; and perhaps the most that can be hoped at present is that connections can be made between diverse types of struggle, that all should develop a critical appreciation of the efforts of others who are trying to bridge the gap between ideals and reality. Nobody can pretend to have found *the* path to *the* revolution.

Jos Kingston

TANZANIAN
MINISTRY OF INFORMATION

ESCAPE ROUTE FOR THE POOR

Well-meaning attempts by advocates of 'Development' to export the centralised, capital-intensive technologies of the industrial nations as a foundation for the economies of Third World countries have almost always led to results which are the reverse of the naive intentions of their instigators.

Inequities of wealth and power are increased, not decreased; unemployment rises; traditional economies and social structures are undermined — often fatally.

In this article Jimoh Omo-Fadakah explores some saner ways of helping the poor to help themselves.

Peasants training cattle for use in ploughing. Initially the cattle are trained to pull logs.

Many of the non-industrialized countries are characterized by the same problems—the wealth of a few, the brutish quality of life of the masses (unemployment, under-employment, malnutrition, starvation, illiteracy, diseases and sickness). In a nutshell, poverty. How is this problem to be solved?

A REDEFINITION OF DEVELOPMENT

The cause of poverty in non-industrialized countries is not backwardness but the decay of the rural structure. Most of the development plans drawn up in these countries up till now have altogether bypassed the rural areas—and about 80-90 per cent of the population of these countries live in the rural areas, in villages. It is in the rural areas that one finds oneself in the midst of abject poverty.

The first thing non-industrialized countries have to recognize is that for the foreseeable future the great mass of their populations will be peasants. Only by sustained agricultural productivity can industrial development be possible.

The second thing to recognize is that the problems confronting these countries cannot be solved by industrialization *per se.* Any attempt to superimpose a highly developed industrial system upon a society highly unstable economically and socially will only worsen the problem of poverty. The type of development needed is one that will produce enough food to feed the whole of the population and that will absorb the labour. In this type of development agriculture should be the key factor, not industry. In effect, this means a pattern of high densities of population, producing their own food, running small workshops and factories when they are not working on the land, and with a limited number of large-scale capital-intensive modern industrial centres.

The third thing to recognize is the lack of capital for development. Non-industrialized countries are caught in a dilemma. On the one hand, they want all that is modern in technology for their development. This is totally understandable. On the other hand, they have limited capital resources and unlimited manpower, largely unskilled, lying idle. The crux of the matter is how to strike a balance between the two and use the resources in the manner that is most profitable to the country. In many of the non-industrialized countries, industry accounts for less than a quarter of the national product and employs less than one-fifth of the workers. Readily available are land and human effort. Emphasis should be placed on the use of *men* not *money.*

STRATEGY FOR CHANGE

◆ *(a) Agriculture—land reform* In order to increase agricultural productivity to meet the needs of an expanding population, a complete restructuring of rural societies through land reform is essential. Land reform could take several forms depending on the conditions. In all countries the family is an economic as well as a social unit. From the point of view of productivity any land reform should aim to give each family a piece of land so that they can invest their labour and whatever funds they have in raising yields and improving their land also.

Large-scale farmers and producers who are primarily concerned with cash crops for export and secondarily with subsistence farming should be replaced by small-scale farmers and producers whose first concern is subsistence farming and whose second is with cash crops. According to Barbara Ward and Rene Dubos,

"the small farmer working with his own labour on a family holding, has been shown in a wide variety of developing countries—India, Brazil, Kenya and Colombia—to produce more per acre than big estates. Some of the highest yields are to be found in countries where acre limitations are strictly enforced. This productivity is secured not by heavy machines which drink gasolene and can easily damage fragile soils, but by hard work with light equipment which is by definition less prone to generate ecological risks. Fertilizers and pesticides are less lavishly used, human and animal wastes are more carefully husbanded. Greater personal care keeps terraces in trim, shade trees planted, gullies forested. And earnings are not spent, as is often the case in semi-feudal economies, on acquiring more land for extensive use, thus pushing up land prices and driving working farmers away from the soil. Nor are they withdrawn altogether from the rural economy, by the development of 'Western' standards of consumption or an over-affection for numbered accounts in Swiss banks" (1)

All land should be publicly owned, that is nationalized, and redistributed to landless peasants. There should be a complete decentralization of agricultural activities. Agricultural practice should be based on labour-intensive rather than capital-intensive, labour-saving farming methods. Overall use of chemical fertilizers and spraying with all-purpose insecticides should be avoided as far as possible. Planting and harvesting could be timed to avoid the times of insect infections.

◆ *(b) Rural industry* This should be represented by agriculture and by widely-diffused small-scale industries which are more-or-less traditional and labour-intensive. Economic activities should be decentralized and statistical and planning machinery placed under local control. In this way rural labour could be mobilized for economic development. This economic decentralization should be aimed at stimulating development from below which would make possible the release of *spontaneous* initiative of the masses.

◆ *(c) Self-reliance* The development of the spirit of self-reliance with emphasis being moved to the rural areas and to the use of *men* not *money* should be adopted. As far as possible these countries should do things themselves, without foreign aid or assistance. In this way they will eventually become virtually independent. Any aid that is accepted should be related to the needs of the recipient countries, and not to the needs of the donor countries.

At any rate a good many undesirable things come into a country on the back of aid. Often aid creates a psychological dependence on getting still more aid. It saps initiative and enterprise; again, it may foster—as it has in so many non-industrialized countries—a type of development wholly inappropriate to circumstances. Industrial plants are created, instead of basic water supplies being improved. Aspirations are created that can never be fulfilled. The Western or Eastern "expert" wants to bring his whole cultural baggage with him and this can include myths about what happens and what is possible in his own country.

Moreover no one in a position of power and prosperity can offer such aid as would threaten his own security. In a lot of ways aid has become a means of impoverishing and exploiting the non-industrialized countries and making them more dependent.

The gap between the rich and the poor countries is growing wider, and, worse still, so is the gap between the rich and the poor in these poor countries. So aid is only helping to make the rich richer and the poor poorer.

DEVELOPMENT TECHNIQUES. (1) RURAL DEVELOPMENT

◆ *Self-help technology* The non-industrialized countries will need technology to achieve their developmental goals, but it should be a type consistent with the maintenance of healthy self-regulating societies, not a type that destroys them and leads to the growth of amorphous mass societies. Such a technology should: *(i) be cheap enough to be accessible to virtually everyone*. This self-help technology should involve the mass of the people and not just the privileged few. As Mahatma Gandhi put it,

"I want the dumb millions of our land to be healthy and happy, and I want them to grow spiritually. As yet for this purpose we do not need machines . . . If we feel the need of machines, we certainly will have them. Every machine that helps every individual has a place, but there should be no place for machines that concentrate power in a few hands and turn the masses into mere machine-minders, if indeed they do not make them unemployed." *(2)*

(ii) be suitable for application on a small scale. As Aldous Huxley has observed, if inventors, scientists and engineers were to provide ordinary people with the means of "doing profitable and intrinsically significant work, of helping men and women to achieve independence from bosses, so that they became their own employers, or members of self-governing cooperative groups working for subsistence and local markets . . . this differently orientated technological progress would result in a progressive decentralization of population, of political and economic power." Other advantages Huxley said would be "a more humanly satisfying life for more people, a greater measure of genuine self-governing democracy and a blessed freedom from the silly or pernicious adult education provided by mass producers of consumer goods through the medium of advertisement." *(3)*

Small operators, however numerous, are less likely to be harmful to the environment than large-scale ones. Although, as a result of ignorance, small communities can sometimes be guilty of causing serious erosion, this is trifling compared with the devastation caused by large organizations when they are motivated by greed, envy and lust for power. Moreover it is obvious that people who are organized in small communities and units are likely to take better care of their bit of land or other natural resources than large anonymous companies.*(iii) be labour-intensive* And, most important of all, *(iv) be capable of being reproduced locally*. In other words, the technology should stimulate output of indigenous industries, and be compatible with man's need for creativity.

"Industrialization cannot be grafted on to a country like a foreign body," a Chinese official said in an interview in the *Guardian* (April 5th, 1972). "It must grow within the country at grass-roots level."

A new type of literature for the rural population will need to be created—literature on low-cost building materials, low-cost housing, low-cost dams, low-cost energy; low-cost labour-intensive methods, low-cost transport and low-cost medicine; and all those things which the village or self-help or self-regulating or self-sufficient communities need.

In putting self-help technology into practice the

People of Shagiluru village laying plastic water pipes under self-help. The pipes were paid for by the villagers themselves.

following development techniques should be considered.

◆ *Self-help villages* New forms of peasant organizations which would overcome the powerlessness of the individual peasant family need to be created. The technique should be fairly simple. The government should take development to the countryside in a planned, systematic way. This is where 80-90 per cent of the populations of these countries live. The approach should be sixfold: *economic; education for self-reliance; health; security; trade* and *politics.*

The basic structures through which the rural transformations should take place are the villages. Many of the non-industrialized countries are multi-ethnic societies made up of people of different traditions, customs, religions and cultures. Ethnic loyalty is very strong, and in order to avoid civil strife and inter-ethnic wars (which have been frequent up till now) the different national groups should be allowed to develop separately without fear of domination of one group by another. They could collaborate in matters of common interest.

The co-operative or self-help villages should be, as far as is possible and practicable, based on the different national or ethnic groups. The villages should have as an overall aim the building of completely self-reliant, self-sufficient, self-regulating and self-financing human-scale communities.

◆ *Economics* The villages should be run completely on communal lines and all work in them done communally. Communalization of food production (land clearing, sowing, harvesting and threshing) should become the peasants' major economic activity. Cash crops should also be grown communally. Credit and marketing lend themselves readily to the co-operative approach, and members can learn the value of co-operative activity and more particularly the ability to raise levels and quality of production.

New low-cost houses could be built communally so that houses in the villages would no longer be sold when individuals left.

The economic activities in the village or set of villages should be highly diversified. Apart from subsistence agriculture, agricultural activities should be widened to include poultry, fishing, vegetable production and the keeping of livestock for sale. The main branches of industry in the villages should be those closely dependent on agriculture such as the

preparation of animal foodstuffs, the manufacture and repair of agricultural implements, and brick-making.

All cash income from the sale of cash crops earned by the villages should not be automatically distributed to members. Some of the surplus should be re-invested in development projects such as the building of grain stores or poultry houses, or stocking of cattle herds. All developments in the villages should be internally financed.

When not working on the land e g during the period between planting and harvesting, the peasants should be engaged in rural public works projects such as building roads or their own dams for irrigation systems, with the help of agricultural instructors, agronomists, etc. This is the policy of "turning labour into capital" by seasonal "investment" in public works. The villagers could also build their own workshops and co-operative shops, grain mills, timber mills, etc.

As Barbara Ward and Rene Dubos have pointed out,

"Rural mobilization could also be utilized for other aspects of a balanced ecological 'package deal' in agriculture. Before many of the chemical insecticides appeared on the scene, a variety of pests were kept under control by hand picking or by wrapping and covering vulnerable vegetables and fruit—composting in deep pits, judicious use of night soil, building village latrines, are all methods by which rural labour can be used to keep humus in the soil and prevent human wastes from contaminating the local water supply." *(4)*

What agricultural development through farming co-operatives and self-help villages should aim to achieve is the mobilization of the enormous latent potential of the unemployed masses of the rural areas. In this way the huge peasant populations which have, up till now, been an economic burden on the state could accumulate their own capital.

◆ *Education for self-reliance* The self-help technology at village level will require literate farmers. The villagers should run their own adult education classes during the evenings after the day's work. The purpose of this mass literacy campaign is to enable people to improve their economic, social and personal relations as citizens.

The villages should also run their own primary, secondary and training schools and research stations, with government assistance if necessary. This education for self-reliance is the very basis of whatever action-orientated programme may be indulged in.

A good example of education for self-reliance is the education given at Ujamaa village school at Litowa in Tanzania. The education given at this school is designed to enable the pupils to continue to work in the rural areas. The "Work and Study" programmes which include both classroom and production activities appear to complement each other. The aim is to combine education and production as mutually reinforcing aspects of the same process. The school at Litowa has its own farms where pupils learn about water storage, agricultural techniques, preservation of food and grain and the traditional craft of the village. The aim is to introduce practical technologies in the school curricula to which school children can apply themselves.

On a wider level, a rural bias to education also helps to prevent or limit the flow of young people from the land to the cities. (5)

◆ *Health* The villages should also build their own dispensaries, community health centres with trained doctors, nurses and midwives, and nursery schools.

◆ *Security* The villages should become the basic social and welfare groups organizing relief measures should their areas be hit by calamities. Families who are in need because of illness or some other reasons beyond their control could be assisted by a welfare fund of the team to which they belong.

The villages should also have their own militia (people's army) made up of men and women in the villages for the military defence of their communities.

In the day-to-day life of their members, co-operative or self-help villages could integrate the totality of the elements that make up peasant life—food, clothing, housing, education, medicine and defence.

◆ *Trade* The emphasis on self-reliance and co-operative living should be such as to make each village or set of villages understand that they will have as little contact with the world outside *in terms of exchange relations.* This should re-orientate the countries' agricultural production away from world markets dominated by capitalism, and towards first the internal markets of each country which are still underdeveloped, and then towards other countries with which they can enter into agreements at guaranteed 'prices'. In other words, trade by barter.

◆ *Politics* The emphasis on self-reliance should be such as to make each village or set of villages understand that the will to develop co-operative living must come from the peasants themselves. The *spontaneous* approach to development from below where the peasants make their own decisions with little or no government interference, whilst welcoming assistance from the government when needed, should be encouraged.

The importance of the political factor in development should assert itself in this context. Great emphasis should be placed on the importance of dedicated leadership which should be provided by a party (such as TANU in Tanzania) and a score of trained party cadres. What is required from the party is that it should provide from within its ranks advanced sections of the peasantry, coming out of the areas where co-operative and self-help villages are being built, teaching and working with the peasants in the process. What is not required is the wholesale importation of officials from outside the area, even from regional headquarters, instructing the peasants as to their tasks but taking no physical part in it themselves.

On the political level the general principle could be established that the villages should be the demo-

Setting up a school building; manual projects are part of Tanzanian education under self-reliance programme.

cratic political control agencies. They should have representatives who are democratically elected and who are subject to democratic control and dismissal.

Development should be based on the peasantry not on the urban privileged. The only way the non-industrialized countries can rescue themselves from poverty is by radical changes which have a popular base and popular support. The peasants and workers should be allowed to enact their own revolutionary life experience to its logical conclusion. This is vital. Political change in non-industrialized countries will remain of little long-term value unless it is accompanied by cultural change. But cultural change becomes possible only when men and women fight out their own mental battles with themselves.

DEVELOPMENT TECHNIQUES (2) URBAN DEVELOPMENT

Labour-intensive technology The major means of production should be under public control. As a first step, all foreign banks, insurance, import-export and wholesale businesses should be nationalized. Thus all foreign investments would be eliminated.

The second step should be their redirection to serve the needs of the people. Certain services may need to be provided at the national rather than provincial or village level. However, there should be no attempt at industry on too large a scale.

The third step should be the development of community types of industries. This can only be achieved by a complete decentralization of industrial and economic activities. If there is need for large-scale industry, this should not exclude small ones in the villages.

Within the urban-based industry itself there should be a parallel development of small-scale, labour-intensive and large-scale capital-intensive industry. This economic development should become "dualistic" with on the one hand a modern large-scale capital-intensive sector in the urban centres and on the other a traditional labour-intensive sector. The Chinese experience is relevant here. The development of this "dualistic" economy is what the Chinese call "Walking on two legs"—"the technique of combining agricultural and industrial development, new and traditional techniques, small-scale labour-intensive local industry and large-scale capital-intensive modern industry within a developing economy". (6)

The aim is to build a diversified economy, balanced between industry and agriculture; light and heavy industry; and to develop in each region of the country the energy basis on which industry must rest.

CONCLUSION

It is clear from what has been said that the problems confronting non-industrialized countries cannot be solved by the adoption of Western patterns of free enterprise capitalism. Many of the problems confronting these countries started with this type of development which was a result of their colonial past. Given the pressure of time (constantly aggravated by the increase of population) the free enterprise capitalist system is incapable of handling problems as complex and deep-rooted as those faced by these countries.

Soviet achievements have an obvious appeal because of the speed at which modernization of the Soviet economy was carried out. During the initial stages of their development, Soviet planners faced the same problem as those faced by non-industrialized countries: the modernization of a backward peasant economy. But the Soviet model is unlikely to provide the answer. There are negative sides to its achievements. Firstly, the implementation of Soviet planning has been on authoritarian lines. The "forced march" towards an industrialized—and socialist—society has been characterized by an enforced austerity, the deliberate holding down of living levels while the resources needed to create a modern industry were accumulated, and the systematic exploitation of the peasant masses. Secondly, the pace of growth in the agricultural sector of the Soviet economy has been slow. Soviet-type agriculture is still in the dumps, and its yields, after more than fifty years of revolutionary government, still compare unfavourably with those of 1913. Thirdly, there has been an increasing pre-occupation of workers in a technologically developed society with material possessions; and the emergence of new and privileged classes.

Until recently, when countries with peasant economies became the subjects of analytical interest, all economies were perceived through one of the two theoretical frameworks: the first was the tradition of conventional economics from Ricardo to Keynes, designed to analyse the industrial capitalism of Western Europe and the United States. Marxian economics, the other grand theoretical scheme, was designed to analyse the very same set of capitalist economies.

Classical economics and the ideology of laissez-faire, as well as Marxist socialism, came out of the English nineteenth century Industrial Revolution. They bear no relevance to conditions in non-industrialized countries. The Soviet bloc is no more capable of solving the problems of these countries any more than its Western Imperialist rivals. The economies of non-industrialized countries are markedly different from those of the Soviet Union, Western countries or Japan. They are agrarian, small-scale. Organization of production is controlled by social institutions—the local face-to-face communal ties of family, kinship, neighbourhood, common ancestry and religious obligation.

As President Julius Nyerere of Tanzania has pointed out, socialism and communism are meant to apply to large-scale industrialized economies with highly centralized planning. He points out that although there is some validity in the notion of African Communism, African societies are communalistic rather than communist, and that their communalism is of small-scale communities whose economic arrangements express a community ethos of "Democratic Socialism" rather than the kind of socialism associated with the Soviet Union. (7)

The non-industrialised countries should pioneer a new pattern of development that draws on the experience of other countries, but is based on the indigenous traditions, as in China and Tanzania, or in Albania, North Korea, Vietnam, Burma and Cambodia.

This approach is more likely to solve their problems. The countries need to develop on their own, to invest their traditional concepts with new meanings, not slavishly accept the standards of the industrialized countries. The almost universal adoption of centralized political, economic and social systems should be abandoned. This in effect means developing an economic system, an appropriate self-help technology, a pattern of trade and political institutions that are best suited to a country's own specific traditional, cultural and indigenous requirements. The country should be committed to pluralism and decentralized decision-making.

The types of societies that will emerge from adopting these strategies and techniques will be a conglomeration of stable, self-governing, self-regulating and self-supporting communities.

It must be admitted that the adoption of these strategies *in toto* by many of the non-industrialized countries is unlikely. But self-help technology with many of its development techniques—such as labour investment, "work study" programmes of education, decentralization of decision-making, and above all the psychological drive to show the peasants that they can initiate development themselves, that they need not limp along supported by the twin crutches of outside expertise and outside aid—can have direct applicability to the solution of their problems.

Self-help technology with its development techniques, is the only escape route from poverty for the non-industrialized countries.

Jimoh Omo-Fadaka

REFERENCES
(1) Ward, Barbara and Dubos, Rene: *Only One Earth (The care and maintenance of a small planet)* Harmondsworth: Penguin, 1972 p.235.
(2) Quoted from *The Economics of Permanence* by Dr E.F. Schumacher in *Resurgence*: Vol 3 No 1 May/June, 1970. London.
(3) Huxley, Aldous: *Science, Liberty and Peace*. London: Chatto and Windus, 1947 pp. 23—24.
(4) Ward, Barbara and Dubos, Rene: Ibid. p. 234.
(5) Omo-Fadaka, Jimoh: *Tanzanian Way to Self Reliance, Ecologist* Vol 2 No 2 February 1972. London.
(6) Buchanan, Professor Keith: '*The Transformation of the Chinese Earth* London: G. Bell, 1970 p.311.
(7) Nyerere, Julius K: *Communitarian Socialism* in *The Seeds of Liberation* Paul Goodman (Editor) New York; Brazilier 1964. Reprinted in *African Socialism*, Stanford University Press; Friedland, W.H. and Rosberg, Jr. C.G. (Editors) 1964.

HOMESPUN PHILOSOPHY

Community Technology or the Technology of Self-Reliance was the springboard of India's Independence movement and the crux of Gandhi's vision of a new society. The spinning wheel symbolized the whole movement of technology for self-reliance. Gandhi said that the British Raj had been able to strengthen itself only by breaking the network of village industries, handicrafts and labour-intensive technology. Now (he argued) if we wanted to weaken and destroy the foreign domination of our country we had to strengthen and create a kind of technology which would not require our dependence on centralized, heavy technology. And then it would become impossible for the British to continue to exploit us. Gandhi asked,

'What is the cause of the present chaos? It is exploitation of sister nations by sister nations. It is the heavy machinery and impersonal technology that has enabled these nations to exploit others. Therefore the Europeans have to remodel their outlook if they are not to perish under the weight of the comforts to which they are becoming slaves.'

Gandhi went on to say,

'Sooner or later the fact must be recognized that the people will have to live in villages and small communities and not in impersonalized urban jungles. In the cities people may be getting big profits and good wages but all that has become possible only by sucking the blood of the rural masses.'

Gandhi's opposition to mechanization and industrialization was based on the conviction that they create more competition and enable a few to concentrate wealth in their own hands in total disregard of millions of men and women whose bread is snatched out of their very mouths. In the Indian context it must be considered a complete madness to devise capital-intensive machines to save labour where capital is scarce and labour is in abundance. Therefore Gandhi said,

'We save labour until thousands of people are without work and die of hunger on the streets. I want to secure employment and livelihood not only for part of the human race but for all. I will not have the enrichment of a few at the expense of the community. What may be hoped for is that Europe will realize the obvious and retrace her steps and find a way out from the demoralizing industrialism.'

Gandhi believed that mass production would result in a great world tragedy unless there were simultaneous distribution on an equally mass scale.

'Mass production takes no note of the real requirements of the consumer. If mass production were in itself a virtue it should be capable of indefinite multiplication, but mass production comes within its own limitations. If all countries adopted the system of mass production there would not be a big enough market for their products. Mass production must then come to a stop.'

Gandhi was firmly convinced that the mania for mass production is responsible for the world crisis. It is responsible for the concentration of production in particular areas. Therefore distribution is inequitable. If both production and distribution take place in the areas where the things are required then automatically the distribution is little problem. The decentralization of production means the people are producing for themselves, and technology for self-reliance should be such that it will help people to get rid of exploitation by the few. Technology at present makes it easy to exploit people; a technology

Visiting Britain for negotiations in 1931, Gandhi brought a pair of goats to keep him in milk.

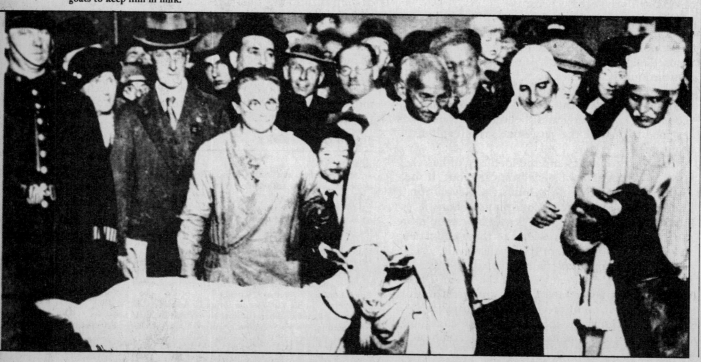

of self-reliance should minimize the possibility of exploitation.

Gandhi said,

'When production and consumption both become localized the temptation to speed up production indefinitely, and at any price, disappears. All the endless difficulties and problems that our present day economic system presents would then come to an end. Distribution can be equalized when production is localized, in other words, when the distribution is simultaneous with production. Distribution will never be equal so long as you want to top other markets of the world to dispose of your goods. So we have to do away with centralized mass production and the technology of mass production and achieve mass production through production by the masses. The technology of self-reliance will enable us to have mass production in people's own homes. Such a technology will not herd people together in crowded, unhealthy factories but will multiply individual production millions of times and fulfil the real requirements of our society. The production by the fewest possible number through the aid of highly complicated machinery is sheer madness and a clever way of exploitation. The technology of self-reliance must be a technology of simplicity so that it can be put in the homes of the millions of people of the world. For such a technology it is labour which is the current coin not metal. Any person who can use his/her labour has that coin and has wealth.'

Gandhi saw centralized technology as the surest way to unemployment.

'In an organized and industrialized country there are only fixed and limited avenues of employment: the workers become highly skilled in the use of one particular kind of machinery. They cannot shift from one job to another in a day and unemployment becomes a tremendous problem. The centralized technology is the technology of dependence for the masses and the privilege and monopoly of the few. Whereas decentralized technology is the technology of self-reliance for all.'

Moreover the centralized technology requires people to adapt to machines, whereas the technology of self-reliance can adapt to the human being. The technology of self-reliance should help and support crafts, not destroy them. That is why Gandhi experimented with various models of spinning wheel, and designed a new one while he was in prison. That particular spinning wheel was called after the prison (*Yervada chakra*). It is a wheel fixed in a wooden box and easily portable. Gandhi used to spin with this wheel while attending large political meetings and during discussions and interviews. He spun all the cloth he used. And, following his example, hundreds of thousands of Indians who had completely forgotten this art again started to spin. There were mass spin-ins where thousands of people would gather together for an hour or two and all that they had spun in that time they would contribute to the independence movement, a great

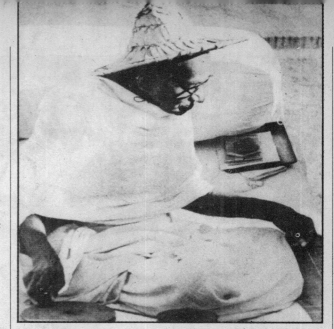

Operating the portable spinning wheel designed in Yervada Prison

mountain of hanks. This was an example of production by the masses. At the same time as organizing boycotts and public bonfires of factory produced British clothes he was reviving the indigenous hand-spinning industry. The British had destroyed it so that Indian cotton would be exported to England to be manufactured into cloth and re-exported to India. But Gandhi did not want Indian capitalists to replace British capitalists and build factories in Indian cities to exploit their own brothers, he wanted a technology which could be used in every village and in every home. He announced a prize for the person who could invent a spinning wheel which would enable the spinner to earn as much at home as he could do in a factory. This did not happen in his lifetime, but after his death Ambar Nath invented a wheel with four spinners. This wheel realized Gandhi's dream and he was given an award. The wheel is called *Ambar Chakra*.

For Gandhi the technology of self-reliance was not limited to spinning and weaving. He set up a laboratory to experiment and invent appropriate tools and technology for producing paper, shoes and sugar, and for husking, pounding, grinding, ploughing, printing, etc. The energy for these machines was either muscle-power or animal-power and, where necessary, methane. He attacked the Hindu prejudice against using human excrement and the village practice of burning dried cow dung as fuel. He advocated the use of methane from human and animal excrement and the use of the manure as fertilizer. Methane gas proved very successful since the Indian climate provides the right temperature for anaerobic decomposition. The gas is used for cooking and lighting. He not only encouraged handicrafts and production by small scale technology but also he insisted that people use only what is produced by these methods.

Gandhi found that the traditional mill stones were very heavy and slow to operate, so he devised a small technological improvement. Instead of a wooden centre piece he used a screw on a ball bearing. This enabled the top stone to be raised or lowered in

OTHER PERSPECTIVES

On his 1931 visit to London, Gandhi stayed in the East End and was enthusiastically welcomed.

order to grind finer or coarser. For the first time people were able to grind enough flour every day for their own daily bread and free themselves from dependence on the mills which destroy part of the food value of the wheat.

Gandhi saw that agriculture depending on tractors and on imported oil to run the tractors would make India vulnerable to foreign domination. And the bullocks which are traditionally used for ploughing would be made superfluous. Keeping them for beef would mean using land which is already over-populated. Ultimately, he predicted, human beings must dig and plough for themselves, so he invented certain ploughs by which two persons formed the ploughing team, one pulling the plough and the other pushing the plough through the earth and keeping the furrow straight. He also devised a sowing plough for two people—again one person pulling the plough, the other releasing the seeds one by one through a tube so that the seed would not be wasted, as in the hand-broadcasting of traditional farmers. He called this *rishi-kheti* (the agriculture of the sages).

Gandhi not only invented tools, but set up communities to use them, shops to sell them and the goods produced by them, and schools to teach the use of the technology. Thousands of shops sold handicrafts, whole foods, leather goods made from animals that had died naturally, *Khadi* (hand spun, hand woven, hand printed cloth) and recycled hand-made paper. In Gandhian ashrams and communities thousands of workers were specially trained and then sent to the villages to renew, re-establish and rein-state the dying community technology. The genius of Gandhi was not in having these ideas but inspiring a movement which could put these ideas into practice.

Of course traditional technologies are still flourishing in India and do not need reviving. In the city of Benares alone 20,000 families are supported by the weavers of silk saris who interweave silk with gold thread. Before the British this kind of art would have been spread throughout India and now it survives only in pockets.

In the villages everybody knows house building. People build their own houses from wood, mud, stones, leaves and straw. The bucket water-wheels still survive for irrigation of land. But a new interest of a new confidence has been created in the indigenous and traditional techniques and in their capacity for adaption and improvement.

But it would be wrong to assume from its many successes that this is the mainstream of development in India.

The bulk of the government departments, the Ministry of Industry, the Planning Commission, the western educated elite, the city industrialists still consider it important to industrialize India on the western pattern and to centralize the modes of production. However, the failure of heavy industry in the West might make Indians think again and avoid committing the mistakes of the West.

When the Westernized Indian elite sees that the massive and complicated technology with its gigantism and inherent violence, dinosaur-like, is nearing its collapse then they may look with new eyes at Gandhi's prophetic vision of small-scale, decentralized, simple, non-violent and labour-intensive technologies, and seek truly Indian solutions to India's problems.

Satish Kumar

CHRISTIAN SCIENCE MONITOR

PEASANTS' COMMUNAL COMMANDS AND POPULAR POWER IN CHILE 1970—73

'The power of the Communal Commands, the Popular Power, is not created by decree, but it is born out of the class struggle in the country and in the commune, therefore its formation can't be the product of an administrative and bureaucratic decision' (Chilean poster).

Note: The historical process which led to the formation of the Communal Commands in Chile (1970—73)—linking industrial and agricultural workers, students and *pobladores* (squatters) is extremely complex; to discuss them requires knowledge of a series of concepts. The length of this article obliges me to make statements that may seem unsupported; I have no choice but to make reference to other sources.

Since the Greeks, Western thinking has established the struggle for the ownership of land as fundamental for the peasantry. Marxist analysis starts from a feudal situation of small and big landowners. Much has been written by Marxists about the subordination of the peasants' struggle to the industrial workers' struggle.

In pre-Colombian Latin America, the Indian cultures had a communal system of land property and a fundamentally different concept of 'ownership' and 'privacy'. Spain didn't transplant feudal relations from the old to the New World, for Spain itself was already in transition from feudalism to capitalism and "the conquest had a capitalist purpose: the exploitation and commercialisation of precious metals".[1]

The Indian population was transformed into 'agricultural workers' and the land was organised in a system of large estates (*latifundia*). The social conditions essential to its survival were and are: "a relatively closed system of social stratification; misery and marginality of the agricultural labour force; predominance of a primary system of labour relationships".[2] In countries with considerable native populations—Peru, Mexico and Bolivia—the struggle to regain the land has been a historical constant, the primary condition for ethnic survival.[3] In the rest of Latin America, the pressure for change from the country has been basically economic, brought to bear by workers demanding improvements in working conditions and, later, the effective application of the Agrarian Reforms.

The legal rights gained in such struggles have only been observed when the workers' movement is strong; when it is weak, the ruling class does not hesitate to disregard them. This is a recurrent phenomenon in Latin American history.[4]

The banner reads 'Che Guevara Encampment — Homeless Citizens' Movement — House or Death, We will Win'. This is not empty rhetoric. In many countries squatters have been killed resisting eviction by the police or armed forces.

An economy dominated by export capitalists with no interest in internal development has generated an unbridgeable gap between the forces of production and the relationships of production in Latin America.[5] The Agrarian Reforms achieved by pressure from the agricultural workers could not afford to break the economic unity of agriculture; collective ownership is likely to be the pattern in the peasantry. The small landowner (*minifundia*) plays a minor role in the economy.

Since the Second World War, the United States has been dumping her agricultural surplus on the

1 Luis Vitale, in *Latin America: Reform or Revolution*, ed. J. Petras and M. Zeitlin. Vitale is now a prisoner of the Chilean Junta.
2 Almino Affonso, "El sindicato campesino: agente de cambio", *Ceres*, September 1970.
3 Movement of Zapata, Mexico, 1910; Rojas in Cochabamba, Bolivia, 1947; the *comuneros*, Hugo Blanco, Peru, 1963.
4 In Mexico, in spite of the agrarian sector being fundamental in the 1910 revolution (and in spite of the Agrarian Reform Law of the 1917 Constitution) no land was distributed in Yucatan, Comarca Lagunera, etc., in the late 'thirties.

5 Che Guevara's writings to Bettleheim, *Ceres*, September 1970.

world market. National production in Latin America was unable to compete with US prices and the ruling class shifted its capital resources from the country to the industrial cities, generating massive unemployment among the agricultural workers; insufficient agricultural production, an increase of imports and a growing national debt were the unavoidable results.

To protect its interests and those of the agro-industrial national elites, the USA has helped to perpetuate the *latifundia.* In the early 'sixties—as a response to the turmoil generated by the Cuban revolution—the USA launched a development programme for Latin America: the 'Alliance for Progress'. Its line on agricultural development was 'productionism', ie increase production through efficient land usage and technological modernisation, without land re-distribution. This would ensure a larger share of the export market, stabilise the currency and increase importation of farm machinery. In reality AID (Agency for International Development) funds have merely been used to subsidise US exported agricultural and industrial goods, and provide protection for the interests of the agrarian elites.

For the Left it was clear that "rather than working only towards modernising agriculture and expanding exports, the agrarian reform is an aspect of social change that will eradicate inequalities in rights and income, thereby minimising inequalities of access to the political system".[6] A change in the structure of land ownership was essential. In agriculture the gap between the forces of production had widened so much that changes in the industrial, political and commercial structures were necessary for the reforms to be effective. There is no possibility of success for a revolutionary movement in Latin America without a revolutionary change in the agricultural sector, nor can it succeed if it ignores the revolutionary potential of the agricultural workers. The major impetus for land reform had to be mass mobilisation.

It is in this context that I am going to consider the role of the agricultural workers' councils during the Popular Unity Government in Chile (1970—73).

CHILEAN AGRICULTURAL SITUATION IN THE 'SIXTIES

Since the 'twenties Chilean attempts at agrarian reform have been ineffective[7]. In the 'sixties the situation was as follows:
● 25% of the labour force worked in agriculture.
● 80% of workable land was *latifundia*, employing 40% of the labour force and providing 60% of the agricultural production.
● Small landowners represented 25% of the agricultural population and owned 2% of the workable land.
● 70% of the agricultural workers had an average income of $100 per year.

● There were three urban dwellers for each country man.
● Illiteracy in the country was 30—40% whilst in the city it was less than 10%[8].
● During the 'sixties agricultural exports amounted to $30—40 million while imports reached $200 million so the advantages gained by industrialisation were lost by agricultural stagnation.[9]

In 1962 an Agrarian Reform law was passed under Alessandri (of the Conservative Partido National), as part of the Alliance for Progress. It was formulated by the landowners' organisation—*Sociedad Nacional de Agricultura.* The idea was to create a middle-class peasantry. Two agencies were formed: *Corporacion de Reforma Agraria* (CORA) for the establishment of co-operative reform settlements (*asentamientos*) and the *Instituto de Desarrollo Agricola* (INDAP). "INDAP helps restrain the pressure on CORA for land by encouraging the peasants under its control to seek alternative goals" (wages, profit sharing, workers participation).[10] By 1966 it was apparent that the land tenure system "was a primary contributing factor to agricultural stagnation".[11]

In 1967, during Frei's administration (Christian Democrat, 1964—70) the congress passed a new law which "enables the state to expropriate not only abandoned or poorly developed lands [as had been the case before] but all those belonging to a single owner exceeding 80 Ha. in the fertile Central Valley or equivalent".[12] Under the pressure from the radical sector of the CD (led by Chonchol), in this same year a law was passed making truly effective the laws permitting formation of agricultural labour unions. By 1970, 10% of the agricultural workers were unionized under the control of INDAP.

The *asentamiento* was introduced to the social structure of the state; the peasant made an alliance with it which generated a dependence on its institutional framework. Perhaps the main characteristic of the CD model—"revolution in liberty"—is its lack of a unified national strategy for reform, and therefore, its weak administrative action. Frei's administration only managed to redistribute land to one in every 30 landless families and 90% of it was land without water. The resettlements received neither technical nor financial help.[13] During the last 20 months of Frei's administration, 400 land occupations took place.

The failure of the CD model dragged the country into a deep crisis in the power structure. Two strategies became clear: the parliamentary road to socialism of the Popular Unity (UP) coalition[14]

6 J. Petras, *Political and social structure in Latin America,* Monthly Review Press, 1970.
7 In 1924 a law legalizing agricultural workers' unions in principle was passed, but had no influence on the condition of the peasants.

8 Solon Barraclough, "Reforma Agraria: Historia y perspectivas", Int. Dir. ICIRA.
9 Jacques Chonchol (later Allende's Minister of Agriculture), "Poder y Reforma Agraria en la experiencia Chilena", *Ceres,* June 1970.
10 "New Chile", NACLA, pp.66, 118.
11 Study published by International Committee for Agricultural Development (CIDA).
12 "New Chile".
13 Only one in every 30 beneficiaries received ownership titles. The total cost for the six years was $500 millions, most of it spent in irrigating dry land.
14 Communist and Socialist parties as a majority, with the MAPU, Radical and others.

and that of the MIR (*Movimiento de Izquierda Revolucionaria*).

The UP strategy aimed to solve the crisis in the power structure by the democratisation of the bourgeois state. Mass mobilisation for the UP was a method of alliance with sectors of the bourgeoisie which would make such democratisation possible. This policy of alliances—and the conception of the revolutionary process taking place in stages—constituted the core of the UP political proposals.

The MIR was the most important political group left of the UP. It was formed in 1965 in the University of Concepcion and during Frei's administration it went underground.

The MIR political line was that of sharpening the crisis in the system of domination to destroy the bourgeois state and create a new popular state. Mass mobilisation was an end in itself. The MIR saw its role as that of organising and orienting the spontaneous forms of struggle of the people, integrating backward sectors of the sub-proletariat into the class struggle, guided by the working class. It operated in branches reaching these different sectors of the people: FTR (workers), FER (students), MPR (*pobladores* or squatters), and MCR (peasants' revolutionary movement).

POPULAR UNITY (1970—73)

The UP's basic programme considered agrarian reform "simultaneous and complementary with the

'Tierra o muerte' — Land or death. Farm taken over and defended by the Peasants Revolutionary Movement.

general transformations that are desired in the country's social, political and economical structure . . ."

It gave importance to workers' participation and sought their organisation; it advocated regional planning; to guarantee credit it proposed to nationalise banks; it gave preference to collective ownership and special attention to irrigation and conservation. The Cautin province was the first target for the UP programme. 69% of its population are Mapuche Indians, who hold 19% of the workable land; it is the province with the densest and poorest rural population. (Since 1968—9 militants of the MIR (*Miristas*) have been working with the Mapuches.)

In November 1970, Indians, agricultural workers, *Miristas* and the left-wing of the Socialist Party (PS), started land seizures in Cautin. The tactic was called *corrida de cercas* (fence moving). Most of these were of short duration, with little or no violence or property damage. Some were re-occupation of land which—by title—belonged to the Mapuches; other seizures were made of estates that were to be expropriated, to prevent the owners from selling off livestock and machinery and leaving only the bare ground for the reform beneficiaries. Yet others were undertaken to protest against the non-payment of wages. Almost all the occupied

'The only unemployed will be the children'.

farms were either expropriated, returned to their former owners, or else made subject to government intervention as a result of the owners' illegal actions against the workers.[15]

The combined result of the government's and workers' actions was that in the first eight months of Allende's administration more land was distributed than in the six years of Frei's government. By July 1972, practically all the remaining large estates had been incorporated into the Social Area of Property (*Propiedad del Area Social*).

REACTION OF THE BOURGEOISIE

Though there was very little violence against the landowners, each incident was blown up out of proportion by the opposition press. At the same time very little was said about the "economic crimes" committed by the bourgeoisie with direct collaboration from the judicial powers: landowners refused to plant crops, sacked workers, dismantled equipment, slaughtered breeding stock, sabotaged production, burned forests, smuggled cattle and wood to Argentina. They organised para-military training, arms dealing and sales on the black market.[16]

Cautin was the scenario of continuous terrorism by landowners using para-military forces: as early as October 1970, a priest working with the Mapuches was murdered.[17] The taking back, by force, of the legally expropriated land was a recurrent event in which many workers lost their lives.[18]

THE PRODUCTION BATTLE

The entry of the Left into the state apparatus generated a duality of power: the executive power with Allende representing the interests of the working class, and the parliament and judicial powers representing the interests of the ruling class and imperialism. In this situation, the need to increase efficiency in the expropriated sector was seen as a priority by UP. The policy of the UP was that of 'modernising' agriculture in the capitalist mode. During the first year, the main worry for the 15,000 civil servants of the agrarian sector was administrative restructuring. Everything could be solved if the right hierarchical line was established,

if the right bureaucratic structure was found. The problem of leadership (leader-led relationship) was understood to be quantitative rather than qualitative. "Expropriation was not understood as a blow to the ruling class—the bourgeoisie—but as means to overcome outmoded forms of ownership, feudal or semi-feudal."[19]

The organisations the UP used for implementing Frei's law were basically the same: the *asentamiento* is an expropriated farm put under the administration of the family heads, supervised by a local unit of CORA. (These local units comprised several *asentamientos*; all over 16 years of age participated in their administration.) "Instead of undertaking a big campaign for the development of local CORA units—as a unit of production superior than the *asentamiento*—all energy was channelled into maintaining the interests, ideology and form of the capitalist production."[20]

In order to promote unity among the four peasants' unions, the UP established a National Peasants' Confederation. Here we have to consider the kind of consciousness generated by peasant trade unionism (*fundo sindicalista*). If the unity established at leadership level has no corresponding class solidarity at grass-roots level, the trade unionism will not generate a class consciousness able to fight opportunism and insularity. This limits the development not only of a class consciousness but also of hegemonic consciousness, ie the consciousness of a class that it has the right and competence to create a new social order.

In spite of the fact that production increased more than 6% during the first year of the UP, the opposition press managed to blame the agrarian reforms for the scarcity which soon became a reality. By increasing salaries and freezing the prices of primary goods, the UP had increased the buying power of the working class; but the increased demand exceeded increased production. Taking advantage of this, American rumour-mongers created public hysteria about the shortages of non-essential goods, which led to hoarding of supplies.

The 'invisible' blockade by the US fitted perfectly: shortages of imported goods—such as spare parts—produced by the lack of international credits were aggravated by sabotage in fertilizers, transport, etc.

THE POPULAR OFFENSIVE: WORKERS' RESPONSE

"Valenzuela, the Cautin CORA director, favored the introduction of a sliding wage scale depending on how much work each person accomplished per hour, enforced by the Production Council. *The workers of this property, however, insisted that group politization was the remedy for low productivity.*"[21]

To overcome the agrarian crisis it was necessary to go beyond capitalist production, and, thus, beyond capitalist society; to create the conditions necessary for production to develop under new relationships. *This was the task of the whole working class.*

15 CORA would appoint a temporary administrator to set up the *asentamiento*.
16 "Que vale mas: un campesino o un mercenario?", *Punto Final*, 24/4/73.
17 Wilfredo Alarcon, Perquenco.
18 "Cautin: la region del fascismo devoto", *Punto Final*, 3/7/73.
19 Conacho, "La crisis agraria", *Punto Final*, 30/1/73.
20 "La crisis agraria".

Within the image: SE INVIERTE EN COMPRAR / LO QUE EL PAIS NO PRODUCE

Peasant Communal Command takeover in Southern Chile.

The original mistake in the UP policy was to isolate the agricultural workers from the class struggle of the society as a whole. It failed to conceive a path of social development based on the class struggle and the real power of an amalgamated working class, rather than on bureaucratic power. The decision-making process should have been transferred from the bureaucracy to the workers.

Chilean agricultural workers of the MCR and PS tried to create new organisations to fight against the bourgeois state, not against the government. The *Consejos Comunales Campesinos* (Communal Peasants Councils) "put together all existing organisations and non-organised peasants, with the objective of establishing the control of the production process and exerting the popular power in the country, contributing in this way to the transformation of the institutional apparatus."[22]

The CCC were proposed before Allende's election and became even more important in the following three years, particularly after the "bosses' strike" in October 1972.[23] They became, in some cases, a real alternative to the bourgeois state, the basis for a new social order. They covered many regions. Within them, the agricultural workers were united in their struggle with industrial workers, students and women's organisations, and integrated isolated groups into the struggle. Here, the workers developed a sense of how their work related to national and international economic and political development, and acquired self-confidence and political maturity.

With the CCC and the CCT (Workers Communal Commands), for the first time in Latin America workers undertook a political struggle of world-wide historical significance. Ranquil, Nuble, Maipú, Chillán, Temuco, Cautín, Entre Lagos, Concepción, Antofagasta, Talcahuano, Constitución . . . and in Santiago, Barrancas, Conchali, Nuñoa-Macul, and Estación Central.[24]

By mid 1973 it was clear—to the vanguard of the working class—that Chilean "democratic" institutions had been violated by the same class that created them. The UP was operating under the illusion of a democratic framework which no longer existed. More and more left-wing parties[25] were gravitating towards developing popular power based on organisations such as the CCC and CCT. It was also apparent that the Armed Forces would play a decisive role in the alignment of forces established by the class struggle; the polarization depended on the leadership capacity, ideological coherence, strength of objectives and homogeneity in the command shown by the classes in conflict.

But the reformist elements failed to understand the political significance of the working class revolutionary offensive. In the same way they now blame the Left for the coup—they fail to understand that it wasn't the MIR but the Chilean working class who went far beyond their mistaken leaders.

"Await the response of the constitutional elements of the Army", Allende said in a broadcast from La Moneda[26] on the morning of September 11th 1973 . . .

It is very difficult to know how many thousands of people—workers, students, professionals, journalists, artists, trade unionists, women and young people—have been murdered in Chile.[27] The Junta launched a programme for "national reconstruction" and returned factories, land and banks to their previous owners, a class which has proved its inefficiency for revitalising capitalism. This has jeopardised the policy that—in theory—could have economically consolidated the Junta, ie "to turn towards a local industrial capitalism linked to the multinationals achieving the reproduction of capital by the only way possible, external markets, based on agricultural and mineral extraction."[28]

The prices of primary goods have increased by up to 2,500%. Salaries have increased at only half the inflation rate. In this way the Junta has alienated its middle-class base. The repression—now organised by ex-Nazi members—has even alienated the Catholic Church.[29] The Chilean story has not ended. "Today, the resistance is a mass process inevitably growing into an overwhelming social force."[30]

Josefina Mena

21 "New Chile", NACLA, p.78.
22 Speech by Altamirano, Sec. PS, *Punto Final*, 13/3/73.
23 Unions, managers and professionals went on strike to paralyze the country. Workers' mobilization prevented the strike from being successful.
24 Santiago is the capital city; its population of nearly four millions represents 40% of the country.
25 For example, MAPU (Movement of Popular Unified Action) and IC (Christian Left).
26 Presidential Palace where Allende was killed, machinegun in hand.
27 From 30 to 80,000. More than 100,000 have left Chile (among them 73% of Chilean scientists). Amnesty International reports that 16,000 are still being tortured in more than twenty concentration camps.
28 *Le Monde*, April 13th, 1974.
29 The strong opposition of Cardenal Silva Henriquez represents a real threat to the Junta, which has now accused the Pope of being part of an international communist plot.
30 *El Rebelde*, MIR newspaper, published underground in Chile, August 1974.

THINK BIG, THINK LITTLE

By now, readers of the Western press know that the Chinese recycle their industrial wastes, fertilize the land with human excrement, and use lots of compost. Heroes of the self-sufficiency and organic farming movements, such as Robert Rodale and Helen and Scott Nearing, have been to see the Chinese countryside and reported favourably. Clearly the Chinese have a lot to be proud of.

And yet foreigners who ask the Chinese, "How can we be like you?" are directed not to the compost heaps and the rice-transplanting machines, but to the rifle and the writings of Chairman Mao. For many in the West this is disturbing. Here are undoubtedly the world's leading practitioners of "radical technology" brushing the whole business aside as if it were an unimportant sideline. A further paradox is that the Chinese speak with equal pride of solar cookers and of oil refineries, of methane digesters and of nuclear tests— they feel none of the distrust of Big Technology which has seized the West.

The 'ecological consciousness' which exists in China is different from that of Western environmentalists. Man is seen as 'conquering' nature, rather than living in harmony with it. Chinese ecology is very pragmatic, not at all mystical. Western city-dwellers can easily fall in love with Mother Nature at first sight. Chinese peasants, who know what a bitch she can be when the river floods or the crops fail, regard her as a useful ally only when kept well under control.

There has been a campaign for pollution control

Non-polluting solution: bring the pests to the poison, don't take the poison to the plants. This insect trap lights up at night.

in China during the past few years. It is based on an attack on the very concept of 'waste'. "Environmental pollution in modern times", writes Fang Hsin (*Peking Review* 1973, No.29) "is mainly created by industrial waste, gas, liquid and residue. In the absolute sense, however, there is no such thing as 'waste'. There are unused materials in the world but there are no materials which cannot be used." Chairman Mao has called for "multi-purpose use" of materials, and factories now make hundreds of new products—notably fertilizers, animal feed, chemical products and building materials—out of what used to be wasted.

Environmental problems are seen in China not as a *by-product* of economic growth but more as an *obstacle* to economic growth. It is of course possible that the Chinese stress on growth may alter, in ten

The leap from donkey-cart to electric bus almost by-passed the car.

ALL PHOTOS: TONY DURHAM

or twenty years time, once a high level of prosperity has been achieved. The West has already had enough growth, too much even. China has not. The Chinese also reject the view that damage to the environment is a consequence of population growth. (Despite this they have "the best family planning programme in the world", as judged by an International Planned Parenthood Federation representative who visited China in 1972.) "The history of mankind has proved that the pace of development of production, science and technology always surpasses the rate of population growth," said Tang Ke, leader of the Chinese delegation at the UN Conference on the Human Environment in Stockholm in 1972. He went on, "The possibility of man's exploitation and utilization of natural resources is constantly extending." It is important to remember that China does have enormous domestic resources of coal, oil and minerals and that consumption is still relatively modest compared with that of the United States or the Soviet Union. For the time being, China is unscathed by the so-called global resource crises.

Why then do we find so much small-scale, community-controlled, ecologically sound technology in use in China? Cynics will argue that what we see is the fast-disappearing remnant of the traditional society; that they'll stop using wooden looms as soon as they can get steel ones, and they'll give up compost when the chemical fertilizers arrive in bulk. It may not be so simple. There may well have been a period immediately after Mao Tse-tung's victory in 1949, when traditional Chinese technology was undervalued and Soviet-influenced modernization was in vogue. But during the 'sixties, and especially during the Cultural Revolution, there has been a tremendous effort to revitalize traditional methods.

Joseph Needham draws attention to three significant Chinese phrases, *yang fa, t'u fa* and *hsin fa. Yang fa,* he says, simply means "foreign ways of doing things", implying that the "foreigners are always right"; everything has to be done in that way, or not at all. *T'u fa,* on the other hand, literally means "earth methods". These local, down-to-earth techniques are now being revitalized and put to good use. Many of them are thousands of years old and, as Needham himself has shown, Western technology itself incorporates a rich variety of ideas originally imported from China, of which gunpowder, printing and magnetism are merely the three best-known. Chinese traditional medicine gave us the drug ephedrine, and immunization against smallpox. Now, after five thousand years, the West is recognizing the value of acupuncture, the traditional Chinese needling therapy. This is a direct result of the revived interest in traditional methods in China itself. It was during the Cultural Revolution of 1966—9 that Chinese medical workers discovered how to use acupuncture to prevent pain during surgery. Chinese researchers have also been testing out hundreds of old herbal remedies and trying to identify active ingredients.

The third phrase, *hsin fa,* means "entirely new

Even uncultivated ground feeds into the human ecological cycle: children collect "green manure".

methods". Most of these don't achieve fame: they are innovations made by thousands of workers and peasants which improve production, reduce waste or save labour. Western factory workers, of course, could produce dozens of such ideas, just like the Chinese. But they keep quiet about them, rather than risk talking themselves out of their jobs.

China's socialist revolution occurred when its industrial revolution had hardly begun. Traditional methods were never eclipsed by early capitalism as in Europe. Both the people and the knowledge are still there, in the countryside. And the people now have official encouragement to put the traditional knowledge to good use. The Chinese attitude to nightsoil is a good example. A common story told by city-dwellers who have come to do their stint in the countryside runs like this (in the words of a young man at the July 1st People's Commune near Shanghai): "At the beginning when I shouldered the nightsoil buckets I felt this kind of work was very dirty. When some drops got on my clothing I felt it was very dirty and was very upset. But the peasants didn't care about those things, what they cared about was getting the work done, and this moved me very much". The peasants take the sound view that the contents of the privy are precious, a valuable fertilizer.

Another favourite source of manure in China is waste ground that has not been brought under cultivation. Children and teenagers are often to be seen collecting great bundles of wild plants for use as 'green manure'. Needless to say, this is much better for the soil structure than chemical fertilizers. Perhaps in the old days, to fertilize your fields with shit and weeds was to make an ecological virtue of necessity. But the Chinese peasants show no sign of abandoning these practices as they move into an era of unprecedented prosperity.

The West is only now discovering the soya bean (as a food for humans, I mean). In China, of course, it has been a staple source of high-quality protein for centuries. The bland beans are usually converted into more savoury forms: bean-curd or soy sauce. An acre of soya beans produces about ten times as much edible protein as the same acre could produce in the form of meat. Not that the Chinese are averse

Protein-rich juice squeezed from soya beans.

to meat-eating. Most peasant households have a pig, who recycles garbage as useful fertilizer, and is eventually recycled at the dinner table. But despite rapid growth in livestock numbers, pork, beef, chicken and duck still account for a relatively modest fraction of the Chinese diet. Professor Jean Mayer, the Harvard nutritionist, summed up the situation as follows: "Americans, as meat-eaters, need 2,200 lbs of grain per head per year to feed them (140 lb direct, and all the rest for their cattle). Chinese people use 400 lb per head per year, 360 lb direct, and 40 for their cattle. 1,500 Chinese could live off what 270 Americans eat." In spite of this national shortage of hot-dogs and hamburgers the Chinese are not merely physiologically well-nourished but quite visibly enjoy their food greatly.

Whatever the virtues of nightsoil, compost and soya beans, it is most unlikely that Chinese agricultural production could have reached its present level by traditional methods alone. Chairman Mao has said that "the fundamental way out for agriculture lies in mechanization". This may surprise those who imagine everything is done in China by armies of workers toiling with their bare hands. There have of course been some spectacular, labour-intensive construction projects. But these have generally been timed for the slack periods of the year. Visit a Chinese commune when the rush is on to reap the early rice and plant the late rice, and you will find the people working in the fields from dawn to dusk. There is simply too much

work for bare hands. Even simple forms of mechanization—such as the many rice-transplanting machines devised in different parts of China—can help to ease these annual bottlenecks. I suggest that anyone who thinks machinery has absolutely no place in agriculture should try a twelve-hour stint of transplanting rice by hand, bent over double and up to his knees in water.

Mechanized farming in China does not mean (as it does in the West) an agriculture which consumes more energy in oil than it produces in food, nor does it mean (as in the USSR) fleets of magnificent combine harvesters which lie crippled and unrepaired while the ripe grain rots in the fields. Chinese agricultural machinery is often manufactured within the county, and can be repaired locally. Chungshan County in the south China province of Kwangtung now has over 170 county-run factories and workshops making 330 types of machinery serving agriculture, including generators, motors, threshers and complete sets of irrigation and drainage equipment. Tractors and other big machinery still come from large state-owned factories elsewhere. On the other hand there is now a farm machinery repair plant in each of the county's twenty-one people's communes, and a lesser repair centre in each of the 314 production brigades. (A production brigade is a village-size unit of anything from 150 to 500 households. There are usually between eight and twelve brigades in each commune, sometimes more.) These commune repair plants are not just garages which bolt on spare parts manufactured 500 miles away. They have lathes, milling machines and welding equipment. The lathes themselves are in many cases made locally.

I saw the same policy in practice at Hsing Long production brigade, one of the eleven "villages" which make up July 1st People's Commune near Shanghai. The brigade's tractor repair shop was a spacious single-storey building. Of the four tractors in the building, one was stripped down, apparently for repairs to its transmission. Obviously quite major repairs could be done on the spot, though of course the workshop depended on spares from outside the brigade. The real surprises came in two other workshops. One of them was producing electric motors for irrigation pumps and threshing machines. Again, of course, some city-made components were indispensable; but think of the psychological significance of a village making its own electric motors: this most magical of all technological products held no more mysteries for the peasants of Hsing Long.

A third workshop made farm implements. The methods here really did approach self-sufficiency. We were shown, with some pride, an electrically driven circular saw and mechanical hammer, both built on the spot. They were apparently made by fixing bits of wood and scrap metal together until you got something of the right shape and strength. Despite their Heath Robinson appearance, both machines were fast and precise in operation.

Chairman Mao insists that industry should serve agriculture. Here in the West, the countryside has

become more and more dependent on the city's factories. In China, however, the products supplied by the city to the country are often such as to *enhance* the countryside's self-sufficiency. A small but pleasing example comes from the Shanghai No.15 Radio Factory, which recently turned out 1,000 solar energy stoves for peasants on the outskirts of the city and in other parts of China. The stove is shaped like an inverted umbrella, and consists of a reflector, a support, and a rack for cooking vessels. It takes fifteen minutes to cook one kilogramme of rice.

Iron and steel, cement, and even chemical fertilizer production is being disseminated into the countryside. Between 1970 and 1972, Shanghai factories sent 300 kits for small synthetic ammonia plants to various parts of the country. Small plants like these now make over half of China's synthetic ammonia. Again, these plants cannot be regarded as totally self-sufficient since they need outside energy supplies. There could also be environmental dangers, but the Chinese may still show us how to maintain soil structure with organic manure and at the same time get a little extra yield by adding synthetic nitrogen.

The lifeline of agriculture, according to Chairman Mao, is water conservation. One of the most impressive achievements of the Chinese peasants has been the sinking of 1.2 million pump wells in North China alone. Dotted over the countryside **are** these little diesel or electric motors, and the sound of the water gushing into the irrigation

(Above) Confidence is more important than having the right materials or blueprints. *(Below)* Sodium nitrate fertilizer: the contents of this sack were once factory effluent.

channels is as much part of the aural landscape as
are sheep, chickens, or cicadas. Drilling a pump well
to a depth of thirty metres or more is beyond the
capacities of a small farmer's cooperative. It was
only after the founding of the people's communes
in 1958, says a New China News Agency report,
that the peasants began to sink pump wells on a
large scale, relying on their growing collective
strength. So this particular technology depends on
the existence of a political grouping somewhat
larger than the village.

The total installed power of pump wells in China
is about 15 million kilowatts. They would need
eight of the largest power stations to run them. But
in practice those wells which are not diesel-powered
are often supplied with electricity from small, local
hydro-power stations. Water running downhill in
one place pumps water out of the ground in another
place some miles away. There are now over fifty
thousand of these small hydro-power stations. The
electricity is used not only for pump wells but also
for lighting and for irrigation pumps and other farm
machinery. It is another component of the policy
of rural self-reliance.

But once again, the Chinese *always* refuse to
'think small'. Three great river basins, the Yangtze,
the Yellow River and the Haiho, have been the
scene of gigantic projects in flood control, drainage,
irrigation and hydro power. One of the biggest
projects now under construction is the 2.5 kilometre-
long Tanchiangkou dam on the Yangtze's biggest
tributary. A hundred thousand people have taken
part in the design and building.

Even this gigantic operation is dwarfed by the
'river-taming battles' of the Haiho river basin, which
includes the cities of Peking and Tientsin. In 1974
five hundred thousand people from 700 communes
joined in, working on dykes, canals and reservoirs.
In other years, the figure has been as high as a
million people. But perhaps the most significant
fact is that at the same time, back in their own
communes and brigades, millions more were engaged
in levelling farmland, sinking pump wells, and
building small reservoirs, ponds, ditches and other
improvement projects. Perhaps the difficulties with
large water-control projects elsewhere, such as
Aswan and Kariba, have been due in part to the lack
of involvement of local people in schemes which
were thrust on them from above. Millions used to
die in floods in China, and I don't think the Chinese
see any alternative to large-scale water control
projects. Their policy is one of "walking on two
legs". The two legs are, roughly speaking, Big
Technology and Little Technology. We may admire
the Little, but we must not forget the Big behind it.

Fascinating snippets of information emerge from
China from time to time. It seems there is an
experimental geothermal power station near Peking,
which has a turbine propelled by vapour from an
unspecified liquid of low boiling point. There are
sealed pits in which many communes bury the stalks
of plants, grass and leaves: the methane gas released
by this fermenting matter is piped to houses for
lighting, and in at least one place it has replaced

(Upper): **Lin Hsien peasants channelled water across the mountains
to their parched valley. Now their fields are lush and they have a new
source of energy: hydro-electricity.** *(Lower):* **Traditional tools are
quick and effective in the sympathetic hands of a craftsman.**

diesel oil as the fuel for rice-husking and sugar-cane
pressing machines. In thousands of fields, apparently,
two or even three different crops are grown
simultaneously in alternating rows.

The Chinese have developed the "5406" bacterial
fertilizer, which is also said to protect plants against
disease and promote germination, and the "920"
hormone, claimed to increase yields of wheat,
cotton, maize and rice. There have been experiments
with biological pest control in which chalcid wasps
were used against cutworms. And an assault has
been made on a cotton pest, the pink bollworm,
with a synthetic pheromone—a man-made version of
the chemical with which the insect attracts its mate.

The Chinese report these achievements but do
not exaggerate their importance. Many of them
have been surpassed in countries which do not have
a socialist system. You could find better examples
of geothermal power in use in Italy, or solar power
in Israel, or methane in India. The Chinese would,
I think, admit this, but they would also point out
that the crucial difference between China and, say,
India, is not in the technologies the two countries
use, but in their respective class structures and
political systems.

Tony Durham

DIRECTORY: Bibliography

2 GENERAL

This section contains basic sources and contacts, bibliographies and works on the 'theory' of Radical Technology (such as it is); and ideological background reading which at other times and places must be foreground.

2.1 BASIC DIRECTORIES AND BIBLIOGRAPHIES

These are all fundamental sources and well worth getting hold of for reference. The first five are American and the rest British.

◆ *Energy Primer: solar, water, wind and bio fuels* (Portola Institute: $4.50 in USA/ $5.50 elsewhere; available from the Whole Earth Truck Store, 558 Santa Cruz Avenue, Menlo Park, CA 94025) [CO]. On the technical aspects of 'alternative energy' this is the best single source you can get. Compiled by New Alchemy (West), Whole Earth Truck Store, Ecology Action/Palo Alto and ASE, it is the definitive textbook on small-scale renewable sources of energy. As the title says, it is a *primer* — a textbook on the basic principles, written with care, clarity and excellent illustrations. It is not a series of blueprints, yet not more than a step or two this side of practicality. As an access tool, it blows my mind: there are thousands of references and contacts, many of them painstakingly annotated. It covers a lot more than just energy. The bio-fuel section deals with agriculture and aquaculture as well as methane, alcohol and wood. There are also sections on architecture and integrated systems. Throughout the book it is emphasised that renewable energy sources only make sense if much less energy is consumed and living-patterns alter accordingly. It sets a new standard of thoroughness and realism for this kind of information.

◆ *Whole Earth Epilog* (Point/Penguin, 1974: £1.75) [CO, OB, MB]. The pagination follows on from the latest edition of *Whole Earth Catalog (WEC)* which is not yet available in Britain. The *Epilog* is generally more relevant to 'AT' than the old *Catalog* (which was useful enough), and is in my opinion an indispensable aid to digging up sources and contacts. It is classified into broad sections as follows: whole systems; land use; shelter; soft technology; craft; community; nomadics; communications; learning. It is very well indexed and cross-indexed, but is naturally rather US-oriented.

◆ *Public Works*, compiled and edited by Walter Szykitka (Links, New York and London, 1974: $10.00). [CO, MB] Subtitled 'A Handbook for self reliant living', it is just that: I don't know how I did without it all these years. Size of a telephone directory, 1,024 pages, two million words of 'how to' articles culled from publicly available sources, under the following general categories: first aid and survival; child care; health; food; farm and home; tools and construction; transport and communication; government; money: all good down-to-earth stuff. See also *Coevolution Quarterly* (2.223).

◆ *Shelter*, edited by Lloyd Kahn (Shelter Publications, Box 279, Bolinas, CA 94924, USA, £3.20) [AD]. Dazzling successor to *Domebook 2*, and a labour of love from cover to cover. Basically oriented towards vernacular building, but leaves space for many simple construction recipes; 'Domebook 3'; an extensive and personal annotated bibliography, and some songs of experience about 'whiteman technoplastic prowess'.

◆ *Alternative Sources of Energy: Practical Technology and Philosophy for a Decentralised Society* (ASE, Rt 2, Box 90A, Milaca,

1 INTRODUCTION

1.1 REMARKS ABOUT THE TERM 'RADICAL TECHNOLOGY'

'Radical Technology' is a very vague term we decided to use because, having rejected 'Mutiny on Spaceship Earth', 'Moulin Rouge', 'Bicycles of the Gods' and other such gems, we couldn't think of a better title for the book. For a long time we referred to it as 'The Alternative Technology Book' because 'alternative technology' — or 'AT' as it is known in the trade — is by far the most widely accepted umbrella term for wind-generators, methane-digestors, autonomous houses, solar stills, etc, etc. But this was exactly its problem. It was too much associated with pure gadgetry, especially of the merely environmental variety, for use by the affluent to soothe their consciences and amaze their friends at a safe distance from the cities.

We wanted to express an ideal of technological organisation that was part of a total movement towards a new form of society; but at the same time to assert the belief that technology itself matters, not *just* who controls it — that, in other words, not only the relations of production, but the *means themselves* must be changed to permit the achievement of a just, stable and fulfilling society.

Since this last is a notion that most radicals would not accept, we adopted the word 'radical' with some diffidence, reinforced by the fact that most of the material in the book is purely technical and has no overt political content at all. But other explicitly political labels were even more misleading or susceptible to misinterpretation. 'Socialist Technology', 'Anarchist Technology' or 'Utopian Technology' could all have done at a pinch (let no-one call us sectarian!) but the terms are so muddied that the relatively anodyne 'Radical Technology' was wheeled in *faute de mieux*.

This does not dispose entirely of the term 'alternative'. You get quite fond of it after so many years, and after all it does seem a bit ridiculous to talk about 'the radical approach' to, say materials, or wind power, and I shall frequently revert to the term 'alternative' or just 'AT'. In these cases, I either want to distinguish the approach I take from one which might more normally be called 'radical'; or I want to imply a certain ambivalence, that the radical aspect is not inherent and requires a context of other truly radical changes.

These 'other changes' I take for granted, and in most sections of the directory I have only hinted at them. For example, under 'Energy' I don't discuss miners' wage struggles, or under 'Shelter' unionisation in the construction industry. I don't wish to minimise these issues, but many of them are obviated by the very nature of **Radical Technology**; others are dealt with in section 2; others are beyond the scope of this book. I had to draw the line somewhere!

1.2 HOW THE DIRECTORY IS ORGANISED, AND OTHER REMARKS

It might look a bit complicated, but don't be frightened.

MN 56353, USA: $4.00). A great big book, nearly 300 pages long, an epitome of the first 10 issues of the magazine. It has an enormous bibliography (several hundred items) classified as follows: energy and power; solar energy; wind energy; water energy; agriculture and organic fuels; energy storage; energy conversion devices; direct energy conversion; architecture and the arts. Unfortunately the items are only slightly annotated, and it suffers from trying to be too comprehensive: a lot of rubbish mixed with the good stuff, and no indication which is which. See 2.33 for ASE Lending Library. The holdings lists in *ASE* 15 themselves make a useful bibliography. *ASE* 17, 'Spectrum', is a directory of alternative technology equipment.

◆ *Survival Scrapbooks* by Stefan Szczelkun (Unicorn Books, Nat Gwilw, Llanfynnydd, Carmarthen, Wales: £1.50) Actually this is a series of six, of which Stefan did 1:*Shelter*;

2: *Food*; and 5: *Energy*. The others are *Access to Tools* (Vol 3), *Play* (Vol 3½) and *Paper Houses* (Vol 4). Stefan's ones are very beautifully done, especially the first two, and they are fine to start off with, but lack the detail to carry anything through unless you already know. Their real strength lies in their bibliographies, classified and partly annotated. Worth having. In US published by Schocken, New York.

◆ 'Designing for Survival', a special section of *AD*, July 1972, edited by Colin Moorcraft. [AD] A melee of very varied material spanning eco-architecture, apocalyptic tub-thumping, Third World and China, alternative rural development, and astronauts' water-recycling gear. Classified bibliography covering: energy in general; solar energy; wind energy; water supply; water energy; geothermal energy; biological energy; heat energy; bricks; cob, pise and stabilised earth; fibres; fabric weaving, dyeing and spinning;

ALTERNATIVE ENGLAND & WALES

The directory does not precisely follow the categories of the book, though it cross-references. I have tried to make it relatively independent so you don't need to refer to the book for explanations. Bibliographies can go on for ever, but I have preferred to give relatively few items and annotate them properly, rather than exhaustive lists of bare titles. But I'm pretty inconsistent at times.

Each section has a short introduction giving reasons for including some things and not others, and why they might be considered 'Radical Technology'. The sections are subdivided into convenient categories, and within each subdivision the items move from the general to the specific, the elementary to the advanced, and the theoretical to the practical. I tend to give bibliographies first, then collections of essays or general works, textbooks, then more specialised items and finally 'lollipops' — things that are particularly illuminating, fun to read, or that just turned me on. Mixed in with publications are references to organisations, or in some cases individuals, who can at least tell you where to ask next. Where there are borderline topics not covered, I have tried to indicate what's missing and suggested where you might start to look.

Nearly all the publications are British or North American. The reasons for this rather narrow scope are: (1) 'Radical Technology' in the sense here used seems to be largely restricted to the Anglo-Saxon world, although of course its spirit is universal; (2) we're a terribly parochial lot and don't have much contact with those outside the fraternity, especially if they don't speak English. Where the foreign stuff *is* known it is included to give at least an initial lead, should anyone want to start something in the country concerned.

There might be problems finding some of the books or periodicals mentioned. In the USA, the Alternative Sources of Energy Lending Library should be helpful (see 2.33). In Britain, much of the material is to be found in 'movement' bookshops, of which a list can be got from Rising Free (see box 2). For browsing, it's very difficult. Compendium bookshop is probably best (see box 2). Or one might be able to use the AA library or get access to the excellent collection of material at AHS (both by prior arrangement). On the political side, the Public Library, 197 Kings Cross Road, London NW1. Otherwise, keep plugging the public libraries, both on principle and because if they order the material it helps to get it around to people who would otherwise never see it. See box for further information on where to find things.

The numbering of sections is just for easy cross-reference. The system is very simple. Separate sections are numbered in sequence, 1,2,3 . . . but a subdivision adds a digit: 3.1, and its own subdivisions 3.11, 3.12, etc. If the system bugs you, just ignore it.

This may all seem a bit involved, but I'm trying to make it fool-proof for those who want to chase things up, and at the same time provide a coherent package tour for the idly curious. One other thing, often asked — I have not read all the books.

the magazine of radical science and peoples' technology

UNDERCURRENTS
number 6

WINDMILLS•ELECTRONICS•DOME-GROWN FOOD•HEAT PUMPS•
WATER POWER•SCI—FI•NEWS, REVIEWS and lots more....

inside...
it's a
G.A.S.
conversion!

around; strangers; bits that don't fit in elsewhere. Useful far beyond London.

This famous work now has two cousins:
◆ *Alternative England and Wales* (Nicholas Saunders, 65 Edith Grove London SW10: £2.50) [OB,MB] and *Alternative Scotland* (Wildwood House, London, 1975)[OB,MB] which cover many alternative technology projects and related topics.

In France, the equivalent is:
◆ *Manuel de la Vie Pauvre* by Les Enfants D'Aquarius (Vivre/Stock 2, Paris, 1974: 28F) France's answer to *Alternative London*. A guide to most aspects of the cheap 'n simple life, including excellent directories of periodicals, bookshops and libraries, and a special chapter on energy alternatives.
◆ *An Index of Possibilities: Energy and Power*, edited by The Catalog, (Clanose Publishers/Wildwood House in conjunction with Arrow Books, London: £2.50, Pantheon, New York) [OB,MB]. A kind of alternative cyclopaedia, big format and remarkable graphics. Very strong on the freaky side. Contains one short but well-annotated bibliography on AT (p. 120) and column-miles of access information on *really* alternative technologies (wierd psychic abilities etc). It can hardly be called *radical* but it's a lot of fun.

2.2 PERIODICALS

Remember that by the time this book comes out, all the subcription rates will have gone up, and some mags will have died.

2.21 BASIC
These are the fundamental journals, focusing on the small-scale hardware, but frequently including discussion of the wider issues.
◆ *Undercurrents* (275 Finchley Road, London NW3: £2.50 for six issues anywhere or $7.50 US airmail; back issues 50p; bi-monthly)[MB,SB]. Frankly indispensable. There are plenty of hardware recipes, but also political analysis and news about what's going on. Just as a good read, it's hard to beat. See also 2.311.
◆ *Alternative Sources of Energy* (Route 2, Box 90-A, Milaca, MN 56353, USA: $5.00 for six issues, approximately bi-monthly). *ASE* has been getting fatter and fatter and better and better ever since it was a scruffy old cyclostyled newsl-sheet. Plenty of hard information, but this doesn't prevent them speculating wildly if it's needed. Apart from articles, there are always dozens of reviews and endless letters, contact lists, reports of meetings, surveys; they seem to work terribly hard. Indispensable if you live in the USA or Canada. See also 2.33.

---

stone; grasses; rushes, bamboo, wood. Almost a period piece by now.
◆ *The Rational Technology Unit at the Architectural Association*, 1973-74 (AA:40p). [AA]. A collection of thirteen concise articles on various small-scale technical alternatives, and a series of excellent annotated bibliographies and contact lists in the following categories: general; sulphur; rammed earth and soil cement; nutrition and food production; wind power; water power; solar energy; aerobic composting; methane production — anaerobic decomposition; heat pumps. See also AA library bibliographies, no 14 on Self-Help Housing, Squatters and Housing Associations, and no 15 on Solar and Wind Energy.
◆ *Comtek 74* (from Jenny Hiles, 13 Bedford Street, Bath, Avon: 25p). Has an extraordinary address list left over from the last festival of community technology.
All the above share a style which can only

be described as 'alternative'. Two excellent, systematic books with a more scholarly manner are: *Energy Environment and Building*, by Philip Steadman (Cambridge University Press, London, 1975) and *The Autonomous House* by Robert and Brenda Vale (Thames & Hudson, London, 1975). They are more exactly described in 3.2, but are full of carefully assembled general reference material.
Other 'access tools' (as they say in America) to areas closely related to Radical Technology, follow.
◆ *Alternative London*, by Nicholas Saunders (Nicholas Saunders and Wildwood House, London, 1973: 85p) [OB]. Covers many of 'AT's' natural bed-mates in a small volume bursting with well-researched information and contacts on: housing; home-making; eating; money; in trouble; communications; self-development; drugs; sex; crafts; community development; liberation; getting

◆ *In the Making* (221 Albert Road, Sheffield S8, Yorks, England: 60p a year for two full directories and supplements, or 15p for annual issues) [MB,CO,RF]. ' A directory of proposed productive projects in self-management or radical technology, and people who want to start work in them'. A running guide to projects and people looking for projects. It also contains short articles and letters from people commenting about the state of the self-management movement. Invariably contains a brief directory of Radical Technology sources, and all sorts of special news and information you won't get any other way. See also 13.2.

◆ *Journal of the New Alchemists* (New Alchemy Institute [East], PO Box 432, Woods Hole, MA 02543, USA; normally obtainable through Associate Membership of the Institute [$25] but they might make special arrangements if you write. It comes out very rarely, but is beautifully produced; contains a unique mixture of completely straight scientific papers (eg 'Studies of the Ecology of the Characid Fish *Brycon Guatamalensis* in the Rio Tirimbina, Heredia Province, Costa Rica, with Special Reference to its Culture as a Food Fish'), reports of activity on the New Alchemy farm, freaky graphics, and a general air of whimsy. How science could be, if only . . .

◆ *Alternative Energy Sources Newsletter* (PO Box 134, Kingston, Surrey KT2 6PR; comes with membership of CTT Association [2.311] £3.78 a year). Technically oriented — methane, wind, sun, hydro, domes, etc, emphasising D.I.Y. aspects.

◆ *Appropriate Technology* (Intermediate Technology Publications, 9 King Street, London WC2: £3.50 a year quarterly). This is the recently started journal of the Intermediate Technology Development Group. Mostly Third-World oriented, it is both newsy and practical, and it covers economic questions also, but appears to shy away from any political questions.

◆ *The Mother Earth News* (PO Box 70, Hendersonville, NC 28739, USA: $6.00 a year, bimonthly, $8.00 outside the USA). [CO]. Extremely useful source of practical information, and exhaustive lists of contacts, with a truck store to match. One has to read between the slabs of rather cloying homespun philosophy.

◆ *De Kleine Aarde* ('The Small Earth') (Munsel 17, Boxtel NB, The Netherlands: 20 guilders a year, quarterly). This is a really excellent magazine basically dealing in eco-tech. It's a pity it's so inaccessible for reasons of language.

2.22   FRIENDS, RELATIONS AND COMRADES
These are journals that carry occasional articles on radical or alternative technology, or cover related areas.

2.221 *Ecological*
Architectural Design (26 Bloomsbury Way,

Abbreviations

There are certain sources and organisations which are referred to so frequently in the text that I have abbreviated them. This might be confusing at first but most of them crop up so often you get to learn them fast enough. Detailed descriptions of these items can be found in the sections indicated by the numbers. Abbreviations in **bold** are organisations; abbreviations in *italics* are publications; abbreviations in [square brackets] indicate where an item might be found, and a list of these is given in the next box.

AA	Architectural Association	2.31
AARTU	*Architectural Association Rational Technology Unit Report*, 1973-74	2.1
AD	*Architectural Design* (periodical)	2.22
ADDS	Special issue of *Architectural Design*: 'Designing for Survival', July 1972	2.1
AHS	Autonomous Housing Study, Technical Research Division, Department of Architecture, University of Cambridge	2.31
ASE	*Alternative Sources of Energy* (periodical)	2.21
ASEB	*Alternative Sources of Energy* (book)	2.1
ASEbib	Lists of holdings in ASE lending library, in *ASE* nos 9 and 15.	2.1
BSSRS	British Society for Social Responsibility in Science	2.312
CTT	Conservation Tools and Technology	2.311
EP	*Energy Primer*	2.1
HDRA	Henry Doubleday Research Association	2.312
ITDG	Intermediate Technology Development Group	2.312
PW	*Public Works*	2.1
SH	*Shelter*	2.1
SS	*Survival Scrapbook* series	2.1
TMEN	*The Mother Earth News* (periodical)	2.21
UC	*Undercurrents* (periodical)	2.21
VITA	Volunteers in Technical Assistance	2.33
WEE	*Whole Earth Epilog*	2.1
WEC	*Whole Earth Catalog*	2.1

London WC1: £8.40 a year, £6.00 for students, overseas £13.20; expensive, isn't it? — that's the trouble with overground magazines, salaries, overheads . . .) [CO,AD]. This is not strictly ecological, but it has an excellent track-record of articles and special columns on 'eco-tech', all mixed up with the flotsam and jetset of the latest architectural gimmickry.

◆ *The Ecologist* (Catesby, Molesworth Street, Wadebridge, Cornwall: £3.00 a year, monthly) [OB]. Frequent articles on technical alternatives among the cries of doom.

◆ *Environment* (438 N. Skinker Boulevard, St Louis, Missouri 63130: $10.00 a year in US, $2.00 more for foreigners). Frequent, very well researched articles on alternatives, generally for application on a fairly large scale. This is a useful corrective to the constitutional miniaturism of 'AT' freaks.

Two new ecology magazines that are practically oriented:

◆ *Aether* (Cairnleith Croft, Ythanbank,

Ellon, Aberdeenshire, Scotland) [MB].

◆ *Radical Ecologist* (PO Box 87, Carlton South, Vic. 3053, Australia).

And two French ones:

◆ *La Gueule Ouverte* (10 Rue des Trois - Portes, 75005 Paris. Weekly). Radical ecology in the *Charlie Hebdo* style, with regular AT stuff in cartoon form. Highly polemical and funny.

◆ *Le Sauvage* (11 Rue d'Aboukir, Paris 75002). A more glossy, bourgeois affair altogether. Bit like *The Ecologist* but smarter.

◆ *Self-Reliance Newsletter* (29 Dartmouth Avenue, Huddersfield, Yorks: bimonthly, £1 a year). A nice little mimeo job on the determinedly arcadian front.

2.222 *Science*
Science for People (9 Poland Street, London W1: £2.00 a year, quarterly) [MB]. Journal of the British Society for Social Responsibility in Science. Radical orientation, focuses on institutional science, and alternative

Where to find things

Many of the sources cited in the directory will be difficult to find through the normal channels of libraries and high-street bookshops, and I have occasionally added a suggestion as to where they are likely to be found.

[OB]   Ordinary Bookshops, like Smiths.

[SB]   Specialist Bookshops, like Foyles, Dillons, or university bookshops.

[MB]   Movement bookshops, the kind that sell political material or underground magazines, of which two important ones are:

[CO]   Compendium (240 Camden High Street, London NW1; tel 01-485 8944) — split into two parts, one political, the other freaky; very wide range, and lots of foreign stuff that is otherwise inaccessible. Write for *Catalogue No. 5 Alternative Technology and Ecology*: 200 items and —

[RF]   Rising Free (197 Kings Cross Road, London WC1; tel 01-837 0283) — very good on radical magazines, booklets, general ephemera, and pleasantly scruffy reprints of Great Works. They produce a list of MB's in Britain, and run The Public Library.

[AA]   Architecture Association library or bookshop (34 Bedford Square, London WC1; tel 01-636 0974).

[AD]   Obtainable from Architectural Design, (26 Bloomsbury Way, London WC1; tel 01-405 6325).

[LO]   Libraries only — or second hand bookshops (out of print).

[HMSO]   Her Majesty's Stationery Office. Lists of publications can be seen in any public library.

Other useful places to get stuff mentioned in the lists:

Blackwells, Broad Street, Oxford: write for a catalogue; straight stuff.

The Public House Bookshop (21 Little Preston Street, Brighton; tel 28357) very good on anarchist and freak stuff, often with American and continental titles otherwise unobtainable.

Housman's Bookshop, (5 Caledonian Road, London N1; tel 01-837 4473) is particularly good on ecology and the non-violent revolutionary literature.

In USA all I can suggest (which not a trifle) is the Alternative Sources of Energy lending library.

patterns of organisation. Chris Ryan, contributor of the textiles article in this book, was formerly its editor.

◆ *Radical Science Journal* (9 Poland Street, London W1: £1.50 a year, 3 times a year) [MB,SB]. (Libertarian) Marxist perspective oriented towards the question 'What is socialist science and technology?'. Heavy stuff, but hearts of gold.

◆ *New Scientist* (128 Long Acre, London WC2: £10.80 a year, weekly) [OB]. Very good indeed for keeping up with the straight science world; plenty of social comment and occasional material directly relevant to Radical Technology.

◆ *Science Bulletin* (10p, irregular). Produced by the Communist Party. A bit dry, but trying hard. No time for windmills.

◆ *Survivre et Vivre* (6 Rue Chappe, 75018 Paris, France: 3.50F, monthly). French radical science magazine, hard-hitting.

◆ *Science For The People* (9 Walden Street, Jamaica Plain, MA 02130, USA, bimonthly)

[CO, or from BSSRS]. The main radical science journal in the US. The 'the' in the title differentiates it from the BSSRS's magazine and indicates a more Leninist approach.

◆ *Spark* (CSRE, 475 Riverside Drive, New York NY 10027). Also radical, mainly oriented towards institutionalised engineering, but more sympathetic to alternatives than *Science For The People*. You can get it by joining the Committee for Social Responsibility in Engineering ($10) at the above address.

2.223 The movement
Peace News (8 Elm Avenue, Nottingham: £5 a year, weekly) [MB]. Very thorough coverage of movement events from a non-violent revolutionary point of view, with frequent articles of interest to radical technologists. It includes the occasional *CLAP Bulletin* (see BIT, 2.312). For simply keeping in touch, it's excellent.

◆ *Resurgence* (275 King's Road, Kingston, Surrey: £2.50 a year, bimonthly) [MB]. 'Journal of the Fourth World', ie small, mutual-aid groups, dedicated to a kind of green decentralism, more gentle and respectable than the usual anarchist stuff. Frequent material on technical alternatives.

◆ *Communus* (3 Endsleigh Street, London WC1: 15p, monthly). This is the magazine of the ecology/community action project of the National Union of Students and is another good organ for keeping in touch. A good mixture of disparate concerns, including radical technology.

◆ *Wildcat* (Box 999, 197 Kings Cross Road, London WC1: £2.50 a year, monthly) [MB]. The link-journal of the active libertarian Left. Every issue has a special in-depth supplement. Back issues 15p.

◆ *Vannbaereren* (Regnbuetrykk, Boks 13, 9155 Karlsoy, Norway: 10NKr a year, quarterly). I'm afraid this is in Norwegian, but if you can surmount that barrier it's one of the liveliest freak magazines anywhere and contains plenty of technics, theory and practice.

◆ *Coevolution Quarterly* (558 Santa Cruz, Menlo Park, CA 94025, USA: $6.00 a year). This is the journal of the Point Foundation, and periodical arm of the *Whole Earth Catalog* and *Epilog*. It is organised in the same sections as the *Epilog*, including 'Soft Technology', but with an even more heavy-survivalist bias. Being essentially Stewart Brand's creature, its scope (to delicate radical sensibilities) is shocking. Nothing is taboo, unfortunately. Unlike most freaky mags, it is rich and fat enough to carry long articles that can go into things properly, and to reprint great classics that we have been

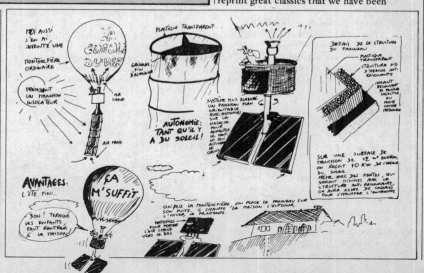

looking for all these years. For adrenalin jags and bits of Zeitgeist, it's a bargain turn-on.

You may find this selection a bit wishy-washy. *Chacun à son goût.* For stronger meat washy. For stronger meat try *Liberation, Solidarity, Anarchy, Telos, Ramparts, Bulletin of the Institute for Workers' Control, Catonsville Road Runner, Review of Radical Political Economics, Socialist Register, New Left Review, International Socialism,* or even *Marxism Today.*

2.3 CONTACTS

This is a list of groups concerned in one way or another with radical or alternative technology. I should emphasise at the outset that the activities pursued by many of them can be severely disrupted by too many enquiries and visitors, so be sensitive, and be prepared to take no for an answer. If you write and get no reply, try again and make the letter funny.

I have organised the entries geographically, but have excluded Third World groups. They are found in section 12.3.

2.31 BRITAIN

2.311 Generalists

These groups play around with technical alternatives in general, although of course each has its *specialites de la maison.*
◆ **Undercurrents Limited** (11 Shadwell, Uley, Dursley, Gloucestershire; tel. Uley 636 or 01-891 0989). A non-profit company limited by guarantee. The group that produces *Undercurrents* under the benign guidance of Godfrey and Sally Boyle, many members of which helped to produce this book. They have developed a wide network of contacts in all aspects of Radical Technology, and if you want to get the feel of what's going on, there are weekly meetings in London (phone one of the above numbers for details).
◆ **Street Farm** (The Vicarage, 21 Flodden Road, London SE5; tel 01-274 3045). Have a look at the interview with them in the book. Clever and funny, practical anarchists and guerilla architects. Built the first eco-house and now working on an old church. Lots of practical experience.
◆ **Radtech** (71 Thirlwell Road, Sheffield S8; tel 0742-583741 583856). This is a radical technologists' collective set up in a large industrial city with the intention of producing useful goods in a small co-operative factory. Good on electronics, and planning a range of alternative technology projects. Jos Kingston, who wrote the article 'It's Been Said Before . . . ' in the book, is a member of Radtech.
◆ **Architecture Association** (36 Bedford Square, London WC1; tel 01-636 0974). This is a major centre for radical activity (well, mostly talk, but that's necessary too) of all kinds, and particularly alternative technologies. Gerry Foley's Rational Technology Unit is well represented in this book (see articles on wind and subsoil building by the Taylor brothers) and in *AARTU.* Another AA contributor to the book is Tom Woolley (self-build housing), who with John Turner (author of *Freedom to Build,* 2.51) has set up a study of 'Alternatives in Housing' in the Graduate School. Other AA people concerned with technical alternatives are John Shore (see 3.72), George Kasabov, and Martin Pawley, well-known for *The Private Future* (2.53) and his advocacy of 'garbage housing' (3.5).
◆ **Autonomous Housing Study** (Technical Research Division, Dept of Architecture University of Cambridge, 1 Scroope Terrace,

Cambridge; tel Cambridge 54265). Several important theorists are connected with this group. Alex Pike has designed an extremely fancy autonomous house featured in the article on autonomous units. James Thring and Gerry Smith have done sterling work on the economics of alternative technologies. Phil Steadman's painstaking survey *Energy, Environment and Building* is eulogised in 2.1 (85 Norwich Street, Cambridge). Robert and Brenda Vale (The Horse and Gate, Witcham Toll, Sutton, Ely, Cambs.) have contributed articles to the book (solar energy and vernacular building), written a definitive textbook on autonomous servicing, and are now converting an old country pub. Robert is director of the Autonomous House project at Brunel University.
◆ **Conservation Tools and Technology Ltd** (PO Box 134, Surrey KT2 6PR). Formerly 'Low-Impact Technology Ltd', now reorganised, offering sales or consultancy on bits of AT gadgetry (windmills, fireless cookers, composting toilets, etc). There is a quarterly newsletter *Alternative Energy Sources,* and a CTT Association has been formed offering discount rates. A lonely attempt to go commerical. The Design Wing is Ian Hogan, a veteran alternative gadgeteer (Hillside Cottage, Wotton-Under-Edge, Gloucestershire). Write for excellent little booklet giving details of stock and publications.
◆ **Comtek** (Community Technology) (13 Bedford Street, Bath, Avon; tel 63717). They do all sorts of things (housing, transport, recycling, smithing) but are most famous for their festivals of alternative technology (write for Comtek '74 catalogue — 'over 600 useful addresses').
◆ **The National Centre for Alternative Technology** (Llwyngwern Quarry, Pantperthog, Machynlleth, Powys, Wales; tel Machynlleth 2400). An earnest and pretent-

iously titled but well-intentioned attempt to bring respectability to alternative technology by careful testing and practical demonstrations. They have worked very hard and it deserves to succeed. Worth a visit.

2.312 Specialists

These groups have focused on specific aspects of radical technology.
◆ **British Society for Social Responsibility in Science** (BSSRS) (9 Poland Street, London W1; tel 01-437 2728). This is the main radical science organisation in Britain and anyone working for radical change in science or technology should join. It has focused on issues of factory safety and riot control, but its concerns are wide-ranging. Write for series of excellent pamphlets. Two contributors to this book, Charlie Clutterbuck ('Agribusiness') and Alan Dalton ('Chemicals from Biological Sources') are part-time workers.
◆ **Intermediate Technology Development Group** (Parnell House, 25 Wilton Road, London SW1; tel 01-828 5791 4). A very important source of advice and material on small-scale technologies for the Third World. Not noted for its radicalism, but represents a great deal of accumulated experience. Its publications, apart from the journal *Appropriate Technology,* include a guide to hand-operated and animal-drawn equipment, a manual on building construction, another on simple methods of water treatment, and technical specifications for a metal-bending machine and an oildrum forge. A list can be obtained on request.
◆ **Council for Small Industries in Rural Areas** (CoSIRA) (35 Camp Road, Wimbledon, London SW19; tel 01-946 5101). This body provides advice and assistance for groups intending to set up medium-scale industries in rural areas.
◆ **BIT** (146 Great Western Road, London

W11; tel 01-229 8219) is an information service on every facet of alternative living. It has contacts throughout Europe, and publishes a very useful information digest which changes its name every issue (call it *Bitman*: £1 a year or 25p an issue). It also co-ordinates CLAP (Community Levy for Alternative Projects) whereby financially successful ventures support others, while they get started. 'AT' projects are particularly welcome, and on past experience, have a good chance of getting money. CLAP is an extremely important experiment. If you earn any kind of wage you should contribute 4% CLAP tax.

◆ **Henry Doubleday Research Association** (20 Convent Lane, Bocking, Braintree, Essex, UK). Headed by the indefatigable Laurence D. Hills, who wrote the article 'Compost Culture' in this book. It has carried out decades of research on small-scale organic gardening, and has initiated a decentralised programme of experiments with subscribers all over the country. An annual subscription of £3 will secure quarterly newsletter reports and materials. The newsletters by themselves are 15p each. Absolutely fundamental for would-be organic gardeners, and cannot be too highly recommended.

◆ **Soil Association** (Walnut Tree Manor, Haughley, Stowmarket, Suffolk). This is another organic husbandry research organisation which puts out useful pamphlets.

◆ **Future Studies Centre** (15 Kelso Road, Leeds LS2 9PR). Into various alternative projects (ie not chrome-plated gee-whiz futurology), such as weekend Dig-ins.

◆ **Centre for Living** (Fachongle Isaf, Newport, Pembrokeshire, Wales). This is a project initiated by John Seymour (author of article 'Across the Hungry Gap' in the book, and of the well-known *Self-Sufficiency*) to train people in the many skills of self-sufficiency. (See *UC* 10.)

Other contacts can be found in *In the Making* (2.21), *The Survivalists* (2.51), *Comtek 74* (2.21), and in Nigel Turner's *Makin' It: A Guide to Some Working Alternatives* (Paper Tiger Publications, The Loft, The Manor House, River Lane, Petersham, Surrey TW10) [MB] .

2.32   EUROPE

Belgium

◆ **Mass Moving** (41 Lebeau Street, 1000 Brussels, Belgium). A radical street theatre group with great technological skill. One of their most spectacular exhibits is a focusing solar collector that generates steam at 700ºC, which is used to blow a solar raspberry on a 12-foot brass trumpet (see picture p.65).

Finland

◆ **Agitkrop** (Katajanokankatu 3B10, Helsinki 16, Finland). A group of British expatriates very strong on water power and situationalist politics, see *UC* 5 and 6, especially 'An Agitkrop Communique'. That one really burns the page. George Woolston, one of the group, contributed the articles on water supply and hydropower to this book.

France

A useful list of contacts in France can be found in *UC* 9.

◆ **Nature et Progres** (3 Chemin de la Bergerie, 91700 Sainte Genevieve du Bois). Organic agriculture – a large organisation.

◆ **Amis de la Terre** (15 Rue du Commerce, 75015 Paris). Friends of the Earth.

◆ **Fiches Ecologiques** (Daniel Fargeas, 14 Rue de la Poste, 66600 Rivesaltes). Concise information sheets on a wide range of ecological technologies, some straight, some very strange. Write for catalogue.

◆ **Jacques Michel** (14 Rue des Poissonniers,

92204 Neuilly sur Seine). Originator of the passive solar wall (see article on solar energy in the book).

◆ **Philippe Arreteau** can be contacted at La Terisse', La Ribeyre, 0714 Les Assions.

Germany

◆ **Project Das Neue Technik** (c/o Peter Owsianowski, 1000 Berlin 12, Sybelstrasse 46). A group connected with Robert Jungk at the Free University of Berlin (see interview with Jungk in the book: he can be contacted through the above address, or Steingasse 31, A-5010 Salzburg, Austria.)

The Netherlands

◆ **Project 'De Kleine Aarde'** (Small Earth) (Munsel 17, Boxtel, NB). An experimental farm run on a fairly large scale with some official support. It was founded by Sietz Leeflang, interviewed in the book, who also edits *De Kleine Aarde* (2.21). (See also Jaap t' Hooft [3.72])

◆ **Roel van Duijn**, Nieuwe Leliestraat 37, Amsterdam. The *primus inter pares* of the Kabouter movement, Kropotkin's prophet on earth, and explorer of liberatory technologies for the cities.

Norway

◆ **Vannbaereren** (c/o Jan Bojer, Regnbue-trykk, 9155 Karlsoy). 'Aquarius': produce the magazine (2.223) from somewhere up beyond the arctic circle.

Sweden

◆ **Per Janse** (Vikingagatan 10, S-11342 Stockholm). A journalist and agitator working in various political, environmental and radical technology projects. (See 'A Low-Energy Society – But How?' [4.13])

◆ **Eko-Bygg** (c/o Hans Nordenstrom, Postgraduate Studies, Dept of Architecture,

Lund Institute of Technology, Box 725, S-22027). An extensive graduate programme on 'ecological building'.

◆ **Gothenburg Alternative Technology Group** (c/o Bjorn Eriksson, Institute of Theoretical Physics, Chalmers Tekniska Hogskola Fack, S-40220 Goteborg). Working on an inventory of 'resource-frugal' technologies, and other things.

Switzerland

◆ **Alternative-Katalog** (GD1, Park im Gruene, CH-8803 Ruschlikon: 10 Sw. Fr). A 'Whole Swiss Catalog' covering building, communities, communications, transport, recycling.

◆ **Barglutli** ('mountain gnomes') (c/o Marco Bischof, Wasserman-Centrum, 3186 Dudingen, Fr). More German-speaking Swiss freaks (!) inspired by Sergius Golowin's *Lustige Eidgenossen* (Atlantis-Verlag, Zurich 1972) and believing that alternative culture (and technology) is the true heir of the authentic independent spirit of Switzerland.

◆ **BLABLA** (*Blaues Blatt*) (Box 97, CH-2900 Porrentruy: £3 a year, fortnightly). A magazine (in German), covering technological alternatives.

2.33   NORTH AMERICA

◆ **Alternative Sources of Energy.** The group of people connected with the magazine. Contact Eugene and Sandy Eccli (928 2nd Street, SW, Apt 4, Roanoke, VA 24016, USA); or Don and Abby Marier (Route 2, Box 90-A, Milaca, MN 56353, USA);or Jim and Elizabeth DeKorne (Box 5, El Rito, NM 87530, USA). They work hard keeping in touch with things in North America and are essential contacts. They publish the magazine (2.21), the book (2.1) and various pamphlets, maintain a carefully classified catalogue of contacts, and run a lending library. If you wish to join the communications network, send details of your particular interests to Don Marier at the above address. Details of holdings and lending charges for the library can be found in *ASE* 15, or write to ASE Lending Library also c/o Don Marier. A list of interest-profiles of members of the network – can also be found in *ASE* no. 15.

◆ **New Alchemy Institute East** (PO Box 432, Woods Hole, MA 02543). The philosophy behind it can be gauged from the interview with John Todd in the book. Their slogan is 'To restore the lands, protect the seas, and inform the earth's stewards', which might sound a bit airy-fairy, but many of them are dropped-out biologists from the Oceanographic Institute at Woods Hole and they know how to do research. Aquaculture is one of their specialities (I suppose you could say they had fish fingers), and they get grants for research on fish nutrition and other matters. Other things they do on their experimental farm on Cape Cod are reported in their *Journal of the New Alchemists* (2.21). They have been carrying out a programme of decentralised 'people's research' through the journal *Organic Gardening and Farming* (Rodale Press, E Minor Street, Emmaus, PA 18049). Associate membership of the Institute costs $25.00. A list of published literature is available on request. (See also articles by John Todd referred to in 2.42.)

◆ **New Alchemy Institute West** (Box 376, Pescadero, CA 94060, USA). They have specialised in organic agriculture and methane generation (Richard Merrill and John Fry), and collaborated in producing the stupendous *Energy Primer*. Richard's book *Radical Agriculture* should hatch one day. Peter van Dresser, interviewed in this book, has been associated with the New Alchemists on various projects.

◆ **Community Technology** (1520 New Hampshire Avenue, NW, Washington DC 20036). An extremely promising group getting it together in the back-streets of megalopolis. Their main current projects are basement fish-farming, small-scale solar cookers with a heat-store; community textile production with small power looms; alternative employment for graduate engineers and technicians; and a nice line in communal social theory. Send $1.00 and stamps for more details, or see article in *Spark*, vol 4, no. 2, Fall 1974.

◆ **Project Ouroboros** (University of Minnesota School of Architecture, 110 Architecture Building, Minneapolis, MN 55455). 'Ouroboros' (the snake that bites its tail) is the name of a house constructed by staff and students (see 3.72) to withstand the extreme summers and winters of Minnesota without external servicing. Publish *Ouroboros East* ($5.00) with plans for conversion of standard houses. See also article on autonomous units in the book.

◆ **Full Circle**, c/o Tom Bender/Lane DeMoll, 760 Vista Avenue, SE, Salem, OR 97302. Its goals are 'to help in the development of localised economies and self-reliant communities in the Pacific Northwest; to generate lower-cost and higher quality community services; to work toward energy-conserving, satisfying living and working patterns; and to sponsor labour-intensive, intermediate technology production processes.' Their projects include autonomous houses, credit unions, alternative employment projects etc. Tom Bender's work is particularly illuminating — 'Living Lightly'; 'Sharing Smaller Pies', and 'Environmental Design Primer' — all from above address.

◆ **Zomeworks Corporation** (PO Box 712, Albuquerque, NM 87103, USA). A fountain of brilliant designs, mostly to do with solar energy (see 4.24).

◆ **Max's Pot Center for Maximum Potential Building Systems** (6438 Bee Caves Road, Austin, Texas 78746). A group connected with the School of Architecture at the University of Texas, Austin. They do everything: organic gardening, algae ponds; methane, solar walls, wind generators, integrated systems. Several reports are in preparation.

◆ **Shelter group and Lloyd Kahn** (Shelter Publications, Box 279, Bolinas CA 94924). If you want to know what they're into, just look at *Shelter* (2.1) and read 'Smart but not Wise', Lloyd Kahn's manifesto of the neo-primitive.

◆ **The Farallones Institute** (PO Box 700, Point Reyes, California CA 94956). Another group with experience in integrated systems, having built a small, low-cost dwelling with 'AT' gadgetry. Report available for $2, with more to come.

◆ **VITA (Volunteers in Technical Assistance)** (3706 Rhode Island Avenue, Mt Rainier, MD 20822, USA). They have tended to concentrate on Third World problems, as such publications as 'Bat Control' and 'Smoking Fish in a Cardboard Smokehouse', would tend to indicate. But *The Village Technology Handbook* ($7.00) is a great asset anywhere. Write for a list of publications — some good ones on wind and water.

Two important radical groups in the USA are:

◆ **SESPA** (Scientists and Engineers for Social and Political Action)/Science for the People (9 Walden Street, Jamaica Plain, MA 02130). A very active federation of groups all over the US, publishing *Science for the People* (2.222) and numerous other books and pamphlets (see especially *Science Walks on Two Legs*, 12.1), and co-ordinate radical activity connected with science.

◆ **Committee for Social Responsibility in Engineering** (CSRE) (475 Riverside Drive, New York NY 10027). 'Seeks to challenge the present orientation of engineering and to explore ways in which engineering skills can be used to solve the obvious and growing ills of our society'. Organising among engineers, less university-oriented than SESPA, and more sympathetic to 'positive' radical technology. Publish *Spark* (2.222).

Canada:
   Two very important Canadian Organisations:

◆ **Brace Research Institute** (McDonald College, McGill University, St Anne de Bellevue, 800 Quebec, Canada). This group

specialises in Third World problems, but produces an extremely competent series of technical pamphlets which could be useful anywhere. It is particularly strong on wind power (see SS5 for a brief list). Write for list of publications, Miscellaneous publication no. 17.

◆ **Minimum Cost Housing Group** (School of Architecture, McGill University, Montreal, Quebec, Canada). Their most notable activity has been the construction of cheap dwellings from building blocks made from waste sulphur, see *The Ecol Operation* (1972) $4.00; and an investigation of methods of waste treatment (see 6.2). Information is published in a series of booklets entitled 'The Problem Is'. I get the impression they are a bit snobbish about amateur technologists with ideological axes to grind, so if you write to them, try and get hold of some headed note-paper.

2.34   Australia
Contact with Australia is regrettably weak (at the moment), but an excellent contact can be found in Chris Ryan (c/o Prof S Hammond, 3 Story Street, Parkville, Victoria 3052); or Hugh Saddler (School of Biological Sciences, University of Sydney, NSW 20006).

STREET FARMERS

2.4 ARTICLES

These are of a general nature and could serve as a quick introduction to various aspects of Radical Technology. Regular articles appear in the journals in 2.21; less frequently those in 2.22; on the political side see the journals listed at the end of 2.223.

2.41 SPECIAL COLLECTIONS

◆ *Alternative Technology*, vol. 1, edited by Horace Herring (Smoothie Publications, c/o John Noyce, Flat 2, 83 Montpelier Road, Brighton, Sussex BN1 3BD, UK). Five articles covering a wide range, some of them reprints from elsewhere; general articles on the philosophy of AT, alternative energy sources, workers' self-management and Third World-appropriate technologies.

◆ *Sources*, edited by Theodore Roszak (Harper Colophon, New York, 1972). More famous reprints, including two by Schumacher, one by Bookchin, the *Berkeley Tribe's* 'Blueprint for a Communal Environment' and related material, plus an 'access section' to groups and magazines with an unusual (head trip, consciousness-raising) slant, now unfortunately rather dated.

◆ *Man-Made Futures*, edited by Nigel Cross, Dave Elliott and Robin Roy (Open University Press, Milton Keynes, 1974) is another catalogue of golden oldie reprints (shards of Illich, Roszak, Bookchin, Papanek, Bodington, Jungk, Robin Clarke, etc.).

The other two contain all original articles:

◆ AARTU (see 2.1) 'Appropriate Technology', special issue of *Impact of Science on Society*, vol. 23, no. 4, October-December 1973 (UNESCO), containing articles by Robin Clarke, Mansur Hoda, Josefina Mena, Philippe Arreteau , Jon Sigurdsson and myself.

2.42 INDIVIDUAL ARTICLES

'Towards a Liberatory Technology', by Murray Bookchin, has been perhaps the single most influential piece of writing on radical technology. Reprinted endlessly, it can be found entire in *Post Scarcity Anarchism* (2.51) and *Anarchy* 78, August 1967; or dismembered in *Sources* and *Man-Made Futures* (2.41).

Of similar vintage, but from a less conventionally radical viewpoint, are E.F. Schumacher's essays 'Buddhist Economics', *Resurgence* vol. 1, no. 11, 1968; and 'The Economics of Permanence', *Resurgence* vol.3, no. 1, May-June 1970. Both these are reprinted in *Sources* (2.41).

John Todd (interviewed in the book) has written an agreeable series of articles in *Organic Farming and Gardening* magazine (Rodale Press, E Minor Street, Emmaus, PA 18049, USA): 'Shaping an Organic America' (Sept 1971); 'Designing a New Science' (Oct 1971); 'The Organic Gardener and Farmer as Scientist' (Nov 1971); 'The 21st Century Homestead' (Dec 1971).

Robin Clarke's writing is also deservedly well-known: 'The Soft Technology Research Community', *UC* 2; reprinted as 'The Biotechnic Research Community' in *Futures*; 'Technology for an Alternative Society', *New Scientist*, January 11th, 1973. 'The Pressing Need for Alternative Technology', in *Impact of Science on Society*, vol. 23, no. 4, reprinted in *Man-Made Futures* (2.41).

'Community Technology' by Karl Hess ('the man who used to write Goldwater's speeches'), in *Spark*, vol. 4 no. 2, 1974 is fine stuff, reprinted in UC 12.

Some of my articles could perform an introductory function: 'In Search of Allies for the Soft Technologies' in *Impact* (2.41); 'Notes on "Soft Technology"' *Theoria to*

Theory vol. 8, nos 2 and 3 (Gordon and Breach Scientific Publishers, 1974). See also Breach Scientific Publishers, 1974).

All the above tend to eulogise their subject. More critical treatments can be found in the following, all in *Undercurrents*: 'Ramifications and Propagations of Street Farm', by Graham Caine and Bruce Haggart (no. 4); 'Transfiguration Among the Windmills', by Peter Harper (no. 5); 'What's *Left* of Alternative Technology?' by Peter Harper (no. 6). (These two reprinted in *Alternative Technology*, 2.41) 'A.T. in the Shade', by Peter Harper (no. 7). 'The Future of Alternative Technology', Dave Elliott and Colin Stoneman (no. 10).

Last but not in the least least, three excellent and highly recommended essays. Make nice introductions, from different angles, if you can find them . . . 'Is Indian Science Truly Indian?' by A.K.N. Reddy (12.2). 'Living Lightly' by Tom Bender, unpublished, University of Minnesota School 70 Vista Avenue, S.E., Salem, OR 97302, USA. And Walter Szykitka's introduction to *Public Works* (2.1).

And as an encore, two political lollipops to help you make sense of it all: 'Introduction to Alternative Culture', by "Woody", *UC* 10, 11, 12 & 13; 'An Open Letter to Leszek Kolakowski', by E. P. Thompson, *Socialist Register*, 1973.

2.5 BOOKS

On the whole the specialised technical practice of Radical Technology is covered in sections 3-13. The books in this section cover the more theoretical aspects. This is how they are organised: 2.51 contains basic 'start here' books, equivalent to the articles in 2.42; 2.52 covers critiques of the existing dispensation (if you don't think there's anything wrong, what's the point of all this sound and fury?); 2.53 contains rebuttals of these critiques and 2.54 presents the ragbag anarcho-utopian-visionary-revolutionary tradition which seems to constitute the main political ancestry of the spirit of Radical Technology.

Readers whose concern is restricted to building windmills out of old bike parts (in itself an honourable part of our enterprise) might wonder what all this 'politics' is doing here. The reason, as indicated already in 1.1, is that the spread of groovy small-scale technical capabilities just ain't enough. The main problem is a *collective* one which we mustn't duck out of.

2.51 BASIC

◆ *Post-Scarcity Anarchism*, by Murray Bookchin (Ramparts Press, San Francisco, 1971; Wildwood House, London, 1973) [SB,MB]. A book of vintage Bookchin, containing a number of celebrated essays, including 'Towards a Liberatory Technology', 'Ecology and Revolutionary Thought' and 'Listen, Marxist!'.

◆ *Fields, Factories and Workshops Tomorrow*, by Peter Kropotkin, edited, with introduction, abridgments and notes by Colin Ward. (Allen & Unwin, London, 1974; Benjamin Blau, New York, 1968.) This is a bringing up-to-date of Kropotkins' analysis of the possibilities for Radical Technology in his era, showing that what was feasible in 1900 is long overdue in 1976.

◆ *Alternative Technology and the Politics of Technological Change*, by David Dickson (Fontana, London, 1974) [OB]. An essentially political assessment with a discussion of technics sandwiched in the middle. It is a good theoretical introduction, and has been adopted as the basic textbook for the Open University 'Man-Made Futures' course. David is the only Englishman I know who can write like Habermas or Marcuse.

◆ *Small is Beautiful: Economics as if People Mattered*, by E. F. Schumacher (Blond and Briggs, London, 1973; Harper & Row, New York, 1974). A paean to the intermediate scale by a 'Buddhist Economist'. Quaintly inspiring, with a dash of old-time religion.

◆ *Tools for Conviviality*, by Ivan Illich (Calder and Boyars, London, 1973; Harper & Row, New York, 1974). This is a brilliant and tantalising book. Illich tries to discover the reasons why satisfaction does not increase *pari passu* with the development of technology. Does he do it? One is always on the edge of crystallising his underlying conception of *nemesis*, which overcomes *hubris*, but . . . is it all an illusion? Romantic sociology? Soteriological politics? I dunno. Anyway, he's on our side. This and his other books are a good read (*Deschooling Society*, *Energy and Equity*, *Medical Nemesis*). His attempts to find alternative practical criteria for technology (instead of efficiency, convenience, power, etc.) are extremely valuable contributions.

◆ *The Survivalists*, by Patrick Rivers (Eyre-Methuen, London, 1975). As I write this I haven't seen it, but I know it's an attempt to survey the more ecological aspects of the

Street farmers till their land

Radical Technology movement, the results of Patrick's peregrinations round Britain and the United States. It should be a helpful list of contacts, with plenty of comment. Patrick's interviews with Peter van Dresser and John Todd in *this* book were part of his research.

The following three books are more specialised than the others, but have nevertheless a generally philosophical approach.

◆ *Freedom to Build*, John Turner and Robert Fichter (Macmillan, London, New York, 1972). This is a book of essays about self-building and user-involvement, in one of the most mystified areas of technology. It is mainly Third-World oriented, but the implications for industrial societies are obvious. 'Housing as a Verb'. It's terrific.

◆ *Design for the Real World*, by Victor Papanek (Paladin, London, 1974; Bantam, New York, 1973). This is, in a sense, a very obvious book about designing for people rather than profit, but it needs saying, over and over again. The question as to the partition of design *for* people and design *by* people is given less attention in this book, but his heart is very much in the right place (and one day, Vic, you may say the same of me).

◆ *Self-Sufficiency*, by John and Sally Seymour (Faber and Faber, London, 1973). John Seymour is the exact reincarnation of William Cobbett, and this is his revised *Cottage Economy*, full of handy hints, good-humoured prejudice and rugged ruralism. See his article in the book, 'Across the Hungry Gap' and 'Animal Farm'.

2.52   CRITIQUES OF INDUSTRIAL SOCIETY

Radical Technology justifies itself by its critique not only of capitalism, but of all known forms of advanced industrial society — and perhaps any possible form, although personally I'm a bit scared of following that line of thought too far. But industrial society is a many-headed beast, and it's hard to construct a unified critique, so I have divided the material up into various categories of 'reaction against modern society': anti-science, mystical, arcadian, New Left. These will be discussed in turn. They all have a bearing on Radical Technology.

2.521 *The anti-science reaction*
This is a rather indiscriminate condition ascribed both to those who are against the

supposed effects of science, and those who are against science itself. Formally, these are distinct: a debate about technological determinism and its consequences and a debate about the role played by scientific rationality in moulding our consciousness and behaviour. But in practice they tend to go together. On the one side there are the enthusiastic advocates of pure science and of technology applied in a 'scientific' manner — a tradition that includes Adam Smith, Andrew Ure, H. G. Wells, Thorstein Veblen, and today (am I being unintentionally satirical?) Bucky Fuller and Herman Kahn. On the other side are those who (often hypocritically) reject the scientific worldview altogether, with its (supposed) expression in the form of advanced technology — a tradition which includes Blake, Carlyle, Ruskin, Morris, Tolstoy (as social critics) and in this century, Lewis Mumford, Jacques Ellul and Ivan Illich. I tremble to say more, but here are some books on the subject.

A more-or-less neutral standpoint is taken in the following:
◆ *Science in the Modern World*, by A.N. Whitehead (Cambridge UP, 1926).
◆*Mechanisation Takes Command*, by Siegfried Giedion (Oxford UP, London, 1974; Norton, New York, 1969).
◆ *The Unbound Prometheus*, David Landes (Cambridge UP, London, New York, 1969).
◆ *Science and Society*, by Hilary and Steven Rose (Penguin, Harmondsworth, 1971; Peter Smith, New York).
◆*Politics and Technology* by Raymond Williams (Macmillan, London, 1971).
◆ *Scientific Knowledge and its Social Problems*, by J.R. Ravetz (Oxford UP, London, New York, 1971).
◆ *Technology and Society*, by Robin Roy and Nigel Cross (Open University, Man-Made Futures Design and Technology Course Units 2-3, 1975).

These are critical and committed:
◆ *Technics and Civilisation*, by Lewis Mumford (Routledge & Kegan Paul, London, 1934; Harcourt, Brace & World, New York, 1963).
◆ *The Myth of the Machine*, by Lewis Mumford (Secker & Warburg, London, 1967 Harcourt Brace and Jovanovich, New York)
◆ *The Pentagon of Power* by Lewis Mumford (Harcourt Brace and Jovanovich, New York, 1971).
◆ *The Technological Society*, by Jacques Ellul (Knopf, New York, 1964).
◆*One-Dimensional Man*, by Herbert Marcuse (Sphere, London, 1969; Beacon Press, New York, 1964).
◆ *Tools for Conviviality* (see 2.51)

Most of these take a liberal approach politically, but the Roses, Williams and Marcuse are more radical. Illich is unclassifiable. Other radical analyses of science and technology can

be found in *Ideology and Science*, ed. Steven and Hilary Rose and *The Control of Technology*, by David and Ruth Elliott (both at press as I write), and in any issue of *Radical Science Journal* (2.222). See also Andre Gorz's seminal article 'Technical Intelligence and the Capitalist Division of Labour' in *Telos* 12, Summer 1972.

Two books which I feel stand apart from most of the others, partly by virtue of their particular concern with the scientific worldview as a destructive idiology — not so much with technology — and partly because they are more vivid, passionate and romantic:
◆ *Where the Wasteland Ends: Politics and Transcendence in Post-Industrial Society*, by Theodore Roszak (Anchor, New York, 1973; Faber and Faber, London, 1974) [OB,MB] . A manifesto of transcendental radicalism; alternatives to materialist desiccation in radical politics; loads of Blake; some nice footnotes; what more could you want? It could be shorter . . .
◆ *Liberation and the Aims of Science: The Obstacles to Building a More Beautiful World*, Brian Easlea (Chatto and Windus, London, 1974; Rowman, New York, 1973) [OB,SB] . There's such a lot in this book: history, heroes, villains, scholarship, poetry, hope, care. He can see where the 'dead universe' vision of science has led us, but as an ex-physicist he cannot shake off the memory of that terrible beauty. Can we have science *and* life?

The problem with all this is that if the scientific worldview (whatever it is — it's not easy to pin down to a few sentences, although it should be, shouldn't it?) is as pernicious in its alienating effects as the critics fear, then an alternative Radical Technology would need completely different forms of systematic enquiry as a theoretical basis. But how can this be? Surely there is only one science, towards which we constantly move? But on the other hand, one thinks of Giordano Bruno, of Newton in his alchemical thought, of Fechner, William James, Whitehead, Bose, George Washington Carver, Wilhelm Reich, Jung, Laing . . . and all the others who didn't quite fit into the orthodox mould, but seemed (in their several ways) to have alternative methods of procedure which brought the universe back alive rather than in a bottle. It's a pity that such a list also includes Velikovsky, Lysenko . . . (we know they're nutty, don't we?) so perhaps after all it's better to stick with the devil we know, until perhaps we find the grail that is 'a stable alternative to the ideal of objectivity'. I draw back from the brink. Those who pressed on regardless are dealt with in next section.

2.522 *The Mystical Reaction*
Although partisans often present this as a rejection of rational thought, much of it can be presented in a clear and reasoned way. I shall consider in turn four claims which seem to me fairly typical.

(a) It may be occasionally more rational from the point of view of a 'deep' human welfare to explore and apply technologies for changing consciousness, or 'exploring inner space' (which, it is claimed, is vastly more complex, interesting, yet ordered, than is usually supposed), than messing around with the outer world, which is costly, gets in people's way, and is full of kickbacks, ecological and otherwise.
◆*The Centre of the Cyclone, An Autobiography of Inner Space*, by John C. Lilly (Calder and Boyars, London, 1973; Julian Press, New York, 1972).
◆ *The Psychology of Consciousness*, by Robert E. Ornstein (Freeman, London, 1972).
◆*The Nature of Human Consciousness*, ed. Robert E. Ornstein (Freeman, London, 1973).

◆ *Altered States of Consciousness*, by Charles C. Tart (Wiley, London, New York, 1969). See also the article in the book by Pete Russell, 'Inner Technologies'.

(b) New sciences and technologies could emerge from as-yet unrecognised principles.

◆ *Supernature: The Natural History of the Supernatural*, by Lyall Watson (Coronet, London, 1974; Bantam, New York, 1974).

◆ *Psychic Discoveries Behind the Iron Curtain*, by Sheila Ostrander and Lynn Schroeder (Abacus, London, 1974).

◆ *The Secret Life of Plants*, by Peter Tomkins and Christopher Bird (Allen Lane the Penguin Press, London, 1974).

◆ *Wilhelm Reich: Selected Writings*, ed. by M. B. Higgins (Vision Press, London, 1961).

◆ *Apparitions*, by G. N. M. Tyrrell (Collier, New York, 1963).

◆ *The UFO Experience: A Scientific Enquiry*, by J. Allen Hynek (Abelard-Schuman, New York, 1972).

(c) Sciences and Technologies based on different principles from our own were practised in prehistoric times, and could be recovered by suitable research, much of the hardware being extant in the form of menhirs, wells, trackways, mounds, etc, whose real significance is not recognised. A good concise introduction to this idea is John Michell's essay 'Megalithic Science' in his *The Old Stones of Land's End* (Garnstone, London, 1974). The same author's *The View Over Atlantis* is a longer (and less clear) treatment (Abacus, London, 1973; Ballantine, New York, 1972).

◆ *Megalithic Sites in Britain,* by Alexander Thom (Oxford UP, London, New York, 1967).

◆ *Megalithic Lunar Observatories*, by Alexander Thom (Oxford UP, London, New York, 1971).

◆ *Quicksilver Heritage*, by Paul Screeton (Thorsons, Northants, 1975). See also article 'Mysterious Energies' in *UC* 11 by Chris Hutton-Squire, and the periodical *The Ley Hunter*, edited by Paul Screeton (Egton Drive, Seaton Carew, Hartlepool, Cleveland TS 25 2AT; £1.50 a year, bimonthly). A more academic style is favoured by the Research into Lost Knowledge Organisation (RILKO) (36 College Court, Hammersmith, London W6).

(d) A deeper and healthier relationship (complementary? dialectical?) between 'objective' and 'subjective' sensibilities can be achieved, and should be sought.

◆ 'Sensuous-Intellectual Complementarity in Science', by Thomas R. Blackburn, in *The Nature of Human Consciousness*, ed. Ornstein (Freeman, London; 1973; Viking, New York, 1974). See also Ornstein's *The Psychology of Consciousness* (Freeman, London, 1973; Viking, New York, 1973).

◆ The theme is treated with great feeling in Robert Pirsig's *Zen and the Art of Motorcycle Maintenance* (The Bodley Head, London, 1974; Morrow, New York, 1974).

The significance of these matters for Radical Technology is potentially manifold. As Pete Russell points out in his article in the book, in a world of shortages on the supply side, it makes sense to pay at least some attention to the demand side, as long as we don't relapse into escapism and individual palliatives ('Don't worry about your environment, Mrs Brown, there's nothing you can do, just keep taking the pills . . . etc.). These technologies seem to be very light on non renewable resources, and ecologically clean. Maybe it's because they don't work very well? But the most interesting feature is that there seem to be inherent limits to the extent to which

they can be alienated and turned into commodities or controlled by experts. Since they necessarily require care and involvement from their users, they cannot be mechanised, marketed and merely consumed. As Illich might say, they are 'structurally convivial'.

Of course, it might all turn out to be rubbish, but you can see why the interest is there. It's not just escapism. The only trouble with the mystic lot is that they tend to be out on a limb and rarely connect with either the politics or the straight technology.

2.523 *The arcadian reaction*

A common reaction to complex modern urban culture has been a hunger for the simple, the old and the rural. It might be a direct emotional response, or it might be elaborately justified by appeal to various theories of human nature, society, or latterly, ecology. It leads in various directions: the ideal of self-

sufficiency (either of a traditional homesteading kind, or the more fancy 'autonomous house' variety); efforts at 'ecologically sound' husbandry; and a concern with outdated technologies and traditional crafts.

Historically, this ideal of a return to some simpler, more ideal, more natural state of existence, can be seen in the Peasants' Revolt of the fourteenth century, the Diggers' movement during the Commonwealth, the Owenites and other utopian socialists of the nineteenth century (see Jos Kingston's article in the book) and in modern populism. A book which puts a lot of this in perspective is Raymond Williams's *The Country and the City* (Paladin, London, 1974; D.U.P., New York, 1973). One of the essays in it shows each generation locating its 'Golden Age' a few centuries before, but when we travel back to examine the 'Golden Age' we find that they, too, felt themselves lapsed from some former state of grace: before the coming of the machines: before the enclosures and clearances: the Elizabethan yeomanry; the medieval freemen; before the 'Norman Yoke' — the true Saxon peasantry of Alfred, the pre-Saxon Kingdom of Arthur, and so on. He calls this 'the arcadian fallacy'. Radical Technologists need to

take careful account of this, to avoid empty fantasy and the charge of 'going back', which in an age which worships 'progress' is an unanswerable anathema. Personally, I'm a complete sucker for the arcadian fallacy, and here are some of its fruits:

Rural Rides (Penguin, Hamondsworth, Dutton, New York) and *Cottage Economy*, (New Portway Reprints, London, 1966; Kelley, New York) by William Cobbett, are both great classics, the former including dreadful fulminations about 'The great Wen' (London — if he could see it now!) and the latter about the evils of tea and the potato. Another famous classic of utopian arcady is *News from Nowhere* by William Morris (Routledge, London, New York, 1970). Morris wrote this in reaction to another utopian socialist novel, Edward Bellamy's *Looking Backward*, which is worth reading to contrast the urban, technological, progressive vision

with the arcadian one. Probably fictional treatments are the best way to get to grips with this (Shakespeare — eg *As You Like It*; the Romantic Poets, Borrow, Ruskin, Tolstoy, Gorky, Lawrence, Huxley, and endless SF stories today). In the non-fictional sphere, indulgent but precise accounts of the country ways and crafts can be found in the books of George Ewart Evans: *The Farm and the Village, The Pattern Under the Plough, Ask The Fellows Who Cut the Hay, The Horse in the Furrow, Acky, The Leaping Hare* (various dates, all Faber). More sardonic is *Total Loss Farm* by Raymond Mungo (Dutton, New York 1970), a saga of radical urban hippies trying to make it in the country. Quite a mess. On the other hand, to show that you don't need to be bred to it, as long as you have a fair supply of good old bourgeois discipline, *Living the Good Life*, by Helen and Scott Nearing (Schocken, New York, 1960), is a chronicle of formidable success by two (now octogenarian) ex-C. P. members creating everything out of nothing but hard work. Another amazing back-to-the-land story is *Hey Beatnik! This is the Farm Book*, by Stephen and The Farm (The Book Publishing Company, The Farm, Summertown, Tennessee

38483, USA) [MB]. It is about more than 600 totally vegetarian freaks living (apparently) happily ever after on a big farm in Tennessee. They have a counterculture style, but are rather strict, for example they won't make honey — 'It's laying a bad trip on the bees, man.' For Utopian theorists, an important case to study. (See also section 13).

On the revival of interest in obsolete technologies, numerous reprints bear witness: *On Architecture*, by Vitruvius (Dover, New York; Heinemann, London); *De Re Metallica*, by Agricola (Dover, New York, London); *Pirotechnia*, by Biringuccio (MIT Press). George Sturt's *The Wheelwright's Shop*, (Cambridge UP, London, New York, 1963), nearer our own time but still culturally exotic, is an absolute delight. There are now countless books on windmills and watermills, industrial archaelogy, thatching, potting, smithing and every conceivable rural craft (see 5.3). A collector's piece on all these, complete with beautiful graphics, childlike whimsy and hip-Victorian flavour is *Country Bizarre's Country Bazaar*, by Andy Pittaway and Bernard Scofield (Architectural Press, London, 1974). It has an excellent bibliography. For photographs, Gordon Winter's *A Country Camera 1844-1914* (Penguin, Harmondsworth; Gale, New York) is riveting.

2.524 The New Left reaction

The post-war generation of radicals had to face the fact that capitalism was, in its own peculiar way, delivering the material goods. The old concerns remained: elementary economic justice, rights of working people, racism, imperialism, seizure of power, and so on; but these had to move over to make room for a *cultural* critique. Alienation was back in town. Furthermore, whereas previous generations of socialists had thought science was their own thing — to be liberated from the fetters which capitalism placed on it — it was obvious to the post-war generation that science and technology flourished nowhere so well as under mature industrial capitalism. As it consorted so cosily with the enemy, they would have none of it, and in this they differed from the Rational Materialist 'Scientific Socialists' of the preceding period. They also differed in their suspicion of authoritarianism; their concern with consciousness as well as power, the personal as well as the political; their willingness (and, occasionally, ability) to use real moral language; and their willingness to recognise the problems inherent in industrialism — not to escape the need for searching analysis by blaming it all on capitalism. All this merged at one end with the 'counterculture' and the revival of the utopian tradition, for which see 2.54 and 13. Here are some influential works:

◆ *The Movement Towards a New America: The Beginnings of a Long Revolution*, ed. Goodman (Knopf, New York, 1970).
An amazing compendium of the movement in America since 1956, but mainly the blossoms of the late '60s; unsurpassed, but now a little dated.

◆ *The New Left Reader* ed. Carl Oglesby (Grove Press, New York, 1969).

◆ *The May-Day Manifesto*, ed. Raymond Williams (Penguin, Harmondsworth, 1968).

◆ *Obsolete Communism: The Left-Wing Alternative*, Daniel Cohn-Bendit (Penguin, Harmondsworth, 1969; McGraw Hill, New York, 1969).

◆ *One-Dimensional Man* (Sphere, London, 1969; Beacon Press, New York, 1964) and *Eros and Civilisation* (Beacon Press, New York, 1974), by Herbert Marcuse.

◆ *Workers' Control*, ed. Ken Coates and Tony Topham (Panther, London, 1970).

Along with these went a hundred other

developments: the women's movement, the radicalisation (and proletarisation) of 'professionals', the rise of community politics, greater self-definition among oppressed and minority groups, etc. These pointed towards something frighteningly new: the revolution of everyday life. The groups that came closest to questioning the real fundamentals of modern society (ie hierarchical organisation, bureaucracy, the need for order and control — because the technical nature of production demands it — otherwise the system will break down and we'll all starve, so stop singing and get back to work, etc, etc) were the yippies (in America) and the Situationists (in Europe): partisans of the 'total freedom jag': Abbie Hoffman and Jerry Rubin in stoned, hilarious shocking, irresponsible, repetitious and often pathetic books like *Do It!*, *Revolution for the Hell of It*, *Woodstock Nation*, *We Are Everywhere*, *Steal This Book*, etc; and 'the incomplete work of the Situationist International, now elegantly collected and translated in *Leaving The Twentieth Century*, ed Christopher Gray (Free Fall Publications, New York,

1974) [RF]. The greatest manifestation of all this was doubtless Paris May '68. The spirit is well expressed in *The Beginning of the End*, by Angelo Quattrocchi and Tom Nairn (Panther, London, 1968).

This kind of thing, of course, begets its own reaction, discussed in the next section.

2.53 SOME PESSIMISTS AND BLUE MEANIES

Romanticism is all very well in novels and poetry, but when carnival becomes a way of life, and people start taking their dreams seriously, they have to be refuted, if only for their own good. Radical Technology in certain of its manifestations, as well as many of its friends and relations, has put a direct challenge to 'modernity' as it has come to be understood, and has posed the question whether there *can* be a viable alternative to the large, well-regulated, centralised, specialised, bureaucratic, materialistic, advanced-technological, safe, rational, hierarchical societies that we call 'industrial' or 'modern', whether 'capitalist' or 'socialist'. The orthodox view is that once 'modernity' is established there is, roughly speaking, a single pattern of development, albeit with minor variations, to which all nations must accede, under the subtle but ultimately determining forces of technology and the need for suitable social control to keep the complex system working. Attempts to break away from this basic pattern will prove either futile or disastrous. The thesis is a very powerful one on a number of levels, and serious utopians must reckon with it if they are to make their visions credible beyond the circles of the faithful.

A good one to start on is *Industrialism and Industrial Man*, by Clark Kerr, John T. Dunlop, Frederick Harbison and C.A. Myers (Penguin, Harmondsworth, 1973, 2nd ed; originally Harvard UP, 1960). This book is a product of the 'convergence theory' (that the USA and USSR would become structurally more alike) which grew out of the 'end of ideology' period of American sociology. One of its ringing slogans is *There is one best tech-*

THE ANARCHIST COLLECTIVES, SAM DOLGOFF. FREE LIFE Pub.

SOLIDARITY

nology: a concise statement of the one-dimensional thesis.

Although the authors acknowledge the possibility of small local variations (eg measures of workers' control), and in the 'ten years after' edition recognise the influence of 'the new Bohemianism' (that's us — nice to see such a charming old term made to walk again) as an unexpected factor of the post-industrial period, they see the future as roughly more of the same, and the evidence they gather is quite impressive.

More worrying, because it understands the counter-modern tendencies so well, is *The Homeless Mind*, by Peter Berger, Brigitte Berger and Hansfried Kellner (Penguin, Harmondsworth, 1974; Random House, New York, 1973). Yes, they agree, modern societies are pretty gruesome. But the only conceivable alternatives are far worse. Much the same sort of argument is presented by Martin Pawley in *The Private Future* (Thames and Hudson, London, 1973, Random House, New York, 1974) but with a nastier twist. He describes the process of 'privatisation' and the growth of alienation with such venomous glee that you feel he must in the end have a golden alternative to release the dramatic tension and put us out of our misery. But no, he says, *this is what people freely choose*, and is the inevitable destiny of advanced societies. Again there is plenty of evidence to back up the thesis, needing some clever footwork to refute.

Another gloomy vision is presented by Peter Laurie in *Meet Your Friendly Social System* (Arrow, London, 1974), who makes Britain in the '70s look somewhat worse than the Third Reich.

The most chilling tract of all is Barrington Moore's *Reflections on the Causes of Human Misery* (Harvard UP, 1972), which is so obviously sincere, and he so hates to come to his doleful conclusions, that you know he has no axe to grind for pessimism. In the end you feel there cannot be a single loophole of hope left. I must confess this quenches even my optimism. But having suffered these fine scholarly vivisections 'from the centre' as it were, it is always good to realise that the Right has only the soggiest and bluntest of instruments. For light relief, read Ayn Rand's *The New Left,: The Anti-Industrial Revolution* (New American Library, New York, 1971).

The descent into hell should fortify us for the creation of a set of assumptions that sidestep the numbing logic of the academics, rationalists, materialists, technocrats, blue meanies and all other varieties of grown-ups. Ones that can't really be disproved and can always remain a basis for hope. For example that humans can be generous, co-operative, willing agents rather than reactive, self-interested social atoms (because life is more fulfilling that way); that people appear to 'choose' privatisation because they are trapped into it (or maybe it's just a phase that they'll get over); that *many* possible purposes and criteria can be applied to technology, yielding a mosaic of completely different technological patterns; that it *is* possible to produce *enough* with technologies that do not degrade the environment and do not require total social regimentation; that most bureaucratic functions can be reliably transferred to affinity groups without intolerable group pressures or the growth of irksome patterns of obligation; decentralised societies *can* work, now above all times because we have the means; etc , etc. Documentation of these and other unlikely-sounding beliefs can be found in the works cited in the next section.

Anarchist Peasants in rural Spain

2.54 A POLITICAL TRADITION FOR RADICAL TECHNOLOGY

Philip Toynbee has proposed an apt genetic analogy for classifying left-wing groups. What you tend to see if you look about is the 'dominant' left, basically Marxists and Social Democrats, who share the progressive economic values of the liberals and also their view of the role of technology and the basic forms of productive apparatus. This is stony ground for Radical Technologists, and, looking elsewhere for places to put down political roots, they are rediscovering the 'recessive Left' of anarchists, utopians and visionaries, which tends only to manifest itself when dominant genes like Lenin or Harold Wilson are off doing something else. Here are some heroes at random (the tradition is not noted for its coherence): Lao Tzu, John Ball, Gerald Winstanley, Godwin, Cobbett, Blake, Paine, Owen, Fourier, The Rochdale Weavers, the Paris Communards, Proudhon, Thoreau, Tolstoy, Morris, Edward Carpenter, Ebenezer Howard, Geddes, Kropotkin, Luxemburg, Makhno, G. D. H. Cole, Bertrand Russell, Arthur Morgan, Gandhi, Borsodi, Simone Weil, Orwell, Buber, Dolci, Goodman, Djilas, C. Wright Mills Chomsky . . . get the idea?

This is an atmosphere radical technologists tend to find congenial, but of course other political traditions must be respected and worked with. There are after all great weaknesses in the recessive tradition. Being fundamentally a *moral* force, it always gets zapped by determined 'realists' if it gets in their way (see Benjamin Barber's *Superman and Common Men* [Penguin, Harmondsworth; Praeger, New York] for an account of the perennial failures of anarchism). And it has rarely matched the staggering intellectual fire-power of the great dominant heavies. But times are changing. It is getting hard to tell who's who politically these days, except by the labels. The stylistic differences between political groups seem greatly to outweigh the doctrinal ones. The gap seems to be closing. As we move into the post-industrial era, a synthesis seems possible that could unite the best features of the dominant and recessive traditions. On the theoretical front, this is expressed in the exploration of new forms of radical economics, and a resurgence of interest in the more rugged and tested urban forms of participatory politics: 'council communism'/'communist anarchism'/'anarcho-syndicalism'/libertarian socialism. On the practical side it is manifest as a tremendous growth of community organisation; grassroots movements for workers' self-management; and tentative confrontations with 'the

revolutionisation of everyday life'. This is discussed further in section 13. The following are representative works:

◆ *Mutual Aid* (Prism Press, 1975). *The Conquest of Bread* (Allen Lane the Penguin Press, London, 1972; Blom, New York, 1968). *Fields, Factories and Workshops Tomorrow* (2.51) These are three of Peter Kropotkin's great classics.

◆ *Post-Scarcity Anarchism*, by Murray Bookchin (2.51).

◆ *The Anarchist Collectives: Workers' Self-Management in the Spanish Revolution 1936-1939* by Sam Dolgoff (Free Life Editions, New York, 1974). They did it.

◆ *Anarchy In Action*, by Colin Ward (Allen & Unwin, London 1973; Harper & Row, New York, 1974). The author was formerly editor of *Freedom* and *Anarchy*. He sees the seeds of liberation everywhere, and is that endearing kind of anarchist whose subversive proposals don't strike one as political at all, but just obvious commonsense.

◆ *Communitas: Means of Livelihood and Ways of Life*, by Paul and Percival Goodman (Vintage, New York, 1960). Originally written in 1947, this remains a timeless statement of alternative ways of organising production and community life. More details of a decentralist model can be found in Paul Goodman's *People or Personnel: Decentralising and the Mixed System* (Vintage, New York, 1968).

◆ *A Landscape For Humans*, by Peter van Dresser (Biotechnic Press, El Rito, NM, 1971). A discussion of the principles, economics and technology of decentralisation applied to the uplands of New Mexico where the author lives. (See interview with van Dresser in the book.)

◆ *Anarchism, From Theory to Practice*, by Daniel Guerin (Monthly Review Press, New York, 1970). Well, what it says.

◆ *Workers' Councils and the Economics of a Self-Managed Society* (Solidarity Pamphlet no. 40, 123 Lathom Road, London E6). Extensive proposals for libertarian socialist organisation of society dating from 1957 in the wake of the Hungarian uprising; translated from the French, with contemporary comments from *Solidarity*. Delightfully embellished with hedgehog cartoons. On similar lines is Anton Pannekoek's *The Workers' Councils* (Freedom, 84b Whitechapel High Street, London E1, reprinted).

◆ *The Breakdown of Nations*, by Leopold Kohr (Routledge and Kegan Paul, London, 1957). This is a critique of centralised organisation, and proposals for decentralisation, from a standpoint that can hardly be described as Left — just human, perhaps. Similar ideas are applied to the pre-industrial condition in *Development Without Aid* (Christopher Davis Ltd, Llandybie, 1973) but with a strain of paternalism.

◆ *Paths in Utopia*, by Martin Buber (Beacon Press, Boston, 1958). An erudite discussion of the basis of utopian thought and its moral and social necessity.

◆ *Strategy for Labour*, by Andre Gorz (Beacon Press, Boston, 1968). An attempt to break out of the stultifying 'waiting for the revolution' mentality without relapsing into reformism. How would you really like it to be? Well start now, build towards it and don't give an inch.

◆ *The Case for Participatory Democracy*, ed. by George Benello and Dimitrios Roussopoulos (Grossman, New York).

◆ *Neighbourhood Government*, by Milton Kotler (Bobbs-Merrill, New York, 1974).

◆ *A Blueprint for Survival*, The Ecologist (Penguin, Harmondsworth, 1972; Houghton Mifflin, New York, 1972). An attempt to plan a decentralised society not primarily out of preference but the sheer necessities imposed by environmental and resource constraints — a dimension missing in nearly all other treatments. One can quibble with it politically, but it is a valuable contribution. A revised version is in preparation.

See also items in 2.51; read *In the Making* (2.21). *The Movement Towards a New America* (2.524); see section 13, and once again, the articles by Woody and Edward Thompson in 2.42, for an inspiring optimism tempered in the fires of defeat. We can do it!

3 SHELTER

The critiques of existing housing practices come from a number of different directions. The gripes are: that current patterns of housing encourage or compel privatisation and passive consumption of goods and services; that they are stultifying to live in and increasingly expensive to build and run; that they lead to over-use of non-renewable resources.

The traditional political debate about housing has focused on the private *v.* the public; owner-occupation, rented accommodation and local authority housing. Radical Technologists would emphasise other dimensions: user involvement, especially at a local collective level; the growth of a sense of community; self-building and self-maintenance; moves towards more ecologically sound servicing; a 'new regionalism' in construction, through the use of local methods and materials especially in connection with a re-population of rural areas; rehabilitation of existing buildings rather than new starts; grants for the installation of autonomous servicing on the basis of 'whole life costing'; and flexible communalisation of natural units such as blocks or terraces. Most of this is not new in radical circles, and the following items focus primarily on the technical aspects.

3.1 BASIC ACCESS

On the technical aspects:

◆ *WEE* has a whole section on 'shelter' broken down as follows: architecture; building carpentry; adobe-plaster; masonry and thatch; shacks and pole and buildings; repairs/wood heat; natural forces; woodwork; furniture; craft; tipis and yurts; tensile structures, domes.

◆ *SH* has a fine annotated bibliography angled towards the vernacular stuff.

◆ *Survival Scrapbook No. 1: Shelter (SS1)* has an **excellent** classified bibliography on most aspects of shelter, including clothing.

On the social aspects:

◆ The AA Communications Network (36 Bedford Square, London WC1B 3ES). A referral agency, documentation Centre, and information exchange covering: aided self-help; housing associations; co-operatives; communes; tenant management and takeovers; squatting; community action, etc. It has only just started but should be extremely useful. £5 a year should go a very long way.

A number of building co-ops have been set up in recent years:

◆ Sunderlandia (General Graham Street, Sunderland, Tyne & Wear).

◆ Common Ground (45 Kensington Park Road, London W11).

◆ A Buncha Builders (c/o "New Church", Flodden Road, London SE5).

◆ Urban Building Renovation Group (Eastbourne House, Bullards Place, London E2).

◆ Centre for Alternatives in Urban Development (Lower Shaw Farm, Shaw, Swindon Wilts).

See *In the Making* no. 3 for further details.

An excellent compendium of articles on both technical and social aspects of shelter is *The Future of Shelter* (Open University Man-Made Futures Units 4 & 5, Futures Access File, 1975).

Source Catalog No 2: Communities/ Housing (Swallow Press, Chicago, 1972) [SB, MB,CO]. A community-oriented directory of activity and sources in 250 pages in the following sections: organising for basic tenant rights; legal; city-wide organising; public housing; open housing; elderly and handicapped; temporary housing; Third World; rural; changing national urban housing policy. An extraordinary quantity of material.

3.2 BASIC GENERAL TEXTS

Lloyd Kahn's *Shelter (SH)* is a great introduction, strongest on traditional building methods from many cultures but with plenty of practical stuff as well.

The Owner-Built Home ($7.50) and its 2-volume sequel *The Owner-Built Homestead* ($5.00), by Ken Kern, (Ken Kern Drafting, Sierra Route, Oakhurst, CA 93644) [CO] are the practical bibles for building if you have a bit of land.

On the principles of self-building and user-control: *Freedom to Build*, edited by John Turner & Robert Fichter (Macmillan, 1973: £3.75) [AD] is outstanding. Not a directory but a manifesto, with case studies in both Third-World and industrial countries. It forms the basis for a programme at the AA Graduate School in 'Alternatives in Housing' run by John Turner and Tom Woolley, who wrote the article on user involvement in housing in the book.

See also *Shelter and Society* by Paul Oliver (Cresset, 1969), and *Supports: An Alternative to Mass Housing*, by N. J. Habraken (1972).

Energy, Environment and Building, by Paul Steadman (Cambridge UP, London, 1975) [SB]. An absolute *tour de force* on energy and building. It minutely analyses the entire pattern of energy input and output of building and discusses methods for improving energy use. There is a wealth of examples of real projects and a massive bibliography.

'Bad Gir' wind
deflectors for
cooling; Pakistan

Left margin (rotated): ENERGY, ENVIRONMENT & BUILDING, PHILIP STEADMAN   CLASS WAR COMIX, CLIFFORD HARPER   SHELTER

3.3 VERNACULAR CONSTRUCTION

While *SH* is quite good enough here, Bernard Rudovsky's *Architecture Without Architects* (Doubleday, New York, 1964) [SB] is deservedly famous. Less exotic for Britons is R. W. Brunskill's *Illustrated Handbook of Vernacular Architecture* (Universe Books, 1970) [SB].

More information from references in these books, or from Paul Oliver (Dartington Hall, Totnes, Devon, England) and Ron Lewcock (Clare Hall, Cambridge, England), who has made a special study of traditional building outside Europe. On indigenous housing in tropical arid areas — as the most practical, not just the prettiest, solution — see 'Indigenous Housing and the Third World' *AD* 4/75, by Allan Cain, Farroukh Afshar and John Norton.

3.4 SPECIAL METHODS AND MATERIALS

WEE shelter section, *SH* and *SSI* have endless references on thatch, adobe, brick, sod stone, log, pole, and timber construction. Brenda Vale's papers *A Survey of Indigenous Building Materials* and *The Use of on-site Building Materials (AHS)* are pleasing companions to all these, and are the basis for her article on traditional building methods in this book.

On subsoil construction, Colin Taylor, author of the article on that subject in the book, has produced an extensive annotated bibliography (*AA,AARTU*). I cannot refrain from mentioning *Building in Cob, Pise and Stabilised Earth* by Clough Williams-Ellis and J & E Eastwick-Field (Country Life, London, 1919, 3rd edn, 1947) [LO] still commonly found in second-hand bookshops.

Sulphur is all the rage as a building material these days — see bibliography in *AARTU* and *The Ecol Operation* (3.5), and contact Mike Critchley at the AA for crazy schemes to grow sulphur bacteriologically as a by-product of methane generation.

Paper Houses by Roger Sheppard, Richard Threadgill and John Holmes is the latest (no. 4) in the *SS* series to appear [SB], and is fine for the job, as far as I can judge (practical), with a largish bibliography.

For handling other materials see section 5.

3.5 LOW-COST BUILDING

Plenty of references can be found in *AA bibliography no. 13, SS1, WEE* and *SH.* Two sources which stand out are:
The Ecol Operation (Minimum Cost Housing Group, School of Architecture, McGill University; Montreal 101, Canada, 1972). The group is worth contacting, as their work continues. See 2.33 for a longer description; also 6.2.
A Manual on Building Construction by the Rev. Harold K. Dancy (ITDG 1973) [CO], an old missionary handbook resuscitated.

On Low-cost materials, see Martin Pawley's 'Garbage Housing', *AD* 12/1973, 'Recycling Building Components', *AD* 11/1972, and 'The work of Mike Reynolds', *AD* 3/75.

The doyen of temporary structures among the '60s freaks was the dome, of which the *locus classicus* is Lloyd Kahn's *Domebook Two* (Shelter Publications, 1971) [AD], extended in 'Domebook Three' which is incorporated in *SH.* See also *Dome Builder's Handbook* by John Prenis (Running Press Philadelphia, 1974) [CO]. A cousin of the dome is the zome, information from Zomeworks Corporation (Box 712, Albuquerque NM 87103). On yurts, see *AD* 1/75, p. 20.

For songs of experience on plastic structures and all forms of gee-whiz architecture, read Lloyd Kahn's essay 'Smart but not wise' in *SH.*

3.6 SELF-BUILD AND USER INVOLVEMENT

AA bibliography no 14 is a good access to sources. *Freedom to Build* and *The Owner-Built Home* have already been mentioned. For house maintenance, *PW* is excellent.

For the more militant side of user-involvement, see *Tenants Take Over* by Colin Ward (Architectural Press, London, 1974: £3.95) [SB]. BIT's *Squatters' Handbook* (BIT, 146 Great Western Road, London W11), *Source Catalogue No 2,* (3.1) and contact the AA Graduate School 'Alternatives in Housing' programme (3.2).

A practical bible for house maintenance is *The Self-Help House Repairs Manual* by Andrew Ingham (Penguin, Harmondsworth, 1975; 60p) which takes you through everything in beautiful step-by-step pictures. It is particularly thorough on electricity and plumbing, and follows from years of experience in making squats habitable. A really useful book.

3.7 AUTONOMOUS HOUSES

The most conspicuous aspect of 'AT' building has been the 'autonomous house' — in principle a micro-ecosystem of self-sufficiency and the ultimate in consumer privatisation. Many have been designed, and a fair number built. There are many different types, naturally. Some parameters of variation are: size, style of life presumed for the inhabitants, completeness of the attempt at autonomy, level of technology of materials. See the 'autonomy' section of the book.

3.71 GENERAL SOURCES AND CONTACTS

A comprehensive textbook on the subject is *The Autonomous House,* by Robert and Brenda Vale (both contributors to this book) (Thames & Hudson, London) [SB]. Phil Steadman's *Energy, Environment & Building* (3.2) [SB] will also provide references to virtually any aspect of the topic.

The Autonomous Housing Study group at Cambridge (2.311) has amassed a formidable collection of material and published a number of seminal papers. One should write for the list of publications.

EP has a concise section on eco-architecture, including many reviews and articles on American building codes, insulation and natural air-conditioning.

Other groups working on similar lines are the following:
◆ Steve Baer's **Zomeworks Corporation** (Box 712, Albuquerque, NM 87103).
◆ **Ouroboros Project** student projects, *real,* both rural and urban. (2.33).
◆ Robert Reines' **Integrated Living Systems** (ILS) (Star Route 103, Tijeras, NM 87059) have designed and constructed what are probably the most effective energy-autonomous units to date, at a very low cost.
◆ **Minimum Cost Housing Group,** McGill University (Montreal 101, Canada) trying to reduce the cost of construction as well as of running.
◆ **Malcolm Wells** (Box 183, Cherry Hill, New Jersey, NJ 08034) has been advocating and

Interior of Red Rockers' communal dome

designing 'eco-architecture' for years — see *ADDS*, or *The Future of Shelter* (3.1).

For more details on these groups, see *WEE* pp. 534-5. Also see **New Alchemy Institute, Brace Research Institute, Max's Pot** (2.33); **Ekologiskt Byggande** (2.32); **Conservation Tools and Technology** (2.311).

3.72   SPECIFIC DESIGNS FOR AUTONOMOUS HOUSES

There is no simple method of classification that will allow me to list these in a rational manner. On the whole, such buildings are either expensive, ineffective, or poky. The examples cited here are all discussed in the section on 'Autonomy' in the book.

Of the very costly variety, none have actually been built yet; probably the first two will be Alex Pike's box (*AD* 11/74 pp. 681-9) and Brenda Vale's award-winning design, which is planned to be built on the campus at Brunel University, Uxbridge. Brenda's husband Robert has been appointed director of the project.

The cheap/non-poky/unreliable variety is favoured by those experimenters whom Alex Pike patronizingly styles 'enthusiasts'. Of these Graham Caine and his Living-Shed-Greenhouse (Street Farm House, Thames Polytechnic Playing fields, Kidbroke Lane, London SE9) is an outstanding example. Best to go and have a look soon as it's likely to be pulled down; for such a national monument, this is sheer philistinism (see the interview with Graham and Bruce Haggart in the book).

Of the cheap/poky/reliable variety, Robert Reines' designs at ILS (3.71) obviously have a great future, but fearing commercial rip-offs, they guard the designs closely. Basically they are steel domes lined with polyurethane foam, studded with port-holes, and with detached solar collectors and wind generators. Cost is comparable with 'mobile homes'.

Most accessible in this bracket is Jaap t' Hooft's dome at The Small Earth project in Holland (Munsel 17, Boxtel, NB, The Netherlands). This is a reinforced concrete dome with cork/cement insulation, home-made thermoglass windows (the 7 triangular wind windows alleviate the poky feeling) and detached solar collector wind generator and

methane digester. Cost is under £2,000. There is an article on this house in *UC* 11. Technical specifications (in English) can be obtained from Jaap at the address given.

In the same nuclear-family-size category are a number of designs not yet built, with widely varying characteristics:

James Thring and Gerry Smith of the Cambridge AHS group designed a dwelling similar to Pike's in many respects, but slightly smaller and octagonal in plan, with goats on the ground floor. Gerrard Crouch of the same group has designed an A-frame building in which the whole of one side is a vast 90 m^2 solar collector. These are both fancy jobs and would be pretty costly.

John Shore at the AA, apart from designing a tiny autonomous dome for *one* person (see 'Organic Living Experiment', *UC* 6) has designed a compromise between spaciousness, effectiveness and cost with a really cheap glasshouse structure for growing vegetables, and a tiny well-insulated room in the centre with all essential services, to which he can retire when even socks and sweaters cannot keep the cold at bay.

Back in the costly sphere, Simon Longland at the University of Edinburgh (22 Panmure Place, Edinburgh EH3) has designed an autonomous house constructed from prefabricated modular units for mass-production but permitting a certain variety of arrangement.

For a really cold-climate design, one of the most interesting of all autonomous houses is Ouroboros (2.33). This house has to cope with 8,000 heating-degree-days, 4 months of snow, and temperatures down to -35°F. Nevertheless it meets 100% of its space and water heating needs with inter-seasonally stored solar energy, plus wood burning to top it up. The plan form is trapezoidal; it has a greenhouse, a 4kW wind generator, an aerobic composter, earth berms, and a sod roof for summer cooling angled so as to hold snow in the winter.

Large autonomous houses are much more economical than small ones. The house at Biotechnic Research and Development (BRAD) in Wales is well-known (see Fig E1 in 'Autonomy', report in *UC* 8 and solar roof in 4.23).

Robert and Brenda Vale have designed a second collective house (for 16 people) for

the BRAD site, in their preferred 'long, low, south-facing' form.

Another design which takes my fancy is a large, circular communal building with a conical roof built round a central chimney. The large room round the fireplace in the centre of the ground floor is completely surrounded by other rooms and is therefore very cosy in the winter, when the inhabitants would spend most of their time there. This is an idea of Herbert Girardet's (8a Leighton Crescent, London NW5) (see 'The Radial House', *Resurgence*, Nov/Dec 1973 and 'New Villages Now', *UC* 10). For other autonomous designs, see the article in the book.

3.8   CITIES

If a dwelling is not merely a shelter, this is even more true of a city. The emphasis on software comes into its own. Naturally Radical Technologists think big cities are too big and don't work very well as places to live and love. Colin Ward's essay 'Anarchist Cities', *UC* 10, is a good introduction building on the ideas of Kropotkin, Howard, Geddes and Goodman. Murray Bookchin's *The Limits of the City* (Harper and Row, New York, 1974) is a critical analysis of city planning and a vision of alternative city life, with a deep historical perspective. Other 'anti-planning' books are Robert Goodman's *After The Planners* (Penguin, Harmondsworth; 1972; Simon & Schuster, New York, 1973); Richard Sennett, *The Uses of Disorder* (Penguin, Harmondsworth; 1971); and Jane Jacobs's celebrated *The Death and Life of Great American Cities* (Penguin, Harmondsworth, 1968; Knopf, New York, 1970) — an antidote to urbanophobia. But principles of collective organisaton are still needed. An ecological approach is taken in *Design with Nature* by Ian McHarg (Doubleday, New York, 1969). Various aspects of local participation are dealt with in *Policy and Participation* by Dave Elliott (Open University Man-Made Futures Unit 6, 1975); *Neighbourhood Government* by Milton Kotler (Bobbs-Merrill, New York, 1974); and in 'Blueprint for a Communal Environment' by *The Berkeley Tribe*, reprinted in *Sources* (2.41).

See also 13.3.

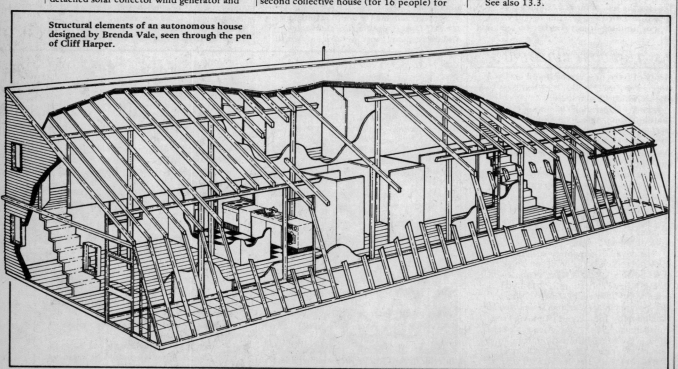

Structural elements of an autonomous house designed by Brenda Vale, seen through the pen of Cliff Harper.

VALE AUTONOMOUS HOUSE, CLIFFORD HARPER

4 ENERGY

PETER BROOKES

DE KLEINE AARDE

The aim of alternative energy usage should be to do it fairly, cheaply, cleanly, and without unduly depleting non-renewable resources. This is easier said than done.

The section concentrates mainly on alternative *sources* of energy, but these certainly could not provide for current, let alone prospective, demand without drastic reorganisation of production and consumption patterns. Explorations, both technical and social, of *how to use less* are just as important as the search for alternative sources. See the article on autonomous units in the book, and section 3.7.

The practical future of the alternatives discussed in this section depends very much on what happens in the field of nuclear power generation — the great white hope of the mega-technological optimists. For not unbiassed accounts of the nuclear issue, see *Nuclear Power: Technological Bases for Ethical Concern,* by Amory Lovins (Friends of the Earth, 9 Poland Street, London W1); *UC* 9 special issue on nuclear energy; various back numbers of *Science for People* (2.222) and *Environment* (2.221), which, as well as careful critiques of the US nuclear power programme, often contains articles on larger-scale energy alternatives (geothermal, hydrogen) which have been rather neglected in this book.

4.1 GENERAL

4.11 PERIODICALS

For alternative energy you cannot do without the bimonthly *Alternative Sources of Energy (ASE)* [CO]. It's worth getting the back-issues book *Alternative Sources of Energy (ASEB),* a real bargain at $4.00; also *ASE* back numbers 11-15. Detailed coverage of sources and contacts, articles, reviews.

For other journals, *Alternative Energy Sources* Newsletter — *Undercurrents, Journal of the New Alchemists, The Mother Earth News* see 2.21.

4.12 BASIC ACCESS

The bibliographies in *EP* are definitive.

The *ASE bibliography* is fine, although unannotated. The journal *ASE* always has an excellent reviews section for new books. *ASE* also runs a communications network which asks readers to check items on a comprehensive questionnaire and publishes profiles, so as to put people with common interests in touch with each other. As it stands it is probably the best way of finding others who are working on the same things as yourself. In North America, *ASE*'s lending library service is a useful way of sharing resources. A list of holdings and rates for borrowing (to cover postage and new purchases) can be found in *ASE* 15.

Other alternative energy bibliographies and contact lists may be found in *SS5, AARTU,* AA library, *ADDS,* in the *WEE* 'soft technology' section, and from CTT, 'New Energy Sources' (2.31). In particular, Derek Taylor at the AA is a constant fountain of information and bibliographies on alternative energy.

For alternative energy *hardware* in Britain, see CTT (2.311); in USA, *ASE*'s *Spectrum* (2.21), *WEE* and *EP.*

4.13 GENERAL TEXTS

EP, of course. On energy in general, *The Energy Crisis* by Tad Szulc (Franklin Watts, New York, 1974), and the Ford Foundation's

PIFRE'S SUN-POWER PLANT OF 1878 DRIVING A PRINTING PRESS.

A Time to Choose: America's Energy Future (Ballinger, Cambridge, 1974) seem to sum up the present situation very well, to judge from the *New York Review of Books.*

A sober analysis of the technical options, given the existing economic and social dispensation, is found in *New Energy Technology: Some Facts and Assessments* by Hottel & Howard. (MIT Press, 1972) [SB] mainly focussed on what *we* would call conventional energy technologies.

Most proponents of alternative energy see it as a deliverance from the baleful hand of big business, but the same 'crisis' that has fanned the fires of Radical Technology has also boosted the energy industry to top position in capitalism. If you prudently feel a need to keep a watchful eye on Big Brother, Environmental Information Centre Inc publish two annually up-dated reference works intended for the up-to-the-minute executive: *The Energy Index* catalogues key information about the energy industry (mostly US) with 2,800 abstracts: *The Energy Directory* profiles more than 3,000 energy-related organisations in the USA ($50 each, $75 together; from EIC, Professional References Dept. 124 East 39th Street New York, NY 10016). Probably available in reference libraries.

On the use of energy, Steadman's *Energy Environment and Building* (2.1) contains an excellent summary. A good textbook of over-

all energy use is *Total Energy* by R. M. E. Diamant (Pergamon, London, 1970) [SB]. For critical analyses of current energy use, books are expected shortly from Gerry Foley (AA); Gerald Leach (3 Tanza Road, London NW3); and Peter Chapman of The Open University. (Milton Keynes Bucks). See also *The Energy Crisis — A Matter of Profits* (URPE/PEAC, Box 331 Cathedral Station, New York NY 10025) and Illich's *Energy and Equity* (2.51).

On saving energy, Steadman's analysis (regarding building) is comprehensive, while Eugene Eccli's forthcoming *Save Energy Through Shelter Design* (from ASE) will be excellent and practical. A foretaste can be had in his basic guide to insulation in *ASE* No 13: 'Conservation of Energy in Existing Housing'.

Derek Taylor's *AA* bibliography on insulation is useful — about thirty entries, including a list of Dept of Environment Advisory Leaflets. See also *EP,* p. 174.

Less specialised treatments are *Technology of Efficient Energy Utilisation,* ed. E. Kovach (NATO Scientific Affairs Division, 1974) [SB] for the big stuff; and for the small: *350 Ways to Save Energy (and Money)* by Spies, Konzo, Calvin and Thoms (Crown Publishers, New York, 1974). These are always talking in terms of 10% savings here and there. But a real impact on energy consumption can only be made by 'Living Lightly', as argued by Tom Bender in his essay of that title (2.42).

At this point I must plug *Living on the Sun* by Godfrey Boyle (Calder & Boyars, London, 1975) an analysis of current public energy policies and the alternatives open to us. Straight from the shoulder. Another treatment of the same theme is *A Low-Energy Society — But How?,* (Alternativ Stad, Per Janse, Vikingagatan 10, S-11342 Stockholm, Sweden; £1.00).

General coverage of alternative sources of energy can be found in:

Producing Your Own Power, ed. Carol H. Stoner (Rodale Press, Organic Park, Emmaus, PA 18049, USA, 1974; $8.95). Contains many very competent articles, and has excellent source listings.

SS No 5: Energy by Stefan Szczelkun (qv in *AT1*) [MB,CO]. A good introduction, attractively produced, but lacking detail. Also covers psychic energy, which is unusual.

Energy Book 1: Sources and Backyard Applications by John Prenis (Running Press, 1974) [CO]. Good, practical, honest.

The Mother Earth News Handbook of Home-Made Power (Bantam, New York, 1973) [CO].

EP, however, eclipses and supercedes all, except that great classic, *New Sources of Energy* (United Nations, 1964, sales no. 63/1/41) [LO], 7-volume proceedings of a conference in 1961 on geothermal, solar and wind energy. Remarkable how little it seems to date.

4.2 SOLAR ENERGY

4.21 PERIODICALS
Apart from *ASE*, the best way of keeping in touch with trends in the (mainly straight) world of solar energy research is a subscription to the monthly *Solar Energy Digest* (PO Box 17776, San Diego, CA 92117, USA; $27.50 a year). It's pretty expensive, and I reckon *ASE* at $5.00 is quite adequate. The technical journal *Solar Energy* comes as part of the $20 subscription to the International Solar Energy Society (PO Box 52, Parkville, Vic. 3052, Australia).

4.22 GENERAL ACCESS
EP solar section: general, distillation, drying, collectors, water heating, space heating, concentrating collectors, audio-visual, loose ends, and 21 pages of books, groups and manufacturers, mostly American.

Annotated bibliographies: *AA bibliography no. 26*: *AARTU* or Derek Taylor's personal sun bibliography; *WEE*, p. 529 ff. *ASEB* has an unannotated bibliography classified as follows (which is representative): general: solar collectors: cookers; cooling and refrigeration; distillation; dryers; furnaces; greenhouses; house heating; water-heating; solar measurement; electricity. The Building Research Establishment (Garston, Herts) has a library bibliography (No 220) on 'Utilisation of Solar Energy', somewhat out of date. I have not seen it, but it seems that *Solar Energy Directory* from Environmental Action of the University of Colorado (1100 14th Street, Denver CO 80202) at $15.00 is compendious, containing reference to books and articles, manufacturers, research, and solar buildings. John May of the Catalog discovered another good source: If you write to the Library of Congress (Science and Technology Division, 101st Street S.E., Washington DC 20540) and ask for a 'Tracer Bulletin' on Solar Energy, they send you a complete list of American Sources updated every month. And another American one: *Reference List of Major Publications on Solar Energy* of the

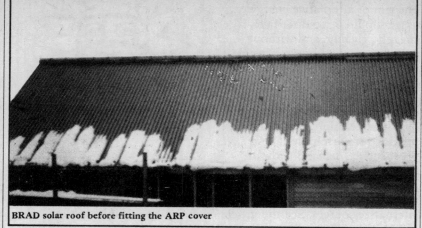

BRAD solar roof before fitting the ARP cover

Institute of Solar Energy Conversion (University of Delaware, Newark, DE 19711).

4.23 BASIC TEXTS
Yellot's article in *EP* is a fine introduction. *Direct Use of the Sun's Energy* by Farrington Daniels (Ballantine, New York, 1974) [CO] is still unsurpassed as a general introduction to the field. Less technical is B. J. Brinkworth's *Solar Energy for Man* (Compton Press, Wilts., 1972) [CO]. Probably the best guide for the would-be builder is *Solar Energy Handbook* by Henry Landa (FICOA, 2901 S. Wentworth Avenue, Milwaukee, W1 53207, USA): all the formulae and numbers are there. Colin Moorcraft's concise and punchy introduction to solar energy in building can be found in *AD* 10/73. A simple pamphlet on solar energy by Ian Hogan can be had from CTT (3.21) for 35p.

A huge number of conferences have been held on solar energy, with very repetitive proceedings. Three which are particularly worth digging up are:
◆ *New Sources of Energy* (4.13) Vols. 4-6.
◆ *Proceedings of the Solar Heating and Cooling for Buildings Workshop*, (Washington DC, 1973. Dept of Mechanical Engineering, University of Maryland 1973).
◆ *The Sun in the Service of Mankind* (Unesco, Paris 1973).

And here are some lollipops from the enormous literature:
◆ *Analysis of Forms for an Autonomous House* by Robert Vale (AHS WP10: £0.40).
◆ *Economics of Solar Collectors, Heat Pumps and Wind Generators* by Gerry Smith (AHS WP3: £0.60).
◆ *BRAD's Solar Roof Plan* (£0.35 + sae from Eithin y Gaer, Churchstoke, Powys, Wales): all the details needed to roll your own, including the electronic control circuit. Parts of these are to be found in the solar energy section of this book.

The design owes something to:
◆ *Solar Houses and Solar House Models*; and *Solar House Plans* by Harry Thomason ($1.00 and $10.00 respectively from Edmund Scientific Co., 150 Edscorp Bldg Barrington, NJ 08007, USA, 1972).

4.24 SPECIFIC APPLICATIONS
Solar Energy and Building by S. V. Szokolay, who has been researching the subject for years at the Poly of Central London (Architectural Press, London: £6.00) [SB]. An illustrated technical review of some thirty solar houses from all over the world, complete with all published details and performance data. Also covers collection and uses of a solar energy, planning implications, economics, a survey of existing 'solar industry', and provides a design guide.

A survey of 58 solar-heated buildings at various latitudes in the USA is to be found in *Solar Heated Buildings: A Brief Survey* by William A. Shurcliff (Solar Energy Digest, PO Box 17776, San Diego, CA 92117).

A similar survey of installations in Britain was carried out by a group of students at the Polytechnic of Central London: They really did go around and see every goddam one, and they've got slides to prove it. Their report can be found in the proceedings of The International Solar Energy Society (UK), July 1974 (4.25).

A useful series of D.I.Y. plans for solar installations can be obtained from Zome-works Corp (PO Box 712, Albuquerque, NM 87103, USA: Solar Booklet, $3.00; Solar Water Heater Plans, $5.00; Drum Wall Plans, $5.00; Beadwall System, $15.00). A set of colour slides about these systems can be obtained for $12.00.

Other applications: see 'Solar House at Rickmansworth' by Ed Curtis in *AD* 9/74, which also features the application to standard housing estate design at Milton Keynes by David Hodges, Architecture Dept., Polytechnic of Central London.

Schoolhouse Newsletter No 17 and other material from Educational Facilities' Laboratories, Inc. (477 Madison Avenue, NY 10022, USA) — vast arrays of collectors for schools, and real.

4.25 OTHER CONTACTS
◆ **International Solar Energy Society** (UK) (c/o Dr Mary Archer, The Royal Institution, 21 Albemarle Street, London W1). They meet roughly quarterly.
◆ **Solar Energy Developments**, Box 10, 16 South Wharf Road, London W2 1PF. A solar oriented architecture practice, trying out applications of photovoltaic effects as control systems.
◆ **Laboratoire d'Energie Solaire** (CNRS, Pyrenees, France). The main centre of solar energy research in France (see *AD* 1/75 pp 13-17).
◆ A leading research worker on passive solar walls is Jacques Michel (14 Rue des Poissonniers, 92204 Neuilly-Sur-Seine, France).
◆ **Paul Yaneske**, Dept of Architecture and Building Science, University of Strathclyde (Rottenrow, Glasgow 4, Scotland) has developed a helpful computer programme to calculate expected receipts of solar energy under a host of different conditions (wind too).
◆ **Mass Moving** (41 Lebeau Straat, 1000 Brussels, Belgium): see 3.32.
◆ In Switzerland, contact **SSES** (Leonhardstr. 27, CH-8001 Zurich).

For other contacts, see *EP*.

Assembling a small flat-plate collector

Grandpa's knob: The biggest wind mill ever built, 1.25 MW

NEW ALCHEMISTS   ENERGY, ENVIRONMENT & BUILDING, PHILIP STEADMAN   ALTERNATIVE SOURCES OF ENERGY

4.3 WIND ENERGY

4.31 GENERAL ACCESS

Once again *EP*'s bibliography is overwhelming, with 17 pages classified as follows: general, climate, storage, generators and alternators, mechanical (blades, towers, etc), water pumping, wind electrics, plans and kits, wind hardware, research groups.

There is a short but well-annotated bibliography in *WEE*, p. 536. This is extracted from *Wind Energy Bibliography* by Windworks (Box 329, Rt 3, Mukwonago, W1 53149, USA, 1973: $3.00) which is probably the most comprehensive available.

The *ASE bibliography* wind section is unannotated but classified as follows: general; propellers and aerodynamics; towers; water pumping; old windmills; wind measurements; wind electricity.

The best bibliography of all (forthcoming) will be *Wind Energy Bibliography*, from Library Administration, Technical University, PO Box 513, Eindhoven, The Netherlands.

Relevant periodicals are *ASE*, *UC*, *Alternative Energy Sources*, *Journal of the New Alchemists*, and *De Kleine Aarde*.

4.32 BASIC TEXTS

The great classic text on modern wind machines is E. W. Golding's *The Generation of Electricity by Wind Power* (Spon, 1955) [LO] now sadly only found in libraries.

Another very well-known work on large-scale machines is *Power From the Wind* by P.C. Putnam (Van Nostrand-Rheinhold, New York, 1948) [SB]. A wealth of research papers is to be found in vol. 7 of the UN *New Sources of Energy* (4.13).

Two more modern, small-scale, practical sources are: *Wind and Windspinners* by Michael A. Hackleman, (Earthmind, 26510 Josel Drive., Saugus, CA 91350, USA) which is mostly about Savonius rotors, and *Electric Power from the Wind* by Henry Clews (Solar Wind, PO Box 7, East Holden, ME 04429).

See also Jim Sencenbaugh's contribution in *EP*, p. 77, and CTT's concise *Wind Power Booklet*.

Derek Taylor's wind book, published by the AA, is a definitive zoology of the windmill. His extensive article in this book is just a .aster . . .

4.33 SPECIFIC DESIGNS (FOR D.I.Y.)

◆ **Windworks** (Box 329, Rt 3, Mukwonago, W1 53149), as well as their commendable bibliography, publish a number of proven plans, and a design for new type of tower.

(25ft diam. sailwing plan, $10, propeller-type $15.)

◆Another high-speed design can be obtained from **Jim Sencenbaugh** (678 Chimalus Drive, Palo Alto, CA 94306: $12).

◆ **Brace Research Institute** (2.33). There's a complete list of publications in *EP*, p. 102, one of which is 'How to construct a cheap Wind Machine for Pumping Water', by A. Bodek (1973: $1.00), the famous oil-drum Savonius, for which also see *UC 5*, and **VITA** Savonius plans no. 11132-1 ($0.75).

◆**VITA** also has plans for multiblade windmills (nos. 11133.1 and 11133.3; $1.00 each), and sail-type windmills (no 11131.1).

◆ **New Alchemy Institute (East)** (2.33) also has a fine sail design, including parts, gearing tower, sails and a flow-chart to tell you the sequence for assembly (see *Journal of the New Alchemists*, no. 2 which also contains an excellent article on wind electrical systems).

Several practical designs are to be found in the French publication *14 Eoliennes* in the D.I.Y. series 'Systeme D' (no. 9) (Societe Parisienne D'Édition, 43 rue de Dunkerque, 75010 Paris, France). English translations of parts of this work have appeared in *UC* 6 and 8. *UC* 11 has a nice tried-and-tested (and simple) design, and a report of one of the AA's famous 'wind days'. See also CTT's

New Alchemy Daedalus prepares to fly

booklets *Free electricity* (well yes but . . .) and *Winco Electric*.

On the now trendy 'Darrieus' vertical-axis designs, Derek Taylor has built a couple of models, but it's not all that easy. Details can be obtained from the *National Research Council of Canada* Ottawa, (reports LTR-LA-74, LTR-LA-105, and PNW-73-303).

For a list of sources on electrics, generators, batteries, etc, see *ASE bibliography*.

In addition to these specialized items, *EP* and *Producing Your Own Power* (see 4.13) are replete with helpful material on D.I.Y. wind applications.

4.34 MANUFACTURERS

A list of Windmill Manufacturers, by Gerry Smith (*AHS M1*: £0.15) [CO] has the lot. *WEE* also carries a list of American dealers on p. 537. In Britain the best agents are CTT (2.311). See also ASE *Spectrum* (2.1).

4.35 ECONOMICS

The Economics of Solar Collectors, Heat Pumps and Wind Generators, by Gerry Smith (*AHS WP3*) [CO] covers small-scale, off-the-shelf generators.

Putman's *Power from the Wind* deals with large-scale generators.

4.36 CONTACTS

See *EP*, especially pp. 100-105.

In USA, contact with experienced wind-workers can be gained through the *ASE* network (4.12) or direct to eg:

◆ **Marc Sherman at New Alchemy East** (2.33), or *EP*, p. 101.

◆ **Henry Clews at Solar Wind** (4.32)

◆ **Hans Meyer at Windworks** (4.31)

◆ In Britain, the grand old man of wind work is Golding's old collaborator, A. M. Stodhart (still at the Electrical Research Association, Cleeve Road, Leatherhead, Surrey). J. R. Tagg is also at the **ERA**. *EP* has a complete list of ERA publications.

◆ **Dr. N.G. Clavert** (U. Liverpool) has

developed cheap sailwing designs under 10kW, and advocates the use of hydraulic couplings.

◆ **Dr Elliot** of Lanchester Polytechnic, Coventry has carried out comparative studies of various blade shapes and configurations.

◆ **Derek Taylor** and **John Shore** at the AA have both made a number of machines, as have **Kit Pedler** (119 Park Hill, London SW4); **Cliff Collins** (Poly of Central London, NW1); **Tony Williams** (Royal Ballet School, 155 Talgarth Road, London W14); **Rob Hitchings**, (1 Mafeking Place, Annan, Dumfriesshire, Scotland), whose design is described in *ASE* 14; the Street Farmers (2.311); and Dave Andrews, c/o Comtek (2.311). Several of these heroes have contributed material to this book — and not all on wind machines. Truly they are free-range and not battery-technologists, roaming wide and free.

In Holland, Rinie v.d. Brand and a group at the Technologistche Hogeschool at Eindhoven have produced some detailed reports on optimizing designs for small-scale generators, while F.D. Eelman (N.V. Texelsche-Electriciteits-Maatschappij, Texel, Oudeschild) has developed a simple method for converting traditional pumping mills to generate electricity.

4.37 OLD WINDMILLS

The sources most commonly cited — deservedly — are *Windmills and watermills* by John Reynolds (Praeger, New York, 1970) [CO] and *The English Windmill* by Rex Wailes (Routledge and Kegan Paul, London, 1954). But the ultimate collector's item, without any doubt, is the *Transactions of the Second International Symposium on Molinology*, edited by Hans Jespersen (Selskabet Danske Mollers Venner, Brede, Lyngby, Denmark), a staggering tour de force of editorial perfectionism.

On the life of millers, J. W. Freese's *Windmills and Millwrighting*, (David and Charles, 1973) is charming. In Holland you can take courses in milling (Het Gilde van Vrijwillige Molenaars, Herengracht 75b, Amsterdam). If you want to talk to a real live miller with flour on his eyebrows, visit the North Laverton windmill, Nottinghamshire.

4.4 WATER ENERGY

Unlike sun or wind, water power can easily be monopolised because not everyone can get to the river. In the middle ages, water mills could throng in favourable locations like grapes on a vine, each miller trying to trim his upstream neighbour's head of water by raising his own dam. Nowadays in Britain, it's very hard to run a small-scale water power installation because there's a tax on the water you use. Therefore it is again monopolised, supposedly in the public interest, by the Central Electricity Generating Board. The question of big *v.* small water-power (and at any scale it is in principle a renewable resource — although the Colorado River sometimes disappears before it reaches the sea, doubtless crying 'water! water!') is ably discussed by the irascible George Woolston in *UC* 5 and *UC* 6, and here in the book.

4.41 GENERAL ACCESS

EP has 6 pages of reviews and a list of 50 water-power equipment manufacturers.

AARTU contains a helpful bibliography including a small list of manufacturers specialising in small-scale equipment.

The *ASE bibliography* is classified as follows: general; geothermal; hydraulic rams; old water mills; water-wheels and turbines; tidal power; wave energy; water-power measurement; dams and hydroelectric power; temperature gradients.

4.42 BASIC TEXTS

On the big stuff, the textbook is *Hydro-electric Engineering Practice* by J. G. Brown, 3 vols. (Blackie, London, 1958) [SB]. *Power from Water* by T. A. L. Paton and J. G. Brown (Leonard Hill, 1961) [SB] is more popularly accessible.

For small-scale work, a handy basic primer is *Low-Cost Development of Small Water-Power Sites* by Hans W. Hamm, from VITA. See also Robin Saunder's contribution in *EP*, p. 52. *TMEN* 13 and 14 contained reprints of some *Popular Science* articles which are reprinted in *The Mother Earth News Hand-Book of Home Made Power* (4.13) and again

These waterwheels drove the fountains at Versailles

in *Cloudburst: A Handbook of Rural Skills and Technology* (Cloudburst Press, Box 74, Brackendale, B.C., Canada, 073), along with some of the VITA text, which itself is reprinted in *Producing Your Own Power* (4.13). *TMEN* 22 has an article about hydraulic ram installation.

Hydropower by Andrew McKillop (Wade bridge Ecological Centre, Molesworth Street, Wadebridge, Cornwall, England, or CTT) reprints a number of useful designs.

4.43 OLD WATERMILLS

On old watermills, see *Windmills and Watermills* and *Trans. Sec. Int. Symp. Molinol* (both 4.37). For the car-borne tourist, *Discovering Watermills* by J.T. Vince (Shire, 1970) [OB]. On traditional tide mills *Tide Mills* by Rex Wailes (Society for the Protection of Ancient Buildings, London 1957) [SB]; and on bigger things *Tidal Power* by T. J. Gray and O. K. Glashus, (Plenium, London, 1972) [SB].

TRANS. 2ND. INT. SYMP. MOL.

4.5 BIOLOGICAL ENERGY

EP is the only directory I know which covers this field as a whole; its articles on methane, alcohol, and wood are excellent.

Another concise general intro (without bibliography) is Colin Moorcraft's 'Plant Power' in *AD* 1/74, covering basic principles, yields, combustion, fermentation, methane production, nitrogen sources, fuel crops, sewage farming, hydroponics, fodder factories.

4.51 FUEL CROPS
Virtually any green plant could be grown as a means of fixing carbon by solar energy, which can then be converted by eating, burning, fermenting, etc. But some plants are more efficient than others for these purposes. The most commonly considered prospects are algae, grasses, sugar cane, wood and root storage crops (the latter championed by one Mangelsdorf, which always amuses me).

The algal process usually involves conversion to alcohol or methane as an intermediate step, and is generally associated with sewage disposal as a source of nitrogen. The masters of the field are W. J. Oswald and C. Golueke of the Sanitary Engineering Research Laboratory (Dept of Engineering, University of California, Berkeley); see for instance 'Solar Power via a Botanical Process', *Mechanical Engineering*, February 1964, and 'An Algal Regenerative System for Single Family Farms and Villages', *Compost Science*, vol. 14, no. 3, 1973. See also 6.1.

A case for the use of higher plants rather than algae is made by N. W. Pirie in 'Power from Leaves' in *Proceedings of the New Delhi Symposium on Wind and Solar Energy* (UNESCO, 1958, p. 216), which volume, incidentally, also contains plenty on sun and wind power, but is rather out of date.

On wood as a fuel, see *EP* and *ASE bibliography* and *Services for an Autonomous Research Community in Wales,* by Robert Vale (*AHS WP5*) which contains details about cropping a hazel coppice. The general feasibility of wood as a fuel is discussed by Clinton Kemp and George Szego in 'Energy Forests

Oil drum digestor

and Fuel Plantations', *Chemtech*, May 1973.

For wood pyrolysis products (wood gas and methanol), see *ASE bibliography* and *ASE* 11 and 14, which also contains stove designs and a list of manufacturers.

For more small-scale wood-burning equipment, *EP* wood section and *WEE*, p. 518; VITA *stove plan, no. 5100*; and *The Wood-Burners Handbook*, by David Havens (Media House, Box 1770, Portland, ME 04104, USA) [CO]. The most fashionable wood-burning stoves right now are the Norwegian Jotuls (imported by Brobarts Ltd, 12 Gold Square, Aberdeen, Scotland, or direct from Aksjeselskapet Jotul, Post box 6206, E.T., 05106, Norway).

4.52 METHANE
The generation of methane gas from organic wastes is currently the popular favourite form of biological energy in 'AT' circles. The literature is vast, but in temperate climates its application on a small scale can be problematic.

4.521 Methane: basic texts
Good introductions are Colin Moorcraft's 'Methane Power' in *AD* 2/72 and Richard Merrill's quickie in *EP*, p. 144.

A short article and concise bibliography can be found in *AARTU EP's* bibliography thoroughly reviews ten basic texts, then gives a 100+ list classified as follows: methane digestion (municipal/industrial, agricultural wastes); popular overviews and scaled-down designs; biology/chemistry; sludge (analysis; gardening and farming; algae systems — growth, harvesting and digestion; algae systems for methane power; algae for livestock feed; hydroponics); digester privies. Other bibliographies are in the works cited.

The most accessible texts in Britain are probably:

Methane, Fuel of the Future, by Bell, Boulter, Dunlop and Kieller, (Andrew Singer, The Mill House, Coles Hill, Highworth, Wilts, England: £0.75) [MB,CO]. A concise description of existing theory and practice, with some speculation about where it will all lead. Not very helpful for rolling your own, but with outstanding classified bibliography of 133 items, glossary, list of periodicals, and further contacts.

Practical Building of Methane Power Plants, by L. John Fry (D. A. Knox, 'Staddlestones' Penton Mewsey, Andover, Hants SP 11, England) [MB,CO]. This is a handsome distillation of Fry's unsurpassed practical experience, and definitely worth

having, although £4.00 is just as definitely a rip-off.

Much of the same material is in:

Methane Digesters for Fuel Gas and Fertilizer (New Alchemy Institute Newsletter no. 3, Spring 1973: $3.00/£1.50) [CO] by Richard Merrill and John Fry. This is a model of 'AT' publishing: theory, estimates of yields, rules of thumb, blueprints for two tested working models and a 69-item unannotated bibliography.

Methane (Atomic Rooster's Here) from the Wadebridge Ecological Centre (Molesworth Street, Wadebridge, Cornwall, England: £1.60) [CO] has a number of alternative designs, but they are untested.

Other sources:

Composting: Sanitary Disposal and Reclamation of Organic Waste by Harold B. Gotaas, (W. H. O. monograph no 31, 1956) [LO]. Has a useful section on methane.

Bio-gas Plant: Generating Methane from Organic Wastes (£2.00). *Bio-gas Plant Designs with Specifications* (£2.50) both by Ram Bux Singh (Gobar Gas Research Station Ajitmal, Etawah, U.P., India) [CO]. These are principles and plans based on a great deal

of experience, and are evidently very effective in Indian conditions.

The case for the development of such methane plants in tropical climates is persuasively argued in an exceptionally competent paper, 'Bio-Gas Plants: Prospects, Problems and Tasks', *Economical and Political Weekly* (Bombay) vol. 9, Special Number August 1974, by C. R. Prasad, K. K. Prasad and A. K. N. Reddy. (Copies can be obtained from Professor Reddy, (12.4).)

But in colder climates, it's very hard to get small digesters to give out more energy than they need to keep them warm. Some cautionary tales are told in 'Muck Power', by Michael Gaisford, *Farmers Weekly*, May 31st, 1974.

4.522 Methane: contacts
The following have at least built digesters:

◆ **Les Auerbach,** (242 Copse Road, Madison CT 06443, USA). He sells 50 pages of plans for £4.50.

◆ **Steve Sampson** c/o CTT.

◆ **Jiri Skopek** (Shenley Park House, Shenley Church End, Milton Keynes, Bucks, England). See 'A methane digester: a progress report' in *AARTU.*

◆ **Jaap t' Hooft** (3.72) a highly insulated, solar-heated, underground digester, a promising design.

◆ **J. Howarth** ('South View' Haxey, Doncaster, S. Yorks, England) built a medium-scale farm digester and sells plans for £5.00. He reckons it works.

◆ **Richard Merrill**, New Alchemy Institute

Farm methane gas holders

(West) (Box 376, Pescadero, California, CA 94060), editor of *EP* bio-fuel section, worked with John Fry on the celebrated tractor inner-tube digester.

◆ **Biogas Plant** (Easebourne Lane, Midhurst, Sussex GU29 9AZ, tel Midhurst 3913/3169). They produce a series of digesters which are large enough to look feasible in temperate climates, but keep costs down by various design tricks. See *UC* 11, p. 31. Write for booklet *Bio-Gas Today*.

4.6 MISCELLANEOUS ENERGY

4.61 HEAT PUMPS
A good short introduction to the subject of heat pumps is Pete Stellon's 'The Heat that Comes in from the Cold' in *UC* 6. This contains a concise bibliography and a list of practitioners.

A more advanced text is *Heat Pumps and Electric Heating*, by E. Ambrose (Wiley, London, 1966) [SB].

A detailed bibliography is *Electricity Council Bibliography*, B58 (Intelligence Section, 30 Millbank, London SW1).

EP's coverage of heat pumps is modest and has no reference, but there's an agreeable 1-page intro on p. 73.

4.62 ANIMAL ENERGY
I don't know much about this. The best text is ITDG's *Guide to Hand-Operated and Animal-Drawn Equipment* (£1.50) [CO]. In Britain horses come to mind. Someone running half a 150-acre farm with horses is Charlie Pinney at The Cottage, Bettiscombe Manor Farm (Bettiscombe, Bridport, Dorset, England). See also Heavy Horse Preservation Society, in section 9.

Stefan Szczelkun lumps dowsing, acupuncture, tai-chi and orgones into this category, with references, in *SS5*. See also article on occult technologies in the book.

4.63 OTHER ENERGY TOPICS
The case for hydrogen as a non-polluting medium of energy transmission in industry, housing and transport is propounded in *Energy: A Solar Hydrogen Alternative* by J. M. O. Bockriss, (Architectural Press, London: £13.50) [SB].

On total energy systems and stationary engines see Kit Pedler's article in the book, and *Total Energy*, by R. M. E. Diamant (4.13).

On geothermal energy, see vols. 2 and 3 of the UN *New Sources of Energy* (4.13).

On other topics (storage, direct conversion compressed air, fuel cells, flywheels, peat-burning, district heating, industrial waste-heat recovery and all the other issues I can't think of now), see bibliographies in *EP*, *ADDS*, *SS5*, *ASE6*.

5 MATERIALS, TOOLS & DESIGN

The essence of the Radical Technology approach, I suppose, is to use renewable materials, long-lasting materials (yes, even aluminium and stainless steel) or waste products; and processes that lend themselves to 'convivial', co-operative production and use — to be sufficiently well-equipped with tools to make and maintain what you need. 'Who makes the tools?' is the other half of the story, for which, see 2.524 and 13.2.

5.1 GENERAL ACCESS

WEE has a whole section on craft. See also pp. 542-5. *PW* is extraordinary — 274 pages on tools and construction , with lots of diagrams. *SH* is also good. On the general use of ordinary materials, consult the local library.

5.2 TOOLS

On the general principles of 'alternative tools', see (at the most abstract level):

Tools for Conviviality, by Ivan Illich (2.51).

A more obviously 'radical' approach is taken in the splendid Open University text *Design and Technology*, by Nigel Cross (Man-Made Futures Unit 9).

More practically, *Design for the Real World* by Victor Papanek (2.51), or more practically still, *The Sensuous Gadgeteer*, by Bill Abler (Running Press, 38 S. 19th Street, Philadelphia, PA 19103) [CO].

On how things work, see:

How Things Work, by C. Van Amerongen, 2 vols (Paladin, London, 1972) [OB], and its 19th century analogue, Andrew Ure's *Dictionary of Manufacturers*, 3 Vols, Longman, London, 1831, 1860, etc.).

For the old stuff on tools and the craft atmosphere, *The Wheelwright's Shop* by George Sturt (Cambridge UP, London, New York) [OB] is remarkable.

For dreams about restoring such a dispensation, see a series of essays on 'The Community Workshop', *Anarchy* 30, 1966. But actually there's often a community workshop within reach already — I paid 75p for a term of metalwork evening classes, and had access to lathes, drills, welding gear, a forge, hand tools — the lot, and met some lovely people too.

If you want to make your own tools, these two books by Alexander Weygers are highly recommended: *The Making of Tools* (1973) and *The Modern Blacksmith* (Van Nostrand Rheinhold, New York, 1974) [CO].

5.3 TRADITIONAL CRAFTS

On the traditional craft materials and skills (wood, leather, ceramics, wax, jewellery, glass, basketry and all the textile crafts), *WEE* has a very good selection.

The Foxfire Book (1972) and *Foxfire 2* (1973), edited by Eliot Wigginton (Doubleday Anchor, New York) [CO] contain an extraordinary selection of interviews with old country people in the Georgia Appalachians describing the crafts which they have always practised, but which are now dying out. See also *The Book of Country Crafts* by R. W. Johnston (Barnes, London, 1964); and the amazing *Country Bizarre's Country Bazaar* (2.523). These days any library or bookshop will have endless books on the crafts. The remaining items might not be so easily found.

For the textile crafts, the best source of information in Britain is K. R. Drummond (30 Hart Grove, Ealing, London W5). Write for the comprehensive catalogue. The Guild of Spinners, Weavers and Dyers publishes the *Quarterly Journal of the GSWD* (Ruth Hurley,

47 East Street, Saffron Walden, Essex). In the USA the main journal is the *Handweaver and Craftsman* (10 McGovern Avenue, Lancaster, PA). On using natural dyes see Chris Ryan's article in the book. On pottery the finest book I know (earthy technics, no arty bullshit) is *Pioneer Pottery* by Michael Cardew (Blackwells, Oxford, 1969).

On paper, *Paper Making* by Dard Hunter (Knopf, New York, 1974; 2nd ed.). On shoes, *Manual of Shoe-Making*, ed. Jane Clarke (Clarks, 1966), and the articles by Derek Burns (87 Chester Terrace, Brighton, Sussex) and Nick Mellor (37 Severn Street, Leicester) in the book.

On the vernacular materials used in building, see 3.3 and 3.4.

Courses in many of the traditional crafts are offered at West Dean College, Chichester, W. Sussex.

Iranian scythe-maker

6 WASTE TREATMENT & WATER SUPPLY

The categories of composting, excreta treatment and water supply fall together even if you try to keep them apart. The Radical Technology emphasis is on saving valuable resources (nitrogen, water, etc.) and preventing pollution, all at once, which of course is the only sensible thing to do anyway.

The bibliography in *SS2* is not bad.

5.4 MODERN MATERIALS

On two favourite modern materials adaptable to the small scale:

The New Glass Fibre Book, by R. H. Waring (Motor books International, 3501 Hennepin Avenue, S. Minneapolis, MN 55408, USA) [CO]. Plans for things to build in GRP can be had from Trylon Ltd (Wellingborough, Wollaston, Northants, England).

And on ferrocement — *PW* reprints a definitive UN booklet on the subject.

On chemicals, see the article by Alan Dalton 'The Skeptykal Kemyst'; *Charcoal and Other Products from the Thermal Decomposition of Wood*, by P. Dryburgh, Forest Panel of ITDG; *Alternative Sources of Industrially Important Chemicals*, Trevor Bonner, Wolfson Foundation 1974; 'Carbohydrates as an alternative source of petroleum for organic chemicals' by C. Weizmann et al, *Chemistry and Industry* December 13, 1947, p. 769; *Encyclopaedia of Chemical Technology*, Wiley Interscience, 1970.

5.5 WASTE AND SCRAP

On the use of waste products and scrap, Friends of the Earth (9 Poland Street, London W1) publish *Material Gains — Reclamation, Recycling and Reuse* by Christian Thomas (£1) — reclamation techniques for consumers, industry and local government. Also *Packaging in Britain — A policy for Containment* (50p). See also the trade journal *Materials Reclamation Weekly* (PO Box 109, 69 High Street, Croydon CR9, England); and reports on generation, flow, use and disposal of waste by the Warren Spring Laboratory of the DTI (Gunnels Wood Road, Stevenage, Herts).

For small-scale application of scrap parts and metal, contact Rob and Al Hitchings (1 Mafeking Place, Annan, Dumfrieshire, Scotland). Their guide to what to look for in scrap yards is in this book on p.190.

For garbage housing and sulphur construction, see 3.4.

A fascinating book on the most economical possible use of materials is *China at Work* by Rudolf P. Hommel (recently reprinted by MIT Press).

Finally (I didn't know where else to put this), the two volumes of *Nomadic Furniture* by James Hennessey and Victor Papanek (Pantheon, New York, 1973 and 4) contain ideas and designs for furniture that 'folds, inflates, knocks down, stacks, or is disposable and can be recycled' — emphasising use of low-cost or scrap materials.

6.1 COMPOSTING

There are two bibliographies in *AARTU*, one on aerobic composting, one on anaerobic, both well-chosen, concise and annotated. See also *EP*, p. 120.

The journal *Compost Science*, (Rodale Press, Emmaus, PA 18049), mainly deals with large-scale treatment of town refuse.

References on anaerobic composting have already been given in the methane subsection of 'Biological energy' in 4.521. *Composting* by Gotaas, mentioned there, is a basic textbook for all kinds of composting.

A comprehensive survey has been carried out by the Compost Studies Group at the University of Birmingham: 'A Review of Composting' by Gray, Sherman, Biddlestone and Clarke, in *Process Biochemistry* Part 1, June 1971; Part II, Oct 1971; Part III, Oct 1973.

Another textbook is C. Golueke's *Composting: A Study of the Process and its Principles* (Rodale Press, 1973).

See also *An Agricultural Testament*, and *Farmers of Forty Centuries* (7.4).

For a human, the act of shitting is like firing a ball to the top of a pin-ball machine. Just to flush it down the loo is to lose the ball with no points at all. Composting it and getting it back to the land is the least you can do to turn a few lights on. Getting some power out of the carbon before you put the nitrogen back on the soil will improve your score. This can be boosted by an intermediate algal process to fix more carbon.

And here's a real jackpot-winner: a feller I met in Liverpool has found that desiccated human shit, mixed with straw and grit makes a perfect chicken food. This is the obvious first step; *then* collect the chicken shit and grow algae on it; *then* digest the algae to get methane; *then* stick the effluent back on the land. But none of this can be done without complete reform of the sewage-collection systems in cities because of the heavy metals and other toxic ingredients in that golden sludge.

6.2 EXCRETA TREATMENT

The definitive work is without doubt *Stop the Five-Gallon Flush*, by Ortega et al, of the Minimum-Cost Housing Group at McGill (2.33) (1973: $2.00) [CO] — a survey and critical analysis of 50 different types of toilet. It is the complete access guide and gives names and addresses of manufacturers.

The classic textbook on low-cost privies is *Excreta Disposal for Rural Areas and Small Communities*, by E. G. Wagner and J. N. Lanoix (World Health Organisation, WHO, 1958).

Another useful paper, which was devised to complement *5 Gallon Flush*, is *Economics of Water Collection and Waste Recycling* by Gerry Smith, *AHS WP6* [CO].

See also *SS2*, and *Technical Bulletin no. 1*, Farrallones Institute (2.33)

Other references are in *SS2*, *AARTU*, *WEE*; or contact John Shore at the AA for the opinions of a dedicated coprophile.

6.3 WATER SUPPLY

Water Supply for Rural Areas and Small Communities, by E. G. Wagner and J. N. Lanoix (WHO, 1959) is the complement to their monograph on excreta disposal.

The best access source for low-cost applications is *A Bibliography of Low-Cost Water Technologies* by ITDG [CO]. Advice can be had from Simon Watt of ITDG's water panel (National College of Agricultural Engineering, Silsoe, Beds.).

Gerry Smith's paper on economics of water supply and waste disposal (mentioned above) reviews the more costly systems of collecting and purifying water, and gives references.

Less practical but more charming is Dorothy Hartley's *Water in England* (Macdonald, London, 1964).

George Woolston's article in the book presents the social side of water supply.

Graham Caine's fibreglass toilet

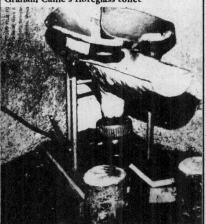

Solar still, roof of Alex Pike's 'autarchic house'

7 FOOD

From the point of view of Radical Technology the purpose of research into food supply is to create an economical, indefinitely-sustainable husbandry that provides food of good quantity and quality without discrimination, exploitation or unneccessary toil. Depending on how these vague specifications are interpreted, various corollaries follow: local production and consumption, minimum inorganic fertilizers and biocides, higher person/land ratio, careful attention to the local nitrogen cycle, reduced meat consumption, alternative sources of protein, special methods for cities and suburbs, new patterns of distribution. Taken together, these seem to imply a completely different character and relationship of town and country, indeed a revolutionary reorganisation of society. Yes.

7.1 GENERAL ACCESS

There are no end of bibliographies. Probably the most exhaustive on everything to do with the land is the *catalogue* of Landsman's Bookshop Ltd (Buckenhill, Bromyard, Herefs, England). This is a small outfit, but they seem to be obliged by their constitution to carry everything on agriculture that's in print. The service is very prompt, and they'll buy things back at 2/3 price if they're in good condition.

Other useful catalogues for ordering are Blackwell's *no. 894* (Broad Street, Oxford); HMSO *Sectional Catalogue no. 1*; for the French literature, La Maison Rustique (Rue Jacob, 75006, Paris); and for the American, Garden Way Publications (Charlotte, VT 05445).

EP's agriculture section has a magnificent annotated and classified directory.

SS2 has a sturdy but unannotated bibliography classified as follows: general, nutrition, air; water; growing; gathering wild food plants; rearing animals; hunting animals; cooking; preserving, processing, etc.; waste; contacts.

Otherwise see *AARTU, WEC*, p. 50 and *WEE*, p. 500, and visit the library of the Royal Horticultural Society (Vincent Square, London SW1).

A *literature list* on biodynamic gardening can be obtained from Biochemical Research Lab (Threefold Farm, Spring Valley, NY 10977).

7.2 PERIODICALS

The most important step is to get plugged into the HDRA (Henry Doubleday Research Association) (2.312). A subscription of £3.00 will generate a flood of bulletins and reports on most aspects of intensive horticulture.

Organic Gardening and Farming and *Compost Science* are both from Rodale Press (33 E. Minor Street, Emmaus, PA 18049, USA, but I don't know the subscription rates).

Nature et Progres (3 Chemin de la Bergerie, 91700 Sainte Genevieve du Bois, France: 45F a year, quarterly).

TMEN is very strong on food topics and food ideas, *Journal of the New Alchemists*, also, in its own scholarly/freaky way.

Seed, (269 Portobello Road, London W11: £3.00 p.a.) [CO,MB]. Monthly organ of the macrobiotic and healthfood freaks, polemical rather than practical.

7.3 GENERAL CONTACTS

Join the HDRA.
◆ **Soil Association** (Walnut Tree Manor, Haughley, Stowmarket, Suffolk, England) has been doing careful research in organic farming for years, and publishes the *Soil Association Journal*.
◆ **Farm and Food Society** (37 Tanza Road, London NW3) campaigns for less chemicals

Algae culture in India

and more kindness to the beasts of the field.
◆ **The Biodynamic Gardening Association Ltd** (Springfield, IL 62701) promulgates the ideas of Rudolf Steiner. In England, contact can be made through **Rudolf Steiner House** (35 Park Road, London NW1).
◆ **Nature et Progres** (address 7.2) — the European Association for Organic Agriculture and Health — has an extensive list of books available by mail order, mostly in French.

7.4 ORGANIC GARDENING AND FARMING

Two textbooks:
Grow Your Own Fruit and Vegetables by Lawrence D. Hills of the HDRA (Faber, London, 1971; Transatlantic, New York, 1974) [CO].
The Encyclopaedia of Organic Gardening by J. I. Rodale (Rodale Press, 1969) [CO].

Two great classics:
An Agricultural Testament by Sir Arthur Howard (Oxford, 1940) — experience in India.
Farmers of Forty Centuries by F. H. King (orig 1911, new edn. Rodale Press, 1974) — experience in China.

Two general-purpose turn-ons:
Self-Sufficiency, by John and Sally Seymour (Faber, London, 1973) [OB,MB]. A grand book, but vegetarians need not apply.
Diet for a Small Planet by Frances Moore Lappe (Ballantine, New York, 1971) [CO,MB]. The argument from resources and ecology — this time, sad reading for carnivores.

Then there are lots of special techniques, for example *Companion Planting* by Helen Philbrick and Richard B. Gregg (Robinson and Watkins, London, 1967), which springs from the biodynamic tradition. A broader text in biodynamic gardening is *The Pfeiffer Garden*

Book, by The Biodynamic Gardening and Farming Association (7.3) and the Great Original is Rudolf Steiner's *Agriculture* (Rudolf Steiner House) (7.3) which has some very strange and wonderful things in it.

'Sward gardening' is another technique for maintaining soil fertility, through the use of clover. See the articles by Tony Farmer in *UC* 8 and 10.

7.5 GROWING IN CITIES

In the city, first one must find what land there is, and secondly one must make the most intensive possible use of it. Or one can create subsitiues for land. Once the food is grown, it should be used as efficiently as possible; this applies also to food you don't grow yourself.

John Shore's 'Looking After Ourselves' in *AARTU* is a good introduction to ultra-intensive food production, and contains a useful bibliography. Pat Pringle's 'Nutritional Requirements and Home Food Production' in the same publication complements it. See also John Shore's article on p.28.

Information about allotments can be obtained at the local town hall. In *The Allotments Campaign Manual*, Friends of the Earth (qv, 25p + 9p p.+p.) suggest ways of turning derelict town land over to allotments and tactics for getting past unco-operative local authorities.

The land should be carefully manured (see 'Composting') and plants chosen to make best use of soil and space: see John Woods' 'Great Pigs from Little Acorns Grow' on p.42.

The construction and use of greenhouses is discussed in *PW*, and in *Plastic Structures for Agriculture and Horticulture*, Ministry of Agriculture document STL 86.

If there is no land, but space for growing-boxes, it is still possible to grow food:

In the open: *Raise Vegetables Without a Garden*, by George and Katy Abraham (Countryside Books, A. B. Morse Co, Barrington, IL 60010, 1974).

Or indoors: *The Complete Book of Gardening Under Lights*, by Elwin McDonald (Popular Library, New York, 1965).

If soil itself is a problem, hydroponics (soilless culture) offers an alternative. *WEE* has a short bibliography of hydroponics as p. 505. The classic texts are those of Sholto Douglas: *Hydroponics: The Bengal System* (Oxford, 1970) [CO]; *The Beginner's Guide to Hydroponics* (Pelham, London, 1972) — his article in the book summarises his work.

Full bibliographies on soilless crop-growing are available from the Secretariat, International Working Group on Soilless Culture (IWOSC) PO Box 52, Wageningen, The Netherlands. Ready-mixed nutrient formulae for hydroponics are available from Phostrogen Ltd, London Road, Corwen, Gwynedd, Wales.

WEE, p. 588ff lists a number of useful sources on healthy, cheap diets, food preservation, and the organisation of food co-ops. On preserving, *PW* is particularly good, but any library will have all the information. See also the article in the book.

7.6 INTENSIVE PROTEIN SOURCES

With a premium on land, economics and rational husbandry swing against meat production on prime agricultural land, excepting scavengers like pigs. Radical Technology practitioners have tried either to find alternatives to animal protein, or to culture animals that can happily live at high density off waste products. On the former side, they have focused on the legumes, particularly the

RICHARD GREENHILL

mighty soybean; so-called 'leaf-protein' and algae; on the latter side, on fish.

On the case for beans in general, see *Diet for a Small Planet* (7.4), and on soybeans, *Soybeans and Soybean Products* by K. S. Mackley (Wiley, London, 1950) and *The Soybean Cookbook* by Dorothea Van Gundy Jones (General Publishing Co, Don Mills, Ontario, Canada). The HDRA has been doing some research on the Fiskeby V soybean, which is intended for use in temperate climates — it was planted by hundreds of enthusiastic bean-freaks last season, but the results have been disappointing.

On leaf protein, the textbook is *Leaf Protein* by N. W. Pirie (International Biological Program, 1971) [SB]. Ordinary grass can give a high yield of excellent quality protein if harvested and extracted at the right time. The result is bright green and tasteless but good for you.

Other plants are also efficient generators of protein. Firstly algae cultured for food: see the extremely suggestive article, 'Algae Research in Auroville' by Robert Lawlor in *ASE* 16: this includes a list of others doing similar research. Secondly, Russian Comfrey, the HDRA's wonder-plant (write for glowing details).

On fish culture, the basic textbook is *Aquaculture* by J. E. Bardach, W. O. McLarney and J. Ryther (Wiley, London, New York, 1972) [SB]. The authors are mixed up with the New Alchemists, whose aquaculture research is perhaps the most advanced and original aspect of their work. *Journal of the New Alchemists* no. 2 contains 'Walton Two: The Compleat Guide to Backyard Fish Farming by Bill McLarney and John Todd, 40 pages of details, reports and instruction. See also the aquaculture section of *EP* for an introduction, reviews, references and contacts; and Community Technology (2.33) for basement fish-culture in cities.

7.7 MISCELLANEOUS

There seems to be a bit of a vegetarian bias about this selection so far. I'm daunted by the enormous literature on animal husbandry, and haven't really got space. There are excellent references in *Landsman's catalogue*, *SS2*, *WEC* and *WEE*. The fashion has been for bees, chickens and goats. (See articles in *UC* 11)

Other topics I have neglected include insect resistance, tree crops, mushroom culture, but these can all be found *inter alia* in the sources already cited.

A marginal category that has spawned delightful literature is that of wild foods. The *SS2* bibliography is good here, and the nicest books are: for Europe, *Food for Free* by Richard Mabey, (Collins, London, 1972; Scribner, New York, 1974)[OB] which persuaded me to eat a giant puffball steak last summer; and for North America, *Stalking the Wild Asparagus, Stalking the Blue-Eyed Scallop*, and *Stalking the Healthful Herbs* by Ewell Gibbons (MacKay, New York, 1970) [MB].

7.8 SOCIAL ASPECTS OF FOOD

On wider questions of food policy, the famine-scare books of the late '60s seem to have given way to more positive treatments. An excellent survey of the global food problem is presented by *The Future of Food*, a collection edited by Oliver Shirley with Robin Roy (Open University Man-Made Futures Course, Design and Technology Units 7 and 8 Futures Access File, 1975). A useful introduction to the more technical aspects of food supply and demand is N. W. Pirie's *Food Resources Conventional and Novel* (Penguin, Harmondsworth; Gannon, New York, 1969).

On the matter of Britain's food supply: *Losing Ground*, and *Britain and the World Food Crisis*, both produced by Friends of the Earth (9 Poland Street, London W1).

Can Britain Feed Itself? by Kenneth Mellanby (Merlin Press, 1975), and an article with the same title by Michael Allaby in *Resurgence* vol. 5, no. 4; not forgetting *A Blueprint for Survival* (2.54) and *Fields Factories and Workshops Tomorrow* (2.51).

A general compendium which has been on the verge of publication for years (and a first cousin to this book) is *Radical Agriculture*, edited by Richard Merrill (Harper and Row, New York). I hope it will finally have appeared by the time *Radical Technology* sees the light of day.

Two good articles on political aspects of food are Charlie Clutterbuck's piece on 'Agribusiness' in this book, and Colin Tudge's article 'Food for the Unthinking', in *World Medicine*, June 5th, 1974, reprinted in *The Future of Food* cited earlier in this section: a critique of the hi-tek food industry and a manifesto of alternatives.

8 MEDICINE

I have never really written down a list on this subject before, but it seems reasonable that 'radical medicine' should satisfy at least some of the following criteria: an emphasis on health rather than sickness, ie preventive rather than curative medicine; demystification of the doctor's role and complete participation by the patient; reduction of institutionalised and high-capital treatment, increased community and family care and a wider spread of medical skills; a shift of emphasis from relatively rare acute conditions to common chronic conditions and occupational health problems, etc; openness to unorthodox methods if they work.

Currently the most widely circulated heresies on medicine are those of Ivan Illich, in *Medical Nemesis* (Calder and Boyars, London,1974) [OB]. He is arguing (among other things) that the provision of capital-intensive institutional medicine destroys something in us which he considers very precious — our ability to look after ourselves. This wouldn't matter perhaps if Big Medicine were capable of making good what is lost, but Illich argues it is not, and cannot be. Likewise does John Powles in his seminal paper, 'On the Limitations of Modern Medicine', 1973, vol. 1, in *Science, Medicine and Man*.

This is a far cry from the position of the traditional Left, who have always argued for *more* institutionalisation, the Socialist Medical Association for example (14 Bristol Street, Birmingham) or Marxists in Medicine (27 Pearman Street, London SE1).

China's new medicine is perhaps somewhere in between, with 'barefoot doctors' taking the load of routine cases, leaving more fully trained doctors to handle rare or difficult cases: see *Away With All Pests* (12.1) and *Serve the People*, by Victor W. Sidel and Ruth Sidel (David White, NY, 1973). The Chinese policy of blending traditional medicine (herbs, acupuncture) with modern methods — walking on two legs — seems to be very effective, but is frowned on in the West, although some unorthodox stuff (cancer treatment by meditation, 'laying on of hands', etc.) seems to be growing in acceptance: see *Fringe Medicine*, by Brian Inglis (Faber, London, 1974).

Preventive medicine which emphasises health rather than sickness suggests a kind of environmental approach, and indeed Powles

FRAID SO, PETE

NOT BORAGE FRITTERS AGAIN

and Illich point out that statistical or 'eco-logical' measures like sanitation have had far more effect on health than the 'engineering' interventions of doctors. But there has to be a place for personal as opposed to strictly functional (ie Hippocratic rather than Galenic) treatment, and it was a desire to find this balance that led to the setting up of the famous 'Peckham Experiment' before the war, where the total environment and personal relationships between patients, and between doctors and patients, could be developed. See George Scott Williamson and Innes Pearse: *Science, Synthesis and Sanity* (Collins, London, 1965) [LO], and *Anarchy* no. 60.

At the time the Peckham Experiment was an isolated event, but the movement towards community medicine now gathers strength, spurred by the Women's Movement — see *Our Bodies Ourselves* by the Woman's Health Book Collective (Simon and Schuster, New York, 1973). *Source Catalog No 3:* by Source, Inc. (Beacon Press, Boston, 1974), a comprehensive guide, is impressive evidence. The idea of an experimental community health-centre where the doctors pool their salaries to support more workers, and encourage like patients to discuss their problems with each other, is currently being canvassed (contact Gail Chester, 163 Clapham Park Road, London SW4).

Meanwhile, we have become far more aware of the chronic problems of occupational health. Pat Kinnersley's *Hazards of Work* (Pluto Press, London, 1974) cannot be too highly praised. Its equivalent in America is *Work is Dangerous to Your Health*, by Jeanne Stellman and Susan Daum (Vintage, New York, 1974). See also Charlie Clutterbuck's guide to the topic, 'Fight Pollution at Work', in *Science for People*, no. 28 (available also as a separate reprint); or contact Charlie at BSSRS (2.312).

A nice lollipop (not an apt metaphor) to end this section is *The Tooth Trip: An Oral Experience*, by Thomas McGuire (Wildwood House, London, 1973; Bookworks, Berkeley, 1972) — a happy case of demystified dentistry, with grotesque drawings of brigand microbes munching bits of tooth like Brighton rock. I hope it sets a precedent for preventive and D.I.Y. medical texts.

9 TRANSPORT

This is another area that Illich has had a go at. His message on transport is never to go over 15 miles an hour. (*Energy and Equity*, Calder and Boyars, London, 1974; Harper & Row, New York, 1974) [OB]. I don't really know what I think about that. Sounds a bit crazy, but there might be something in it. The very first words in Illich's book are 'Socialism can only come on a bicycle': equity is destroyed if some people perpetually move much faster than others. So we should walk or cycle — even buses and trains are suspect.

All Change to Bikes is a campaign to promote the cause of cycling in transport planning and to lobby local authorities (see *AD* 1/74 p. 47). It is sponsored by the cycle trade association: The British Cycling Bureau (director, Nicholas Cole) (Greater London House, Hampstead Road, London NW1 7QX). They are bringing out *Give Way*, which is to be published by Friends of the Earth (9 Poland Street, London W1V 3DG).

On the practicalities of cycling, there's a good section in *WEE* (pp. 638-41).

On general transport policy, *Changing Directions*, the report of Bishop Montefiore's Independent Transport Commission (Coronet, London, 1974: 75p) [OB] is likely to be influential.

If you must have a car, *PW* is excellent on maintenance, and if you think that converting it to propane gas will save the world, don't use Harold 'Mr. Chickenshit' Bate's device; look at *UC* 6, or write to Jerry Friedberg (Arrakis Volkswagen, PO Box 531, Point Arena, CA 95468) and ask for *How to Convert Your Auto Engine to Propane: A Manual of Step by Step Procedures for the Complete Idiot.*

There could be many fewer cars if we all shared them. Perhaps the 'White Car' (silent, slow, small, collectively owned) would be nice to have around: contact the inventor, Luts Schimmelpenninck (Oude Zyds Achterburgwal 125, Amsterdam).

Community Transport (29 Poland Street, Manchester M4 AZ. Martin Bould is projects director) provides services which are not catered for by established transport facilities in a number of British towns. An offshoot is NACTO — National Association of Community-based Transport Operations (secretary Nick Lowther-Harris, 22 Caldecott

Road, Manchester 9), which co-ordinates transport operations of the nation's charities.

On canals, contact the British Waterways Board (Melbury House, Melbury Terrace, London NW1).

On airships (such are the cliches of the movement) Max Rynish (Environmental Consulting Office, 10-11 Great Newport Street, London WC2).

On horses, contact the Heavy Horse Preservation Society (Old Rectory, Whitchurch, Salop).

On the deeper (?) implications of transport (?) see Robert Pirsig's remarkable *Zen and The Art of Motorcycle Maintenance* (The Bodley Head, London, 1974; Morrow, New York, 1974).

LIFESTYLE, W. A. ALLEN

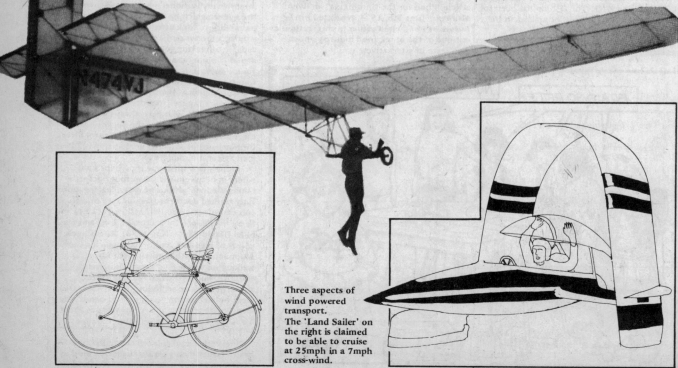

Three aspects of wind powered transport.
The 'Land Sailer' on the right is claimed to be able to cruise at 25mph in a 7mph cross-wind.

10 COMMUNICATIONS

This comes next to transport because some hope and others dread that transport will be replaced by 'communication'. Fortunately communication has other meanings and other uses, although the debates in Radical Technology circles on the role of advanced communication technology are often bitter.

References are no problem here. *Source Catalog No 1: Communication* (Swallow Press, 1970) covers such topics as listener-controlled radio, video groups, boycotts, guerilla theatre, etc.

WEE has a 40-page section headed 'communications.'

UC 7 was a special issue dedicated to the liberation of communications (mostly electronic).

For periodicals, see *TAP* (10.5) and *Interferences* (10.4). See also the 'Communications' section in the book.

10.1 PRINT

Personally I never feel quite at home with all this newfangled stuff, so let me start with some shreds of Gutenbergiana:

Print from Rising Free (197 Kings Cross Road, London WC1). A clear and concise introduction to the various methods of printing, when they are appropriate, and how to do them. A clever touch: different pages printed by the method being described. Part of this is used in the book here. *Printing It,* by Clifford Burke (Wingbow Press, 2940 7th Street, Berkeley CA 94710, 1972).

The Publish It yourself Handbook, ed. Bill Henderson (Pushcart Book Press, Box 845, Yonkers, NY 10701).

For tales of experience in running small presses, try Richard Moseley, Black Wedge, Graphics Workshop (Gloucester Street, Brighton, Sussex, England), or Andrew Singer (The Mill House, Coles Hill, Highworth, Wilts, England).

On what comes off these small presses, consult the *Directory of Alternative Publications,* 11th edition from Smoothie Publications (83 Montpelier Road, Brighton, Sussex, England) (and incidentally, from the same address, *Librarians for Social Change* (magazine) which I suppose fits into this section; Libraries are one of the great institutions), or in America, *Alternatives in Print,* from Glide Publications (330 Ellis Street, San Francisco, CA 94102, USA).

On alternative news, Peoples News Service (119 Railton Road, London SE 24): Excellent weekly bulletins.

10.2 FILM

Now I have to get on with all that McLuhan stuff.

For lively possibilities in film, *Challenge for Change,* newsletter of the National Film Board of Canada, (PO Box 6100, Station A, Montreal, Quebec, MC3H5) is a pace-setter — the best out of nos. 1-5 have been reprinted.

See also, *Independent Film-Making* by Lenny Lipton (Straight Arrow, San Francisco, 1972).

10.3 VIDEO

Theory The classic handbook-turned text-book is *Guerilla Television* (Holt, New York 1971) by Michael Shamberg and Raindance Corporation, a group of New York (now West Coast) video-freaks, who also started *Radical Software* (Gordon and Breach, New York and London; bimonthly, sometimes) and compiled the *Prime Time Survey* (TVTV 1974, Box 48-455 Los Angles, CA 90048): if there's one

book to read, that's it.

For critical analysis of public TV policy, in US: The Network Project (104 Earl Hall Columbia University New York); in UK: Hoppy and others at the Centre for Advanced Television Studies (CATS, 15 Prince of Wales Crescent, London NW1) and the Standing Conference on Broadcasting (9 Poland Street, London W1).

More abstractly, see Gene Youngblood's *Expanded Cinema* (Studio Vista, London 1973), and Raymond Williams's *Television: Technology and Cultural Form* (Fontana, London 1974).

Practice Use manuals produced in your own country because you and the writer are likely to be using the same generation equipment. Contact: (Instead of listing publications that may be difficult to obtain or out-of-date, I've decided to list organisations to contact.) In the USA, TVTV (see above); Videofreex (Maple Tree Farm, Lanesville, New York 12450), who have written *The Spaghetti City Video Manual* (Praeger, New York, 1973): Johnny Videotape, alias H. Allan Fredericksen, (695 30th Avenue, Santa Cruz, California 95060), who has written *Community Access Video.* In the UK, *CATS Video Training Manual* and a UK *Video Index,* a useful list of practitioners and relevant organisations; Inter-Action (14 Talacre Road, London NW1), a large community-orientated action group; the Greater London Arts Association (25 Tavistock Square, London WC1); the Association of Video Workers (18 Wyatt Road, London N5).

(My thanks to John Howkins for this little lot).

10.4 RADIO

On amateur radio, see *WEE,* p. 702, and read the amazing *Sex and Broadcasting: A Handbook on Starting a Radio Station for the Community,* by Lorenzo W. Milam, 2nd edn (KIAO, 5 University Avenue, Los Gatos, CA 95030, USA). 'The People's Radio Primer' in *UC* 7 is a good practical introduction to the hardware involved, and 'Opening up the Airwaves' in *UC* 8 explains some of the problems of running a pirate transmitter. Cop McDonald is worth contacting (PO Box 483, Rochester, MN 55901, USA), as is *Undercurrents'* own radio correspondent, Rick Martin (this is a pseudonym) (c/o *UC,* 275 Finchley Road, London NW3).

In France, the magazine *Interferences* (94 Quai Jemmapes, 75010 Paris; 44F a year, quarterly). Specialises in alternative radio but covers all aspects of mass communications.

10.5 MISCELLANEOUS

On 'phone phreaking', see again *UC* 7, or subscribe to the phone phreaks' own journal, *TAP* ($2.00 a year, $4.50 outside US, from Room 504, 152 W. 42nd Street, New York, NY 10036), which also contains quantities of information on how to render mass technological systems 'inoperative'.

On the social uses of computers, see Stephen Bodington's *Computers and Socialism* (Spokesman Books, 1973).

Meanwhile the people's computer service at the Galdor Centre (52 Brighton Road, Surbiton, Surrey KT6) always needs more hands to drive the venerable ICT 1301A. Any offers?

11 ODDS AND SODS

11.1 CIVIL AID & DISASTER TECHNOLOGY

This requires the same *bricoleur's* mentality as the practice of Radical Technology.

Walter Lloyd (Duckworth Farm, Shawforth, Rochdale, Lancs) is national co-ordinator of Civil Aid, and a great authority on creating things out of nothing.

Diana Manning (12 Argyll Mansions, London W14) is author of the definitive bibliography on disaster technology.

See also *AD* 1/75 on housing that was knocked up after the Managua earthquake.

11.2 ENVIRONMENT & ECOLOGY

The 'Ecology Movement' may be considered an aunt or uncle of Radical Technology.

See *WEE,* pp. 461-75.

Environmental Information Centre Inc. produce *Land Use Planning Abstracts,* which covers environment, ecology, pollution, natural resources, etc. A 500-page hardback of American info, with 2-300 abstracts from

journals and official reports since 1970 as well as statistics and laws. ($50 from EIC, Land Use Reference Dept, 125 East 39th Street, New York, NY 10016).

The Environmental Handbook: Action Guide for the UK ed. by John Barr (Ballantine, New York, 1971: 40p).

Contact Friends of the Earth (9 Poland Street, London W1V 3DG), who supply a list of publications; or Conservation Books, 28 Bearwood Road, Wokingham, Berks, RG11 4TD.

See *Environment* and *The Ecologist* (2.221).

The currently most fashionable piece of neo-doomsday theory is Howard Odum's essay, 'Energy, ecology and economics', reprinted in *WEE* — an extraordinary example of an ideological wolf in scientific sheep's clothing. Somebody ought to get down to analysing Odum's work from a radical perspective. *Radical Science Journal,* where are you hiding? Meanwhile, we have 'A Critique of Political Ecology' by Hans-Magnus Enzensberger, *New Left Review* 84, March/April 1974, which is not bad.

11.3 LAND HOLDING

See special issue of *Resurgence* (ATI) on land (Sep 1974), and manifesto 'Land for the People' in *UC* 10. This represents the Radical

Technology approach to land very well. *People and Land* published by the Centre for Rural Studies (345 Franklin Street, San Francisco, CA 94102; 50c) is a journal devoted specifically to the subject of land reform (it's free: I wonder where they get their money?).

A new idea in land-holding is the 'community land trust'. In Britain contact Dr D. S. Warren (3 Salubrious, Broadway, Worcs. WR12); in America the International Independence Institute (West Road, Box 183, Ashby, MA 01431). The III's book *The Community Land Trust: A Guide to a New Model for Land Tenure in America* (Centre for Community Economic Development, 1878 Massachussetts Avenue, Cambridge MA 02140; 1972) is an excellent survey of various patterns of collective tenure, and the possibilities for further extensions of the idea.

A sobering assessment of government-sponsored land resettlement schemes is Dave Elliott's article 'How the Land Turned Sour' in *UC* 11.

11.4 SCIENCE

This is largely dealt with in section 2.521. The main organisations are BSSRS (2.312), SESPA/Science for the People (2.33), and The Committee for Social Responsibility in Engineering (2.33). The journals are listed in 2.222. *Undercurrents* also has material on pure science and institutionalised science, and anyway there's a lot of cross-fertilisation in the different radical science groups. *Science for People*, no. 25, Jan/Feb 1974 has a bibliography on 'Science and Society'. I cannot pass by without a fond word for the *Radical Science Journal*, which contrasts so starkly with *Undercurrents*. It is destined for great things, taking care to give the references and footnotes on the way. Academia, what progeny you bear!

11.5 LEARNING

The textbook of the new countercourse movement is *Countercourse*, ed. Trevor Pateman, (Penguin Education, London, 1972) — another treat for bibliography freaks, with 87 pages of it.

On Learning and Social Change, by Michael Rossman (Vintage, New York, 1970). Intelligent and funny essays by a 'Taoist, middle-aged radical'.

Somewhere Else, a living-learning catalog edited by Center for Curriculum Design (Swallow Press, 1973; $3.00).

Keith Paton's golden oldie, *The Great Brain Robbery* is long out of print but can still be found in odd corners of movement bookshops.

12 THIRD WORLD

I enter this section with some diffidence, as I know very little about Third World countries and what might count as Radical Technology in that context. Some idea of the striking variety of interpretations can be gathered from the various articles in this book on China, Gandhi, Chile, and Intermediate Technology.

12.1 CHINA

It seems to me that, on the whole, the Chinese have got the right idea about technology, so I'll start off with a plug for them.

WEE has a magnificent 7-page annotated China bibliography, which should be enough to get anyone started.

Here is a selection of other books:

◆ *Feng Shui*, by E. J. Eitel (1873, now reprinted and available from Cockaygne, 1 Jesus Terrace, Cambridge) [CO] . A rather arrogant missionary's view of the ancient Chinese science/art of ecological building, garden and landscape planning. This and *China at Work* (qv under 'Materials, tools and design') indicate that the Chinese had some fine traditions with which to create the new China.

◆ *Doing Battle with Nature: Landscape Modification and Resource Utilization in the People's Republic of China*, by Christopher Salter (Occasional Paper no. 1, Asian Studies Committee, University of Oregon) [OR] . A comprehensive bibliography of every English-language source on environment, resources and development in China.

◆ *Away with All Pests: An English Surgeon in People's China*, by Joshua Horne (Monthly Review Press, 1971) [CO,SB] . Alternative medical practice.

◆ *Science Walks on Two Legs*, by Science for the People (Avon Publishers, 1974; available from Science for the People, 9 Walden Street, Jamaica Plain, MA 02130). A report of a group visit, focusing specifically on Chinese science and technology.

◆ *Science and Civilisation in China*, by Joseph Needham, 7 vols (Cambridge) is the great historical source book on Chinese science and technology.

◆ *Economic Management in China*, by Joan Robinson (published by SACU, 152 Camden High Street, London NW1: 30p).

◆ *AD* 3/74 and 4/74: eight essays on various aspects of planning in China.

More information on China can be obtained from Society for Anglo-Chinese Understanding, SACU (152 Camden High Street, London NW1).

12.2 DEVELOPMENT AND TECHNOLOGY

China's pattern of development is unusual, but similar ideas crop up elsewhere. See for instance:

Ujamaa, Essays on Socialism, by Julius

Nyerere (Oxford, 1967) [SB] , and the well-known *Small is Beautiful*, by E. F. Schumacher (2.51).

A collection of essays on 'appropriate technology' subjects appear in *Impact of Science on Society* (UNESCO) vol. 24, no. 3, 1973; while cautionary tales on the use of large-scale technologies for development are found in *The Careless Technology*, edited by M. T. Farvar and J. Milton (Natural History Press, New York, 1971) [SB] .

The best two theoretical papers I have read on technology for the Third World are:

'Self-Help Technology: Escape-Route for the Poor' by Jimoh Omo-Fadakah (a version of which is published in this book) and 'Is Indian Science Truly Indian?' by A. K. N. Reddy, *Science Today*, Jan 1974.

12.3 APPROPRIATE TECHNOLOGY GROUPS OUTSIDE THIRD WORLD

On more practical matters, several organisations specialise in appropriate technology for development in low-capital situations:

◆ In Britain, **ITDG (The Intermediate Technology Development Group)** (see also 2.312, 3.5, 4.62, 6.2).

◆ In Canada, **Brace Research Institute** (McDonald College, McGill University, St Anne de Bellevue, 800 Quebec) (2.33, 4.33) and **Minimum Cost Housing Group** (School of Architecture, McGill University, Montreal) (2.33, 3.4, 3.5, 6.2).

◆ In the USA, **VITA (Volunteers in Technical Assistance)** (2.33, 4.33, 4.42).

All the above have done sterling work. One should write for catalogues of publications, which are continually being extended. ITDG has a number of expert panels on various topics such as water energy, building, etc, and publishes the journal *Appropriate Technology* (2.21).

◆ **VCOAD (Voluntary Committee on Overseas Aid and Development** (same address as ITDG) publishes: *Synopses of appropriate technology projects* which is a directory of Third-World-orientated projects being undertaken by technical students in British institutions of higher education, and it includes wind-power studies, water power, animal power, methane, refrigeration, pumps, low-cost transport, workshop equipment, materials, and water supply.

Brace and VITA are particularly strong on windmill design.

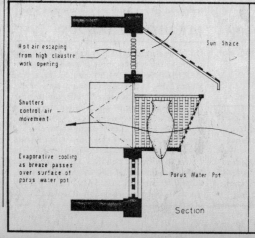

Hot air escaping from high claustre work opening

Sun Shade

Shutters control air movement

Evaporative cooling as breaze passes over surface of porus water pot

Porus Water Pot

Section

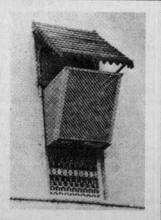

12.4 OTHER CONTACTS

This list is perhaps rather arbitrary — people I happen to know; but they all know where they're at and would be very useful contacts for serious enquirers.

◆ **Dr Marcel Antonorsi** (Conicit, Apartado 70617, Los Ruices, Caracas, Venezuela). An economist seeking radical alternatives to standard development. He has written a critical thesis on 'soft technology' which offers a more-or-less comradely critique from a radical Third World perspective. It's in Spanish, but a French translation, *Technologie Douce: Un Essai d'Interpretation Critique* Cahier de l'Ecodeveloppement no. 4, Centre International de Recherches sur l'Environment et le Developpement, can be obtained from the Ecole Pratique des Hautes Etudes, (54 Rue de Varenne, 75007 Paris, France).

◆ **Farroukh Afshar**, Architectural Association, (2.31), is an Iranian architect who has been making a special study of traditional housing practices in Third World Countries, particularly the Middle East. See 'Indigenous Housing' in *AD* 4/75 (3.3).

◆ **Bob Congdon** (Technische Hogeschool Eindhoven, Buro Entwicklingssamenwerking, Eindhoven, The Netherlands) worked for ITDG and UNESCO and is an old intermediate technology hand with lots of contacts.

◆ **Dr Harry Dickinson** (Dept of Electrical Engineering; University of Edinburgh) — organised a conference on 'Appropriate Technology' in Edinburgh; been everywhere, including China. A shrewd eye.

◆ **Dr Taghi Farvar**, Centre for Endogenous Development Studies, Alashtar, Lorestan, Iran. Did his Ph.D. with Barry Commoner, edited *The Careless Technology* (12.2), and is now head of a new centre for indigenous rural development.

◆ **Jimoh Omo-Fadakah** (208b Camberwell Grove, London SE5). Accomplished theorist of self-help politics and technology, especially for Africa. Contributed the article to this book.

◆ **Professor A. K. N. Reddy**, Cell for the Application of Science and Technology to Rural Problems (Indian Institute of Science Bangalore 560012, India) see also 4.521 and 12.2 and Dr. Mansur Hoda, Appropriate Technology Group, (Gandhian Institute of Studies, PO Box 116, Rajghat, Varanasi, India) will both know what is going on in that part of the world.

(vertical left margin) CALIFORNIA's UTOPIAN COLONIES, ROBERT V. HINE

13 STRATEGY & SOCIAL CHANGE

Knowing where we're going is very important, as long as we don't get too rigid about it. That is what section 2.54 is about, defining our dreams better. This section follows on from there. What do we do now? The trouble is that all the aspects of contemporary capitalist society are woven together, and very little is free to change by itself. Institutions, technology, work, life-styles, consciousness, what we expect of each other and what we hold each other to — all lock into place and resist change. It is not surprising that many people submit to the fallacy that nothing can change until it all does — and therefore nothing can change. This leads either to total compliance, escapism, or the 'waiting for the revolution' syndrome. The utopians reckon you should just start building the post-revolutionary society here and now, clearing away little areas and getting on with it, knowing that every battle will end in defeat except the last.

Revolutionary situations do occur, when the pulse of a whole people may quicken in a new-found realisation of their own power: Paris 1871; Russia 1917; Spain 1936; Hungary 1956; and again Paris 1968. But these have to be prepared for, and you have to know (roughly) where you are going. It's no good wasting your strategical imagination on insurrections, only on what they permit to be implemented: the new structures which have been growing all these years, which we as temporary custodians of the tradition must invent, guide and nurture with all our care and passion. That is all I shall say about revolution.

13.1 SOME GENERAL DISCUSSIONS OF STRATEGY

Discussions of strategy are often dominated by the question of parties, but this does not appeal to me, although the debates on the subject in *Liberation* have been interesting (see *Liberation* Dec 1973, vol. 18, no. 4; and William Domhoff's rather arrogant but entertaining essay 'How to Commit Revolution in Corporate America' (Entwhistle-West, Goleta, California, 1968). The following emphasise organising on all fronts rather than having parties:

◆ *Strategy for Labour,* by Andre Gorz (2.54)
◆ *Strategy for a Living Revolution,* by George Lakey (W. H. Freeman, London, 1973; Grossman, New York, 1973).

◆ 'Towards Liberation' by Michael Randle, in *Peace News,* May 30th, 1975
◆ *Organisers Manual,* by OM Collective (Bantam, New York, 1971). *Amazing* bibliography
◆ *Socialist Alternatives for America: A Bibliography,* by Union of Radical Political Economics (c/o Sandy Orlow, Office of Organisational Services, Michigan Union, Ann Arbor, MI 48104)
◆ *Manual for Revolutionary Leaders,* by Michael Velli, ed. Lorraine and Freddy Perlman (Red & Black, Detroit 1972). Brilliant, funny, graphically extraordinary. Required reading.

See also the journals listed at the end of 2.223, and, in a different vein from the above, Illich's *Tools for Conviviality* (2.51)

13.2 WORK AND PRODUCTION

The ultimate aim is a directly fulfilling decentralised production system in which stupid jobs have been abolished, tasks and responsibilities are rotated, people equitably and voluntarily adjust their own balance of work-hours and work-satisfaction, and the patterns of production are controlled both by producers and consumers. The possibilities for economic decentralisation are indicated in

Members of the Kaweah Colony before the Karl Marx Tree (now more widely known as the General Sherman Tree), California, 1889.

LONG LIVE THE LANDLORD

YOUR HOME IS HIS CASTLE

2.54. See especially Goodman's *Communitas*; also 'Work and Surplus' by Keith Paton, *Anarchy* 118, 1970; 'What's *Left* of Alternative Technology?', *UC* 6, and the Open Universities Futures Access File *The Future of Work* (Man-Made Futures, 1975). China constitutes a proof that decentralisation and political rather than economic development can be very effective. See 12.1, and Jack Gray's article 'The Chinese Model: Some Characteristics of Maoist Policies for Social Change and Economic Growth', in *Socialist Economics*, ed. A. Nove and D. M. Nuti (Penguin, Harmondsworth, 1972).

There are two aspects to immediate strategy. One is the relocation of economic activity in the community or the home rather than the factory or office, reversing a trend inevitably fostered by commodity-society and now virtually complete. This is taken up in 13.3. The other aspect is to transform the nature of factory production, either by taking over existing enterprises or starting new ones.

Quite a few workers' co-ops have come into being in Britain recently (Fakenham, Meriden, Scottish Daily News, Fisher-Bendix; Lucas Aerospace, next?) and they seem bound to increase. A good discussion of this is found in Robin Fielder's article 'The Institute for Workers' Control and the Workers' Co-ops' in *In The Making* no. 3 (2.21). The IWC has been articulating the theory a long time now, and has produced some very helpful books and pamphlets, see *Workers' Control* (2.524) and *Can the Workers Run Industry?* by Ken Coates (Sphere, London, 1968). The *Bulletin of the Institute for Workers Control* can be obtained for £1.50 subscription or membership of the Institute for £3.00 (IWC, Bertrand Russell House, Gamble Street, Nottingham NG7 4ET).

Another new departure has been the setting up of 'Community Development Projects' (CDP's) with Home Office backing to foster the growth of common-ownership co-operative enterprises in economically depressed regions. See again, *In The Making*, no. 3. *In The Making* also lists new productive projects being set up, both urban and rural — essential reading for anyone interested in 'alternative work'.

A particularly hopeful development is that the Combined Shop Stewards Committee at Lucas Aerospace, representing the entire workforce, have sent out requests for suggestions to various Radical Technology groups on alternative products to replace the cutbacks in defence contracts. Contact Mike Cooley (75 Talbot Avenue, Langley, Berks).

13.3 COMMUNITY PRODUCTION AND SERVICES

At the moment the distant specialised workplaces dominate production. We spend most of our waking hours in them or travelling to them. At the end of the day we buy the products or services back again, with money exchanged for the hours spent. Ignoring the question of whether the deal is fair or not, we could spend many of those hours more happily nearer home, meeting many of our needs by direct local production with family, friends and neighbours. In other words, a better balance needs to be created. This is already happening in the growth of community services such as food co-ops, repairs, creches, community medical and law centres, swap-shops, transport, information, and so on; and in small local productive projects such as community workshops (see The Community Workshop, *Anarchy*, no. 30, August 1963), co-operative **gardening** (see **Vision No 1** in this book) or allotments, basement fish-farming (see Community Technology, 2.33) and endless projects described in *In The Making* (2.21).

Another step could be to revive the torpid co-operative Societies with the votes of a few hundred activists establishing legal control. Local people could then take an active part in running the retail outlets. Join your local Co-op now! In America, guides to community services can be found in the various regional editions of *Peoples Yellow Pages* (see *WEE*, p. 577). In Britain, consult BIT (2.312), RF, *Alternative London, Alternative England & Wales* or *Alternative Scotland* (2.1).

13.4 LIVING: COMMUNES AND INTENTIONAL COMMUNITIES

In the 'Visions' in this book, we have tried to express an ideal of co-operative work and co-operative living. Of course, not everybody finds it congenial to live with groups of other people, but it can have a lot of advantages, economically, practically and personally. It seems to me that for many reasons we will have to learn to share a lot more, particularly those goods which hang around doing nothing most of the time, and this is made a lot easier when people live in groups, if they can stand the hassles. The record of success of

communes and communities set up since the industrial revolution is not particularly encouraging. See Jos Kingston's article in the book, and R. M. Kanter's *Commitment and Community* (Harvard University Press, 1972). But among contemporary communities there are plenty of success stories, albeit like chocolate in a Maryland cookie of unstable groupings, many of which will dissolve, recirculate and start again. It takes time to learn new ways.

Journal of the New Harbinger (Co-op Periodicals, Box 1301, Ann Arbor, MI 48106, USA: $6.00 year, bimonthly).

Community Association Newsletter (704 Whittaker Street, Cottage Grove, OR 97424: $15.00 a year).

Communities, Openings, Leaves of Twin Oaks, Twin Oaks Property Code, By-Laws and Working Government (all from Twin Oaks Community, Box 426, Louisa, VA 23093, USA).

Getting Back Together, by Robert Houriet (Abacus, 1973).

Families of Eden, by Judson Jerome (Seabury, NY, 1974).

People Together, by Clem Gorman (Paladin, London, 1975).

See also *Hey Beatnik! This is the Farm Book* (2.523).

A chain of heavily political 'pioneer villages' in Europe seems to be very successful in otherwise dying agricultural regions: contact Longomai (c/o Klinger, Grellingerstr 80, 4000 Basel, Switzerland), and see *In The Making*, no. 3.

In Britain, contact the Communes Network (75 New North Road, Huddersfield, Yorks, subscription is £3 a year, 12 stamped addressed envelopes). The best guidebook to setting up communities is *Legal Frameworks Handbook for Communes and Collectives* (Laurieston Hall, Castle Douglas, Kirkudbrightshire, Scotland: 25p). It is reprinted entire in *Alternative England and Wales* (2.1).

13.5 INSTITUTIONS AND FUNDS

For legal and organisational reasons, it is helpful to be clear about the range of forms through which a group project can work: co-operatives, Credit Unions. Housing Associations, Companies, Trusts, Charities, Partnerships. Advice about such things can be obtained from Dave Treanor (largely responsible for the *Legal Frameworks* booklet (13.4), Robin Fielder (221 Albert Road, Sheffield 8), or Nicholas Saunders (65 Edith Grove, London SW10).

A guide to sources of loan finance to co-operative ventures is given in *In The Making*, no. 3. This covers government and non-government sources. The alternative movement's own Development Bank is CLAP — Community Levy for Alternative Projects (see under BIT 2.312), which has paid out over £20,000 since it began, all raised from small contributions and levies.

13.6 CONCLUSION

Well, that seems to be all I can think of right now. The important thing is to work on all fronts at once, the home, the neighbourhood and the workplace. Such a balance is the essence of utopian strategy. Likewise we must be realistic *and* full of fantasy, attend to public needs *and* individual consciousness, create a balance of mental *and* manual work for everyone, a measure of city *and* country life, focus on immediate problems *and* build for the future, live in earnest *and* just for fun, confront *and* compromise. Have our cake *and* eat it? Why not?

Peter Harper

The first bus built in the workshops of the collectivised General Autobus company in Barcelona during the Civil War. CNT was the anarcho-syndicalist labour federation.

ANARCHIST COLLECTIVES

INDEX

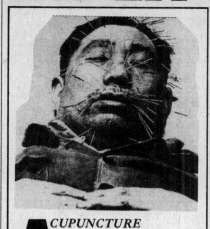

PAOLO KOCH/PHOTO RESEARCHERS

ACUPUNCTURE

BICYCLE

COMFREY CAKE!

CLIFF HARPER

COMMUNE

DERVISH

EARTH

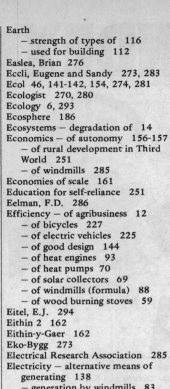

BIOLOO

COUGH COUGH

FAECES

GUEVARA

HEMP

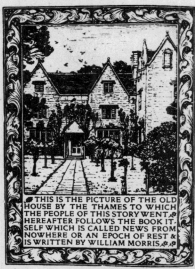

ENERGY PRIMER

THIS IS THE PICTURE OF THE OLD HOUSE BY THE THAMES TO WHICH THE PEOPLE OF THIS STORY WENT. HEREAFTER FOLLOWS THE BOOK ITSELF WHICH IS CALLED NEWS FROM NOWHERE OR AN EPOCH OF REST & IS WRITTEN BY WILLIAM MORRIS

NEWS FROM NOWHERE

JOHN ROSS

OUROBOUROS

PYRAMIDS

QUIXOTE

NEW ALCHEMISTS

TILAPIA

CLIFF HARPER

UNDERCURRENTS

VIDEO

RICHARD ELEN

SHELTER

WOMAN, WOOD,
WORK

SUMMARY: For the lazy reviewer

Radical Technology: Food and Shelter, Tools and Materials, Energy and Communications, Autonomy and Community. Edited by Godfrey Boyle and Peter Harper, and the editors of *Undercurrents.*
Wildwood House, London; Pantheon Books, New York, 1976. 304pp, A4, illustrated, index. Hardback ISBN 0 7045 0218 6; paperback ISBN 0 7045 0159 7.

Radical Technology is a large-format, extensively illustrated collection of original articles concerning the reorganisation of technology along more humane, rational and ecologically sound lines. The many facets of such a reorganisation are reflected in the wide variety of contributions to the book. They cover both the 'hardware' — the machines and technical methods themselves — and the 'software' — the social and political structures, the way people relate to each other and to their environment, and how they feel about it all.

The articles in the book range from detailed 'recipes' through general accounts of alternative technical methods, to critiques of current practices, and general proposals for reorganisation. Each author has been encouraged to follow her or his own personal approach, sometimes descriptive, sometimes analytic, sometimes technical, sometimes political. The contributors are all authorities in their fields.

The book is divided into seven sections: Food, Energy, Shelter, Autonomy, Materials, Communication, Other Perspectives. Over forty separate articles include items on fish culture, small-scale water supply, biological energy sources, a definitive zoology of the windmill, self-help housing, building with subsoil, making car-tyre shoes, the economics of autonomous houses, what to look for in scrap yards, alternative radio networks, utopian communities, and technology in China. Between the main sections are interviews with prominent practitioners and theorists of Radical Technology, including John Todd of the New Alchemy Institute; Robert Jungk, author of *Humanity 2000;* the Street Farmers, a group of anarchist architects; Peter van Dresser; and Sietz Leeflang, editor of *Small Earth,* the Dutch journal of alternative technology.

Also included between the main sections of the book is a series of visionary drawings by the gifted illustrator Clifford Harper, evoking the spirit and practice of Radical Technology: 'how it could be'. These drawings, or 'visions' include a communalised urban garden layout; a household basement workshop; a community workshop; a community media centre; a collectivised terrace of urban houses; and an autonomous rural housing estate.

The book ends with a comprehensive directory of the literature and active organisations in Radical Technology. This notes inevitable gaps in the book's coverage, points the reader to where more information can be found, and provides also an overall picture of a growing movement.

It is an unusual book.

Y IN, YANG

Z OME

Index generated by Chris Hutton-Squire